1970

# GEOMETRY

# GEOMETRY

**EDWIN E. MOISE**  Graduate School of Education and
Department of Mathematics, Harvard University

**FLOYD L. DOWNS, Jr.**  Hillsdale High School
San Mateo, California

**ADDISON-WESLEY PUBLISHING COMPANY**
MENLO PARK, CALIFORNIA · READING, MASSACHUSETTS
LONDON · DON MILLS, ONTARIO

**SECONDARY
MATHEMATICS
SERIES**

THIS BOOK IS IN THE ADDISON-WESLEY
SERIES IN SCIENCE AND MATHEMATICS EDUCATION

*Consulting Editors*

RICHARD S. PIETERS           PAUL ROSENBLOOM

GEORGE B. THOMAS, JR.        JOHN WAGNER

# Preface

In recent years, there has been extensive discussion about the content of the geometry course ordinarily taught in the tenth grade. An examination of the Table of Contents for this book will indicate that we have closely followed the recommendations of the Commission on Mathematics of the College Entrance Examination Board and have been strongly influenced by the text entitled *Geometry*, written by the School Mathematics Study Group (SMSG). Thus, in our choice of topics we have been guided by ideas which these groups, and others, have commonly accepted.

The easiest way for us to explain the spirit and method of this book is to acknowledge at once our immense indebtedness to our colleagues in the SMSG. We had the privilege of participating in that activity and were stimulated by the long and serious discussions of the style and method of teaching mathematics. Naturally, we have written our own book on the basis of our own judgment, after several years of work, reflection, and experience in tenth-grade classrooms; and our innovations are so numerous that we cannot claim for our book any backing of SMSG authority. On the other hand, our views on fundamentals have not changed very much since the summers of 1958, 1959, and 1960; the philosophy of the SMSG book seems as valid now as then; and we considered that our task was primarily to improve its execution.

The leading features of the treatment are as follows.

(1) The concepts of space geometry are introduced early, in Chapter 3, and are used thereafter. They appear not only in later chapters on the geometry of space but also in the problem sets of chapters whose text is devoted to the geometry of a plane. Thus the student has had a long and varied intuitive experience with space geometry by the time we return to a systematic study of it in Chapter 8.

(2) Coordinate systems on a line are introduced in Chapter 2, and algebra is used freely thereafter. Distances and angles are measured with numbers, and the methods of algebra are used in dealing with them. This makes it easy to introduce coordinates in a plane, in Chapter 13, as soon as the student knows about similarity and the Pythagorean Theorem.

(3) Area theory is commonly taught at the end of a geometry course. Here we present it in about the middle, in Chapter 11. There are two reasons for this. In the first place, area should come early, because it is easy, except for the demands that it makes on algebraic skills. (These

skills need to be kept alive anyway.)  In the second place, it is useful in the rest of the theory: it gives an easy proof of the Pythagorean Theorem (p. 306) and an easy proof of the proportionality theorem (p. 330) on which the theory of similarity depends.

(4) In nearly every case, concepts are explained intuitively, by informal discussions, and usually by figures, before being formally defined.  See, for example, the definition of a convex set, on p. 63.

(5) Figures are used very freely in the exposition, and are marked so as to convey as much information as possible.  See p. 114, where we explain the use of marks to indicate congruence.  See also p. 128, where we explain the use of exclamation points in figures.  These are used to indicate *conclusions*.  Thus the figure on p. 134 conveys the entire content of the Isosceles Triangle Theorem.  At the bottom of p. 135 there is a figure which conveys, in the same way, the converse of the theorem.  And the figure in the middle of p. 445, with its markings, tells us that an angle inscribed in a semicircle is a right angle.

(6) We have tried to think of names for as many theorems as possible, so as to make them easier to remember and refer to.  See, for example, the Hinge Theorem, on p. 203, and the Ruler Postulate, on p. 34.

(7) A basic purpose of this book is to teach the student to read mathematics as well as to write it.  This is not an easy task.  If students are to learn to use mathematical language, they must be furnished with terms and notations which convey meaning quickly and accurately.  It is not customary to do this.  For example, in many books the same notation $AB$ is used to denote (a) the line that contains $A$ and $B$, (b) the segment from $A$ to $B$, (c) the ray from $A$ through $B$, and (d) the distance between $A$ and $B$. It is also not uncommon for a book first to explain the distinction between a segment and a line, and then to ignore the distinction.  When language is used as loosely as this, the student is likely to conclude—correctly—that his textbook does not deserve thoughtful examination.  We have tried very hard to earn the students' thoughtful attention by means of consistent clarity and accuracy.

Thanks are due to the staff of Addison-Wesley Publishing Co., Inc., for their able and cooperative work in the production of the book, in full accord with the intentions of the authors.

The teachers' edition of this book has been prepared by Mr. Gerhard Wichura, of Wellesley High School, Wellesley, Mass.

Acknowledgment is hereby made for permission to reprint in this volume portions of the SMSG text, *Geometry*, copyright by Yale University.  However, this permission must not be construed as an endorsement by the School Mathematics Study Group of the present volume.

E. E. M.
F. L. D., Jr.

# ILLUSTRATIONS

# Contents

## 8   PERPENDICULAR LINES AND PLANES IN SPACE

## 9   PARALLEL LINES IN A PLANE

## 10   PARALLEL LINES AND PLANES

## 11   POLYGONAL REGIONS AND THEIR AREAS

# 1 | Common Sense and Exact Reasoning

## 1–1. TWO KINDS OF PROBLEMS

Consider the following problems.

(1) A certain rectangle measures 6 in. by 8 in. The area enclosed is cut into two pieces by a line segment.

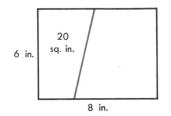

If the area of one piece is 20 square inches (sq. in.), what is the area of the other piece?

(2) In a certain rectangle, the sum of the length and the width is 14 (measured in inches). A second rectangle is five times as long as the first, and three times as wide. The perimeter of the second rectangle is 91. What are the dimensions of the first rectangle?

You should be able to get the answer to Problem 1 without having to think very hard. The answer is 28 sq. in., because $6 \cdot 8 = 48$ and $48 - 20 = 28$. Of course, we could solve the problem algebraically, if we wanted to, by setting up the equation

$$20 + x = 6 \cdot 8,$$

and then solving to get $x = 28$. But this seems a little silly because it is so unnecessary. The chances are that you solved more difficult problems than this, with arithmetic, before you studied algebra at all. And if all algebraic equations were as superfluous as the one we have just set up, then no serious-minded person would pay any attention to them.

Problem 2, however, is quite another matter. If we denote the length and width of the first rectangle by $x$ and $y$, then the length and width of the second rectangle are $5x$ and $3y$. Therefore

$$5x + 3y = \tfrac{91}{2},$$

because the sum of the length and width is half of the perimeter. We also know that

$$x + y = 14.$$

This gives us a system of two equations in two unknowns. To solve, we multiply each term in the second equation by 3, getting

$$3x + 3y = 42,$$

1

and then we subtract this last equation, term by term, from the first. This yields

$$2x = 45\tfrac{1}{2} - 42 = 3\tfrac{1}{2} = \tfrac{7}{2}$$

or

$$x = \tfrac{7}{4} = 1\tfrac{3}{4}.$$

Therefore

$$y = 14 - 1\tfrac{3}{4} = 12\tfrac{1}{4}.$$

It is now not difficult to check that our answer satisfies the conditions of the problem.

In a way, these two problems are rather similar, but in a very important way, they are quite different. The first is what you might call a common-sense problem. It is easy to guess what the answer ought to be, and it is also easy to check that the natural guess is also the right answer. On the other hand, guessing the answer to the second problem is almost out of the question. To solve it, we need to know something about mathematical methods.

There are cases of this kind in geometry. Consider the following statements.

(1) If a triangle has sides of length 3, 4, and 5, then it is a right triangle, with a right angle opposite the longest side.

(2) Let a triangle be given, with sides of length $a$, $b$, and $c$. If

$$a^2 + b^2 = c^2,$$

then the triangle is a right triangle, with a right angle opposite the longest side.

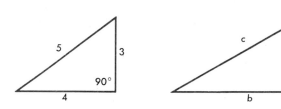

The first of these facts was known to the ancient Egyptians. They checked it by experiment. You can check it yourself by drawing a 3-4-5 triangle, as exactly as possible, and then measuring the angle opposite the longest side with a protractor. You should bear in mind, of course, that this check is only approximate. Suppose, for example, that the angle is really $89° \, 59' \, 59\tfrac{1}{2}''$ (that is, 89 degrees, 59 minutes, and $59\tfrac{1}{2}$ seconds) instead of $90° \, 0' \, 0''$ exactly. In this case, you would hardly expect to tell the difference with a protractor, no matter how carefully you sharpened your pencil and drew your figure. Nevertheless, the "Egyptian method" is a sound common-sense method of checking an experimental fact.

The Egyptians were extremely skillful at making physical measurements. The edges of the base of the Great Pyramid of Gizeh are about 756 feet (ft) long, and the lengths of these four edges agree, with an error of only about two-thirds of an inch. Nobody seems to know, today, how the builders achieved such accuracy. (The more you think about this problem, the more difficult it will probably seem to you.)

Statement 2 above was not known to the Egyptians. It was discovered much later, by the Greeks. It is quite impossible to check this statement by experiment, for the simple reason that there are infinitely many cases to be considered. For instance, you would have to construct triangles, and take readings with a protractor, for all the following cases:

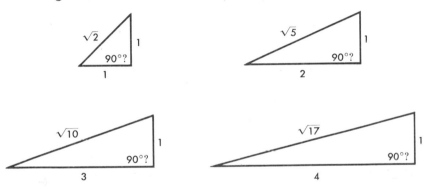

and so on endlessly. Thus it is hopeless to verify our general statement by experiment, even approximately. Therefore, a reasonable person would not be convinced that Statement 2 is true in all cases until he had seen a logical reason why it *has* to be true in all cases.

In fact, this is why it was the Greeks, and not the Egyptians, who discovered that our second statement is true. The Egyptians were very good at measurement, and they made some very clever guesses, which later turned out to be true. But the Greeks discovered a new method which was vastly more powerful. This was the method of exact geometrical reasoning. By this method they turned plausible guesses into solid knowledge, and they learned some rather startling things that nobody would have believed without seeing them proved. In this way, the Greeks laid the foundation for modern mathematics and hence for modern science in general.

## Problem Set 1–1

1. How good are you at guessing? Try this experiment. Take a piece of string, about 5 feet (ft) long, and place it on the floor in a loop with the ends free:

Then pull the ends of the string, gradually making the loop smaller, and stop when you think the loop is the size of your waist. Mark the string where it crosses itself, and check your guess by putting the string around your waist. *After* you have made this check, read the remarks on Problem 1 at the end of this set of problems.

2. This is also a problem in guessing.

A page of a newspaper is not very thick, about 0.003 inch (in.), and you often have seen a stack of newspapers. Suppose you were to place one sheet of newspaper on the floor. Next you place another sheet on top of the first, then two more sheets, then four, and so on, building up a pile of newspaper. Each time you add to the pile as many sheets as are already there. After the tenth time you would have a pile about 3 in. high. If you were able to continue until you had added to the pile for the fiftieth time, how high would the pile be?

One of the answers (a) through (d) below is the correct one. All you have to do is guess, or calculate, which one it is.

(a) About as high as your classroom.

(b) About as high as a four-story building.

(c) About as high as the Empire State Building.

(d) More than twice as high as the Empire State Building.

*After* you have made your choice, read the remarks on Problem 2 at the end of this set of problems.

3. The first of the pair of questions below can be answered by "common sense." State only its answer. The second requires some arithmetic or algebraic process for its solution. Show your work for it.

(a) What is one-sixth of 12?

(b) What is one-sixth of 5,255,622?

4. Follow the directions for Problem 3.

(a) One-third of the distance between two cities is 10 miles (mi). What is the distance between them?

(b) The distance between two cities is 10 mi more than one-third of the distance between them. What is the distance between them?

\* **5.** Follow the directions of Problem 3.

 (a) If a 5-in. piece of wire is cut into two parts so that one part is four times as long as the other, what is the length of the longer part?

 (b) If a 5-in. piece of wire is cut into two parts such that a square formed by bending one part will have four times the area of a square formed by bending the other part, what is the length of the longer part?

**6.** If two students carefully and independently measure the width of a classroom with rulers, one measuring from left to right and the other from right to left, they will probably get different results. Try it! Which of the following is a plausible reason for the difference?

 (a) The rulers have different lengths.

 (b) Things are longer (or shorter) from left to right than from right to left.

 (c) The discrepancies resulting from the change in the position of the ruler accumulate, and the sum of these small errors makes a discernible difference.

 (d) One person may have lost count.

**7.** Show that $n^2 - 2n + 2 = n$ is true if $n = 1$. Is it true when $n = 2$? Is it always true, that is, is it true for $n$ equal to any number?

**8.** An important part of learning mathematics is learning to recognize patterns which suggest general truths. For example, looking at the statements,

$$3 + 5 = 8, \qquad 9 + 5 = 14, \qquad 11 + 17 = 28,$$

you might guess that the sum of two odd numbers is an even number. Can you think of two odd numbers whose sum is an odd number? Does your answer prove that two such odd numbers do not exist?

**9.** Consider these statements:

$$1^2 = 1, \qquad 3^2 = 9, \qquad 5^2 = 25, \qquad 7^2 = 49.$$

 (a) Look for a pattern involving odd numbers. Write a statement generalizing your observation.

 (b) Justify the truth of the generalization.

**10.** Divide each of $3^2$, $5^2$, and $7^2$ by 4.

 (a) What is the remainder in each case?

 (b) What pattern is evident here?

 (c) How many odd integers would you have to square and divide by 4 to guarantee that the remainder would always be the same?

**11.** Consider the following figures and the pattern suggested.

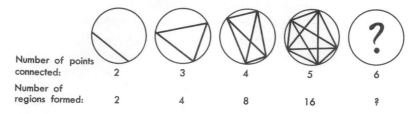

| Number of points connected: | 2 | 3 | 4 | 5 | 6 |
|---|---|---|---|---|---|
| Number of regions formed: | 2 | 4 | 8 | 16 | ? |

(a) Replace the question mark under the 6 by the number you think belongs there.

(b) Draw a circle and connect any six points on it in all possible ways. Count the regions thus formed. Does the result agree with your answer to part (a)?

(c) What does this problem indicate about showing whether a generalization is true or false?

**12.** The following optical illusions show that you cannot always trust appearances to decide upon a fact.

(a) Is *CD* a continuation of *AB*? Test your answer with a ruler.

(b) Are *XY* and *YZ* the same length? Compare the lengths with your ruler or compass.

(c) Are *MN* and *PQ* straight line segments?

(d) Which line at the right of the rectangle is the continuation of the line at the left?

(e) Which is longer, *AB* or *CD*?

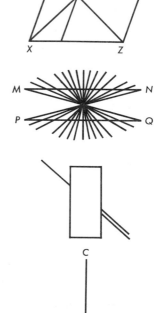

**13.** Consider the expression $n^2 - n + 11$. If we let $n = 1$, the expression equals 11. For $n = 2$, the expression equals 13. For $n = 3$, the expression gives 17. The numbers 11, 13, and 17 are prime numbers. (A prime number is a number greater than 1 which is divisible only by itself and 1.) Do we always get a prime number when we substitute whole numbers for $n$ in the expression?

\*+ **14.** (a) Show that the expression

$$n^2 - n + k$$

behaves like

$$n^2 - n + 11$$

(see Problem 13) when $k$ is 3 or 5.

(b) What general statement does (a) suggest? Is it true or false?

(c) What is the next number greater than 11 that works for $k$? Does 41 work for $k$?

+ **15.** A jet pilot plans to cover a 1000-mi course at an average speed of 1000 mph. For the first 800 mi the speed is 800 mph. At what rate must the remaining distance be covered?

+ **16.** Use a ruler to check that the measurements of the figure are correct. If the measurements are correct, show by computing the areas of the parts that the sum of the areas of the parts is greater than the area of the rectangle. Odd, isn't it? Can you explain it?

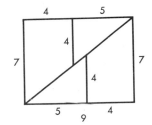

REMARKS ON PROBLEM 1. Almost everybody makes a loop about twice as big as it should be. You can get very satisfactory results if you think somewhat as follows. The circumference of a circle is $\pi$ times the diameter, and $\pi$ is approximately equal to 3. Therefore, the diameter is about one-third of the circumference. Hence, if you know that your waist measure is, say, 24 in., the loop should have a diameter of about 8 in. This may seem unbelievably small, but if you have analyzed the problem mathematically, you will know that your careful logic is reliable.

This is one of many fairly common instances in which even a crude mathematical approach to a problem is better than an outright leap in the dark.

REMARKS ON PROBLEM 2. This is also one of many fairly common situations in which mathematical analysis helps you discover amazing facts that would not occur to you in any other way. The discovery aspect of mathematics is as prevalent and as important as its use in problem solving.

Since each time you add to the pile you are doubling the number of newspaper pages, after 50 times you would have $2^{50}$ sheets. A table of powers of 2, or straightforward arithmetic, will convince you that you would have 1,125,899,906,842,624 sheets. A little more arithmetic will indicate that the pile would be well over 53 million miles high; that is, more than one-half the distance from the earth to the sun.

Even if you reasoned that (d) was the right choice, you probably did not realize it represented so much of an understatement.

## 1–2.   AN ORGANIZED LOGICAL DEVELOPMENT OF GEOMETRY

If you stop to think, you will realize that you know many facts about geometry. For example, you know how to find the areas of various simple figures, and you know the Pythagorean relation for right triangles. Some of the things that you know are so obvious that it might never occur to you to put them into words, let alone to wonder why they are true. An example of this is the following statement.

*Two straight lines cannot cross each other in more than one point.*

But some of them, like the Pythagorean relation, are not obvious at all. In this book we are going to organize the facts of geometry in an orderly way, with a few simple statements at the beginning leading up to the more complicated ones in later sections. We shall see that all the facts of geometry can be derived from a few statements which are simple and obvious. This suggests that we might be able to arrange these facts in such an order that every statement on our list can be derived from the preceding statements by logical reasoning.

Actually, we shall carry out the following program: We shall state definitions for geometric *ideas* as clearly and exactly as we can, and we shall establish the *facts* of geometry by giving logical proofs. The statements that we prove will be called *theorems*.

Although nearly all our statements will be proved as theorems, there will be some exceptions. Our simplest and most fundamental statements will be given without proof. These will be called *postulates*. Similarly, we shall use the simplest and most fundamental terms without making any attempt to define them. These will be called the *undefined terms*.

At first, it may seem better to define every term that we use, and to prove every statement that we make. But it is fairly easy to see that this cannot be done.

Consider first the question of the theorems. Usually, when we prove a theorem, we show that it follows logically from theorems that we have already proved. But proofs cannot always work this way. In particular, the *first* proof that we give cannot possibly work this way, because in this case there aren't any theorems that we have already proved. But we have to start somewhere. This means that we have to accept some statements without proof. These unproved statements are the postulates.

The same principle applies to definitions. Most of the time, when we introduce a new term, we define it, using terms that have already been defined. But definitions cannot always be formulated in this fashion. In particular, the *first* definition that we give cannot work this way, because in this case there aren't any terms that have already been defined. This means that we have to introduce some geometric terms without defining them. Therefore we shall use the simplest and most fundamental geometric terms without even trying to give definitions for them. These fundamental undefined terms will be *point*, *line*, and *plane*.

Postulates, of course, are not made up at random. (If they were, no sensible person would pay any attention to them.) Postulates describe fundamental properties of space. Similarly, the ideas of *point*, *line*, and *plane* are suggested by physical objects. If you make a dot on a piece of paper, with a pencil, you will get a reasonably good picture of a point. The sharper your pencil is, the better your picture will be. The picture will always be only approximate, because the dot will always cover *some* area, whereas a point covers no area at all. But if you think of smaller and smaller dots, made by sharper and sharper pencils, you will get a good idea of what we mean in geometry by the word *point*.

When we use the term *line*, we shall always have in mind the idea of a *straight* line. A straight line extends infinitely far in both directions. Usually we shall indicate this in our illustrations by putting arrowheads at the ends of the part of the line that we draw:

The arrowheads are meant to remind us that the line doesn't stop at the points where the picture of it stops.

We shall have another term, *segment*, for a figure like this:

A thin, tightly stretched string is a good approximation of a segment. A thin piano wire stretched at high tension is a better approximation; and so on.

If you think of a perfectly flat surface, extending infinitely far in every direction, you will have a good idea of what a *plane* is supposed to be.

You should bear in mind that none of the above statements are definitions. They are merely explanations of the ideas that people had in the back of their minds when they wrote the postulates. When we start proving theorems, the only information that we shall claim to have about points, lines, and planes will be the information given in the postulates.

Finally, we give a couple of warnings.

In the first place, there are limits to what logic can do for us. Logic enables us to check our guesses, but it isn't much help in making our guesses in the first place. In your study of mathematics, you are never going to reach a stage where you can get along without ingenuity, or without the guidance of the feelings that you have in your bones.

In the second place, the first few theorems that we prove are not going to be very exciting; you may wonder why we don't just call them postulates and be done with it. This first part, however, will be easy in any case; take the text in your stride, and move on to the problems.

At the beginning of the next chapter, we present a short account of the idea of a set, and a short review of the algebra of the real numbers. Sets and algebra will be used throughout this course. We shall think of them, however, as things that we are working *with*, rather than things that we are working *on;* they will not form a part of our system of postulates and theorems. They are supposed to be available at the start; some of our postulates will involve real numbers, and we shall use algebra in proofs. In fact, geometry and algebra are very closely connected, and both are easier to learn if we establish the connection at the outset.

## EUCLID (THIRD CENTURY B.C.)

Euclid is probably the most successful scientific author who has ever lived. His famous book, the *Elements*, was a treatise on geometry and the theory of numbers. For well over two thousand years, every student who learned geometry learned it from Euclid. And in all that time, the *Elements* served as a model of logical reasoning for everybody.

Nobody knows, today, how much of the geometry in the *Elements* was original with Euclid. Some of it may have been based on earlier books, and some of the most important ideas in it are supposed to be due to Eudoxus, who lived at about the same time. In any case, of the books which have come down to us, the *Elements* is the first one which presents geometry in an organized, logical fashion, starting with a few simple assumptions and building on them by logical reasoning.

This has been the basic method in mathematics ever since. The remarkable thing is that it was discovered so early and used so well. Logic plays the same part in mathematics that experiments do in physics. In mathematics and physics, you may get an idea that you think is right. But in physics, you had better go to the laboratory and try it; and in mathematics, you had better think a little further and try to get a proof.

While Euclid's general method is here to stay, his postulates and the theory based on them are no longer very widely used. Since the development of algebra, the use of numbers to measure things has become fundamental. This method does not appear in the *Elements*, because in Euclid's time algebra was almost unknown.

## Problem Set 1–2

1. A student wanting to know the meaning of the word "dimension" consulted a dictionary. The dictionary listed as a synonym the word "measurement," whose definition the student in turn looked up. He made the following chart.

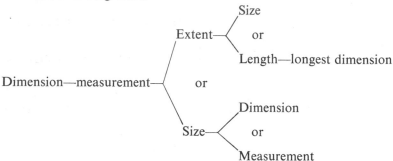

(a) Point out from the chart a circular list of three terms each of which has the term following it as a synonym. (In a circular list, the first term is said to follow the last term.)

(b) Make a circular list having four terms.

+ 2. Make a chart similar to that in Problem 1, starting with some word in a dictionary.

3. What do you think is wrong with the following faulty "definitions"?

(a) A square is something that is not round.

(b) A circle is something that is round.

(c) A right triangle is a triangle whose angles are right angles.

(d) An equilateral triangle is when a triangle has three sides the same length.

(e) A diameter of a circle is a line through the center of the circle.

4. Answer as in Problem 3.

(a) The perimeter of a rectangle is where you take the sum of the lengths of its sides.

(b) The circumference of a circle is when you multiply the diameter by $\pi$.

(c) A plane figure having four sides is a rectangle if its opposite sides have equal lengths.

(d) An equilateral triangle is a triangle which has three sides and three angles and whose sides all have the same length and whose angles all have the same measure.

(e) A triangle is when three lines intersect each other.

+ **5.** After reading Section 1–2 you should be able to decide whether each of the following statements is true or false.

   (a) It is possible to define each geometric term by using simpler geometric terms.

   (b) Theorems are proved only on the basis of definitions and undefined terms.

   (c) Exact geometric reasoning leads to geometric truths that cannot be deduced from measurement.

   (d) The best way of learning to prove theorems is to watch others prove them.

   (e) If you are willing to describe all the steps, each theorem can be proved from postulates and undefined terms, without referring to other theorems.

   (f) Any statement which seems to be true should become a postulate.

+ **6.** Suppose you were able to wrap an iron band tightly around a very large sphere, say the earth at its equator. The band would be about 25,000 mi in circumference. Suppose that you inserted into the band an additional iron strip 6 ft long so that the band would no longer fit tightly around the sphere. The enlarged iron band would stand out from the sphere, and would have a radius slightly greater than the radius of the original band. About how far from the sphere would the enlarged iron band be? (You may use 4000 mi for the radius of the earth, if you need it.)

# 2 | Sets, Real Numbers, and Lines

## 2–1. SETS

You may not have seen the word *set* used in mathematics, but the idea is quite familiar. Your family is a set of people, consisting of you, your parents, and your brothers and sisters (if any). These people are the *members* of the set. Your geometry class is a set of people. A member of a set is said to *belong to* the set. For example, you belong to your family and to your geometry class. The members of a set are also called *elements* of the set; in mathematics, these two terms mean exactly the same thing. A set is said to *contain* its members. For example, both your family and your geometry class contain you. If one set contains every element of another set, then we say that the second set is a *subset* of the first. For example, your geometry class is a subset of the student body of your school, and the student body contains your geometry class. We say that the subset *lies in* the set that contains it.

Note that in defining a subset, we have allowed the possibility that the sets are the same. Thus every set is a subset of itself.

When we say that two sets are *equal*, or write an equality $A = B$ between two sets $A$ and $B$, we mean merely that the two sets have exactly the same elements. Suppose, for example, that $A$ is the set of all whole numbers between $9\frac{1}{3}$ and $14\frac{1}{10}$, and $B$ is the set of all whole numbers between $9\frac{1}{10}$ and $14\frac{1}{3}$. Then $A = B$, because each of the sets $A$ and $B$ contains precisely the numbers 10, 11, 12, 13, and 14. Nearly always, in fact, the same set can be described in two different ways. Therefore, if the descriptions look different, it doesn't follow that the sets are different. The same sort of thing happens in algebra. The expressions $3 \cdot 17$ and $39 + 12$ look different, but they describe the same number; and this is what we mean when we write $3 \cdot 17 = 39 + 12$.

Two sets *intersect* if there are one or more elements that belong to both of them. For example, your family and your geometry class must intersect, because you are a member of both. (The chances are that you are the only person who belongs to both sets.) The *intersection* of two sets is the set of all objects common to both sets.

Passing to mathematical topics, we see that the set of all even numbers is the set whose elements are

$$2, 4, 6, 8, 10, 12, 14, 16, 18, \ldots$$

The set of all multiples of 3 is the set whose elements are

$$3, 6, 9, 12, 15, 18, \ldots$$

The intersection of these is the set whose elements are 6, 12, 18, . . .
(This is the set of all multiples of 6.)

In the figure on the right, each
of the two rectangles is a set of
points, and their intersection is a
set containing exactly two points.
Similarly, each of the corresponding rectangular regions is a set of
points, and their intersection is
the little rectangular region in the
middle of the figure.

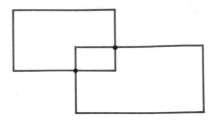

In the next figure, each of the two lines is a set of points, and their
intersection contains exactly one point.

Throughout this book, points,
lines, and planes will be regarded
as sets of points.  (You may regard this statement, if you like, as
our first postulate.)  In fact, *all*
geometric figures will be regarded
as sets of points. On the right we
see two sets of points, each of
which is a rectangular region lying
in a plane.  Their intersection is a
segment, lying in a straight line.

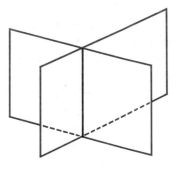

The *union* of two sets is the set of all objects that belong to one
or both sets.

For example, in the figure we see a large rectangular region $R$ which
is the union of two smaller rectangular regions $A$ and $B$.  The vertical
segment near the middle of the figure is the intersection of $A$ and $B$.
The points of this segment belong to the union for two reasons.

For three or more sets, the intersection and the union are similarly defined. Thus a triangle is the union of three sets, each of which is a segment. And a rectangle is the union of four sets, each of which is a segment.

It is sometimes convenient to use the idea of the *empty set*. The empty set is the set that contains no elements at all. This idea may seem very peculiar at first, but in fact it is very closely related to the idea of the number zero. Thus the following three statements mean exactly the same thing.

(1)  There are no white elephants in Chicago.

(2)  The number of white elephants in Chicago is zero.

(3)  The set of all white elephants in Chicago is the empty set.

Once we have introduced the idea of the empty set, we can speak of the intersection of any two sets, bearing in mind the possibility that the intersection may be empty. For example, the intersection of the set of all odd numbers and the set of all even numbers is the empty set. In the preceding figure, the intersection of the triangle and the rectangle is the empty set.

The empty set is denoted by ∅.

*A word of warning:* If you compare the definitions of the words *intersect* and *intersection*, you will see that the use of these terms is tricky. When we speak of the *intersection* of two sets, we allow the possibility that the intersection is empty, but when we say that two sets *intersect*, we always mean that their intersection contains at least one member.

*Another word of warning:* Zero and the empty set are closely related, but are not the same thing. For example, the equation

$$x + 3 = 3$$

has 0 as its only root, and so the set of roots is not the empty set; the set of roots has exactly one element, namely 0. On the other hand, the equation

$$x + 1 = x + 2$$

has no roots at all. Therefore its set of roots is ∅.

## Problem Set 2–1

1. For which of the following sets $A$ and $B$, is set $A$ equal to set $B$?

   (a) $A$ is the set of all whole numbers between $\frac{3}{2}$ and $\frac{25}{3}$. $B$ is the set whose elements are 2, 3, 4, 5, 6, 7, 8.

   (b) $A$ is the set of all girls' names beginning with J. $B$ is the set Jane, Jean, Joan, June, Jackie, Judy.

   (c) $A$ is the set of all countries in Central America whose names begin with $P$. $B$ is the set of all countries in Central America which can be crossed by way of a canal.

   (d) $A$ is the set of all students in your geometry class who are less than 10 years old. $B$ is the set of months of the year whose names begin with R.

   (e) $A$ is the set of all numbers which satisfy $x + 7 = 12$. $B$ is the set of all numbers which satisfy $x^2 = 25$.

   (f) $A$ is the set of all numbers which satisfy $5x + 8 = 8$. $B$ is the set of all numbers which satisfy $7(x^2 + 2) - 5 = 9$.

2. Let
$$P = \{2, 5, 7, 10, 14, 17, 19\}.$$

   [*Note:* Read "$P$ is the set whose members are 2, 5, 7, 10, 14, 17, and 19."]
   Let
$$Q = \{2, 4, 6, 8, 10, 12\}.$$

   What is the intersection of sets $P$ and $Q$? What is the union of the sets $P$ and $Q$?

3. Consider the following sets.

   $S_1$ is the set of all students in your school.

   $S_2$ is the set of all boys in your student body.

   $S_3$ is the set of all girls in your student body.

   $S_4$ is the set of all faculty members of your school.

   $S_5$ is the set whose only member is yourself, a student in your school.

   (a) Which *pairs* of sets intersect?

   (b) Which set is the union of $S_2$ and $S_3$?

   (c) Which set is the union of $S_1$ and $S_5$?

   (d) Describe the union of $S_1$ and $S_4$.

   (e) Which of the sets are subsets of $S_1$?

4. In the figures below, consider the line and the circle as two sets of points. In each case, tell what their intersection is.

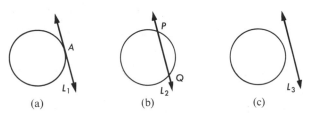

(a)          (b)          (c)

5. In the figure, what is the intersection of the triangle $ABC$ and the segment $AC$? What is their union?

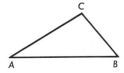

6. Consider the set $E$ of all positive even integers and the set $O$ of all positive odd integers.

   (a) Describe the union of $E$ and $O$.

   (b) Describe the intersection of $E$ and $O$.

7. Consider a set of three boys, $\{A, B, C\}$. Any subset of this set will be called a committee.

   (a) List the subsets of $\{A, B, C\}$.

   (b) How many two-member committees can be formed from the three boys?

   (c) Show that any two of the committees in (b) intersect.

   (d) What does the word "intersect" mean?

8. Let $A$ be the set of pairs of numbers $(x, y)$ which satisfy the equation $3x + y = 15$.

   Let $B$ be the set of pairs of numbers $(x, y)$ which satisfy the equation $2x + y = 11$.

   What is the intersection of the sets $A$ and $B$?

9. Let     $A = \{(1, 12), (2, 9), (3, 6), (4, 3), (5, 0)\}$.

   Let     $B = \{(1, 9), (2, 7), (3, 5), (4, 3), (5, 1)\}$.

   Note that the elements of sets $A$ and $B$ are pairs of numbers. What is the intersection of $A$ and $B$?

**10.** Let $A$ be the set of all solutions of $5r + s = 11$. Let $B$ be the set of all solutions of $3r - s = 5$. What is the intersection of $A$ and $B$?

**11.** Let $A$ be the set of all solutions of $7x - y = 28$. Let $B$ be the set of all solutions of $3x + 2y = 12$. What is the intersection of $A$ and $B$?

**12.** Let $A$ be the set of all solutions of $2m + n = 8$. Let $B$ be the set of all solutions of $4m + 2n = 12$. What is the intersection of $A$ and $B$?

\* **13.** Consider the set of all positive integers divisible by 2. Consider the set of all positive integers divisible by 3.

(a) Describe the intersection of these two sets and list its first four members.

(b) Write an algebraic expression for the intersection.

(c) Describe the union of the two sets and list its first six members.

**14.** Think of a point, $A$, on the blackboard or on a piece of paper. How many lines (straight lines) in the plane of the blackboard or paper are there which contain $A$? The lines containing $A$ form a set. The lines are the elements of the set. How many elements does this set have?

**15.** (a) Given two different points $A$ and $B$. How many elements are in the set of all lines (straight lines) that contain both $A$ and $B$? We often phrase this question differently and ask: How many lines can be drawn through two points, $A$ and $B$?

(b) Given three points, $A$, $B$ and $C$, which do not all lie in a line. How many lines are there each of which contains a pair of the three points?

(c) Given four points, $A$, $B$, $C$, and $D$, such that no three of them lie in a line. How many lines are there each of which contains a pair of the points? If a fifth point is given under the same conditions, how many lines are there?

\* (d) In parts (a), (b), and (c) the same question is asked for different numbers of points. Answer this question if $n$ points are given.

+ **16.** In listing the subsets of a given set, the set itself and the empty set are included as subsets of the set. Thus, the set $\{a, b\}$ has the following subsets:

$$\{a, b\}, \qquad \{a\}, \qquad \{b\}, \qquad \emptyset.$$

That is, a set with two elements has four subsets.

(a) List all the subsets of $\{a, b, c\}$.

(b) How many subsets does a set of four elements have?

(c) How many subsets does a set of five elements have?

(d) How many subsets does a set of $n$ elements have?

## 2-2. ORDER ON THE NUMBER LINE

The first numbers that you learned about were the "counting numbers,"

$$1, 2, 3, 4, 5, \ldots$$

The counting numbers never end, because no matter how far we go, we can always go a step further by adding 1. We may think of the counting numbers as arranged on a line, from left to right:

To the left of 1, we put the number 0:

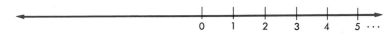

Next we enter the negative whole numbers, from right to left:

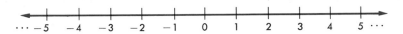

The numbers that we have so far are the *integers* or *whole numbers* (positive, negative, and zero). The counting numbers are, of course, the positive integers, and are often referred to by this name.

Note that there are many points of the line that have no numbers attached to them so far. We need, at least, to put in the fractions $\frac{1}{2}, \frac{1}{3}, \frac{2}{3}, -\frac{1}{2}, -\frac{1}{3}, -\frac{2}{3}$, and so on. There are infinitely many of these between every two whole numbers. In a figure, therefore, all we can do is to indicate some of them, as samples:

What we have mentioned so far are the numbers of the form $p/q$, where $p$ and $q$ are whole numbers and $q$ is not zero. These are called the *rational numbers*. (This term is not supposed to suggest that other numbers are unreasonable. It refers merely to the fact that the rational numbers are *ratios* of integers.)

It is evident that the rational numbers do not fill up the number line completely. There are many numbers that cannot be expressed as ratios of integers. For example, $\sqrt{2}$ is not rational. The same is true of $\sqrt{3}$ and $\sqrt{5}$, and also of certain "peculiar" numbers like $\pi$.

If we insert all these extra numbers so that every point of our line has a number attached to it, then we have the complete set of *real numbers:*

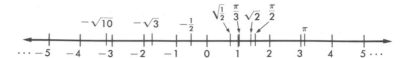

You should check that these numbers appear in the figure in approximately the places where they belong.

The real numbers will be used throughout our geometry. And from now on it is going to be important for us to think of them as being arranged on a line.

A number $x$ is *less than* a number $y$ if $x$ lies to the left of $y$ on the number line, like this:

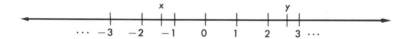

We indicate this fact by writing $x < y$. Obviously every negative number lies to the left of every positive number. Therefore every negative number is less than every positive number. For example,

$$-1,000,000 < \tfrac{1}{10},$$

although $-1,000,000$ may, in a way, seem to be bigger.

Expressions using $<$ are called *inequalities.* Any inequality can be written in reverse: when we write $y > x$, this means that $x < y$. Thus $y > x$ if $y$ lies to the right of $x$ on the number line.

The expression $x \leq y$ means that either $x < y$ or $x = y$. Thus $-2 \leq 1$, because $-2 < 1$; and $2 \leq 2$, because $2 = 2$.

In your study of algebra, you have by now learned a great deal about the behavior of real numbers under addition and multiplication. It is a fact that algebra can be studied in the same way that we shall study geometry in this course. That is, all the algebraic facts that you know can be derived from a few simple postulates. The chances are, however, that you did not study algebra in this manner, and we hardly have time now to begin algebra all over again. In this course, therefore, we shall use nearly all the algebra that you know, without special comment.

We should be careful, however, with inequalities and square roots, because misunderstandings about them are rather common. The relation $<$ is called an *order* relation. Its fundamental properties are the following:

### O-1.  Trichotomy

For every $x$ and $y$, one and only one of the following conditions holds: $x < y$, $x = y$, $x > y$.

### O-2.  Transitivity

If $x < y$ and $y < z$, then $x < z$.

### O-3.  The Addition Law

If $a < b$ and $x \leq y$, then $a + x < b + y$.

### O-4.  The Multiplication Law

If $x < y$ and $a > 0$, then $ax < ay$.

All the usual laws of inequalities follow from these four laws. Finally, we shall need the following:

### R-1.  Existence of Square Roots

Every positive number has at least one positive square root.

There is a rather tricky point in connection with square roots. When we say, in words, that $x$ *is a square root of* $a$, we mean merely that $x^2 = a$. For example, 2 is a square root of 4, because $2^2 = 4$. And $-2$ is also a square root of 4, because $(-2)^2 = 4$. But when we write, in symbols, that $x = \sqrt{a}$, this means that $x$ is the *positive* square root of $a$. Therefore the following statements are true or false, as indicated.

True:   $-2$ is a square root of 4.

False:   $-2 = \sqrt{4}$.

The reason for this usage is simple. If $\sqrt{a}$ were allowed to denote either the positive or the negative root, then we would have no symbol at all for the positive square root of 7. Putting a plus sign in front of $\sqrt{7}$ would get us nowhere, because a plus sign never changes the value of an expression.  If $\sqrt{7}$ were negative, then $+\sqrt{7}$ would be just as negative.  For this reason, we agree that $\sqrt{a}$ always denotes the positive root of $a$.  The negative root of $a$ is $-\sqrt{a}$; and $\sqrt{0} = 0$.

You may find the following statements convenient to refer to when you give reasons for steps that you take in algebra.

### Addition Property of Equality

If $a = b$ and $c = d$, then $a + c = b + d$.

### Subtraction Property of Equality

If $a = b$ and $c = d$, then $a - c = b - d$.

### Multiplication Property of Equality

If $a = b$ and $c = d$, then $ac = bd$.

## Problem Set 2–2

1. Prepare a table with the following column headings: "Real numbers," "Rational numbers," "Integers," "Irrational numbers."  Under the heading "Real numbers" list the following:

$$7, \quad \tfrac{2}{3}, \quad \sqrt{11}, \quad 0.02, \quad \sqrt{4}, \quad 1\tfrac{3}{4}, \quad 14.003, \quad -3,$$

$$\frac{\sqrt{2}}{5}, \quad -\sqrt{\frac{3}{8}}, \quad 0, \quad 1.414, \quad -\sqrt{\frac{9}{16}}, \quad \pi.$$

Complete the table by putting each number under the name of each subset of the real numbers to which it belongs.

2. Tell whether each of the following statements is true or false.

   (a) Negative numbers are real numbers.

   (b) The real number line has at least one end point.

   (c) $-x$ is a negative number for all $x$.

   (d) The point on the real number line corresponding to $\tfrac{7}{8}$ lies between the points corresponding to $\tfrac{6}{7}$ and $\tfrac{8}{9}$.

   (e) There exists a point on the real number line that corresponds to $\sqrt{2}$ which is different from the point corresponding to 1.414.

   (f) If $x$ is a negative number, then $-x$ is a positive number.

   (g) If $x > y$, then $x - y > 0$.

3. In what order would the points corresponding to the numbers in each of the following sets be arranged on a number line in which the positive numbers are to the right of zero?

(a) $\frac{7}{4}$, $1\frac{1}{4}$, $1\frac{5}{8}$.

(b) 4.1, 4.06, 4.012.

(c) $-1.3$, $-0.7$, $-2.14$.

(d) $\frac{8}{5}$, $-1\frac{2}{3}$, $-1\frac{7}{8}$.

4. Write the following using the symbols of order (that is, $<$, $\geq$, etc.):

(a) $x$ is a number greater than 0.

(b) $y$ is a number between $-1$ and 2.

(c) $w$ is a number between $-1$ and 2 inclusive.

(d) $k$ is a positive number.

(e) $m$ is a negative number.

(f) $n$ is a nonnegative number.

5. Restate the following in words:

(a) $AB > CD$.

(b) $m \leq n$.

(c) $-11 < 5 < 8$.

(d) $-2 \leq k \leq 2$.

(e) $x < 0$.

(f) $y \geq 0$.

6. Which of the following are true?

(a) $\sqrt{16} = 4$.

(b) $\sqrt{25} = -5$.

(c) $-\sqrt{64} = -8$.

(d) $-\sqrt{0.36} = -0.6$.

(e) $-\sqrt{0.04} = 0.2$.

7. Which of the following satisfy the condition $\sqrt{x^2} = x$?

(a) $x = 3$.

(b) $x = -3$.

(c) $x = 0$.

(d) $x = 1$.

(e) $x = -1$.

(f) $x < 0$.

(g) $x \geq 0$.

(h) $\dfrac{1}{x} > 0$.

8. Along a number line marked at unit intervals of $\frac{1}{2}$ in., correctly place the following numbers.

$$0, \quad 1, \quad \sqrt{4}, \quad -\sqrt{4}, \quad \sqrt{9}, \quad -\sqrt{9}, \quad \sqrt{16}, \quad -\sqrt{25}.$$

9. If $r$ and $s$ are real numbers other than zero, and $r > s$, indicate whether the following are true for all $r$ and $s$ (T), are true for only some $r$ and $s$ (S), or are never true (F).

(a) $s > r$.

(b) $r - s > 0$.

(c) $\dfrac{r}{s} > 1$.

(d) $s^2 < r^2$.

* 10. Follow the directions of Problem 9 for (a) through (d) below.

(a) $\dfrac{1}{r} > \dfrac{1}{s}$.

(b) $r^3 > s^3$.

(c) $-r < -s$.

(d) $r - 2 < s - 2$.

## 2–3.  ABSOLUTE VALUE

The *absolute value* of a number $x$ is denoted by $|x|$. The meaning of the symbol $|x|$ is readily understood from a few examples:

$$|0| = 0, \qquad |-8| = 8,$$
$$|2| = 2, \qquad |87| = 87,$$
$$|-2| = 2, \qquad |-95| = 95,$$
$$|7| = 7, \qquad |-\sqrt{13}| = \sqrt{13},$$

and so on. Here we are using the following rules:

(1) If $x \geq 0$, then $|x| = x$.

(2) If $x < 0$, then $|x|$ is the corresponding positive number.

If a particular number is written arithmetically, it is easy to see how to write its absolute value. If there is no minus sign in front, we leave the number unchanged. If there is a minus sign in front, we omit the minus sign to get the absolute value.

But when we work algebraically with expressions like $|x|$, $|a - b|$, and so on, it is convenient to have an algebraic form of condition (2). Thus, given a negative number $x$, we wish to have an algebraic way of describing the corresponding positive number. If the negative number is denoted by $x$, then we cannot "omit the minus sign," because there isn't any minus sign to omit. We can get around this difficulty by a simple trick: *if $x < 0$, then the corresponding positive number is $-x$.* Here are some examples:

$$x = -2, \qquad -x = -(-2) = 2,$$
$$x = -3, \qquad -x = -(-3) = 3,$$

and so on.

We can now give a second description of $|x|$.

(1) If $x \geq 0$, then $|x| = x$.

(2) If $x < 0$, then $|x| = -x$.

This second form is more difficult to understand, at first, but it is easier to work with later on. You should try it out on a few numbers, until you are convinced that it really says what we have in mind.

## Problem Set 2–3

1. Evaluate each of the following.

(a) $|5|$.   (b) $|-6|$.   (c) $-|-6|$.
(d) $|2| + (-2)$.   (e) $|2| + |-2|$.   (f) $|8 - 5|$.
(g) $|5 - 8|$.   (h) $|5| - |8|$.   (i) $|-8 - 5|$.

2. Which of the following are true?

(a) $|-3| = 3$.   (b) $|3| = -3$.
(c) $|7 - 9| = |9 - 7|$.   (d) $|0 - 4| = |4 - 0|$.
(e) $|k| = k$ for every real number $k$.

3. Which of the following are true for all values of the variables?

(a) $|-n| = -n$.   (b) $|n^2| = n^2$.
(c) $|x - 3| = |3 - x|$.   (d) $|a - b| = |b - a|$.
(e) $|d + 1| = |d| + 1$.

4. Complete the following statements.

(a) If $k > 0$, then $|k| =$ _____.
(b) If $k < 0$, then $|k| =$ _____.
(c) If $k = 0$, then $|k| =$ _____.

5. The following four figures are graphs on the number line of the algebraic sentences written to the left of each graph.

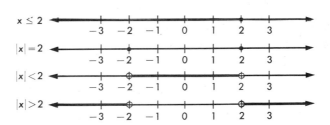

Make graphs for the following sentences.

(a) $x = 1$.   (b) $x$ is a negative number.
(c) $x > 1$.   (d) $x \geq 0$.   (e) $|x| = 1$.
(f) $|x| \leq 1$.   (g) $|x| > 1$.   (h) $|x| \geq 0$.

6. (a) How does the graph of $x < 0$ differ from the graph of $x \leq 0$?
   (b) How does the graph of $|x| = 1$ differ from the graph of $|x| \leq 1$?
   (c) How does the graph of $-1 \leq x \leq 1$ differ from the graph of $|x| < 1$?

* 7. If we consider algebraic sentences with two variables $x$ and $y$, where $x$ and $y$ may be real numbers, we can graph such sentences in the $xy$-plane. You should recall from your previous mathematics course that we graph the set of all ordered pairs $(x, y)$ which make our algebraic sentence true. Thus, the graph of $x - y = 1$ is as shown on the left, and the graph of $x - y \leq 1$ is as shown on the right.

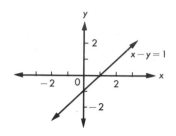 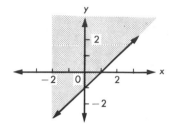

(a) Sketch the graph of $y = |x|$.    (b) Sketch the graph of $y > |x|$.

* 8. Use Problem 7 as an introduction to this problem.
    (a) Sketch the graph of $|x| + |y| = 1$.
    (b) Sketch the graph of $|x| + |y| < 1$.

## 2–4.  RULERS AND UNITS OF DISTANCE

If two points $P$ and $Q$ are no more than one foot apart, we can find the distance between them by laying down an ordinary ruler:

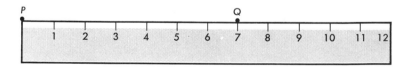

In the figure, the distance is 7 in. Of course, there was no need to place the zero point of the ruler at $P$. We might just as well have laid down the ruler as shown below.

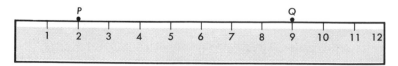

In this case, we find that the distance between $P$ and $Q$, measured in inches, is $9 - 2 = 7$, as before.

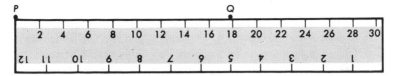

On many rulers one edge is laid off in centimeters. Using the centi-
meter scale, we might have laid down the ruler as shown above. This
gives the distance as about 18 cm, where cm stands for centimeters.

Of course, one foot is 12 in., and one yard is 36 in. One meter (m) is
one hundred centimeters. One millimeter (mm) is one-thousandth of a
meter. We can therefore measure the distance between $P$ and $Q$ in
at least this many ways: 180 mm, 18 cm, .18 m, 7 in., $\frac{7}{12}$ ft, $\frac{7}{36}$ yd.
Thus the *number* that we obtain as a measure of distance depends on
the *unit of measure*.

## Problem Set 2–4A

1. The distance from point $H$ to point $K$, measured in feet, is 4. If we
   choose the inch as our unit, what number is the measure of the distance
   from $H$ to $K$?

2. The distance from $K$ to $M$, measured in inches, is 9. What number
   measures the distance from $K$ to $M$, in feet?

3.

   (a) Rulers marked with various scales are used to measure $PQ$, $PR$, and
       $PT$, and the results are tabulated. Complete the table.

   | Unit of measure | $PQ$ | $PR$ | $PT$ | $QT$ |
   |---|---|---|---|---|
   | Inch | 2 | | | |
   | Foot | | $\frac{1}{4}$ | | |
   | Yard | $\frac{1}{18}$ | | $\frac{1}{9}$ | |
   | Centimeter | 5.08 | | | |
   | Millimeter | | | | 50.8 |
   | Meter | | 0.0762 | | |
   | Palm | | | 0.364 | |
   | Span | 0.54 | | | |

   (b) What is the ratio of $PQ$ to $PR$? of $PQ$ to $PT$?
   (c) Does the ratio of $PQ$ to $PT$ change as different units are used?
   (d) What is $QR$ in inches? in centimeters? in palms?

**4.** Discuss the following questions.

   (a) Why do we have so many units with which to measure distance?

   (b) Suppose we were able to establish just one universal unit with which to measure distance. What advantages would we gain? What disadvantages would result?

**5.** Complete the statements by filling in the appropriate numbers.

   (a) 6 in = _____ ft = _____ yd.

   (b) _____ in = $7\frac{1}{2}$ ft = _____ yd.

   (c) _____ in = _____ ft = $\frac{2}{3}$ yd.

**6.** Complete the statements by filling in the appropriate numbers.

   (a) 2 m = _____ cm = _____ mm.

   (b) _____ m = 50 cm = _____ mm.

   (c) _____ m = _____ cm = 1 mm.

**7.**

$A$, $B$, and $C$ are three points of a line arranged as shown. What is $AC$, given that

   (a) $AB = 6$ in and $BC = 12$ in?

   (b) $AB = 6$ ft and $BC = 12$ ft?

   (c) $AB = 6$ mi and $BC = 12$ mi?

**8.** $A$, $B$, and $C$ are three points of a line arranged in the order shown in Problem 7. What is $AC$, given that

   (a) $AB = 6$ ft and $BC = 12$ in?

   (b) $AB = 6$ in and $BC = 12$ ft?

   (c) $AB = 6$ yd and $BC = 12$ in?

**9.** Note that only the numbers 6 and 12 appear in the statements of Problems 7 and 8. Explain why in Problem 7 the answers to the three parts are the same number, although the units are different, whereas in Problem 8 all the answers are different.

   Logically speaking, one unit works just as well as another. However, using various units in the same problem would cause needless trouble. Let us therefore choose a unit, and agree to use this unit in all our theorems. (It will do no harm to think of this chosen unit as being anything we like. If you happen to like inches, or cubits, or furlongs, you are free to consider that these are the units we are using. *All our theorems will hold true for all units.*)

Thus, once we have chosen a unit, to every pair of points $P$, $Q$ there will correspond a number which tells us how far $P$ is from $Q$. This number is called the *distance* between $P$ and $Q$.

We make this discussion official by stating a postulate and a definition.

**POSTULATE 1.**   The Distance Postulate

> *To every pair of different points there corresponds a unique positive number.*

**Definition**

> The *distance* between two points is the number given by the Distance Postulate. If the points are $P$ and $Q$, then the distance is denoted by $PQ$.

We allow the possibility that $P = Q$, that is, $P$ and $Q$ are the same point. In this case, $PQ = 0$. The distance is defined simply for a pair of points, and does not depend on the order in which the points are mentioned. Therefore we always have $PQ = QP$.

Some of the problems that you will be asked to solve will involve various units such as inches, feet, miles, and so on. As we have already noted, all our theorems will apply to these units, providing that you *consistently use one unit each time you apply a theorem.* In other words, you can make any choice you want, so long as you stick to it, but you can't change units in the middle of a theorem.

## Problem Set 2–4B

1. Allen, Bruce, and Charles measured, in inches, the distance between two points, $P$ and $Q$, marked on a blackboard. Allen said $PQ = 27$, Bruce said $PQ = 27.5$, and Charles said $PQ = 26.75$. How many of the boys could be right? Why? Were any of the boys necessarily right? Discuss.

2. If the distance $PQ$ is 54 in., what is $PQ$ measured in feet? measured in yards?

3. If the distance $RS$ is 15 ft, what is $RS$ measured in inches? measured in yards?

4. Edward and Frank were computing distances between the same points $A$, $B$, and $C$. Edward said, "If $AB = 1$, then $BC = 2\frac{1}{2}$." Frank said, "If $AB = 12$, then $BC = 30$." If both boys were correct, explain how they could get different numbers for the same distances. Does this agree with the Distance Postulate?

5. If the distance $RS$ is $x$ ft, what is $RS$ measured in inches? measured in yards?

\* 6. The distance $AB$ measured in inches is 15 more than 9 times the same distance measured in feet. What is the distance $AB$ in feet?

\* 7. The perimeter of a triangle measured in inches is 10 more than 10 times its perimeter measured in feet. What is the perimeter in feet?

+ 8. If the side of a square is 4 ft, then its perimeter is 16 ft and its area is 16 sq ft. Since $16 = 16$, the statement, "the area of a square equals its perimeter," is true for this square.

   (a) Is the statement true when the side of this square is measured in inches?

   (b) Describe two other squares for which the statement is true.

   (c) What do the three squares for which the statement is true have in common?

+ 9. If the length of a rectangle is 6 ft and its width is 4 ft, the statement, "the perimeter of the rectangle is the sum of twice the length and twice the width," is true for this rectangle.

   (a) Is the statement true when the length and width are measured in inches? in yards?

   (b) Does the truth of this statement depend on a special choice of numbers? on a special choice of units?

+ 10. If the radius of a circle is 2 yd, its circumference ($C = 2\pi r$) is $4\pi$ yd, and its area ($A = \pi r^2$) is $4\pi$ sq yd, then the statement, "the area of the circle equals its circumference," is true for this circle.

   (a) Is the statement true when the radius of this circle is measured in feet?

   (b) Describe two other circles for which the statement is true.

   (c) Does the truth of this statement depend on a special choice of numbers? on a special choice of units?

+ 11. In Problems 8, 9, and 10 you should have observed that some geometric statements are true only for a certain number, no matter what unit is specified. Other statements are true regardless of the choice of numbers or units.

You should verify that each of the following statements is true. Then indicate whether each remains true when the lengths are measured in a different unit. Which statements remain true only if the same number, or set of numbers, is used for all units?

(a) The perimeter of a rectangle 3 ft wide and 4 ft long is 14 ft.

(b) The perimeter of a square 2 ft on a side is twice its area.

(c) The perimeter of a triangle having each side 12 in. long is 36 in.

(d) A triangle whose sides are 3 ft, 4 ft, and 5 ft is a right triangle. (Use the Pythagorean relationship.)

(e) A triangle whose sides are 9 in., 12 in., and 15 in. is a right triangle.

(f) The area of a circle having a 4-ft radius is twice its circumference.

## 2–5.  AN INFINITE RULER

At the beginning of this chapter we laid off a number scale on a line, like this:

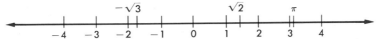

We might, of course, have used a larger scale:

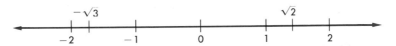

or a smaller scale:

But let us agree, from now on, that every time we lay off a number scale on a line, we are to use the scale given by the Distance Postulate.

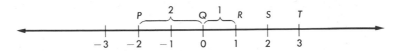

That is, the point labeled 1 is to lie at a distance 1 from the point labeled 0; the point labeled −2 is to lie at a distance 2 from the point labeled 0; and so on.  From the figure we read off the distances

$$QR = 1,$$
$$QS = 2,$$
$$QT = 3.$$

By subtraction, we get

$$RS = 2 - 1 = 1,$$
$$RT = 3 - 1 = 2,$$
$$PR = 1 - (-2) = 3.$$

In fact, it looks as if we can always find the distance by taking the difference of the number labels.

Indeed, this statement is almost right, but not quite.  If we take the points $P$ and $R$ in reverse order, we get the wrong answer,

$$RP = -2 - 1 = -3,$$

which is the *negative* of the right answer.  In fact, subtraction yields a negative answer about half of the time.

It is easy, however, to get around this difficulty: we take the *absolute value* of the difference of the number labels.  When we do this, all our right answers remain right, and all our wrong answers become right. For example,

$$PR = |1 - (-2)| = |3| = 3,$$

and

$$RP = |-2 - 1| = |-3| = 3,$$

as it should be.

Thus we see that the distance between two points is the absolute value of the difference of the corresponding numbers.

We make this common sense official by summing it up in a postulate.

**POSTULATE 2.**   The Ruler Postulate

> *The points of a line can be placed in correspondence with the real numbers in such a way that*
>
> *(1) to every point of the line there corresponds exactly one real number;*
>
> *(2) to every real number there corresponds exactly one point of the line; and*
>
> *(3) the distance between any two points is the absolute value of the difference of the corresponding numbers.*

We call this the Ruler Postulate because, in effect, it furnishes us with an infinite ruler, which we can lay down on any line and use to measure the distance between any two points.

## Definitions

A correspondence of the sort described in the Ruler Postulate is called a *coordinate system*. The number corresponding to a given point is called the *coordinate* of the point.

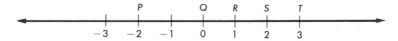

For example, in the figure above, the coordinate of $P$ is $-2$, the coordinate of $Q$ is 0, the coordinate of $R$ is 1, and so on.

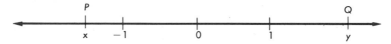

If the coordinate of $P$ is $x$ and the coordinate of $Q$ is $y$, then the Ruler Postulate tells us that

$$PQ = |y - x|.$$

## Problem Set 2–5

**1.**

In the figure a coordinate system, with 0 at $A$ and 1 at $C$, has been established on a line. For clarity of reading, some nonintegral coordinates are written one space lower than the integers. Determine the following distances.

(a) $AC$    (b) $AD$    (c) $EI$    (d) $PR$

(e) $RI$    (f) $AN$    (g) $BH$    (h) $QM$

(i) $AF$    (j) $DJ$    (k) $ND$    (l) $PF$

**2.** Simplify:

(a) $|6 - 2|$        (b) $|2 - 6|$        (c) $|5 - 0|$

(d) $|0 - 5|$        (e) $|0 - (-5)|$        (f) $|4 - (-4)|$

(g) $|x|$        (h) $|x - 0|$        (i) $|x - (-x)|$

(j) $|x| - |-x|$

3. Using the Ruler Postulate find the distance for each pair of points having the following coordinates.

(a) 0 and 8

(b) 8 and 0

(c) 0 and $-8$

(d) $-5$ and $-7$

(e) $-\frac{2}{3}$ and $\frac{1}{3}$

(f) $\sqrt{2}$ and $\sqrt{5}$

(g) $\sqrt{3}$ and $-\sqrt{5}$

(h) $x$ and $y$

(i) $2a$ and $-a$

(j) 0 and $x$

4. If you use an ordinary 12-in. ruler to measure the distance between two points marked on a piece of paper, is it necessary to place the zero at one of the points? Explain.

5. Suppose that in measuring the distance $PQ$ you intend to place the zero of your ruler at $P$ and read a positive number at $Q$. How can you still determine $PQ$ if, instead, you happen to place your ruler so that $P$ corresponds to $\frac{1}{4}$ and

(a) $Q$ corresponds to a positive number?

(b) $Q$ corresponds to a negative number?

6.

In the figure, scale A and scale B use the same unit but assign numbers in a different way.

(a) What are the coordinates of $R$, $P$, and $Q$ on scale A?

(b) Show how to find the distance $RQ$, using scale B; using scale A.

(c) What is the distance $PQ$ on the A-scale? on the B-scale?

7. Consider a coordinate system on a line. Suppose that 3 is added to the coordinate of each point and each new sum becomes the new number assigned to each point.

(a) If $P$ had coordinate 5, what will be its new number? If $Q$ had coordinate $-2$, what will be its new number?

(b) If two points of the line had coordinates $a$ and $b$, what will be their new numbers?

(c) Will each point of the line correspond to a new number? Will each new number correspond to a point of the line?

(d) Show that the formula

$|$(New number for one point) $-$ (New number for other point)$|$

gives the distance between the two points.

(e) Does the new correspondence between points and numbers satisfy each of the three conditions of the Ruler Postulate? Can each new number be called the coordinate of a point? Why?

**8.**

In the figure scale A and scale B use the same unit but assign numbers in a different way.

(a) What is the coordinate of $K$ in scale A?

(b) What are the coordinates of $M$ and $N$ in scale B?

(c) If $x = -6$, what is the coordinate of $M$ in scale B?

(d) If the coordinate of $N$ in the B-scale is $9\frac{1}{2}$, what would $y$ equal?

(e) What is the distance $KM$? the distance $MN$?

**9.** How many real numbers are there? How do you know? Does this tell you anything about the number of points on a line? How many points does a line contain? How does the Ruler Postulate enter into your reasoning?

**10.** In a certain county the towns of Acton, Burnham, and Centerville are collinear (on a line) though not necessarily in this order. The distance from Acton to Burnham is 8 mi. The distance from Burnham to Centerville is 14 mi.

(a) Is it possible to tell which town is between the other two? which town is *not* between the other two?

(b) Use a sketch to determine the distance from Acton to Centerville. Is there more than one possibility?

(c) If you are given the additional information that the distance from Acton to Centerville is 6 mi, then which town is between the other two?

(d) If the distance between Acton and Burnham were $k$ miles, between Acton and Centerville $m$ miles, and between Burnham and Centerville $k + m$ miles, which town would be between the other two?

**11.** $E$, $H$, $K$ are three points on a line. $E$ and $H$ are 3 in. apart and $H$ and $K$ are 5 in. apart. In how many ways can the three points be arranged? Explain with a sketch.

**\* 12.** Three different coordinate systems are assigned to the same line. Three fixed points $A$, $B$, $C$ of the line are assigned coordinates as follows.

In system I the coordinate of $A$ is $-6$ and that of $B$ is $-2$.

In system II the coordinates of $A$ and $C$ are $-4$ and $-3$, respectively.

In system III, the respective coordinates of $C$ and $B$ are 7 and 4.

(a) Which point is between the other two?

(b) Evaluate $AB + AC + BC$.

## 2–6.  THE RULER PLACEMENT POSTULATE. BETWEENNESS. SEGMENTS AND RAYS

The Ruler Postulate tells us that on any line we can set up a coordinate system by laying off a number scale.  Plainly this can be done in many different ways.  For example, given any point $P$ of the line, we can make $P$ the zero point and then lay off the rest of the scale in either direction:

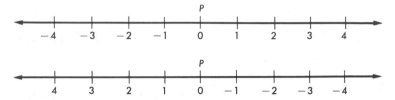

Therefore, if $Q$ is any other point of the line, we can lay off the scale in such a way that the coordinate of $Q$ is positive:

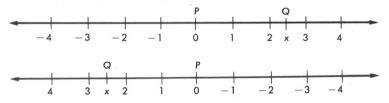

In each case, the scale is laid off so that $x > 0$.

We make this observation official by stating it as a postulate.

**POSTULATE 3.**   The Ruler Placement Postulate

*Given two points P and Q of a line, the coordinate system can be chosen in such a way that the coordinate of P is zero and the coordinate of Q is positive.*

Everybody knows what is meant by the statement that a point $B$ is between two points $A$ and $C$.  It means that the three points lie on the same line, and that they are arranged on the line like this:

or like this:

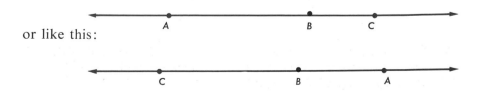

So far, so good.  We doubt that anybody has become confused about the meaning of the word *between*, once a few pictures have been drawn.  But we promised in Chapter 1 that all our geometric terms were going to be defined, except for the terms *point, line,* and *plane*.  To keep the record straight, we had better keep our promise, by giving a mathematical definition of *between* that conveys the idea that we have in mind.  This is easily done.

## Definition

B is *between* A and C if (1) A, B, and C are different points of the same line and (2) $AB + BC = AC$.

It is easily checked that this definition does indeed describe the idea that it is supposed to describe.

There is, however, one rather tricky point in the way this definition is stated.  This is the use of the word *if*.  In a definition, when two statements are connected by the word *if*, then the two statements are considered to be completely equivalent.  Thus, if we know that B is between A and C, we can conclude that both (1) and (2) hold; and if we know that both (1) and (2) hold, we can conclude that B is between A and C.  This use of the word *if* is rather special, because it is different from the usage of ordinary speech.  And the word *if* is not used in this way in postulates and theorems.  Only in definitions does the word *if* mean *is equivalent to*.

## Problem Set 2–6A

1. Consider a coordinate system on a line.  Points R and S have coordinates x and y, respectively.  The Ruler Placement Postulate is applied, that is, the scale is shifted, so that the coordinate of R is 0 and the coordinate of S is a positive number.  What will this positive number be, given that x and y are:

   (a) $x = -3, \quad y = 4$.           (b) $x = -4, \quad y = -10$.

   (c) $x = 8, \quad y = -2$.             (d) $x = \frac{9}{2}, \quad y = -4$.

   (e) $x = 5.2, \quad y = 6.1$.         (f) $x = a, \quad y = b$.

2. A, B, C are three points of a line.  $AC = BC = 5$.  The coordinate of C is 8, and the coordinate of A is greater than the coordinate of B.  What are the coordinates of A and B?

3. $A$, $B$, $C$ are three points of a line. $AC = BC = 10$. The coordinate of $C$ is 8, and the coordinate of $A$ is greater than the coordinate of $B$. What are the coordinates of $A$ and $B$?

4. $M$, $N$, $P$ are three points of a line. $MN = 7$, $NP = 9$, and $MP = 2$. The coordinate of $M$ is 3. What are the coordinates of $N$ and $P$ if

(a) the coordinate of $M$ is less than that of $N$?

(b) the coordinate of $M$ is greater than that of $N$?

5. Suppose $R$, $S$, $T$ are three points of a line. What relation involving $RS$, $ST$ and $RT$ must be true if $R$ is between $S$ and $T$?

6. $P$, $Q$, $R$ are three points of a line. If $PQ = 12$, $PR = 7$ and $QR = 5$, which point is between the other two? Which postulate or definition is a reason for your answer?

7. $G$, $H$, $K$ are three points of a line. The coordinates of $G$ and $H$ are 4 and $-3$, respectively. If $H$ is between $G$ and $K$ and $GK = 13$, what is the coordinate of $K$?

* 8. $A$, $E$, $K$ are three points of a line. The coordinates of $A$ and $K$ are $\sqrt{2}$ and $-\sqrt{18}$. If $AE = EK$, what is the coordinate of $E$?

* 9. $A$, $B$, $C$ are three points of a line with coordinates $a$, $b$, $c$, respectively. If $|a - c| + |c - b| = |a - b|$, which point lies between the other two? Justify your answer.

10. Is the following statement a definition of betweenness for points on a line?

$F$, $G$, $H$ are distinct points on the same line and $FG + GH = FH$ if $G$ is between $F$ and $H$.

How does this wording differ from the statement given in the text?

+ 11. If $A$, $B$ and $C$ are three points on a circle, can you say which point is between the other two? Discuss.

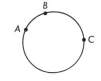

Both of the following statements are obvious.

(1) Let $A$, $B$, and $C$ be points of a line, with coordinates $x$, $y$, and $z$:

If $x < y < z$, then $B$ is between $A$ and $C$.

(2) If $A$, $B$, and $C$ are three different points of the same line, then exactly one of them is between the other two.

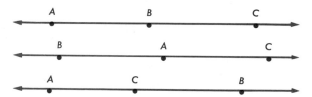

In fact, both of these statements can be proved on the basis of the Ruler Postulate. Without this proof, you may regard both statements as postulates.

We have now reached a stage where we need the following postulate.

## POSTULATE 4.   The Line Postulate

*For every two points there is exactly one line that contains both points.*

The line that contains $A$ and $B$ is denoted by $\overleftrightarrow{AB}$. Here the double-headed arrow over the letters $A$ and $B$ is supposed to remind us of our pictures of lines. The notation suggests that the line is determined when the points $A$ and $B$ are named, and this is exactly what the Line Postulate has just told us. Sometimes, of course, it is simpler to denote a line by one letter such as $L$, $W$, or any other.

A segment is a figure that looks like this:

A more precise description is given by the following definitions.

## Definitions

For any two points $A$ and $B$, the *segment* $\overline{AB}$ is the set whose points are $A$ and $B$, together with all points that are between $A$ and $B$. The points $A$ and $B$ are called the *end points* of $\overline{AB}$.

In the symbol $\overline{AB}$, the horizontal bar on top is supposed to remind us of a picture of a segment. Note that there is a big difference between the segment $\overline{AB}$ and the distance $AB$. In fact, they are objects of completely different kinds: $\overline{AB}$ is a geometric figure, that is, a set of points, while $AB$ is a number which measures the distance between the end points.

## Definition

The number $AB$ is called the *length* of the segment $\overline{AB}$.

A ray is a figure that looks like this:

The figure is meant to indicate that the ray starts at $A$, proceeds through $B$ in a straight line, and then goes on forever in the same direction. In the notation for a ray, we always draw the arrow from left to right, regardless of the direction in which the ray points.  For example, all the rays below would be denoted by $\overrightarrow{AB}$:

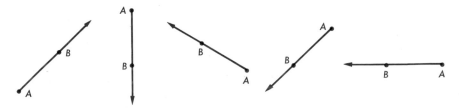

Having explained informally what a ray is supposed to be, we now proceed to give a mathematical definition.

## Definitions

Let $A$ and $B$ be points of a line $L$.  The *ray* $\overrightarrow{AB}$ is the set which is the union of (1) the segment $\overline{AB}$ and (2) the set of all points $C$ for which it is true that $B$ is between $A$ and $C$.  The point $A$ is called the *end point* of $\overrightarrow{AB}$.

The two parts of the ray look like this:

If $A$ is between $B$ and $C$ on $L$, then the two rays $\overrightarrow{AB}$ and $\overrightarrow{AC}$ "point in opposite directions":

**Definition**

If $A$ is between $B$ and $C$, then $\overrightarrow{AB}$ and $\overrightarrow{AC}$ are called *opposite rays*.

Note that a pair of points $A$, $B$ determines at least six geometric figures and one number. The six geometric figures are:

The line $\overleftrightarrow{AB}$

The segment $\overline{AB}$

The ray $\overrightarrow{AB}$

The ray opposite to $\overrightarrow{AB}$

The ray $\overrightarrow{BA}$

The ray opposite to $\overrightarrow{BA}$

The number determined by $A$ and $B$ is, of course, the distance $AB$.

## Problem Set 2–6B

1. $A$, $B$, $C$ are three points on a line with coordinates 7, 3, and 12, respectively. Which point is between the other two?

2. $P$, $Q$, $R$ are three points on a line with coordinates $-5$, $-\sqrt{4}$, and $-\sqrt{12}$, respectively. Which point is between the other two?

3. $G$, $H$, $K$ are three points on a line. Which of the following statements can be true?

   (a) $K$ is between $G$ and $H$, and $H$ is between $G$ and $K$.

   (b) $H$ is between $K$ and $G$, and $H$ is between $G$ and $K$.

   (c) $G$ is between $H$ and $K$, and $K$ is between $G$ and $H$.

   (d) $K$ is between $H$ and $G$, and $G$ is between $K$ and $H$.

   (e) $G$ is between $K$ and $H$, and $G$ is between $H$ and $K$.

4. If three points are on a line, how many of them are not between the other two?

* 5. Three points of a line, $R$, $S$, $T$, have coordinates $a$, $b$, and $a + b$, respectively; $a > 0$ and $a > b$. Which point is between the other two if

   (a) $b > 0$.            (b) $b < 0$.            (c) $b = 0$.

6. *D*, *E*, *F* are three points not all on a line. How many lines do they determine? Name them.

7. *D*, *E*, *F*, *G* are four points no three of which are on a line. How many lines do they determine? Name them.

8. *P*, *Q*, *R* are three points. How many segments do they determine? Name them. How many lines do *P*, *Q*, *R* determine?

9. (a) Is $\overleftrightarrow{AB} = \overleftrightarrow{BA}$? Why?

   (b) Is $\overrightarrow{AB} = \overrightarrow{BA}$? Why?

   (c) Is $\overline{AB} = \overline{BA}$? Why?

10. Is $\overline{AB} = AB$? Why? What is *AB*?

11. (a) Copy the following paragraph, supplying the appropriate symbol, if any, over each letter pair.

    *XZ* contains points *Y* and *V*, but *XZ* contains neither *Y* nor *V*. *V* belongs to *XZ* but *Y* does not. *YZ* + *ZV* = *YV*.

    (b) Make a sketch showing the relative position of the four points in part (a).

12. If $\overrightarrow{RS}$ is opposite to $\overrightarrow{RT}$, which one of the points *R*, *S*, *T* is between the other two?

13. What is the intersection of $\overrightarrow{CD}$ and $\overrightarrow{DC}$? of $\overleftrightarrow{CD}$ and $\overleftrightarrow{DC}$?

14. If *A*, *B*, *C* are three points of a line such that *AC* + *BC* = *AB*, what is the intersection of $\overrightarrow{CB}$ and $\overrightarrow{BA}$? of $\overrightarrow{AC}$ and $\overrightarrow{AB}$? of $\overrightarrow{CA}$ and $\overrightarrow{CB}$?

\*+ 15. Is the following a correct definition of ray $\overrightarrow{AB}$?

    Ray $\overrightarrow{AB}$ is the set of all points *D* of $\overleftrightarrow{AB}$ for which the statement "*A* is between *D* and *B*" is not true.

The following is a consequence of the Ruler Placement Postulate.

**Theorem 2–1.**   The Point-Plotting Theorem

Let $\overrightarrow{AB}$ be a ray, and let *x* be a positive number. Then there is exactly one point *P* of $\overrightarrow{AB}$ such that *AP* = *x*.

**Proof.**   By the Ruler Placement Postulate, we can choose a coordinate system for the line $\overleftrightarrow{AB}$ in such a way that the coordinate of *A* is 0 and the coordinate of *B* is a positive number *r*.

Let $P$ be the point whose coordinate is the given number $x$.   Then $P$ lies on $\overrightarrow{AB}$, because $x > 0$; and $AP = |x - 0| = |x| = x$.   (By definition of the absolute value, $|x| = x$ when $x > 0$.)   Since only one point of the ray has coordinate $x$, only one point of the ray lies at a distance $x$ from $A$.

(Note that this proof copies the procedure that we would use if the ray were drawn on paper and we were plotting the point $P$ with a ruler.   We would put the zero point of the ruler at $A$ and then plot the point opposite the number $x$ on the scale.)

**Definition**

A point $B$ is called the *mid-point* of a segment $\overline{AC}$ if $B$ is between $A$ and $C$ and $AB = BC$.

$$\begin{array}{ccc} A & B & C \end{array}$$

**Theorem 2–2**

Every segment has exactly one mid-point.

**Proof.**   We want a point satisfying the two conditions

$$AB + BC = AC \quad \text{and} \quad AB = BC.$$

These two equations tell us that

$$AB = \frac{AC}{2}.$$

By the preceding theorem, there is exactly one point $B$ of the ray $\overrightarrow{AC}$ that lies at a distance $AC/2$ from $A$.   Therefore $\overline{AC}$ has exactly one mid-point.

**Definition**

The mid-point of a segment is said to *bisect* the segment.

**Problem Set 2–6C**

1.

On $\overrightarrow{ST}$, $S$, $T$, and $V$ are distinct points.   Can $ST = SV$?   Why?

**2.** *P* is a point on a line, and *n* is a positive number. How many points of the line are a distance *n* from *P*? Which definitions or theorems provide reasons for your answer?

**3.** *A*, *B*, *C* are three points of a line. The coordinate of *A* is 0 and the coordinate of *C* is −6. If *B* is the mid-point of $\overline{AC}$, what is the coordinate of *B*?

**4.** *A*, *B*, *C* are three points of a line. The coordinates of *A* and *B* are −2 and 8, respectively. If *C* bisects $\overline{AB}$, what is the coordinate of *C*?

**5.** *B*, the mid-point of $\overline{AC}$, has coordinate 5. If the coordinate of *A* is greater than the coordinate of *C*, and if *BC* = 9, what are the coordinates of *A* and *C*?

**6.** Can you define a mid-point of a line?

**7.** (a) If the coordinates of *P* and *Q* are 4 and 10, respectively, and *M* bisects $\overline{PQ}$, what is the coordinate of *M*?

   (b) What word (or words) completes the following sentence?

   If *M* is the mid-point of $\overline{PQ}$, then the coordinate of *M* is the _____ of the coordinates of *P* and *Q*.

+ **8.** Why is the following statement not a definition of a mid-point of a segment?

   A point *B* is called a mid-point of a segment $\overline{AC}$ if *AB* = *BC*.

*+ **9.** (a) If *A*, *B*, *C* are three distinct points and *AB* + *BC* = *AC*, what is the relationship of the three points?

   (b) If *A*, *B*, *C*, are three distinct points, can *AB* + *BC* > *AC* be true? If not, why not? If true, what is the relationship of *A*, *B*, and *C*?

## 2–7.   CHANGES IN THE UNIT OF DISTANCE

We explained in Section 2–4 that in working problems in geometry, we can choose any unit of distance that we want, provided that in a particular problem we stick to whatever unit we chose. On the other hand, we are free to start all over again with a new unit any time we want.

Suppose, for example, that the distance given by the Distance Postulate uses yards so that for any two points *P*, *Q*, the number

$PQ$ is the number of yards between $P$ and $Q$. If we decide that we would rather use feet, we should multiply all distances by 3. That is, if $(PQ)'$ [pronounced "$PQ$ prime"] is the new distance between $P$ and $Q$, then

$$(PQ)' = 3PQ.$$

The new distance is just as good as the old one. The Ruler Postulate still holds for the new distance, just as it did for the old one.

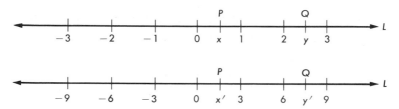

On every line $L$ there is a coordinate system in which

$$PQ = |y - x|.$$

To get a coordinate system that works for the new distance, all we do is multiply each of the old coordinates by 3. Thus, in the figure, $x' = 3x$ and $y' = 3y$. Therefore

$$\begin{aligned}
|y' - x'| &= |3y - 3x| \\
&= 3|y - x| \\
&= 3PQ \\
&= (PQ)',
\end{aligned}$$

just as it should be.

In fact, starting with any two points $A$ and $B$, we can choose a new distance in such a way that $(AB)' = 1$. What we do is to divide *all* the old distances by $AB$; that is,

$$(PQ)' = \frac{PQ}{AB}.$$

Then

$$(AB)' = \frac{AB}{AB} = 1,$$

which is what we wanted. To get a coordinate system on a line, which works for the new distance $(PQ)'$, we divide all the old coordinates by $AB$. That is,

$$x' = \frac{x}{AB}, \qquad y' = \frac{y}{AB}.$$

Therefore

$$|y' - x'| = \left| \frac{y}{AB} - \frac{x}{AB} \right|$$

$$= \frac{|y - x|}{AB}$$

$$= \frac{PQ}{AB}$$

$$= (PQ)',$$

as it should be.

## Problem Set 2–7

**1.**

If, in the figure, $AB = 3$ and $AB = BC = CD = DE = EF$, then $AF = 15$. If $(AB)'$ is the new distance between $A$ and $B$ which uses $AB$ as a unit, what will be the distance $(AF)'$?

**2.** In Problem 1, if $(AC)'$ is the distance between $A$ and $C$ which uses $AC$ as a unit, what will be the distance $(AE)'$? the distance $(AF)'$? the distance $(AB)'$?

**3.** Consider the two statements below and answer the following question for each one: does the truth of the statement depend upon a special choice of unit of distance?

(a) If $A, B, C, D, E, F$ are distinct points of a line such that $AB = BC = CD = DE = EF$, then $AC = BD = CE = DF$.

(b) If $A, B, C, D, E, F$ are distinct points of a line such that $AB = BC = CD = DE = EF$, then $AF$ is exactly divisible by 5. (That is, $AF/5$ is an integer.)

Which of the statements might be considered a more "usable" fact?

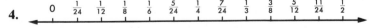

**4.**

The coordinate system indicated in the figure works when distance is measured in feet. Copy the figure on your paper and, placing numerals below the line, indicate a coordinate system which works when distance is measured in inches. Do the same when distance is measured in half-inches; in yards.

**5.**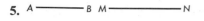

In the figure, the line is marked with two scales. The upper scale uses the length of $\overline{AB}$ as a unit, the lower scale uses the length of $\overline{MN}$ as a unit. Notice that $6AB = 4MN$.

(a) What is the ratio of $AB$ to $MN$?

(b) What is the ratio of $MN$ to $AB$?

(c) How many $AB$'s equal $3MN$?

(d) How many $MN$'s equal $4AB$?

(e) Complete the table below:

| | | |
|---|---|---|
| $1AB = $ _____$MN.$ | $1MN = $ _____$AB.$ |
| $2AB = $ _____$MN.$ | $2MN = $ _____$AB.$ |
| $3AB = $ _____$MN.$ | $3MN = $ _____$AB.$ |
| $4AB = $ _____$MN.$ | $4MN = $ _____$AB.$ |
| $5AB = $ _____$MN.$ | $xMN = $ _____$AB.$ |
| $6AB = $ _____$MN.$ | |
| $xAB = $ _____$MN.$ | |

* **6.** While digging among the ruins of an early civilization a team of archeologists discovered pieces of two old rulers marked with familiar numerical symbols, but each using a different unit of measure. They named one of the scales the "Zee scale" because a symbol similar to a "Z" was carved in the ruler. After some experimenting with the two rulers they found that a square whose side was 1 zee long had a diagonal whose length was a unit of the other scale. Hence, they named this scale the "Diag scale." Making use of the Pythagorean relationship for a right triangle, they then knew that 1 diag $= \sqrt{2}$ zees. A diagram of the two scales appears here.

| 0 Zees | 1 | 2 | 3 | 4 | 5 | 6 | 7 |
|---|---|---|---|---|---|---|---|

| 0 Diags | 1 | 2 | 3 | 4 | 5 |
|---|---|---|---|---|---|

(a) What is the measure, in zees, of a segment whose measure, in diags, is 1? is 2? is 5? is $n$?

(b) Make a table for converting diags into zees up to 10 diags.

(c) What is the measure, in diags, of a segment whose measure, in zees, is 1? is 4? is 5? is 8? is $n$?

(d) Complete this table for converting zees into diags up to 10 zees.

| Number of zees | Number of diags | (Decimal approximation) |
|:---:|:---:|:---:|
| 1 | $\frac{1}{2}\sqrt{2}$ | (0.707) |
| 2 | $\sqrt{2}$ | (1.414) |
| 3 | $\frac{3}{2}\sqrt{2}$ | |
| 4 | | |

## Chapter Review

1. Let $A$ be the set of all months of the year whose names begin with J.
   Let $B$ be the set of all months of the year which have exactly 30 days.
   Let $C$ be the set of all months of the year whose names begin with F.
   (a) What is the intersection of $A$ and $B$?
   (b) What is the union of $A$ and $C$?
   (c) What is the intersection of $B$ and $C$?
   (d) Is set $C$ a subset of set $A$? of set $B$? of set $C$?

2. (a) What is the intersection of $\overline{FD}$ and $\overline{BE}$?
   (b) What is the intersection of $\overline{AE}$ and the triangle $FGE$?
   (c) What is the union of $\overline{ED}$ and $\overline{DC}$?
   (d) What is the union of $\overline{BG}$ and $\overline{BE}$?
   (e) What is the intersection of $\overline{AB}$ and $\overline{EG}$?

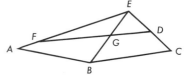

3. (a) How many squares does a given positive number have?
   (b) What is the square of 4?
   (c) How many square roots does a given positive number have?
   (d) Is $\sqrt{4}$ negative?

4. Express the following without absolute value bars.
   (a) $|-6|$
   (b) $|5 - 7|$
   (c) $|5| - |7|$
   (d) $|-5| - 7$
   (e) $|n|$
   (f) $|-n|$
   (g) $|n + (-n)|$
   (h) $|n| + |-n|$

5. (a) If $a < b$, then $a - b$ is _____.
   (b) If $a = b$, then $a - b$ is _____.
   (c) If $a > b$, then $a - b$ is _____.

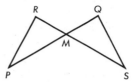

6. (a) What equation defines the relative positions of points $P$, $M$, and $Q$?

(b) Under what conditions would $M$ be the mid-point of $\overline{RS}$?

7. Four points $A$, $B$, $C$, $D$ are arranged along a line such that $AC > AB$ and $BD < BC$. Draw a picture with the four points in place. Is there more than one order possible? Explain.

8. $G$ is the set of all integer pairs $x$ and $y$ whose sum is 21. $H$ is the set of all integer pairs $x$ and $y$ whose difference is 5.

(a) Does the pair 15 and 6 belong to $G$?

(b) Does the pair 9 and 4 belong to $H$?

(c) What is the intersection of $G$ and $H$?

9.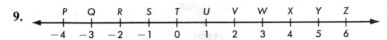

(a) What is the coordinate of $W$? of $S$?

(b) What is the name of the point whose coordinate is 0? $-3$? 5?

(c) Evaluate $RT$, $VZ$, $TW$, $TQ$, $RW$, $PZ$, $XS$, $YQ$.

10. Given a coordinate system on a line. The coordinate of $A$ is 6, of $B$ is $-2$, of $C$ is 1, of $D$ is $x$, of $E$ is $y$.

(a) Which point must be between which two points?

(b) Evaluate $AB$, $BC$, $AD$, $CE$, $BE$, $DE$.

(c) If $x - 6 > 0$ and $y - (-2) < 0$, in what order are the five points arranged on the line?

11. Given a coordinate system on a line. The coordinate of $P$ is 7 and the coordinate of $Q$ is $-12$. What is the coordinate of $M$ if $MP = MQ$?

12. Indicate whether each statement is true or false.

(a) $-5$ is an integer.

(b) $\frac{4}{7}$ is a real number.

(c) 0 is a rational number.

(d) $\sqrt{8}$ is a rational number.

(e) $\sqrt{9}$ is an integer.

(f) $-\dfrac{31}{6}$ is a rational number.

(g) $\dfrac{\sqrt{2}}{4}$ is a rational number.

(h) $-x$ is a negative number for all real $x$.

(i) $-\sqrt{\dfrac{4}{9}}$ is a rational number.

(j) $|x| = x$.

13. If the distance from $A$ to $B$ measured in inches is $k$, what is $AB$ measured in feet?

**14.** If the distance from $P$ to $M$ measured in yards is $t$, what is $PM$ measured in inches?

**15.** The letter pairs in the following paragraph indicate either numbers, lines, line segments, or rays. Copy the paragraph, putting in the proper symbols where they belong.

> $AB + BC = AC$. $DB$ contains the points $A$ and $C$, but $DB$ contains neither the point $A$ nor the point $C$. $A$ belongs to $DB$ but $C$ does not.

Make a sketch showing the relative position of the four points.

**16.** If $A$, $B$, $C$, $D$ are distinct points such that $\overleftrightarrow{AC}$ contains $B$ and $\overleftrightarrow{BD}$ contains $C$, which of these statements must be true?

(a) $B$ is between $A$ and $C$.    (b) $\overleftrightarrow{BC}$ contains $A$.

(c) $\overleftrightarrow{AC} = \overleftrightarrow{BD}$.    (d) $\overleftrightarrow{AC}$ and $\overleftrightarrow{BD}$ intersect at $B$ and $C$ only.

(e) $\overleftrightarrow{AD}$ and $\overleftrightarrow{BC}$ do not intersect.

(f) $\overrightarrow{AC}$ is opposite to $\overrightarrow{DB}$.

**17.** Given a coordinate system on $\overleftrightarrow{AB}$ such that $\overline{AB}$ is the set of all points whose coordinates $x$ satisfy the condition $-5 \leq x \leq 7$. The coordinate of $A$ is less than the coordinate of $B$.

(a) What is the coordinate of the end point of $\overrightarrow{AB}$? of $\overrightarrow{BA}$? of the ray opposite to $\overrightarrow{BA}$?

(b) What is the coordinate of the mid-point of $\overline{AB}$?

**18.** (a) Draw two segments $\overline{AB}$ and $\overline{CD}$ for which the intersection of $\overline{AB}$ and $\overline{CD}$ is the empty set but the intersection of $\overleftrightarrow{AB}$ and $\overleftrightarrow{CD}$ is exactly one point.

(b) Draw two segments $\overline{PQ}$ and $\overline{RS}$ for which the intersection of $\overline{PQ}$ and $\overline{RS}$ is the empty set, but $\overleftrightarrow{PQ} = \overleftrightarrow{RS}$.

**19.** The first numbering of the points of the line below represents a coordinate system. Which of the numberings given in (a) through (e) are not coordinate systems according to the Ruler Postulate and the Ruler Placement Postulate?

| | $-4$ | $-3$ | $-2$ | $-1$ | $0$ | $1$ | $2$ | $3$ | $4$ | $5$ | $6$ |
|---|---|---|---|---|---|---|---|---|---|---|---|
| (a) | $-4$ | $3$ | $2$ | $1$ | $0$ | $-1$ | $-2$ | $-3$ | $-4$ | $-5$ | $-6$ |
| (b) | $-6$ | $-5$ | $-4$ | $-3$ | $-2$ | $-1$ | $0$ | $1$ | $2$ | $3$ | $4$ |
| (c) | $0$ | $1$ | $2$ | $3$ | $4$ | $5$ | $6$ | $7$ | $8$ | $9$ | $0$ |
| (d) | $-10$ | $-9$ | $-8$ | $-7$ | $-6$ | $-5$ | $-4$ | $-3$ | $-2$ | $-1$ | $0$ |
| (e) | $5$ | $4$ | $3$ | $2$ | $1$ | $0$ | $1$ | $2$ | $3$ | $4$ | $5$ |

+ **20.** For each sentence below, consider the set of all points on a line whose coordinates $x$ satisfy the condition.

(a) $x \leq 3$.        (b) $x = 1$.        (c) $5 \geq x \geq 0$.

(d) $x \geq 1$.        (e) $x = -4$.        (f) $x \leq -2$ or $x \geq 2$.

(g) $|x| \leq 2$.        (h) $|x| \geq 0$.

Which of the sets is a ray? a point? a line? a segment? Sketch each of the figures.

# 3 | Lines, Planes, and Separation

## 3–1. INTRODUCTION

In the last chapter we were talking only about lines and the measurement of distance. As a matter of fact, we were talking about lines one at a time, without discussing any relations among them. We shall now begin the study of lines and planes in space. We recall that our basic undefined terms are *point*, *line*, and *plane*—lines and planes are sets of points.

### Definition

The set of all points is called *space*.

In the following section we shall explain some of the terms that we shall use in discussing lines and planes, and state some of the most elementary facts about them. Most of these facts will be stated as postulates. Some of them will be stated as theorems. In a later chapter, we shall see that all the theorems of this chapter can be proved on the basis of the postulates. But in this chapter, we shall not be concerned with their proofs, except in one very easy case. All we are trying to do here is to get a few basic facts straight, and to learn to draw pictures of figures in space.

## Problem Set 3–1

[*Note:* When learning to think about relationships among points, lines, and planes in three-dimensional space, it is often helpful to use pieces of cardboard to illustrate planes, and a pencil to illustrate a line.]

1. Hold your arm straight out in front of you. Consider a point *A*, at the tip of your forefinger, and a point, *B*, at the upper right front corner of your room. How many lines contain both points *A* and *B*? What postulate supports your answer?

2. Take your book or a piece of stiff cardboard. Can you support it in a fixed position on the ends of two pencils? What is the minimum number of pencils needed to support it in this manner?

3. Can three points lie on one line? Must three points lie on one line?

4. Let a corner of your desk represent a point *P*, the light switch on the wall a point *Q*, and a corner of the room a point *R*. Is there a plane containing points *P*, *Q*, and *R*?

5. What is the minimum number of points necessary to determine a plane? Will three points always determine a plane?

6. In this sketch of a pup tent, what line segments must you imagine in order to complete the outline of the tent? What is the intersection of the planes that contain the two sides of the tent?

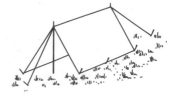

7. The tent in this sketch has a square floor.   What line segments will complete the outline of the tent?

8. Hold two pencils together by their sharpened ends between your thumb and forefinger.  If the pencils represent two intersecting lines, how many planes will contain both these lines?

9. Which sketch do you consider to be a more meaningful picture of a book?  How would you have to hold a book so that it would appear as in sketch (a)? as in sketch (b)?

(a)   GEOMETRY    !!!                                          (b)

10. A board 8 ft long is marked at its middle, that is, 4 ft from either end.  A man carefully saws the board at the mark, yet neither resulting half is 4 ft long.  Moreover, the combined lengths of the two half-pieces does not equal the original length of the whole board.  How can you explain this?

## 3-2.  LINES, PLANES, AND PICTURES

The figure on the left (p. 57) is a picture of a triangular pyramid. The segments $\overline{AB}$, $\overline{AC}$, $\overline{AD}$, $\overline{BC}$, $\overline{BD}$, and $\overline{CD}$ are called its *edges*. Note that the edge $\overline{BD}$ is dashed, because you couldn't see it if the pyramid were solid.  If the figure had been drawn as shown on the right, it would look like a set of points lying in a plane.

The points $A$, $E$, $B$, $C$, and $F$ all lie in a single plane, namely, the plane that contains the upper front face of the pyramid.  Such a set of points is called *coplanar*.  Of course, the points $A$, $B$, $C$, and $D$ are not coplanar.

The points $A$, $E$, and $B$ all lie on a single line, namely, the line $\overleftrightarrow{AB}$. Such a set of points is called *collinear*.  Of course, the points $A$, $B$,

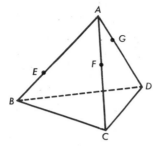 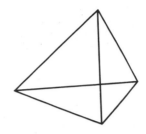

and *C* do not form a collinear set. Similarly, *A*, *F*, and *C* form a collinear set, but *A*, *F*, and *G* do not.

We now repeat these statements more formally.

**Definition**

> A set of points is *collinear* if there is a line which contains all the points of the set.

**Definition**

> A set of points is *coplanar* if there is a plane which contains all points of the set.

[*Query:* In the figure on the left above, the points *E*, *F*, and *G* are not in any one face of the pyramid. Does it follow that *E*, *F*, and *G* are not coplanar?]

To do geometry under the scheme described in Chapter 1, we need postulates that convey the real meanings of our undefined terms: *point*, *line*, and *plane*. For lines, we have already done this. The Ruler Postulate is a good description of what lines look like when you view them one at a time. We have also said that any two points determine a line, when we stated Postulate 4 on p. 41.

**POSTULATE 4.**  The Line Postulate

> *For every two points there is exactly one line that contains both points.*

We now wish to write postulates that will describe planes and space. Our first step is a postulate which says that figures of the kind that we pictured at the beginning of this section really do occur in our geometry.

**POSTULATE 5**

> (*a*) *Every plane contains at least three noncollinear points.*
>
> (*b*) *Space contains at least four noncoplanar points.*

This is merely another way of saying that planes are wide and space is not flat.

Finally, we observe that the Line Postulate conveys some information on the manner in which lines intersect each other.

### Theorem 3–1

If two different lines intersect, their intersection contains only one point.

**Proof.**   If two different lines intersected at two different points $P$ and $Q$, then there would be two lines containing $P$ and $Q$. The Line Postulate tells us that this never happens.

Hereafter, whenever we speak of *two* lines, or *two* planes, we shall always mean that the lines or planes are different. That is, when we speak of two things, we shall always mean that there are indeed two separate items. But if we say merely that $P$ and $Q$ are points, we mean to allow the possibility that $P = Q$.

## Problem Set 3–2

1. Decide by looking at this drawing of a three-dimensional figure whether each following set of points is (1) collinear, (2) not collinear but coplanar, or (3) not coplanar.

   (a) $\{A, B, C, D\}$.
   (b) $\{A, D, B\}$.
   (c) $\{P, D, Q\}$.
   (d) $\{P, B, C\}$.
   (e) $\{A, B, C, Q\}$.

2. How many lines may contain one given point? two given points? any three given points?

3. Given: $P$ and $Q$ are different points. Line $L_1$ contains both $P$ and $Q$. Line $L_2$ contains both $P$ and $Q$.

   What must be true of $L_1$ and $L_2$? What postulate or theorem supports your conclusion?

4. Given: $L_1$ and $L_2$ are different lines. Point $P$ lies on $L_1$ and on $L_2$. Point $Q$ lies on $L_1$ and on $L_2$.

   What must be true of $P$ and $Q$? What postulate or theorem supports your conclusion?

**5.** Write a careful definition of a noncollinear set of points.

**6.** Tell how many lines can be drawn through pairs of the different points *A*, *B*, *C*, and *D* if

(a) *A*, *B*, and *C* are collinear.

(b) no three of the points are collinear.

(c) the points are noncoplanar.

**7.** Given a line *L*, how many planes in space may contain *L*?

+ **8.** Make a model of the figure in Problem 1, using toothpicks and glue.

## 3–3. LINES, PLANES, AND PICTURES (CONTINUED)

The following postulate describes the flatness of planes.

### POSTULATE 6

*If two points of a line lie in a plane, then the line lies in the same plane.*

Our next theorem describes the way in which lines and planes intersect each other.

### Theorem 3–2

If a line intersects a plane not containing it, then the intersection contains only one point.

(Later we shall see that Theorem 3–2 gives no new information; it follows from Postulate 6, just as Theorem 3–1 follows from Postulate 4.)

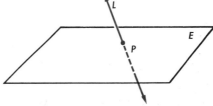

In the figure, we see a line *L* intersecting a plane *E* in the way that Theorem 3–2 says it ought to. You will see many figures of this kind, and you should examine them carefully so that you can learn to draw them yourself. To draw a line, of course, we first draw a segment of the line and then put arrowheads at the ends to indicate that the line isn't supposed to stop.   Usually we indicate a plane by drawing a rectangle in the plane.  When we look at a rectangle edgewise, as we are supposed to in the figure above, the rectangle looks like a parallelogram.  Similarly, a circle seen in perspective looks like an ellipse, as shown on the left below.  If our eyes were in the plane of the rectangle, the rectangle would merely look like a segment, as on the right below, and the drawing would be logically correct, but not instructive.

Postulate 4 told us that two points determine a line.  To determine a plane, we need three noncollinear points.

## POSTULATE 7.   The Plane Postulate

*Any three points lie in at least one plane, and any three noncollinear points lie in exactly one plane.*

More briefly, *any three points are coplanar, and any three noncollinear points determine a plane.*

### Theorem 3–3

Given a line and a point not on the line, there is exactly one plane containing both.

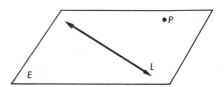

### Theorem 3–4

Given two intersecting lines, there is exactly one plane containing both.

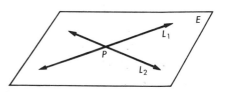

Finally, we state the following postulate.

## POSTULATE 8

*If two different planes intersect, then their intersection is a line.*

It may look as if we were going to continue indefinitely, writing down an endless series of postulates to describe our common-sense ideas about space. It will turn out, however, that we do not need to do this. In this book, we shall study the geometry of space on the basis of only twenty-four fundamental statements. Everything else can be derived from these if you know how. In this text, you will learn how.

Twenty-four should not be regarded as a large number. It is really so small that it makes geometry completely different from a science such as biology for example. In biology, twenty-four facts would get us nowhere; to obtain the thousands of other facts that we need to know, we have to go on working in the laboratory, examining the actual plants and animals. In place of a laboratory, geometry uses logical reasoning, starting with a very small number of fundamental facts.

## Problem Set 3–3

1. How many planes can contain one given point? two given points? three given points?

2. On a level floor, a four-legged table will sometimes rock, while a three-legged table is always steady. Explain.

3. Which postulate does this figure illustrate?

4. Complete the sentence: two different lines may intersect in a _____, and two different planes may intersect in a _____.

5. Given: Plane $E$ contains points $R$ and $T$. What can you conclude about $\overleftrightarrow{RT}$? What postulate or theorem supports your answer? Draw a figure to illustrate this problem.

6. Draw a plane, $E$, using a parallelogram to indicate the plane. Draw a line segment which lies in the plane $E$. Draw a line segment which intersects plane $E$ in only one point, but which does not intersect the other segment.

7. If $\overleftrightarrow{AB}$ and plane $F$ have points $K$ and $M$ in common, what can you conclude about $\overleftrightarrow{AB}$ and $F$? Why?

8. A line may be named by naming two of its points. How many points of a plane must be named, to name the plane?

9. Given: Points $A$, $B$, $C$ lie in plane $E$. Points $A$, $B$, $C$ lie in plane $F$. Can you conclude that plane $E$ is the same as plane $F$? Explain.

**10.** Given: $L_1$ and $L_2$ are different lines. $L_1$ lies in plane $E$. $L_2$ lies in plane $F$. $L_1$ and $L_2$ intersect at point $P$. Point $Q$, different from $P$, lies on $L_1$ and is in $F$. Point $R$, different from $P$, lies on $L_2$ and is in $E$.

What can you conclude about plane $E$ and plane $F$? What postulates or theorems support your answer?

**11.** Examine this figure of a rectangular solid until you see how it is drawn to look like a three-dimensional figure. Then close the book and draw a figure like this from memory. Practice until you are satisfied with the results.

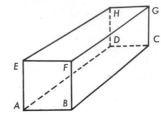

**12.** After doing Problem 11, draw a figure of a cube.

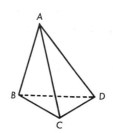

+  **13.** The figure which is the union of all the segments that have four noncoplanar points as their end points is called a triangular pyramid, or a tetrahedron. The four points are the vertices of the tetrahedron.

    (a) Make a definition of an edge of a tetrahedron.

    (b) How many edges does the tetrahedron have? Name them.

    (c) Are there any pairs of edges that do not intersect?

    (d) A face is the triangular region determined by any three vertices. Name the four faces. Are there any pairs of faces that do not intersect?

+  **14.** This figure is a square pyramid whose base, a square, is supposed to be closest to you. Name the planes determined by its vertices. (You should find seven planes.)

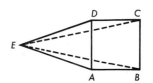

*+ **15.** Consider the following definitions.

> *M-space* is a set whose only elements are four noncoplanar points, $A$, $B$, $C$, and $D$. A *line* is any pair of points belonging to $M$-space. A *plane* is any triplet of points belonging to $M$-space.

Show by carefully examining all point pairs and triplets that $M$-space satisfies Postulates 4, 5, 6, 7, 8 and Theorems 3–1, 3–2, 3–3, 3–4. Such a system is called a four-point geometry.

What postulate has the text included which assures us that ordinary space contains infinitely many points?

## 3-4.  CONVEX SETS

A set of points is called *convex* if you never have to leave the set to take a shortcut.  For example, each of the sets shown below is convex:

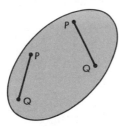  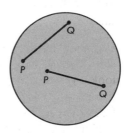

Each of these sets is a whole region in the plane, not just the boundary. In these sets, you can get from any point $P$ to any other point $Q$, moving along a straight line, without leaving the set.  Note the samples shown above.

On the other hand, none of the following sets are convex.

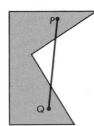 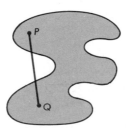 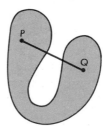

We have indicated why not by giving examples of points $P$ and $Q$ which cannot be joined by segments lying in the set.

Stating all of this more mathematically, we present the following definition.

### Definition

A set $A$ is called *convex* if for every two points $P$ and $Q$ of the set, the entire segment $\overline{PQ}$ lies in $A$.

The sets that we have been talking about so far are "small," but a convex set may easily be large.  For example, every plane is a convex set; and a line in a plane cuts the plane into two sets, each of which is convex and is infinite in extent.  These two 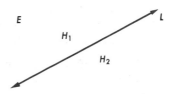 sets $H_1$ and $H_2$ are called *half-planes* or *sides* of the line $L$, and $L$ is called the *edge* of each of them.

Half-planes are convex because if two points are on the same side of the line, the segment joining them never crosses the line.

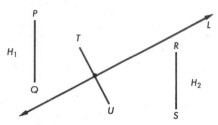

On the other hand, if $T$ and $U$ are points on opposite sides of the line, the segment $\overline{TU}$ *always* intersects the line.

We now summarize the preceding statements in a postulate and some definitions.

**POSTULATE 9.**   The Plane Separation Postulate

*Given a line and a plane containing it.   The points of the plane that do not lie on the line form two sets such that*

*(1) each of the sets is convex, and*

*(2) if P is in one of the sets and Q is in the other, then the segment $\overline{PQ}$ intersects the line.*

**Definitions**

Given a line $L$ and a plane $E$ containing it, the two sets described in the Plane Separation Postulate are called *half-planes* or *sides* of $L$, and $L$ is called the *edge* of each of them.   If $P$ lies in one of the half-planes and $Q$ lies in the other, then we say that $P$ and $Q$ *lie on opposite sides of L.*

Our postulate tells us two things about the way in which a line separates a plane into two half-planes.

(1) If two points lie in the same half-plane, then the segment joining them lies in the same half-plane, and so *never* intersects the line.

(2) If two points lie in opposite half-planes, then the segment joining them *always* intersects the line.

While a line has only two sides in any given plane, every line has infinitely many sides in space.   In the next figure, we see five of the infinitely many half-planes in space that have the line $L$ as an edge.

[*Query:* Is there a difference between the following two statements?

(1) $P$ and $Q$ lie on different sides of $L$.

(2) $P$ and $Q$ lie on opposite sides of $L$.]

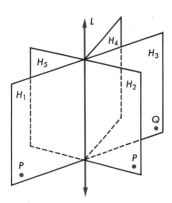

A plane separates space in exactly the same manner in which a line separates a plane.

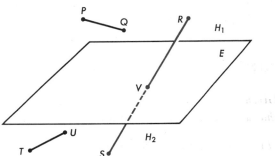

The two sets into which a plane separates space are called *half-spaces*, or *sides* of the plane. In the figure, these are $H_1$ (above the plane) and $H_2$ (below). Each of the two half-spaces is convex. But if $R$ is in one of them and $S$ is in the other, the segment $\overline{RS}$ always intersects the plane.

Again we sum up with a postulate and some definitions.

**POSTULATE 10.**   The Space Separation Postulate

*The points of space that do not lie in a given plane form two sets, such that*

*(1) each of the sets is convex, and*

*(2) if $P$ is in one of the sets and $Q$ is in the other, then the segment $\overline{PQ}$ intersects the plane.*

**Definitions**

The two sets described in the Space Separation Postulate are called *half-spaces*, and the given plane is called the *face* of each of them.

Note that while every line in space is the edge of infinitely many half-planes, every plane in space is a face of only two half-spaces.

## Problem Set 3–4

[*Note:* In answering the problems of this set use your intuitive understanding in situations not covered by our postulational structure.]

1. Be prepared to discuss the following questions orally.

    (a) Is a line a convex set? Explain.

    (b) Is a set consisting of only two points convex? Why?

    (c) If a single point is removed from a line, do the remaining points form a convex set?

    (d) Is a circle a convex set?

    (e) Is the interior of a circle a convex set?

    (f) Is a sphere a convex set?

    (g) Is the space enclosed by a sphere a convex set?

    (h) Does a point separate a plane? space? a line?

    (i) Does a ray separate a plane? does a line? does a segment?

    (j) Can two lines in a plane separate the plane into two regions? three regions? four regions? five regions?

2. Every point on $\overline{AB}$ is contained in the set $K$. Does this mean that $K$ is a convex set? Explain.

3. Is every plane a convex set? Explain. Which postulate is essential to your explanation?

4. Which of the regions named by capital letters are convex sets?

   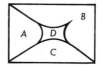

5. If one point is removed from a plane, is the resulting set convex?

6. The interiors, $C$ and $D$, of the two circles are each convex sets.

    (a) Is their intersection a convex set?

    (b) Is their union a convex set?

7. If $L$ is a line in plane $E$, is the set of all points of $E$ on one side of $L$ a convex set?

8. Draw a plane quadrilateral (a figure with four sides) whose interior is convex. Draw one whose interior is not convex.

9. Is the set of points consisting of all points of a sphere and all points in the interior of the sphere a convex set?

10. Is a torus (a doughnut-shaped figure) a convex set?

11. Draw two half-planes which have a common edge and are coplanar. Draw two which have a common edge but are not coplanar.

12. Draw two half-planes which are coplanar but do not have a common edge.

13. $H_1$ and $H_2$ are two coplanar half-planes. Is the union of $H_1$ and $H_2$ the whole plane if

   (a) $H_1$ and $H_2$ have the same edge? Explain.

   (b) the edge of $H_1$ intersects the edge of $H_2$ in exactly one point? Explain.

14. (a) Into how many sets does a point on a line separate the line? What name would you suggest giving to each of these sets?

   (b) Using the terminology you developed in part (a), write a Line Separation Statement similar to Postulates 9 and 10.

15. How does a ray differ from a half-line?

+ 16. Can three lines in a plane ever separate the plane into three regions? four regions? five regions? six regions? seven regions?

+ 17. Into how many sets do two intersecting planes separate space? two parallel planes?

+ 18. What is the greatest number of sets into which space can be separated by three different planes? What is the least number?

+ 19. Is the following statement true or false? The union of any two convex sets which have at least two points in common is a convex set. Defend your answer.

*+ 20. Write a careful explanation of why the following statement is true: the intersection of any two convex sets which have at least two points in common is a convex set. [*Hint:* Let $P$ and $Q$ be any two common points. Which sets must contain $\overline{PQ}$?]

*+ 21. Sketch any geometrical solid bounded by plane surfaces such that the set of points in the interior of the figure is not convex.

## 3-5. THE SEVEN BRIDGES OF KÖNIGSBERG

You might think that there isn't much to the idea of crossing streets, bridges, etc., but as a matter of fact there is a famous problem in mathematics that involves the idea of "crossing" and hardly any other idea at all.

The city of Königsberg is on the coast of the Baltic Sea, at the mouth of the Pregel River. (The ö in Königsberg is pronounced like the *ur* in the English word b*ur*n.) In the river there are two islands, linked to the mainland and to each other by seven bridges, as shown below.

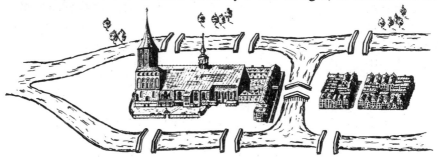

The people who strolled around on these islands found that if they started on the south bank of the river, they could not plan their walk so as to cross each of the bridges exactly once. It seemed that they had to skip at least one bridge:

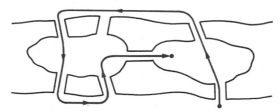

or cross some bridge twice:

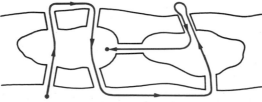

People were convinced that they couldn't cross each bridge exactly once, but nobody was sure. Finally in the year 1735, somebody submitted the problem to the great Swiss mathematician Leonard Euler (pronounced Oiler). Euler discovered that people might as well quit trying. He came up with the following analysis of the problem.

First consider the island on the east:

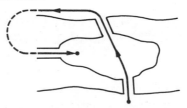

There are three bridges leading to it. Since you started on the south bank, as the problem requires, you must have started somewhere *off* the eastern island. Since you make each of the three crossings exactly once, you end up *on* the eastern island. (Similarly, if the lights are *off*, and you flip the switch three times, then the lights are *on*.)

Next consider the western island.

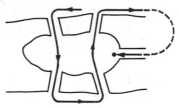

There are five bridges leading to it, and five is an odd number. Therefore, since you started *off* the western island, you must end up *on* the western island. (This is like flipping a light switch five times: if the light was off at the start, it is on at the end.)

But this means that the "Königsberg Walk" is impossible, because you can't end up in two places at once.

Euler's solution of this problem was a very important event because it was the first time that anybody had solved this *kind* of problem. Note that if you draw the map of the islands on a sheet of rubber, you can stretch the rubber any way you like without changing the problem at all.

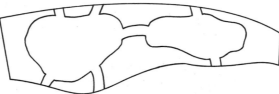

From Euler's analysis of the "Königsberg Walk" developed a whole branch of mathematics, dealing with problems of this kind. This is called *topology*.

Incidentally, if you want to find Königsberg on the map, you should look for it on an old map. The city is now in the Soviet Union, and has been renamed Kaliningrad. Nobody has renamed the problem.

LEONHARD EULER (1707–1783)

Euler's solution of the problem of the seven bridges of Königsberg was typical of his insight and ingenuity. Before his time, it had not occurred to anybody that this sort of problem belonged to mathematics at all. Since then, mathematics has grown fast, in many unexpected directions. Euler's analysis of the Königsberg bridge problem was the first hint of a new branch of mathematics, now known as topology, which has reached its highest development in the twentieth century and is still growing.

Euler was not only very clever but hard working; he produced original mathematics at a rate which has hardly been equaled. His collected mathematical works fill over sixty large volumes. At twenty-eight he lost the sight in one eye; and at fifty he became almost totally blind. But his memory was fabulous—he knew all of Vergil's Aeneid by heart—and he had always been able to carry out long calculations in his head. Thus he was able to go on working, at the same rate as before, for the rest of his life.

# Chapter Review

1. (a) A set of points is collinear if_____

   _____

   (b) A set of points is coplanar if_____

   _____

   (c) May 4 points be collinear?   (d) Must 2 points be collinear?

   (e) Must 4 points be collinear?   (f) May $n$ points be collinear?

   (g) Must 4 points be coplanar?   (h) May $n$ points be coplanar?

2. Which of the statements below are true? Explain.

   (a) If 3 points are collinear, then they are coplanar.

   (b) If 3 points are coplanar, then they are collinear.

3. Comment on the statement, "The top of the table is a plane."

4. Study the three-dimensional figure given (in which $A$, $B$, $C$, $D$ are coplanar) and answer the following questions.

   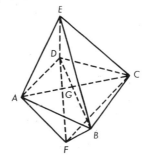

   (a) Are $E$, $D$, $F$ collinear?

   (b) Are $E$, $C$, $B$, $F$ coplanar?

   (c) Do $\overline{AC}$ and $\overline{BD}$ intersect?

   (d) Do $\overline{AC}$ and $\overline{DF}$ intersect?

   (e) Are $E$, $B$, $F$ coplanar?

   (f) Are $F$, $B$, $G$, $D$ coplanar?

5. List all the conditions we have studied which determine a plane. You need only list conditions which we have stated in postulates and theorems. For example, "A line and a point not on the line determine a plane" (Theorem 3–3).

6. How many planes will contain three given points if no one line contains them?

7. Line $L_1$ intersects plane $E$ in $P$, but does not lie in $E$. Line $L_2$ lies in plane $E$, but does not contain point $P$. Is it possible for $L_1$ to intersect $L_2$? Explain.

8. Two planes $E$ and $F$ intersect in $\overleftrightarrow{AB}$. Each of points $P$ and $Q$ lies in both planes $E$ and $F$. Must $P$ and $Q$ lie on $\overleftrightarrow{AB}$? Explain.

9. Indicate whether the following statements are true or false.

(a) Three-dimensional space contains at least four points.

(b) Every half-plane contains its edge.

(c) A ray separates a plane.

(d) Every plane separates space into two convex sets.

(e) If line $L$ separates plane $E$ into half-planes $H_1$ and $H_2$, and if $P$ is a point in $H_1$ and $Q$ is a point in $H_2$, then $\overline{PQ}$ intersects $L$.

(f) Any two half-planes are coplanar.

10. Which of the regions named by capital letters are convex sets?

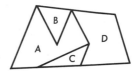

11. What common property do half-planes and half-spaces have?

12. Write a definition of convex set.

13. Is the union of two half-planes always a plane? Is it ever a plane? Explain.

14. Complete the following by referring to the figure.

In the figure, _____ $E$ separates space into _____ $H_1$ and _____. We know that $A$ and _____ are on the same side of _____ since _____ does not intersect plane $E$. Also, $B$ and $D$ are on _____ _____ of $E$, since _____ _____. We can demonstrate that $\overline{AC}$ _____ by showing that $A$ and _____ are on _____ of plane $E$.

15. Draw a line $L$ separating the plane into two half-planes. Label the half-planes $H_1$ and $H_2$. Pick points $D$ and $K$ in $H_1$ and point $F$ in $H_2$.

(a) What is the intersection of $\overline{DK}$ and $L$? Why?

(b) What is the intersection of $\overline{KF}$ and $L$? Why?

+ 16. Each of the planes $E$, $F$, $G$ intersects the other two as shown in the figure. Into how many convex regions do they separate space?

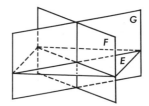

+ **17.** In this problem, you "win" if you can cross each segment of the figure exactly once without lifting your pencil from the paper. Copy the figures on a piece of paper and see whether you can discover in which two of the five figures it is possible for you to "win." Is there a way to make up figures for which you must always "lose"?

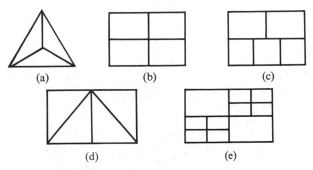

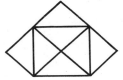

(a)  (b)  (c)

(d)  (e)

+ **18.** Of the three figures shown, two can be drawn without lifting your pencil or retracing a line segment, while the third one cannot. Which two can be drawn in this manner? Try to reproduce each figure on your paper without lifting your pencil or retracing a segment. Is there an easier way of arriving at a conclusion?

# 4 | Angles and Triangles

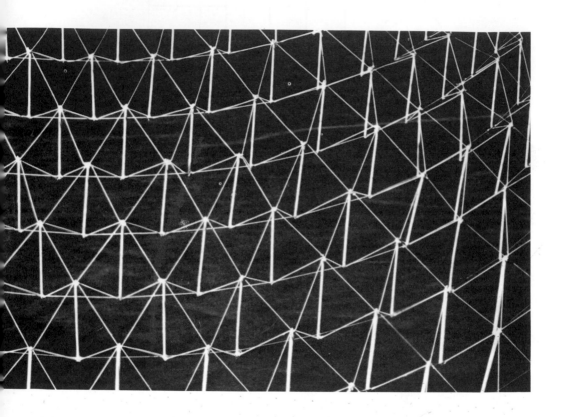

## 4–1. THE BASIC TERMS

An *angle* is a figure like one of these:

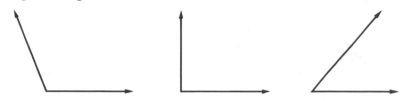

### Definitions

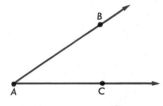

If two rays have the same end point, but do not lie on the same line, then their union is an *angle*. The two rays are called its *sides*, and their common end point is called its *vertex*. If the rays are $\overrightarrow{AB}$ and $\overrightarrow{AC}$, then the angle is denoted by $\angle BAC$ or $\angle CAB$.

It makes no difference which side is mentioned first. In fact, it doesn't matter which point you name on each of the two sides. The angle in the figure on the left below could equally well be described as $\angle BAC$, $\angle DAE$, $\angle BAE$, and so on. For short, we may write simply $\angle A$, if it is plain what the sides are supposed to be.

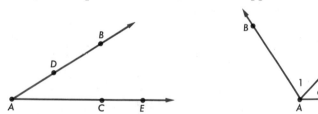

And in figures such as the one on the right above, we may write numbers and letters inside angles, so that we can write $\angle 1$ for $\angle BAC$, $\angle a$ for $\angle CAD$, and so on.

The sides of an angle are rays, not segments. Therefore the figure on the left below is not an angle:

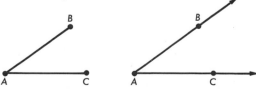

Of course it *determines* an angle, as indicated on the right. (In the same way, a segment *determines* a line without *being* one.)

A *triangle* is a figure that looks like one of these:

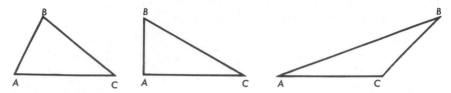

## Definitions

If $A$, $B$, and $C$ are any three noncollinear points, then the union of the segments $\overline{AB}$, $\overline{AC}$, and $\overline{BC}$ is called a *triangle*, and is denoted by $\triangle ABC$. The points $A$, $B$, and $C$ are called its *vertices*, and the segments $\overline{AB}$, $\overline{AC}$, and $\overline{BC}$ are called its *sides*. Every triangle $\triangle ABC$ determines three angles, namely, $\angle BAC$, $\angle ABC$, and $\angle ACB$. These are called the *angles of* $\triangle ABC$. If it is obvious which triangle is meant, we may often denote them by $\angle A$, $\angle B$, and $\angle C$.

Note that when we draw a triangle, we have not necessarily drawn its angles. Just as a school does not contain its own graduates, so a triangle does not contain its own angles. If we wish to draw the angles, we have to extend the sides and use arrowheads as shown in the figure on the left below. Usually there is no need to do this, because it is obvious what the angles are supposed to be.

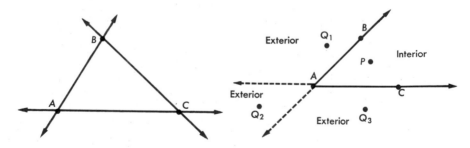

The *interior* and the *exterior* of an angle are as indicated in the figure on the right above.

## Definitions

Let $\angle BAC$ be an angle in a plane $E$. A point $P$ is in the *interior* of $\angle BAC$ if (1) $P$ and $B$ are on the same side of the line $\overleftrightarrow{AC}$, and (2) $P$ and $C$ are on the same side of the line $\overleftrightarrow{AB}$. The *exterior* of $\angle BAC$ is the set of all points of $E$ that lie neither on the angle nor in its interior.

You should check this definition against the figure to make sure that the definition really says what we have in mind. For example, $P$ is in the interior because it satisfies both (1) and (2). $Q_1$ is not in the interior; it satisfies (1) but not (2). $Q_2$ is not in the interior; it satisfies neither (1) nor (2). $Q_3$ satisfies (2) but not (1).

Note that we have defined the interior of an angle as the inter-section of two half-planes. One of these is the side of $\overleftrightarrow{AC}$ that con-tains $B$ and the other is the side of $\overleftrightarrow{AB}$ that contains $C$.

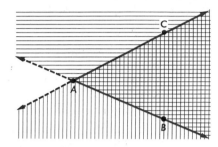

The *interior* and *exterior* of a triangle are as shown in the figure.

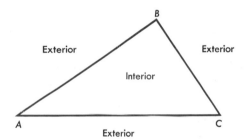

## Definitions

A point lies in the *interior* of a triangle if it lies in the interior of each of the angles of the triangle. A point lies in the *exterior* of a triangle if it lies in the plane of the triangle but does not lie on the triangle or in the interior.

You should check this definition against the figure, as before, to make sure that it says what we really mean. (If we required merely that a point lie in the interiors of *some two* of the angles, instead of all three, would this be enough to describe the interior?) Definitions are much easier to learn if you first examine them in this manner. In fact, when you forget them, this is usually due to the fact that you tried to learn them by rote, without stopping to consider how they express the ideas that they are supposed to express.

Occasionally we will use the symbolism *A-B-C* to mean "*B* is between *A* and *C*," as in Problem 21 of the following set.

## Problem Set 4-1

**1.** Complete the following definition.

    An angle is the _____ of two _____ which have the same _____, but which are not _____.

**2.** Complete the following definition.

    A triangle is the _____ of the three _____ joining each pair of three _____.

**3.** In the figure, points *K*, *P*, and *H* are collinear. Name all five angles.

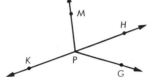

**4.** Given △*ABC*, are $\overline{AC}$ and $\overline{AB}$ the sides of ∠*A*? Explain.

**5.** How many angles are determined by this figure? Name them. How many of them may be named by using only the vertex letter?

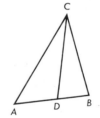

**6.** Can two angles of a triangle ever have a common side? Explain.

**7.** How many angles are in this figure? (There are more than six.)

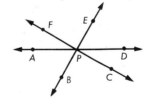

**8.** Is the following statement true? △*ABC* is the union of ∠*CAB* and ∠*CBA*. Why?

**9.** Which points of the figure are in

    (a) the interior of ∠*CBA*?

    (b) the exterior of ∠*EBC*?

    (c) the interior of ∠*ABD*?

    (d) the interior of ∠*ABQ*?

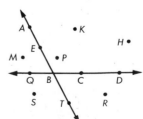

**10.** Is the vertex of an angle in the interior of the angle? in the exterior?

**11.** Into how many regions does a triangle separate the plane of the triangle?

**12.** Into how many regions do the angles of a triangle separate the plane of the triangle?

**13.** Name all the triangles in the figure on the left below. (There are more than four.)

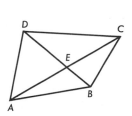 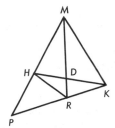

**14.** How many triangles are in the figure on the right above? (One way of attacking this problem is to write *PRHMDK*, then write all possible combinations of three letters, and check each combination with the figure.)

**15.** Is the interior of an angle a convex set? is the exterior?

**16.** Is a triangle a convex set?

**17.** Is the interior of a triangle a convex set? is the exterior?

**18.** Given $\triangle ABC$ and a point $P$ in the interior of $\angle A$ and also in the interior of $\angle C$. What can you conclude about $P$?

\* **19.** (a) Can a point be in the exterior of a triangle and in the interior of an angle of the triangle? Illustrate.

    (b) Can a point be in the exterior of a triangle and not in the interior of any angle of the triangle? Illustrate.

\* **20.** Given $\triangle ABC$ and a point $P$. $P$ and $A$ are on the same side of $\overleftrightarrow{BC}$. $P$ and $B$ are on the same side of $\overleftrightarrow{AC}$.

    (a) Is $P$ in the interior of $\angle ACB$?

    (b) Is $P$ in the interior of $\triangle ACB$?

+ **21.** Given $\triangle ABC$. *A-D-B*, *B-E-C*, *C-D-F*, and *D-G-E*.

    (a) Is $G$ in the interior or exterior of $\triangle ABC$?

    (b) Does $\overrightarrow{BG}$ intersect $\overline{AC}$?

    (c) $G$ and $F$ are on opposite sides of _____?

    (d) How can you be sure of your answer to part (a)?

## 4–2.  SOME REMARKS ON ANGLES

Angles, as we have defined them in this chapter, are simply sets of points.  For example:

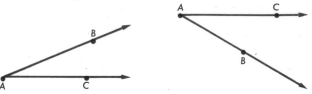

The order in which the sides of an angle are named makes absolutely no difference.

This is the simplest form of the idea of an angle.  It is the idea that is needed for the purposes of this course.  Later on, however, when you study trigonometry, the idea of an angle will appear in a different form.  In trigonometry, it will make a difference which side of an angle is mentioned first:

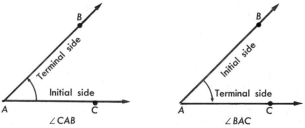

That is, in trigonometry, we distinguish between $\angle CAB$ and $\angle BAC$.  In $\angle CAB$, $\overrightarrow{AC}$ is the *initial side* and $\overrightarrow{AB}$ is the *terminal side*.  In $\angle BAC$, $\overrightarrow{AB}$ is initial and $\overrightarrow{AC}$ is terminal.  Angles such as these are called *directed angles*.  When we use directed angles, we allow "zero angles" and "straight angles."

In this course, directed angles will not be used, because they are not needed in elementary geometry.  For example, the angles of a triangle are never zero angles or straight angles, and there is no reasonable way of deciding in which direction they should go.  To assign directions to them, we would have to proceed at random; and the random directions of the angles would be of no use to us, because they would be unrelated to the problems that we were working on.

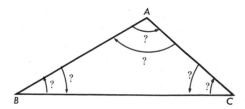

## 4–3.   ANGULAR MEASURE

Just as we measure segments with a ruler, so we measure angles with a protractor.

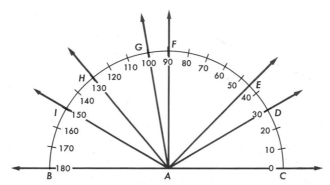

The number of degrees in an angle is called its *measure*. If there are *r* degrees in ∠*PQR*, then we write

$$m\angle PQR = r.$$

Simply from the markings on the protractor, we see that

$$m\angle CAD = 30, \qquad m\angle CAF = 90,$$
$$m\angle CAE = 45, \qquad m\angle CAG = 100,$$

and so on.

Note that we don't need to use the degree sign when we write 30, 45, and so on, because the *m* takes care of this: *m* ∠*PQR* is the *number of degrees* in the angle.

Just as we found distances by subtraction, with a ruler, we can use subtraction to find the measures of angles. For example, we must have *m* ∠*DAE* = 15 because 15 = 45 − 30 = *m* ∠*CAE* − *m* ∠*CAD*. The same device gives us

$$m\angle GAD = 100 - 30 = 70.$$

Note that 180 is not the measure of any angle in the figure. (There is no such thing as ∠*BAC*, because $\overrightarrow{AB}$ and $\overrightarrow{AC}$ are collinear.) We can still subtract from 180, however, to get

$$m\angle BAI = 180 - 150 = 30,$$

$$m\angle BAH = 180 - 130 = 50,$$

and so on.

The following postulates sum up the facts about protractors that we have just been using. In the figures illustrating these facts, we write $r°$, $s°$, and so on, to remind ourselves that these numbers are degree measures of angles.

**POSTULATE 11.**   The Angle Measurement Postulate

*To every angle $\angle BAC$ there corresponds a real number between 0 and 180.*

**Definition**

$m\angle BAC = r.$

The number given by the Angle Measurement Postulate is called the *measure* of $\angle BAC$, and is written $m\angle BAC$.

Anywhere we like, we can construct an angle with any measure between 0 and 180. Of course, if we start with a ray in a plane and a number $r$, we can construct our angle on either side of the line containing the ray. Hence we have the conditions of the following postulate.

**POSTULATE 12.**   The Angle Construction Postulate

*Let $\overrightarrow{AB}$ be a ray on the edge of the half-plane H.   For every number r between 0 and 180 there is exactly one ray $\overrightarrow{AP}$, with P in H, such that $m\angle PAB = r$.*

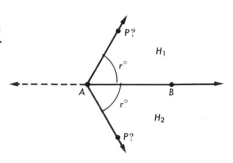

We can calculate measures of angles by addition and subtraction, using the following postulate.

**POSTULATE 13.**   The Angle Addition Postulate

*If D is in the interior of $\angle BAC$, then*
$$m\angle BAC = m\angle BAD + m\angle DAC.$$

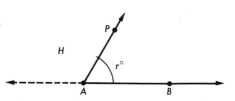

From this we get $m\angle CAD = m\angle CAB - m\angle DAB.$

Two angles form a *linear pair* if they look like this:

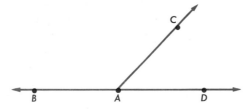

More precisely, we have the following definition.

**Definition**

> If $\overrightarrow{AB}$ and $\overrightarrow{AD}$ are opposite rays, and $\overrightarrow{AC}$ is any other ray, then $\angle BAC$ and $\angle CAD$ form a *linear pair*.

The following definition deals purely with angular measure. It says nothing at all about where the angles are.

**Definition**

> If the sum of the measures of two angles is 180, then the angles are called *supplementary*, and each is called a *supplement* of the other.

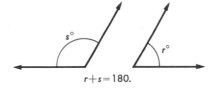

$r+s=180.$

The angles are *allowed*, however, to form a linear pair, and in this case they are always supplementary.

**POSTULATE 14.** The Supplement Postulate

> *If two angles form a linear pair, then they are supplementary.*

These postulates may be referred to, for short, as AMP, ACP, AAP, and SP. These are, of course, abbreviations of Angle Measurement Postulate, Angle Construction Postulate, Angle Addition Postulate, and Supplement Postulate.

You will remember that in our discussion of the measurement of distance, we found that we could use any unit that we wanted. If we decided to change the unit of distance, then we merely multiplied all distances by a certain number, and all the postulates for distance still held. This is not true, however, for angular measure, because the Supplement Postulate determines the unit. Under our definition of *supplementary*, Postulate 14 tells us that if two angles form a linear pair, then the sum of their measures is 180. This condition ceases to hold if we double the measure of every angle, or divide the measure of every angle by 2.

## Problem Set 4–3

**1.** If $m \angle A = 63$ and $m \angle B = 117$, then $\angle A$ and $\angle B$ are said to be _____.

**2.** If, in the figure, $m \angle QPS = 41$ and $m \angle QPM = 37$, what is $m \angle MPS$? What postulate supports your conclusion?

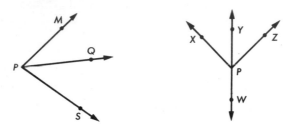

**3.** Given the figure with $Y$, $P$, $W$ collinear and $m \angle XPY = m \angle ZPY$.
   (a) Name two linear pairs.
   (b) Name three sets of supplementary angles.

**4.** Given that $A$-$K$-$F$ and $D$ is a point not on $\overleftrightarrow{AF}$.
   (a) $\angle AKD$ and $\angle FKD$ form a _____.
   (b) $m \angle AKD + m \angle FKD =$ _____.
      What postulate is essential to your answer?

**5.** In the figure, $\overleftrightarrow{GH}$ and $\overrightarrow{PQ}$ intersect, forming four angles.
   (a) If $b = 52$, what does $a$ equal?
   (b) If $a = 110$, what are $b$, $c$, and $d$?

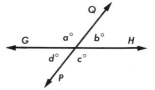

**6.**

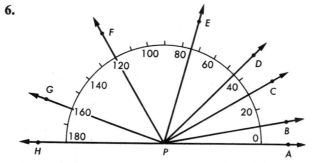

Using the figure, evaluate each of the following.
   (a) $m \angle APC$.
   (b) $m \angle EPD$.
   (c) $m \angle GPA$.
   (d) $m \angle DPB$.
   (e) $m \angle FPC$.
   (f) $m \angle APB + m \angle BPE$.
   (g) $m \angle HPG + m \angle FPC$.
   (h) $m \angle APC + m \angle CPH$.
   (i) $m \angle FPA - m \angle DPA$.
   (j) $m \angle FPH - m \angle FPG$.

7. Use a protractor to evaluate each of the following.

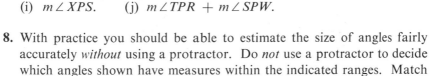

   (a) $m \angle RPS.$      (b) $m \angle VPR.$

   (c) $m \angle VPS.$      (d) $m \angle TPR.$

   (e) $m \angle XPR.$      (f) $m \angle XPY.$

   (g) $m \angle WPS.$      (h) $m \angle XPW.$

   (i) $m \angle XPS.$      (j) $m \angle TPR + m \angle SPW.$

8. With practice you should be able to estimate the size of angles fairly accurately *without* using a protractor. Do *not* use a protractor to decide which angles shown have measures within the indicated ranges. Match the angles on the right with the appropriate range in the left column.

   (a) $80 < x < 95.$

   (b) $55 < x < 70.$

   (c) $40 < x < 60.$

   (d) $90 < x < 105.$

   (e) $20 < x < 45.$

   (f) $110 < x < 125.$

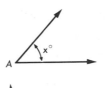

9. Using a straightedge and a protractor, construct angles having degree measures of 30, 60, 15, 90, 100, and 135.

10. Using only a straightedge and *not* a protractor, sketch angles whose measures are approximately 10, 30, 45, 60, 90, 120, 135, 150. Then use a protractor to check your sketches.

11. On the edge of a half-plane take points $M$, $K$, $A$ such that $M$-$A$-$K$. Take $\overrightarrow{AT}$ so that $m \angle TAK = 35$. In the same half-plane take $\overrightarrow{AV}$ such that $m \angle MAV = 85$. Measure $\angle TAV$ with a protractor. Does your finding agree with correct calculation?

12. In the plane figure,

   (a) $m \angle CAB + m \angle DAC = m \angle$ ___?___ .

   (b) $m \angle EAD + m \angle DAC = m \angle$ ___?___ .

   (c) $m \angle EAD + m \angle DAB = m \angle$ ___?___ .

   (d) $m \angle EAC - m \angle DAC = m \angle$ ___?___ .

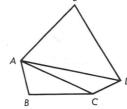

13. Determine the measure of the supplement of an angle whose measure is

   (a) 80.      (b) 48.      (c) 144.      (d) 25.5.

   (e) $n.$      (f) $n + k.$      (g) $180 - n.$      (h) $90 - n.$

**14.** In the figure,

(a) $m \angle SPR + m \angle QPO = m \angle$ ___?___.

(b) $m \angle RSQ + m \angle$ ___?___ $= m \angle RSP$.

(c) $m \angle POQ + m \angle POS =$ ___?___.

(d) $m \angle SRQ - m \angle SRO = m \angle$ ___?___.

(e) $m \angle ROQ = 180 - m \angle$ ___?___.

(f) $SO + OQ =$ ___?___.

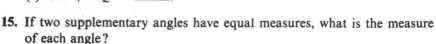

**15.** If two supplementary angles have equal measures, what is the measure of each angle?

**16.** If the measure of an angle is three times the measure of its supplement, what is the measure of the angle?

**17.** The measure of an angle is 24 more than the measure of its supplement. Find the measures of both angles.

\* **18.** Twice the measure of an angle is 30 less than five times the measure of its supplement. What is the measure of the angle?

\* **19.** If, in a plane, $m \angle BAD = 65$ and $m \angle DAC = 32$, what is $m \angle CAB$?

**20.** Given the figure, with $\overleftrightarrow{MN}$ and $\overrightarrow{PQ}$ intersecting at $A$. What postulates or definitions support each of the following statements?

(a) $\angle PAM$ and $\angle QAM$ form a linear pair.

(b) $\angle PAM$ and $\angle QAM$ are supplementary.

(c) $m \angle PAM + m \angle QAM = 180$.

(d) $m \angle QAM + m \angle QAN = 180$.

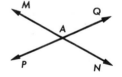

\* **21.** If $m \angle ABC + m \angle DBC = 180$ and $m \angle MAS + m \angle NAS = 180$, does $m \angle ABC + m \angle DBC = m \angle MAS + m \angle NAS$? Why? If we also say that $m \angle DBC = m \angle NAS$, what can we conclude? Why?

## HONORS PROBLEM

Why is the following statement true?

If a line $L$ intersects two sides of $\triangle ABC$ at $D$ and $E$ (and $D$ and $E$ are distinct from $A$, $B$, and $C$), then $L$ does not intersect the third side.

[*Hint:* Refer to Section 3–4, and show that $B$ and $C$ are on the same side of $L$.]

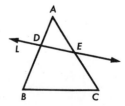

## 4–4.  RIGHT ANGLES, PERPENDICULARITY, CONGRUENT ANGLES

**Definition**

If the angles in a linear pair have the same measure, then each of them is called a *right angle*.

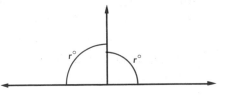

In this case, we have $r + r = 180$, by the Supplement Postulate. Thus we might equally well have written the following definition of a right angle.

**Definition**

A *right angle* is an angle whose measure is 90.

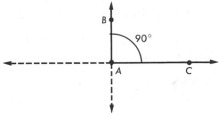

**Definitions**

If $\overrightarrow{AB}$ and $\overrightarrow{AC}$ form a right angle, then they are called *perpendicular*, and we write

$$\overrightarrow{AB} \perp \overrightarrow{AC}.$$

We use the same term and the same notation for lines and segments; thus, if $\angle BAC$ is a right angle, we write

$$\overleftrightarrow{AB} \perp \overleftrightarrow{AC}, \qquad \overline{AB} \perp \overline{AC}, \qquad \overrightarrow{AB} \perp \overline{AC},$$

and so on, for any combination of lines, rays, or segments.

**Definitions**

If the sum of the measures of two angles is 90, then the angles are called *complementary*, and each of them is called a *complement* of the other. An angle with measure less than 90 is called *acute*. An angle with measure greater than 90 is called *obtuse*.

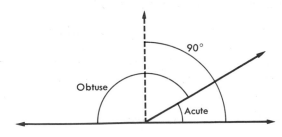

**Definition**

Two angles with the same measure are called *congruent*.

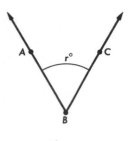

Thus, ∠*ABC* and ∠*DEF* are *congruent* if

$$m\angle ABC = m\angle DEF;$$

in this case, we write

$$\angle ABC \cong \angle DEF.$$

The symbol ≅ is pronounced "is congruent to."

Note that the equation $m\angle ABC = m\angle DEF$ and the congruence ∠*ABC* ≅ ∠*DEF* are equivalent; they mean exactly the same thing. We can replace one of these statements by the other any time we want.

## Problem Set 4–4A

1. In this problem, line segments are meant to be perpendicular if they look perpendicular. Pick out the pairs of perpendicular segments. If you believe that a pair is not perpendicular, state why.

(a) 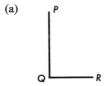   (b) 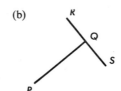   (c)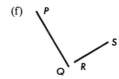

(d)    (e) 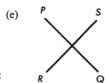   (f)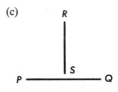

2. In this figure the angles have the indicated measures.

   (a) Name a pair of complementary angles.

   (b) Which postulate makes it possible to assert that $m\angle DAG = 105$?

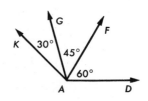

3. Given the figure, with the vertex $M$ of right angle $\angle SMT$ on $\overrightarrow{AB}$, and $m \angle TMB = 50$.

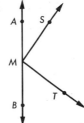

   (a) Name a pair of perpendicular rays, if any occur.

   (b) Name a pair of complementary angles, if there are any.

   (c) Name a pair of congruent angles, if any occur.

   (d) Name a pair of supplementary angles, if any occur.

4. Point $A$ is the end point of two perpendicular rays, $\overrightarrow{AB}$ and $\overrightarrow{AC}$. $D$ is a point in the interior of $\angle BAC$ and $E$ is a point in the exterior of $\angle BAC$ such that $\overrightarrow{AD} \perp \overrightarrow{AE}$.

   (a) Name a pair of complementary angles, if any occur.

   (b) Name a pair of supplementary angles, if there are any.

   (c) Name a pair of congruent angles, if any occur.

5. Complete each sentence to make it true.

   (a) If $m \angle MPS = 39$ and $m \angle THN = 39$, then $\angle MPS$ is _____ to $\angle THN$.

   (b) The supplement of an acute angle is _____ angle.

   (c) The complement of an acute angle is _____ angle.

   (d) If $\angle ADK \cong \angle BEH$, the measures of the angles are _____.

6. If the measure of an angle is twice the measure of its complement, what is the measure of each angle?

7. Determine the measure of the complement of an angle whose measure is

   (a) 20.    (b) 68.    (c) 46.5.    (d) $n$.    (e) $90 - n$.    (f) $45 + n$.

8. What is the measure of an angle, given that the measure of its supplement is 39 more than twice the measure of its complement?

It is easy to see that the following theorems are true, so long as we bear in mind what the words mean.

## Theorem 4–1

If two angles are complementary, then both are acute.

## Theorem 4–2

Every angle is congruent to itself.

(We always have $m \angle A = m \angle A$.)

### Theorem 4–3

Any two right angles are congruent.

### Theorem 4–4

If two angles are both congruent and supplementary, then each is a right angle.

[*Hint:* If they are congruent, they have the same measure $r$. Now show that $r$ must be 90.]

### Theorem 4–5

Supplements of congruent angles are congruent.

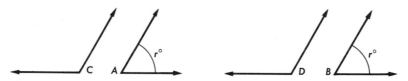

**Restatement.**    If (1) $\angle A \cong \angle B$, (2) $\angle A$ and $\angle C$ are supplementary, and (3) $\angle B$ and $\angle D$ are supplementary, then (4) $\angle C \cong \angle D$.

**Proof.**    Let $r = m\angle A$, as indicated in the figure above. We give the rest of the proof in such a style that you can use it as a pattern in writing proofs of your own.

| STATEMENTS | REASONS |
|---|---|
| 1. $r + m\angle C = 180$. | $\angle A$ and $\angle C$ are supplementary. |
| 2. $r = m\angle B$. | $\angle A \cong \angle B$. |
| 3. $r + m\angle D = 180$. | $\angle B$ and $\angle D$ are supplementary. |
| 4. $m\angle C = 180 - r$. | Step 1. |
| 5. $m\angle D = 180 - r$. | Step 3. |
| 6. $m\angle C = m\angle D$, and $\angle C \cong \angle D$. | Steps 4 and 5. |

There are advantages in the two-column style of writing proofs. If you use this style, it is easier to organize your work, and it is easier to remember that every time you make a statement in a proof, you are supposed to give a reason.

Note also that before we started proving this theorem, we first restated it. This is a device which will often be useful later. Whenever we can, we shall state theorems in words, using very little notation or none at all. The theorems are then easier to read and easier to remember. In the restatement, we introduce the notation that will be used in the proof.

The figure given for this proof shows a very special case: two angles may be supplementary without being lined up in such a way as to make it obvious to the eye that they are supplementary. Supplementary angles may look like this:

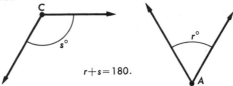

Usually a figure is only an illustration of a theorem or a problem. You should not get the idea that the figures given in this book are in each case the only correct ones.

## Theorem 4–6

Complements of congruent angles are congruent.

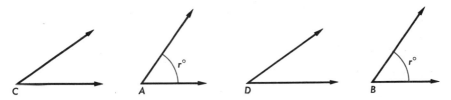

The proof is very much like the proof of Theorem 4–5, and you ought to be able to write it out yourself, using the preceding proof as a pattern. In fact, you *should* do this. Let the figure above help you. Make your own restatement of the theorem.

When two lines intersect, they form four angles. In the figure, $\angle 1$ and $\angle 3$ are called *vertical angles*, and $\angle 2$ and $\angle 4$ are called *vertical angles*. That is:

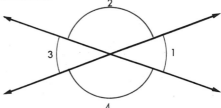

## Definition

Two angles are *vertical angles* if their sides form two pairs of opposite rays.

In the figure, it looks as though the vertical angles are congruent, and in fact this is always the case as is shown in the next theorem.

**Theorem 4–7.**    The Vertical Angle Theorem

Vertical angles are congruent.

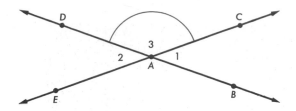

**Proof.**    We have given that $\angle 1$ and $\angle 2$ are vertical angles; that is,

(1) $\overrightarrow{AC}$ and $\overrightarrow{AE}$ are opposite rays, and $\overrightarrow{AB}$ and $\overrightarrow{AD}$ are opposite rays.

Therefore:

(2) $\angle 1$ and $\angle 3$ form a linear pair, and $\angle 2$ and $\angle 3$ form a linear pair.

(3) $\angle 3 \cong \angle 3$.

(4) $\angle 1$ and $\angle 2$ are supplements of congruent angles.

By Theorem 4–5, this means that

(5) $\angle 1 \cong \angle 2$.

**Theorem 4–8**

If two intersecting lines form one right angle, then they form four right angles.

**Proof.**    In the figure, the little square at the vertex of $\angle 1$ indicates that $\angle 1$ is a right angle. This is given. We need to prove that $\angle 2$, $\angle 3$, and $\angle 4$ are right angles. The main steps are as follows. (You ought to be able to give the reason for each step.)

(1) $\angle 3$ is a right angle.

(2) $\angle 2$ and $\angle 1$ are supplementary.

(3) $m\angle 2 + 90 = 180$.

(4) $\angle 2$ is a right angle.

(5) $\angle 4$ is a right angle.

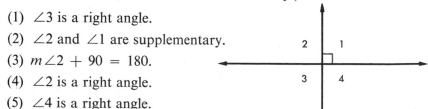

There is a certain theorem which we use as the reason for steps 1 and 5. The reason for step 2 is a postulate. The reasons for steps 3 and 4 are definitions.

GEORGE DAVID BIRKHOFF (1884–1944)

G. D. Birkhoff was one of the most versatile and productive mathematicians of his generation. In his lifetime he wrote a hundred and ninety research papers, in various branches of pure and applied mathematics. His collected works fill three large volumes. He also wrote several books, on mathematics and the theory of relativity.

The postulates for geometry used in this book are modifications of a set of postulates due to Birkhoff. For several centuries, the idea of measurement, for both segments and angles, has been a central idea in geometry. Birkhoff's postulates introduce this idea at the outset; they describe the methods which in fact everybody uses. Thus, while Birkhoff's postulates were not among his great contributions to knowledge, they nonetheless greatly contributed to clarity.

## Problem Set 4–4B

**1.** $\angle ABC \cong \angle DEH$, and $\angle ABC$ is supplementary to $\angle DEH$. What conclusion follows? What postulate, definition, or theorem supports this conclusion?

**2.** If $\angle M$ is supplementary to $\angle K$, $\angle P$ is supplementary to $\angle Q$, and $\angle Q \cong \angle M$, what is true of $\angle K$ and $\angle P$? What statement supports your conclusion?

**3.** If $\angle PAM$ and $\angle MAJ$ are complementary and $\angle KAJ$ and $\angle MAJ$ are complementary, why is $\angle KAJ \cong \angle PAM$?

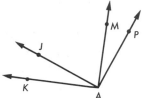

**4.** (a) If two lines intersect, how many pairs of vertical angles are formed?

(b) If the measure of any one of the angles in part (a) is 62, what are the measures of the other angles?

(c) If all four angles of part (a) are congruent, what is the measure of each?

**5.** In the figure, three lines intersect at the same point. Given that $a = 85$ and $e = 30$, find $b$, $c$, $d$, and $f$.

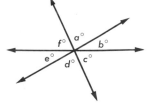

**6.** If one of a pair of vertical angles has measure $x$, write formulas for the measures of the other three angles formed.

**7.** Prove Theorem 4–3.

**8.** Prove Theorem 4–4.

**+ 9.** Given a line, $\overleftrightarrow{AB}$, separating two half-planes $H_1$ and $H_2$. $P$ is a point of $H_1$ such that $m\angle PAB = 30$. If $Q$ is a point of $H_2$ such that $\angle QAB \cong \angle PAB$, then $B$ lies in the _____ of $\angle PAQ$ and $m\angle PAQ =$ _____. If $\overrightarrow{AQ}$ is opposite to $\overrightarrow{AP}$, then $\angle PAB$ is _____ to $\angle QAB$ and $m\angle QAB =$ _____.

**\* 10.** In half-plane $H$, $\overrightarrow{BA}$ and $\overrightarrow{BE}$ are opposite rays, $\angle ABG \cong \angle KBG$ and $\angle KBD \cong \angle DBE$. Find $m\angle GBD$. [*Hint:* Let $m\angle ABG = x$ and $m\angle DBE = y$.]

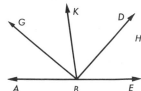

+ **11.** In the figure, plane $E$ intersects plane $F$ in $\overleftrightarrow{AB}$. $\overleftrightarrow{GH}$ and $\overleftrightarrow{KM}$, both in plane $F$, intersect $\overleftrightarrow{AB}$ at $P$.

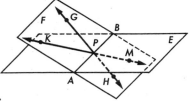

 (a) Name two pairs of vertical angles.

 (b) Name two pairs of supplementary angles.

 (c) If $\overleftrightarrow{GH} \perp \overleftrightarrow{AB}$, name two pairs of complementary angles.

*+ **12.** In the figure, $\overleftrightarrow{AB}$, $\overleftrightarrow{QR}$, $\overleftrightarrow{GH}$, and $\overleftrightarrow{KM}$ intersect at $P$, $\overleftrightarrow{QR}$ is in $E$, and $\overleftrightarrow{GH}$, $\overleftrightarrow{KM}$ are in $F$. $\overleftrightarrow{AB}$ is the intersection of planes $E$ and $F$.

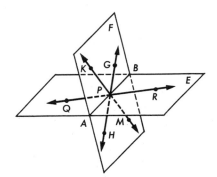

 (a) What two angles are supplementary to $\angle APG$?

 (b) What two angles are supplementary to $\angle HPM$?

 (c) If $\angle BPR \cong \angle KPG$, which other angles must be congruent?

 (d) If $\angle RPG$ is a right angle, which other angles must be right angles?

## 4–5. THEOREMS IN THE FORM OF HYPOTHESIS AND CONCLUSION

Every theorem is a statement that *if* a certain thing is true, *then* something else is also true. For example, Theorem 4–8 says that *if* two intersecting lines form one right angle, *then* they form four right angles. The *if* part of a theorem is called the *hypothesis;* it states what is *given*. The *then* part is called the *conclusion;* it states what is to be *proved*. We can write Theorem 4–8 in the following way.

### Theorem 4–8

>*Hypothesis:* $L_1$ and $L_2$ form one right angle.
>
>*Conclusion:* $L_1$ and $L_2$ form four right angles.

Similarly, we can write Theorem 4–3 as follows.

### Theorem 4–3

>*Hypothesis:* $\angle A$ and $\angle B$ are right angles.
>
>*Conclusion:* $\angle A \cong \angle B$.

Postulates are like theorems, except that they will not be proved. Most of the postulates can be put in the same *if . . . then* form as theorems. For example, the Angle Addition Postulate can be written as follows.

**POSTULATE 13.**   The Angle Addition Postulate

> *Hypothesis: D is in the interior of* $\angle BAC$.
>
> *Conclusion: $m\angle BAC = m\angle BAD + m\angle DAC$.*

In some cases, the hypothesis-conclusion form is not natural or useful. For example, if we wish to say that space contains four non-coplanar points, there is no advantage in writing

> *Hypothesis:* S is space.
>
> *Conclusion:* S contains four noncoplanar points.

It is not necessary, of course, that all theorems be stated in the hypothesis-conclusion form. Regardless of the form in which the theorem is written, it ought to be clear what is given and what is to be proved. Most of the time, however, we ought to be *able* to state a theorem in the hypothesis-conclusion form if we want to, because if we can't, the chances are that we don't understand exactly what the theorem says.

## Problem Set 4–5

1. Identify the hypothesis and the conclusion for each of the following statements.

   (a) If two angles are complementary, then each of them is acute.

   (b) If $a = b$ and $b = c$, then $a = c$.

   (c) If $a = b$, then $a + c = b + c$.

   (d) If two angles are both congruent and supplementary, then each of them is a right angle.

   (e) If the dimensions of a rectangle are $a$ and $b$, its area is $ab$.

   (f) If two planes intersect, then their intersection is a line.

2. Write each of the following statements as an "If . . . then" statement.

   (a) Supplements of congruent angles are congruent.

   (b) The area of a triangle having altitude $a$ and base $b$ is $\frac{1}{2}ab$.

   (c) The intersection of two planes is a line.

   (d) Any three noncollinear points lie in exactly one plane.

   (e) Two angles which form a linear pair are supplementary.

## 4–6. WRITING UP SIMPLE PROOFS

Very soon, writing your own proofs will be a fairly large part of your problem work.  We had better get some more practice in writing up easy proofs, before we tackle more difficult ones in the next chapter. Probably the best way to indicate how your proofs should look is to give some more examples.  In these examples and problems you may assume the figures are coplanar unless otherwise stated.

### Example 1

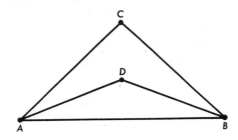

*Given:* $\triangle ABC$ and $\triangle ABD$, as in the figure at the right, with $\angle DAB \cong \angle DBA$ and $\angle CAD \cong \angle CBD$.

*Prove:* $\angle CAB \cong \angle CBA$.

**Proof**

| STATEMENTS | REASONS |
|---|---|
| 1.  $m\angle DAB = m\angle DBA$. | Given. |
| 2.  $m\angle CAD = m\angle CBD$. | Given. |
| 3.  $m\angle DAB + m\angle CAD$ $= m\angle DBA + m\angle CBD$. | Addition property of equality. |
| 4.  $m\angle CAB = m\angle CBA$. | Angle Addition Postulate. |
| 5.  $\angle CAB \cong \angle CBA$. | Definition of congruence of angles. |

### Example 2

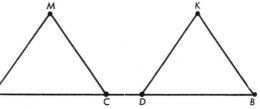

*Given:* Points $A$, $B$, $C$, $D$, as in the figure at the right, with $AD = CB$.

*Prove:* $AC = DB$.

**Proof**

| STATEMENTS | REASONS |
|---|---|
| 1.  $AC + CD = AD$. | Definition of between. |
| 2.  $CD + DB = CB$. | Definition of between. |
| 3.  $AD = CB$. | Given. |
| 4.  $AC + CD = CD + DB$. | Substitution, in steps 1, 2, and 3. |
| 5.  $AC = DB$. | Subtraction property of equality. |

*Example 3*

*Given:* Rays $\overrightarrow{AB}$, $\overrightarrow{AC}$, and $\overrightarrow{AD}$, with $C$ in the interior of $\angle BAD$, and with $m\angle BAC + m\angle CAD = 90$.

*Prove:* $\overrightarrow{AB} \perp \overrightarrow{AD}$.

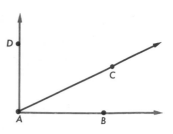

**Proof**

| STATEMENTS | REASONS |
|---|---|
| 1. $m\angle BAC + m\angle CAD = 90$. | Given. |
| 2. $m\angle BAC + m\angle CAD$ $= m\angle BAD$. | Angle Addition Postulate. |
| 3. $m\angle BAD = 90$. | Substitution from steps 1 and 2. |
| 4. $\angle BAD$ is a right angle. | Definition of a right angle. |
| 5. $\overrightarrow{AB} \perp \overrightarrow{AD}$. | Definition of perpendicular rays. |

## Problem Set 4–6

**1.** Copy all of the following and complete the proof.

Given: $m\angle A = 38$, and $m\angle B = 52$.

Prove: $\angle A$ is complementary to $\angle B$.

**Proof**

| STATEMENTS | REASONS |
|---|---|
| 1. $m\angle A = $ _____. | Given. |
| 2. $m\angle B = $ _____. | _____. |
| 3. $m\angle A + m\angle B = $ _____. | _____. |
| 4. $\angle A$ is complementary to $\angle B$. | _____. |

**2.** Copy and supply a proof.

Given: The figure with $PQ = RS$.

Prove: $PR = QS$.

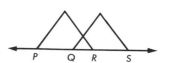

**3.** Copy and supply a proof.

Given: The figure with

$m\angle CAB = m\angle CBA$,

and    $m\angle DAB = m\angle DBA$.

Prove: $m\angle CAD = m\angle CBD$.

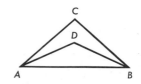

**4.** Copy and complete the proof.

Given: The figure with $\angle PMN \cong \angle PNM$.

Prove: $\angle CMP \cong \angle DNP$.

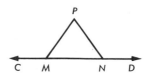

**Proof**

| STATEMENTS | REASONS |
|---|---|
| 1. $\angle CMP$ is supplementary to $\angle PMN$. | Two angles forming a linear pair are supplementary. |
| 2. $\angle DNP$ is _____. | _____. |
| 3. _____. | Given. |
| 4. $\angle CMP \cong \angle DNP$. | _____. |

**5.** Copy and supply a proof.

Given: The figure with

$\angle DBC \cong \angle ECB$.

Prove: $\angle ABC \cong \angle ACB$.

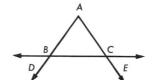

**6.** Copy and supply the reasons.

Given: $\overleftrightarrow{AB}$, $\overleftrightarrow{CD}$, and $\overleftrightarrow{EF}$ intersect at $K$; $a = c$.

Prove: $b = c$.

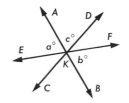

**Proof**

| STATEMENTS | REASONS |
|---|---|
| 1. $\overleftrightarrow{AB}$ and $\overleftrightarrow{EF}$ intersect at $K$. | _____. |
| 2. $\angle AKE$ and $\angle BKF$ are vertical angles. | _____. |
| 3. $\angle AKE \cong \angle BKF$. | _____. |
| 4. $a = b$. | _____. |
| 5. $a = c$. | _____. |
| 6. $b = c$. | _____. |

**7.** Copy and supply a proof.

Given: The figure with $\angle ABC \cong \angle ACB$.

Prove: $\angle DBF \cong \angle ECG$.

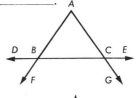

**8.** Copy and prove.

Given: $\overleftrightarrow{AD} \perp \overleftrightarrow{FB}$ and $\angle BAC \cong \angle DAE$.

Prove: $\angle DAC \cong \angle FAE$.

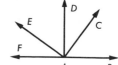

## Chapter Review

In Problems 1 through 15, complete each of the statements given.

**1.** To every angle there corresponds a real number between _____ and _____, called the measure of the angle.

**2.** The instrument used to measure angles is a _____.

**3.** If the sum of the measures of two angles is 90, then each angle is a _____ of the other.

**4.** An angle with measure less than 90 is called _____.

**5.** An angle with measure greater than 90 is called _____.

**6.** Two angles formed by the union of two opposite rays and a third ray having the same end point are called a _____.

**7.** Angles whose measures are equal are called _____ angles.

**8.** Two angles which are complementary must each be _____.

**9.** If two angles are congruent, their supplements are _____.

**10.** Two angles which are both congruent and supplementary must each be _____.

**11.** Every triangle has _____ sides and _____ angles; a triangle contains its _____, but does not contain its _____.

**12.** The sum of the measures of two complementary angles is _____, and the sum of the measures of two supplementary angles is _____.

**13.** The sum of the measures of two _____ angles is always less than 180, and the sum of the measures of two _____ angles is always less than _____.

**14.** If the sides of two angles are opposite rays, the angles are called _____.

**15.** A point $M$ is in the interior of $\angle GHK$ if $M$ and _____ lie on the same side of $\overleftrightarrow{HK}$ and if $M$ and _____ lie on the same side of _____.

Problems 16 through 25 refer to the figure at the top of the next page. (Points that look collinear are collinear.)

**16.** How many triangles are in this figure?

**17.** Is $m \angle BFC = m \angle BFD$?

18. Is ∠*BFC* = ∠*BFD*?

19. Is ∠*FDB* ≅ ∠*EDC*?

20. Name the angle supplementary to ∠*ABF*.

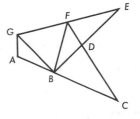

21. $m \angle AGB + m \angle BGF = $ ___?___.

22. $m \angle GFC + m \angle DFE = $ ___?___.

**Figure for Problems 16 through 25**

23. Name a set of vertical angles.

24. If ∠*GBF* is complementary to ∠*FBE*, then $\overline{GB}$ and $\overline{BE}$ must be _____.

25. How many angles are indicated in the figure?

26. The measure of an angle is five times the measure of its complement. Find the measure of each angle.

27. The measure of the supplement of an angle is five times the measure of the complement of the same angle. Find the measure of the angle.

28. Is the sum of the measures of two angles always the measure of another angle? Explain.

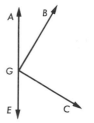

29. Given the figure with $\overrightarrow{GA}$ opposite to $\overrightarrow{GE}$ and $\overrightarrow{GB} \perp \overrightarrow{GC}$. Complete the proof that ∠*AGB* is complementary to ∠*EGC*.

**Proof**

| STATEMENTS | REASONS |
|---|---|
| 1. $\overrightarrow{GA}$ opposite to $\overrightarrow{GE}$. | _____. |
| 2. ∠*AGB* is supplementary to ∠*BGE*. | Supplement Postulate. |
| 3. $m \angle AGB + m \angle BGE = 180$. | _____. |
| 4. $\overrightarrow{GB} \perp \overrightarrow{GC}$. | _____. |
| 5. $m \angle BGC = 90$. | Definitions of perpendicular and right angle. |
| 6. $m \angle BGE = m \angle EGC + 90$. | _____. |
| 7. $m \angle AGB + m \angle EGC + 90 = 180$. | Substitution of Step 6 in Step 3. |
| 8. $m \angle AGB + m \angle EGC = 90$. | _____. |
| 9. ∠*AGB* is complementary to ∠*EGC*. | _____. |

**30.** $\overrightarrow{AB}$ and $\overrightarrow{AC}$ are opposite rays. The points $E$, $F$, and $H$ are on the same side of $\overleftrightarrow{AB}$. Points $E$ and $H$ are on opposite sides of $\overleftrightarrow{BF}$. Points $A$ and $H$ are on the same side of $\overleftrightarrow{BF}$. $\overleftrightarrow{BF} \perp \overleftrightarrow{AC}$, and $\overrightarrow{BE} \perp \overrightarrow{BH}$. $m \angle FBE = 20$. Draw the figure and find:

(a) $m \angle EBA$.           (b) $m \angle FBH$.           (c) $m \angle EBC$.

**31.** Is there a point in the plane of a triangle such that the point is neither in the exterior nor the interior of the triangle and neither in the interior nor the exterior of any angles of the triangle?

**32.** Given $\triangle ABC$ and a point $P$ in the same plane. $P$ and $A$ are on the same side of $\overleftrightarrow{BC}$. $P$ and $B$ are on the same side of $\overleftrightarrow{AC}$.

(a) $P$ is in the interior of which angle?

(b) Must $P$ be in the interior of $\triangle ABC$?

**33.** If you were given that $\angle a$ is complementary to $\angle y$, $\angle b$ is complementary to $\angle x$, and $\angle x \cong \angle y$, what postulate or theorem would you use to prove that $\angle a \cong \angle b$?

**34.** Is the following statement true? If $\overleftrightarrow{PQ}$ and $\overleftrightarrow{RS}$ intersect at $O$, then $\angle POR \cong \angle QOS$.

**35.** Given: In plane $E$, $\overleftrightarrow{AB}$, $\overleftrightarrow{CD}$, $\overleftrightarrow{PQ}$, and $\overleftrightarrow{RS}$ intersect at $O$, and $\overleftrightarrow{CD} \perp \overleftrightarrow{AB}$. Complete the proof that

$$b + g + d = a.$$

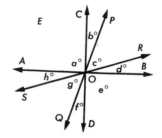

**Proof.** By applying AAP twice we have $m \angle COB = b + c + d$. But since $\overleftrightarrow{CD}$ _____, $m \angle COB = a$. Hence, $a = $ _____. But $\angle POR$ and _____ are _____ angles, so that $c = $ _____. By substituting $g$ for $c$, we conclude that _____.

**36.** Is the following a correct restatement of the Angle Construction Postulate?

Given a ray $\overrightarrow{RS}$ and a number $k$ between 0 and 180, there is exactly one ray $\overrightarrow{RP}$ such that $m \angle SRP = k$.

**37.** Given: The figure with $\overrightarrow{BE} \perp \overleftrightarrow{AC}$ and $\angle ABG \cong \angle CBD$.

Prove: $\angle GBE \cong \angle DBE$.

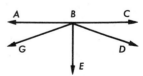

**38.** Given the figure with ∠2 and ∠3 supplementary.    Prove that ∠1 ≅ ∠4.

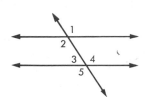 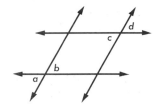

**39.** If, in the figure, ∠b ≅ ∠c, prove that ∠a ≅ ∠d.

**40.** On a line *L*, *A-B-C*.  Points *D* and *E* are on opposite sides of *L* such that, when $\overrightarrow{BD}$ and $\overrightarrow{BE}$ are drawn, ∠*CBD* ≅ ∠*CBE*.  Prove that

$$m\angle ABD = m\angle ABE.$$

**41.** Jim and George were to write the following statement in "If . . . then" form.

"Two intersecting lines intersect in exactly one point."

George wrote, "If *P* is a point, then lines $L_1$ and $L_2$ intersect exactly at *P*." Jim wrote, "$L_1$ and $L_2$ intersect in exactly one point, if they intersect and are different." Was either boy correct?

**+  42.** If $\overrightarrow{OA}$, $\overrightarrow{OB}$, and $\overrightarrow{OC}$ are three distinct rays in a plane such that no two of them are opposite, is each of the following statements true or false? (Recall that just one exception will make the statement false.)
(a) $m\angle AOB + m\angle BOC = m\angle AOC.$
(b) $m\angle AOB + m\angle BOC + m\angle AOC = 360.$

**+  43.** Could the interior of a triangle be defined as the intersection of three half-planes? Illustrate.  If point *X* is any point in the interior of △*ABC*, write a definition of the interior of △*ABC*.  (Refer to the definition of interior of an angle given in Section 4–1.)

**+  44.** Is the interior of △*ABC* completely determined by the intersection of the interiors of any two of its angles?  Illustrate and formulate a definition.  Is it equivalent to the previous definitions?

**\*+  45.** Explain why the following statement is true. If a line *L* intersects △*ABC* at a point *D* such that *A-D-B* and *L* does not intersect $\overline{BC}$, then *L* must intersect $\overline{AC}$ at a point *E* such that *A-E-C*.

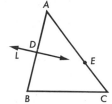

# 5 | Congruences

## 5-1.  THE IDEA OF A CONGRUENCE

Roughly speaking, two geometric figures are congruent if they have exactly the same size and shape.  For example, in the figure below, all three triangles are congruent.

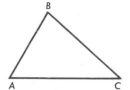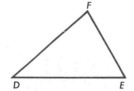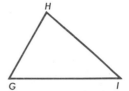

One way of describing the situation is to say that any one of these triangles can be moved onto any other one in such a way that it fits exactly.  Thus, to show what we mean by saying that two triangles are congruent, we have to explain which points are supposed to go where.  For example, to move $\triangle ABC$ onto $\triangle DFE$, we should put $A$ on $E$, $B$ on $F$, and $C$ on $D$.  We can write the pairs of corresponding vertices as follows.

$$A \leftrightarrow E,$$
$$B \leftrightarrow F,$$
$$C \leftrightarrow D.$$

To describe the congruence of the first triangle and the third, we should match up the vertices like this:

$$A \leftrightarrow G,$$
$$B \leftrightarrow H,$$
$$C \leftrightarrow I.$$

How would you match up the vertices to describe the congruence of the second triangle with the third?

A matching-up scheme of this kind is called a *one-to-one correspondence* between the vertices of the two triangles.  If the matching-up scheme can be made to work, that is, if the triangles can be made to fit when the vertices are matched up in the prescribed way, then the one-to-one correspondence is called a *congruence* between the two triangles.  For example, the correspondences that we have just given are congruences.  On the other hand, writing

$$A \leftrightarrow F,$$
$$B \leftrightarrow D,$$
$$C \leftrightarrow E,$$

105

does give us a one-to-one correspondence, but *not* a congruence, because the first and second triangles cannot be made to coincide by this particular matching-up scheme. This correspondence leads to many difficulties. $\overline{AB}$ is too short to be fitted onto $\overline{FD}$, $\overline{AC}$ is too long to be fitted onto $\overline{FE}$, and so on.

We can write one-to-one correspondences more briefly, in one line. For example, the correspondence

$$A \leftrightarrow E,$$
$$B \leftrightarrow F,$$
$$C \leftrightarrow D,$$

which is the first example that we gave, can be written in one line:

$$ABC \leftrightarrow EFD.$$

Here it should be understood that the first letter on the left corresponds to the first letter on the right, the second corresponds to the second, and the third corresponds to the third:

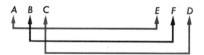

Let us take one more example. The two figures below are of the same size and shape.

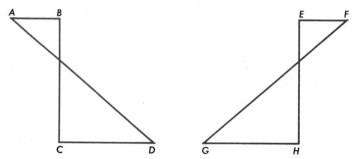

To show how one can be moved onto the other, we should match up the vertices like this:

$$A \leftrightarrow F,$$
$$B \leftrightarrow E.$$
$$C \leftrightarrow H,$$
$$D \leftrightarrow G,$$

This correspondence is a congruence; that is, the figures can be made to fit if the vertices are matched in the given way. For short, we can write the congruence in one line:

$$ABCD \leftrightarrow FEHG.$$

Note that the order in which the matching *pairs* are written does not matter. We could have written our list of matching pairs in this way:

$$D \leftrightarrow G,$$
$$B \leftrightarrow E,$$
$$C \leftrightarrow H,$$
$$A \leftrightarrow F;$$

and we could have described our one-to-one correspondence in one line:

$$DBCA \leftrightarrow GEHF.$$

All that matters is which points are matched with each other.

It is quite possible for two figures to be congruent in more than one way. Here the correspondence

$$ABC \leftrightarrow FDE$$

is a congruence, and the correspondence

$$ABC \leftrightarrow FED$$

is a different congruence between
the same two figures.

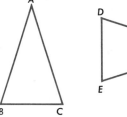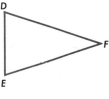

Obviously $\triangle ABC$ coincides with itself. If we agree to match every vertex with itself, we get the congruence

$$ABC \leftrightarrow ABC.$$

This is called the *identity* congruence. However, there is another way of matching up the vertices of this triangle. We can use the correspondence

$$ABC \leftrightarrow ACB.$$

Under this correspondence, the figure is made to coincide with itself, with the vertices $B$ and $C$ interchanged. This is not, by any means, possible for all triangles; it won't work unless at least two sides of the triangle are of the same length.

## Problem Set 5–1

In some of the problems of this problem set you are to decide upon congruences by inspection. That is, correspondences which *look* like congruences if the figures are measured with reasonable care may be called congruences. (No trick effects are involved in the drawings.)

**1.** Which of the following pairs of figures are congruent?

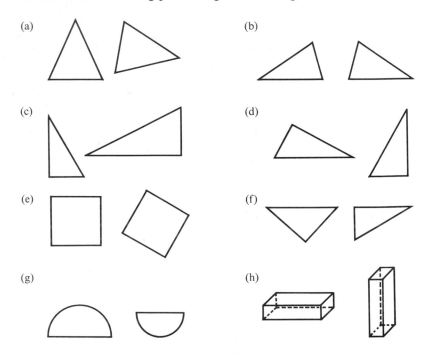

**2.** Which of the figures below do not have a matching counterpart?

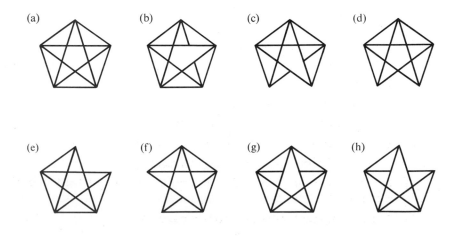

3. Look at the figures below. Write as many congruences as you can between these figures. You should get six congruences. (You may ignore
the identity congruence for all the figures, but you should count the
congruence, which is not an identity, between a triangle and itself if the
triangle has two congruent sides. One congruence is $ACB \leftrightarrow LMN$.)

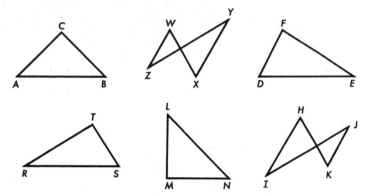

4. Follow the directions of Problem 3 for the following figures.

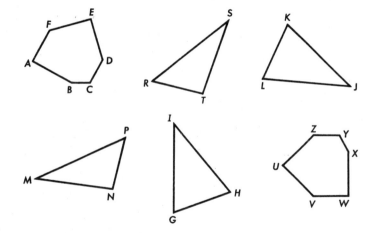

5. (a) Is a figure congruent to itself?
   (b) If each of two figures is congruent to a third, are they congruent to
       each other?
   (c) Are the sides of a square congruent?
   (d) Are the sides of a rectangle congruent?
   (e) Are two opposite faces of a cube congruent?
   (f) Are two adjacent faces of a cube congruent?
   (g) Are two opposite faces of a rectangular block, such as a brick,
       congruent?
   (h) Are two adjacent faces of a brick congruent?

**6.** The triangles in each of the following pairs are congruent. Write the congruences for each pair. (The first one is $AED \leftrightarrow BEC$.)

(a)

(b)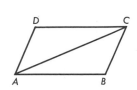

(c)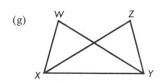

(d)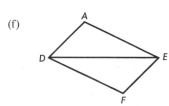

(e)

(f)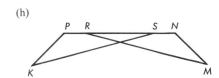

(g)

(h)

**7.** Under what conditions would the following pairs of figures be congruent?

(a) Two segments.  (b) Two lines.  (c) Two angles.

(d) Two circles.  (e) Two squares.  (f) Two triangles.

+ **8.** Consider the five-pointed star $ABCDE$. Write all the congruences between the star and itself, beginning with $ABCDE \leftrightarrow ABCDE$.

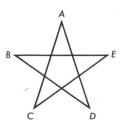

+ **9.** $\triangle ABC$ is equilateral, that is $AB = BC = AC$. Write all congruences between the triangle and itself, starting with the identity congruence $ABC \leftrightarrow ABC$. (There are more than four.)

* **10.** Which of the following plane figures can be fitted onto each other? For each matched pair, tell whether you must turn the figure over in space, or slide it, or rotate it, in order to make the figures coincide.

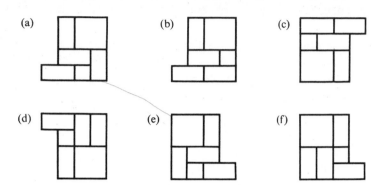

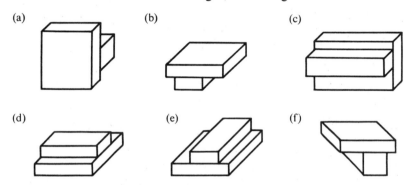

* **11.** Which of these three-dimensional figures are congruent?

*+ **12.** Suppose that the ornamental frieze below extends infinitely in both directions, as a line does. Consider a horizontal motion of the frieze which would take each spike onto the successive spike on the same side of the line. We would say that this motion induces a congruence of the frieze with itself.

(a) Describe motions of a different type that will induce congruences of the frieze with itself. How many such congruences are there?

(b) Describe two types of motions that will induce congruences of the frieze below with itself.

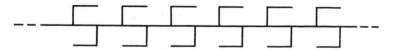

## 5–2.  CONGRUENCES BETWEEN TRIANGLES

In the preceding section, we have explained informally the idea of a congruence.  Let us now give some mathematical definitions so that we can handle the idea mathematically.

For angles and segments, it is easy to say exactly what we mean.

### Definitions

Angles are *congruent* if they have the same measure.  Segments are *congruent* if they have the same length.

Of course, the first of these definitions is a repetition from Section 4–4.  Obviously,

### Theorem 5–1

Every segment is congruent to itself.

The proof is self-evident: because it has the same length as itself.  In later proofs, we shall refer to this theorem by the phrase *identity congruence*.

Just as we write $\angle A \cong \angle B$ to indicate that $\angle A$ and $\angle B$ are congruent, so we write

$$\overline{AB} \cong \overline{CD},$$

to indicate that $\overline{AB}$ and $\overline{CD}$ are congruent.  Thus,

$$\overline{AB} \cong \overline{CD} \quad \text{means that} \quad AB = CD,$$
$$\angle A \cong \angle B \quad \text{means that} \quad m\angle A = m\angle B.$$

Each of the *equations* on the right is an *equation between numbers*.  Each of the *congruences* on the left is a *congruence* between geometric figures.  We do not write $=$ between two names of geometric figures unless we mean that the figures are exactly the same, and occasions of this sort are quite rare.  One example is shown at the right.  Here it is correct to write

$$\angle BAC = \angle EAD,$$

because $\angle BAC$ and $\angle EAD$ are not merely congruent, they are *exactly the same angle*.  Similarly, $\overline{AB}$ and $\overline{BA}$ are

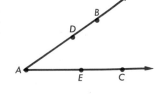

always exactly the same segment, and so it is correct to write not only $\overline{AB} \cong \overline{BA}$ but also $\overline{AB} = \overline{BA}$.

Consider  now  a  correspondence

$$ABC \leftrightarrow DEF$$

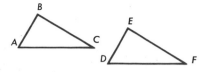

between the vertices of two triangles
$\triangle ABC$ and $\triangle DEF$.  This automatically gives us a correspondence
between the sides of the triangles:

$$\overline{AB} \leftrightarrow \overline{DE},$$
$$\overline{AC} \leftrightarrow \overline{DF},$$
$$\overline{BC} \leftrightarrow \overline{EF},$$

and it also gives us a correspondence between the angles of the two
triangles:

$$\angle A \leftrightarrow \angle D,$$
$$\angle B \leftrightarrow \angle E,$$
$$\angle C \leftrightarrow \angle F.$$

We can now state the definition of a congruence between two
triangles.

**Definition**

Given a correspondence

$$ABC \leftrightarrow DEF$$

between the vertices of two triangles.  If every pair of corresponding sides are congruent, and every pair of corresponding angles
are congruent, then the correspondence $ABC \leftrightarrow DEF$ is called a
*congruence between the two triangles.*

When we write $\triangle ABC \cong \triangle DEF$, we mean that the correspondence
$ABC \leftrightarrow DEF$ is a congruence.  This is a very efficient shorthand: the
single expression $\triangle ABC \cong \triangle DEF$ tells us *six* things at once, namely,

$$\overline{AB} \cong \overline{DE}, \quad \text{or} \quad AB = DE,$$
$$\overline{AC} \cong \overline{DF}, \quad \text{or} \quad AC = DF,$$
$$\overline{BC} \cong \overline{EF}, \quad \text{or} \quad BC = EF,$$
$$\angle A \cong \angle D, \quad \text{or} \quad m\angle A = m\angle D,$$
$$\angle B \cong \angle E, \quad \text{or} \quad m\angle B = m\angle E,$$
$$\angle C \cong \angle F, \quad \text{or} \quad m\angle C = m\angle F.$$

In each of these six lines, the congruence on the left means the same thing as the equation on the right. We can therefore use either notation, according to convenience. Usually, we shall write $AB = DE$ instead of $\overline{AB} \cong \overline{DE}$, because it is easier to write. And for the same reason, we shall usually write $\angle A \cong \angle D$ instead of $m\angle A = m\angle D$. The six facts of the definition above are often referred to by the statement, "Corresponding parts of congruent triangles are congruent."

In figures, it is convenient to indicate congruences between segments and angles by marking the figure as shown below.

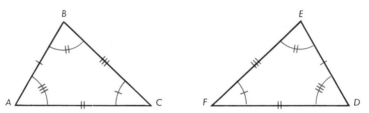

In this case, the six congruences indicated by the marks tell us that

$$\triangle ABC \cong \triangle DEF.$$

In the following figure, the marks tell us less:

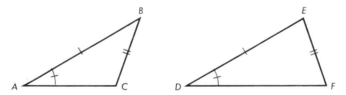

In fact, it is rather easy to see that these two triangles are not congruent under any correspondence whatever.

In some cases, we may be given only partial information, and may still be able to infer that a certain correspondence is a congruence.

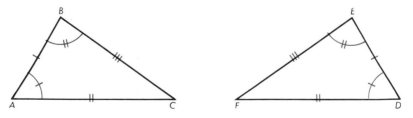

Under the correspondence $ABC \leftrightarrow DEF$, we are told that all three pairs of corresponding sides, and two out of three pairs of corresponding angles, are congruent. It surely ought to follow that $\angle C \cong \angle F$, so that $\triangle ABC \cong \triangle DEF$. And in fact, we ought to be able to get by with even less information. In the latter part of the following problem set, you will discover for yourself the conditions under which we can conclude that a correspondence between two triangles is a congruence. The facts of this matter are not difficult to figure out, as you will see.

## Definitions

A *side* of a triangle is said to be *included* by the angles whose vertices are the end points of the segment.

An *angle* of a triangle is said to be *included* by the sides of the triangle which lie in the sides of the angle.

For example, in $\triangle ABC$ above, $\overline{AC}$ is included by $\angle A$ and $\angle C$. And $\angle A$ is included by $\overline{AB}$ and $\overline{AC}$.

## Problem Set 5–2

1. If $\triangle ABE \cong \triangle DCF$, complete the following statements by supplying the missing symbols. The correspondence $A \_\_\_ \leftrightarrow \_CF$ is a congruence.

   $\angle A \cong \angle D$.        $\overline{AB} \cong$ _____.

   $\angle B \cong$ _____.        $\overline{AE} \cong$ _____.

   $\angle E \cong$ _____.        $\overline{BE} \cong$ _____.

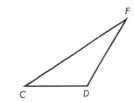

2. Given that $\triangle MQP \cong \triangle NQP$. List the six pairs of corresponding, congruent parts of these two triangles.

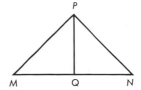

3. For each of the congruences list the six pairs of corresponding, congruent parts.

   (a) $\triangle RQF \cong \triangle ABX$. You may make a sketch of the triangles if you wish.

   (b) $\triangle FHW \cong \triangle MRK$. Do not use a figure.

   (c) $\triangle AZW \cong \triangle BWZ$. Do not use a figure.

4. Write the congruence for the two triangles which is determined by these six pairs of congruent parts:

$$\overline{AK} \cong \overline{BW}; \qquad \angle A \cong \angle B.$$

$$\overline{KT} \cong \overline{WR}; \qquad \angle K \cong \angle W.$$

$$\overline{AT} \cong \overline{BR}; \qquad \angle T \cong \angle R.$$

5. (a) In $\triangle ABC$, which is the included angle of the sides $\overline{BC}$ and $\overline{AB}$?

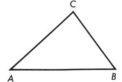

(b) Which is the included side of $\angle A$ and $\angle C$?

(c) Which sides include $\angle C$?

(d) Which angles include $\overline{BC}$?

6. Consider $\triangle GHK$. Without drawing a figure, can you discover an easy method of deciding which sides and angles are included sides and included angles?

(a) Does $\overline{GH}$ and $\overline{HK}$ include $\angle H$?

(b) Does $\angle G$ and $\angle K$ include $\overline{GK}$?

(c) What is the included angle of $\overline{GH}$ and $\overline{GK}$?

(d) What is the included side of $\angle G$ and $\angle H$?

[*Note:* In Problems 7 through 13 you should use a protractor and a ruler to construct angles and segments.]

7. Construct a triangle $\triangle RST$ in which $RS = 2\frac{1}{2}$ in., $RT = 1\frac{1}{2}$ in., and $m \angle R = 35$.

8. Construct a triangle $\triangle ABC$ in which $AB = 2$ in., $m \angle A = 45$, and $m \angle B = 60$. If you construct several triangles $\triangle ABC$ having the given measures, what common characteristic do the triangles share?

9. Construct a triangle $\triangle MNP$ in which $MN = 3$ in., $NP = 2$ in., and $PM = 3\frac{1}{2}$ in. You may find that you will need a compass to complete this construction.

10. Using only your ruler, construct any triangle which has no two sides congruent. Next construct a second triangle congruent to the first triangle and describe the steps that you take. Is there more than one way of obtaining the second triangle from the first? How many of the six parts of the first triangle did you use in forming the second triangle? What is the least number of congruent parts necessary to ensure that the two triangles are congruent?

11. Construct $\triangle ABC$ in which $m \angle A = 40$, $AC = 3$ in., and $CB = 2$ in. Then construct $\triangle DEF$ in which $m \angle D = 40$, $DF = 3$ in., and $FE = 2$ in. Must $\triangle ABC$ and $\triangle DEF$ be congruent?

12. In Problem 8 you should have concluded that all triangles $\triangle ABC$ whose parts have the measures given are congruent; that is, all the corresponding parts are congruent. When this is true, we say that the three given parts *determine* a triangle. In Problem 11 you should have found two triangles which were not congruent but which satisfied the given measures. Does Problem 7 allow for one or more triangles? does Problem 9? Is it possible to assign measures to angles or segments so that no triangle is determined?

\* 13. Construct the triangle determined by each set of measures given below. If the information allows two triangles, construct both. If more than two triangles or if no triangle may be constructed, explain why.

(a) $m \angle M = 30$, $\quad MO = 2$, $\quad m \angle O = 90$.

(b) $m \angle B = 55$, $\quad AB = 5$, $\quad BC = 3$.

(c) $m \angle G = 35$, $\quad GH = 6$, $\quad HI = 4$.

(d) $AB = 5$, $\quad BC = 3$, $\quad AC = 4$.

(e) $m \angle M = 80$, $\quad MO = 2$, $\quad m \angle O = 120$.

(f) $DE = 8$, $\quad EF = 3$, $\quad DF = 4$.

(g) $DE = 4$, $\quad DF = 8$, $\quad m \angle D = 60$.

(h) $m \angle A = 70$, $\quad m \angle B = 60$, $\quad m \angle C = 50$.

\* 14. (a) $\triangle ABC$ and $\triangle DEF$ do not intersect and $M$ is a point between $B$ and $C$. Which of the two symbols $=$ and $\cong$ will fill the blanks to make each of the following a meaningful and possibly true statement?

(i)    $\triangle ABC$ _____ $\triangle DEF$.       (v)        $\angle E$ _____ $\angle F$.

(ii)    $m \angle B$ _____ $m \angle E$.       (vi)    $\angle ABM$ _____ $\angle ABC$.

(iii)    $BC$ _____ $EF$.       (vii) $m \angle ABM$ _____ $m \angle DEF$.

(iv)    $\overline{AB}$ _____ $\overline{DE}$.       (viii)    $AB$ _____ $DE$.

(b) In which blank would both symbols work?

(c) If $\overline{AB}$ had been the same segment as $\overline{DE}$ but $C$ and $F$ were different points, in which blank would $\cong$ change to $=$?

\* 15. Given a triangle $\triangle ABC$. If

$$\triangle ABC \cong \triangle BAC \quad \text{and} \quad \triangle ABC \cong \triangle ACB,$$

what conclusion can be made about $\triangle ABC$? How do you prove that your conclusion is valid?

\* **16.** Given $\overleftrightarrow{PC} \perp \overleftrightarrow{KM}$ with $K\text{-}P\text{-}M$. Points $A$ and $B$ are on the same side of $\overleftrightarrow{KM}$ as $C$, but $A$ and $B$ are on opposite sides of $\overleftrightarrow{PC}$. $A$ is on the same side of $\overrightarrow{PC}$ as $K$. $\triangle ACP \cong \triangle BCP$. Prove that $\angle KPA \cong \angle MPB$.

\* **17.** If

$$\triangle ABC \cong \triangle DEF \quad \text{and} \quad \triangle DEF \cong \triangle GHK,$$

what conclusion can be made about $\triangle ABC$ and $\triangle GHK$? How do you prove that your conclusion is valid? State a theorem generalizing this situation.

## HONORS PROBLEM

An *equivalence relation* is defined as a relation among the members of a set which has the following properties:

If $a$, $b$, $c$ are any members of the set, then

(i) $a * a$.                     (Reflexive)

(ii) If $a * b$, then $b * a$.              (Symmetric)

(iii) If $a * b$ and $b * c$, then $a * c$.   (Transitive)

In applying this definition you should replace the asterisk (*) by the relation. For example, consider the relation, "has the same birthplace as," for the set of all babies born in City Hospital. We would have:

(i) $a$ has the same birthplace as $a$.

(ii) If $a$ has the same birthplace as $b$, then $b$ has the same birthplace as $a$.

(iii) If $a$ has the same birthplace as $b$ and $b$ has the same birthplace as $c$, then $a$ has the same birthplace as $c$.

Since all these statements are true, we say that the relation is an equivalence relation.

(a) Show that congruence for triangles is an equivalence relation. You should explain why each of the three statements is true. You may use Problem 17 above in your proof.

(b) Choose an appropriate set for each of the following relations and then determine which are equivalence relations:

"is less than," "is equal to," "is the reciprocal of," "is a classmate of," "is a resident of the same town as," "is taller than," "goes faster than," "is as wet as."

## 5–3.  THE CONGRUENCE POSTULATES FOR TRIANGLES

As you have, no doubt, discovered for yourself, there are at least three situations in which we can conclude that a correspondence between two triangles is a congruence.

In the first case, $ABC \leftrightarrow DEF$ is called an *SAS correspondence;* by this we mean that two sides and the included angle of the first triangle are congruent to the corresponding parts of the second. ("SAS" stands for "Side Angle Side.")  In this case it follows that $\triangle ABC \cong \triangle DEF$.

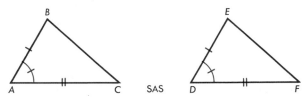

In the second case, $ABC \leftrightarrow DEF$ is called an *ASA correspondence;* by this we mean that two angles and the included side of the first triangle are congruent to the corresponding parts of the second. ("ASA" stands for "Angle Side Angle.")  In this case also, it follows that $\triangle ABC \cong \triangle DEF$.

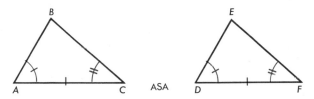

Finally, in the third case, $ABC \leftrightarrow DEF$ is called an *SSS correspondence;* by this we mean that all three sides of the first triangle are congruent to the corresponding sides of the second. ("SSS" stands for "Side Side Side.")  Here we must have $\triangle ABC \cong \triangle DEF$.

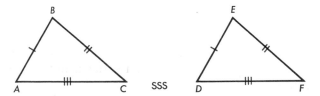

We make these observations official in the following postulates.

**POSTULATE 15.**  The SAS Postulate

*Every SAS correspondence is a congruence.*

**POSTULATE 16.**   The ASA Postulate

*Every ASA correspondence is a congruence.*

**POSTULATE 17.**   The SSS Postulate

*Every SSS correspondence is a congruence.*

In most instances, we shall apply these postulates to correspondences between two different triangles.  We have seen, however, that in some cases we can set up a correspondence between a triangle and itself; and the above three postulates apply in such cases.  Thus an SAS correspondence could be illustrated like this:

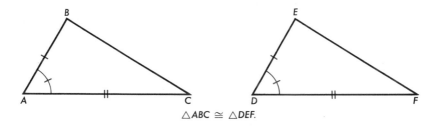

$\triangle ABC \cong \triangle DEF.$

or possibly as in the figure on the right. Here the marks tell us that $ABC \leftrightarrow ACB$ is an SAS correspondence.  We can then apply the SAS Postulate and conclude that $\triangle ABC \cong \triangle ACB.$

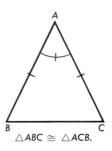

$\triangle ABC \cong \triangle ACB.$

*Warning:* There is no such thing as an SSA Postulate!

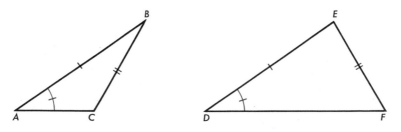

In this figure, $ABC \leftrightarrow DEF$ is an "SSA correspondence"; two sides and a *non*included angle of $\triangle ABC$ are congruent to the corresponding parts of △*DEF*.    But the correspondence is obviously not a congruence; in fact, $\overline{DF}$ is too long, ∠*E* is too big, and ∠*F* is too small.

Of course, if corresponding angles are congruent, it follows merely that the two triangles have the same *shape;* they do not necessarily have the same *size*.

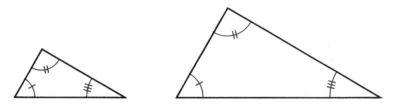

Triangles related in this way are called *similar.*

Hereafter, for short, we shall often refer to our three congruence postulates simply as SAS, ASA, and SSS.

## Problem Set 5–3

**1.** If, in each of the pairs of triangles sketched below, like markings indicate congruent parts, which triangles are congruent by the SAS Postulate?

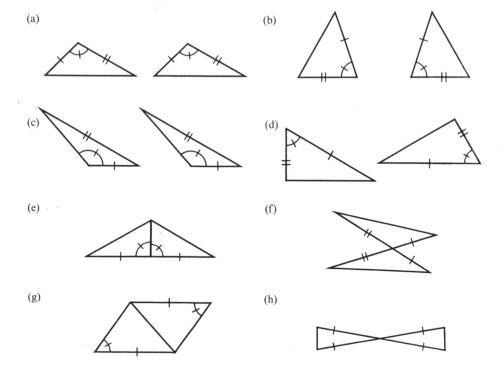

(a)

(b)

(c)

(d)

(e)

(f)

(g)

(h)

**2.** If, for each of the pairs of triangles sketched below, like markings indicate congruent parts, name the congruence postulate (SAS, ASA, SSS), if any, which will prove the triangles congruent.

(a)                                          (b)

(c)                                          (d)

(e)                                          (f)

(g)                                          (h)

(i)                                          (j)

(k)                                          (l)

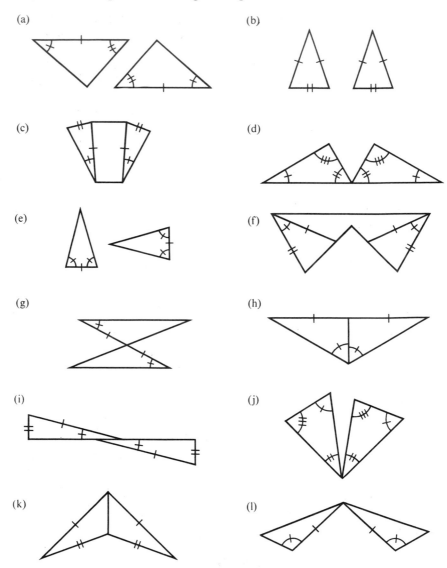

## 5-4.   THINKING  UP  YOUR  OWN  PROOFS

You now have enough basic material to be able to write real geometric proofs of your own.  From now on, writing your own proofs will be a very important part of your work, and the chances are that it will be more fun than reading other people's proofs.

Let us take a couple of examples, to suggest how we go about finding proofs and writing them up.

## Example 1

If two segments bisect each other, then the segments joining the ends of the given segments are congruent.

Starting to work on a problem like this, we should first draw a figure and letter it, using a capital letter for each vertex. Then, state the hypothesis and conclusion in terms of the lettering of the figure.

*Given:* $\overline{AR}$ and $\overline{BH}$ bisect each other at *F*.

*To prove:* $\overline{AB} \cong \overline{RH}$.

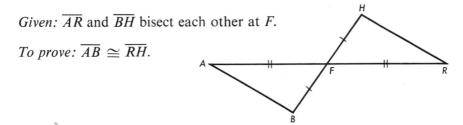

Indicate, by marks on the figure, the congruences that are given.

Next we divide the page into two columns, as usual, and write in the headings "STATEMENTS" and "REASONS."

All this, of course, will not do us a bit of good unless we can think of a proof to write.

Since our object is to prove that two segments are congruent, we must recall what we know about congruent segments. The marks on the figure indicate that $\overline{FB} \cong \overline{FH}$, and this is right, by definition of the mid-point. For the same reason, $\overline{AF} \cong \overline{RF}$. If we want to show that $\overline{AB} \cong \overline{RH}$, our best chance is to show that they are corresponding parts of congruent triangles. To do this, we need to set up a correspondence between the triangles in the figure, and then show that we have an SAS correspondence, an ASA correspondence, or an SSS correspondence. From the figure, it looks as though the correspondence ought to be

$$AFB \leftrightarrow RFH.$$

Two pairs of sides are congruent, because

$$\overline{AF} \cong \overline{RF} \quad \text{and} \quad \overline{FB} \cong \overline{FH}.$$

How about the included angles? If they are congruent too, then we can apply the SAS Postulate. And they *are* congruent, because they are vertical angles. Therefore, by the SAS Postulate, our correspondence is a congruence.  The sides $\overline{AB}$ and $\overline{RH}$ are corresponding sides, and so they are congruent.  This is what we wanted to prove.

Written in the double-column form, our proof would look like this:

*Given:* $\overline{AR}$ and $\overline{BH}$ bisect each other at *F.*

*To prove:* $\overline{AB} \cong \overline{RH}.$

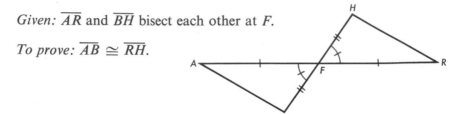

### Proof

| Statements | Reasons |
|---|---|
| 1.  $\overline{AR}$ and $\overline{BH}$ bisect each other. | Given. |
| 2.  $AF = RF.$ | Definition of "bisect." |
| 3.  $FB = FH.$ | Definition of "bisect." |
| 4.  $\angle AFB \cong \angle RFH.$ | Vertical angles are congruent. |
| 5.  $\triangle AFB \cong \triangle RFH.$ | The SAS Postulate. |
| 6.  $\overline{AB} \cong \overline{RH}.$ | Definition of a congruence between triangles. |

This proof is given merely as a sample of how your work might look.  There is a limit to how "standard" we can expect the form of a proof to be.  For example, in steps 2 and 3 we have indicated congruences between segments by writing

$$AF = RF \quad \text{and} \quad FB = FH.$$

We might just as well have written

$$\overline{AF} \cong \overline{RF} \quad \text{and} \quad \overline{FB} \cong \overline{FH},$$

because in each case the congruence between the segments and the equation between their lengths mean the same thing.

We also have a good deal of choice in deciding how many details to give in a proof.  As your knowledge and skill increase, you can write proofs containing fewer details.  Your teacher is the best judge of when you have earned the right to do this, and of how much you may omit.

By now, you should have the idea, and so we give our second example in an incomplete form. Your problem is to fill in the blank spaces in such a way as to get a proof.

## Example 2

Given: $\overline{AH} \cong \overline{FH}$.   $\angle AHB \cong \angle FHB$.

To prove: $\angle A \cong \angle F$.

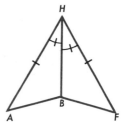

### Proof

| STATEMENTS | REASONS |
|---|---|
| 1.  $\overline{AH} \cong \overline{FH}$. | Given. |
| 2.  $\angle AHB \cong \angle FHB$. | _____. |
| 3.  $\overline{HB} \cong \overline{HB}$. | Every segment is congruent to itself. |
| 4.  $\triangle AHB \cong \triangle$____. | _____. |
| 5.  $\angle A \cong \angle F$. | _____. |

## Problem Set 5–4A

**1.** Copy this problem on your paper and fill in the missing information.

Given: The figure with
$\overline{CD} \perp \overline{AB}$ and $\overline{AD} \cong \overline{BD}$.

Prove: $\triangle ADC \cong \triangle BDC$.

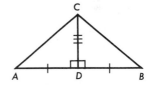

### Proof

| STATEMENTS | REASONS |
|---|---|
| 1. $\overline{AD} \cong \overline{BD}$. | Given. |
| 2. $\overline{CD} \perp \overline{AB}$. | _____. |
| 3. $\angle ADC \cong \angle BDC$. | Definitions of perpendicular and right angle. |
| 4. $\overline{CD} \cong \overline{CD}$. | Identity. (Every segment is congruent to itself.) |
| 5. $\triangle ADC \cong$ _____. | _____. |

**2.** Copy this problem on your paper and fill in the missing information.

Given: $\triangle MKP$ and $\triangle XYZ$ such that $\angle M \cong \angle Y$, $\angle MKP \cong \angle YXZ$, and $MK = XY$.

Prove: $\overline{PK} \cong \overline{ZX}$.

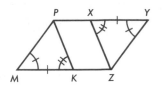

**Proof**

| STATEMENTS | REASONS |
|---|---|
| 1. $\angle M \cong \angle Y$. <br> $MK = XY$. <br> $\angle MKP \cong \angle YXZ$. | _____. |
| 2. $\triangle MKP \cong$ ___. | _____. |
| 3. ___ $\cong$ ___. | Corresponding parts of congruent triangles are congruent (from the definition of a congruence between triangles). |

**3.** In the figure, $\overline{AE}$ intersects $\overline{BD}$ at $C$ so that $AC = DC$ and $BC = EC$. Show that $\angle A \cong \angle D$, by copying the following proof. Supply the missing reasons.

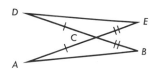

**Proof**

| STATEMENTS | REASONS |
|---|---|
| 1. $AC = DC$. | Given. |
| 2. $\angle ACB \cong \angle DCE$. | _____. |
| 3. $BC = EC$. | _____. |
| 4. $\triangle ACB \cong \triangle DCE$. | _____. |
| 5. $\angle A \cong \angle D$. | Corresponding parts of congruent triangles are congruent. |

[*Note:* Although Statements 2 and 4 look very much alike, one deals with angles and the other with triangles. Consider this in stating Reasons 2 and 4.]

**4.** In this figure, $AB = CD$ and $m\angle x = m\angle y$. Prove that $m\angle ACB = m\angle DAC$.

5. Copy the problem and complete the proof. Prove that if in the figure, $GK = HK$ and $M$ is the mid-point of $\overline{GH}$, then $\angle G \cong \angle H$.

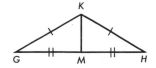

**Proof**

| STATEMENTS | REASONS |
|---|---|
| 1. $GK = HK$. | _____. |
| 2. $M$ is mid-point of $\overline{GH}$. | Given. |
| 3. _____. | Definition of mid-point. |
| 4. _____. | Identity. |
| 5. $\triangle GMK \cong \triangle HMK$. | _____. |
| 6. _____. | _____. |

6. Prove that if in $\triangle GHK$, $GK = HK$ and $G\text{-}M\text{-}H$ such that $\angle GKM \cong \angle HKM$, then $M$ is the mid-point of $\overline{GH}$.

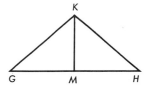

7. Prove that if segments $\overline{AE}$ and $\overline{DF}$ bisect each other at $P$, then $\triangle PDA \cong \triangle PFE$. (Here you must construct your own figure.)

8. Given: A segment $\overline{RS}$ and points $T$ and $U$ on opposite sides of $\overleftrightarrow{RS}$ such that $TR = UR$, $TS = US$, and $UR < US$.
Prove: $m\angle T = m\angle U$.

9. Given: $DG = CH$, $\angle D \cong \angle C$, $\overline{AG} \perp \overline{DK}$, $\overline{BH} \perp \overline{CK}$.
Prove: $AD = BC$.

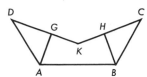

10. Given: Points $A$, $C$, $D$, and $E$ are collinear with $A\text{-}E\text{-}D$ and $A\text{-}D\text{-}C$. $B$ is a point not on $\overleftrightarrow{AC}$ such that $AB = CB$, $EB = DB$, and $AE = CD$.
Prove: $\angle ABE \cong \angle DBC$.

\*+ 11. Given that $\overline{BQ}$ bisects $\overline{PA}$ at $R$, but $BQ \neq PA$. $B$ and $Q$ are on opposite sides of $\overleftrightarrow{PA}$. $S$ and $C$ are points on $\overline{PR}$ and $\overline{AR}$, respectively, such that $RS = RC$, $\overline{BC} \perp \overline{PA}$, and $\overline{QS} \perp \overline{PA}$. Also, $\angle BAR \cong \angle QPR$. Prove that $\overline{PA}$ bisects $\overline{BQ}$ and that $\angle ABC \cong \angle PQS$.

\*+ 12. Given: $\angle HRE$ with $RH = RE$. Points $M$ and $K$ are on the sides of $\angle HRE$ such that $R\text{-}H\text{-}M$ and $R\text{-}E\text{-}K$. $\overline{EM}$ and $\overline{HK}$ intersect at $T$. $\angle HRT \cong \angle ERT$. Prove that $\triangle MTH \cong \triangle KTE$.

After you have finished a proof, you will often find that you can make the figure more instructive by putting more marks on it.

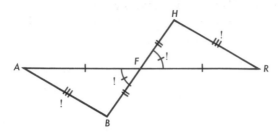

The above figure illustrates Example 1 and its proof. The marks on $\overline{AF}$ and $\overline{FR}$ indicate that the congruence $\overline{AF} \cong \overline{FR}$ was *given*. The marks on $\overline{FH}$ and $\overline{FB}$ indicate that $\overline{FH} \cong \overline{FB}$ was *given*. The marks on $\angle AFB$ and $\angle RFH$, with exclamation points, indicate that the congruence $\angle AFB \cong \angle RFH$ was *proved*. And the marks on $\overline{AB}$ and $\overline{RH}$ indicate that $\overline{AB} \cong \overline{RH}$ was *proved*.

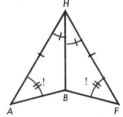

Similarly, the marks on the figure on the right tell us what was given and what was proved in Example 2.

Similarly, our three congruence postulates, SAS, ASA, and SSS, justify all the exclamation points in the following figures.

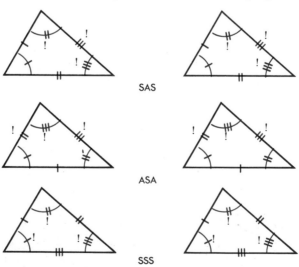

SAS

ASA

SSS

In general, it is a good idea to mark figures in such a way that they will convey as much information as possible. Sometimes we may be able to draw a figure which is a complete picture of a theorem. For example, the following figures are pictures of theorems which appeared in Chapter 4. Which theorems are they?

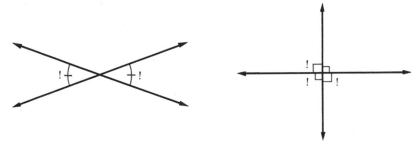

A mistake often made in proofs is that the student *assumes* as true the very thing he is trying to *prove* to be true. Another common mistake is to use as a reason in his proof a theorem which is actually a *consequence* of the statement that he is trying to prove. Such arguments are called circular arguments, and are worthless as logical proofs.

A particularly bad kind of circular argument is the use of the theorem we are trying to prove as a reason for one of the steps in its "proof."

## Problem Set 5–4B

1. Each figure is marked so that it specifies the hypothesis and the conclusion. Write the "given" and the "prove" for each figure.

(a)          (b)

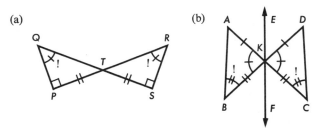

2. Follow the directions of Problem 1 for the figures given below.

(a)          (b)

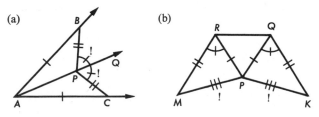

**3.** Copy the problem and complete the proof. Given the figure with $AC = BC$, $DC = EC$, $G$ is the mid-point of $\overline{DC}$, $H$ is the mid-point of $\overline{EC}$, $\angle ACE \cong \angle BCD$. Prove that $AG = BH$.

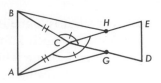

**Proof**

| STATEMENTS | REASONS |
|---|---|
| 1. $AC = BC$. | _____. |
| 2. $DC = EC$. | _____. |
| $G$ is the mid-point of $\overline{DC}$.  __ is the _____. | |
| 3. $DG = GC = \frac{1}{2}DC$. | Definition of mid-point. |
| 4. $EH = HC = \frac{1}{2}EC$. | _____. |
| 5. $GC = HC$. | Steps 2, 3, and 4 and substitution. |
| 6. $m\angle ACE = m\angle BCD$. | Given and definition of congruent angles. |
| 7. $m\angle ACG + m\angle GCH = m\angle BCH + m\angle GCH$. | Angle Addition Postulate and _____ in Step 6. |
| 8. $m\angle GCH = m\angle GCH$. | _____. |
| 9. $m\angle ACG = m\angle BCH$. | Subtraction Principle of Equality. |
| 10. $\triangle AGC \cong \triangle BHC$. | Steps 1, 5, 9 and the _____ Postulate. |
| 11. $AG = BH$. | _____. |

**4.** If, in the figure, $AE = BC$, $AD = BD$, and $DE = DC$, prove that $\angle E \cong \angle C$.

**5.** If, in the figure, $AE = BC$, $AD = BD$, and $\angle EAD \cong \angle CBD$, prove that $\angle BDE \cong \angle ADC$.

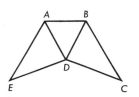

**6.** If, in the figure, $AE = BC$, $AD = BD$, and $\angle E \cong \angle C$, can you prove that $ED = CD$? If so, do so. If not, explain why not.

Figure for Problems 4, 5, 6, 7

\* **7.** If, in the figure, $\angle E \cong \angle C$, $ED = CD$, and $\angle BDE \cong \angle ADC$, can you prove that $AE = BC$? If so, do so. If not, explain why not.

**8.** Given: The figure with $\overline{AB} \perp \overleftrightarrow{MK}$, and $B$ is the mid-point of $\overline{MK}$.

Prove: $\angle x \cong \angle y$.

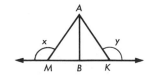

9. Given that ray $\overrightarrow{AE}$ bisects $\overline{BK}$ at $R$ such that $AB = AK$. Prove that $\overrightarrow{AE} \perp \overline{BK}$.

10. In the figure, $CF = CM$, $\angle 1 \cong \angle 2$, and $\angle 3 \cong \angle 4$. Prove that $\angle 5 \cong \angle 6$.

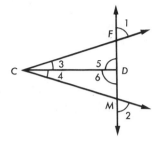

11. Given that $\overline{PQ}$ and $\overline{RS}$ intersect at $T$, with $P$-$T$-$Q$ and $R$-$T$-$S$, such that $RT = QT$, $\overline{PR} \perp \overline{RS}$, and $\overline{SQ} \perp \overline{PQ}$. Prove that $\angle P \cong \angle S$.

12. Prove that if in the figure, $PS = QS$, $PV = QV$, and $\angle x \cong \angle y$, then $\overline{SV} \perp \overline{PQ}$.

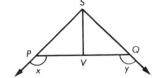

13. If, in the figure, $AB = CB$, $\angle MAE \cong \angle NCD$, and $AE = CD$, prove that $\triangle ABE \cong \triangle CBD$.

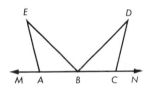

14. If, in the figure, $\angle EAB \cong \angle DCB$, $\angle EBA \cong \angle DBC$, and $\angle E \cong \angle D$, can you prove that $\triangle ABE \cong \triangle CBD$? Explain.

Figure for Problems 13, 14, 15

15. If in the figure, $AB = CB$, $m\angle MAE = m\angle NCD$, and $m\angle ABD = m\angle CBE$, can it be shown that $BE = BD$? If your answer is yes, supply the proof.

16. In the figure on the left below, given that $A$, $B$, $C$, and $D$ are non-coplanar points with $B$, $C$, and $D$ in plane $E$. If $\overline{AB} \perp \overline{BC}$, $\overline{AB} \perp \overline{BD}$, and $BC = BD$, show that $AC = AD$.

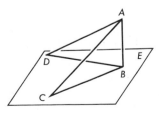

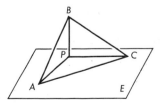

17. If, in the figure on the right above, $\angle ABP \cong \angle CBP$, $\overline{BP} \perp \overline{AP}$, and $\overline{BP} \perp \overline{CP}$, prove that $AB = CB$.

## 5–5  BISECTORS OF ANGLES

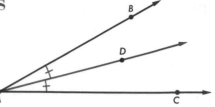

The markings on the figure on the right indicate that $\overrightarrow{AD}$ bisects $\angle BAC$.

In the next figure, $\overrightarrow{AD'}$ does not bisect $\angle BAC$ because it "points in the wrong direction."

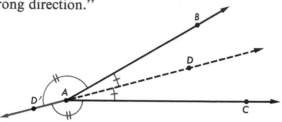

Thus we arrive at the following definition.

**Definition**

If $D$ is in the interior of $\angle BAC$, and $\angle BAD \cong \angle DAC$, then $\overrightarrow{AD}$ bisects $\angle BAC$, and $\overrightarrow{AD}$ is called the *bisector* of $\angle BAC$.

**Theorem 5–2**

Every angle has exactly one bisector.

**Proof.**  (1) In the figure on the left below, choose $B$ and $C$, on the sides of $\angle A$, so that $AB = AC$. Let $D$ be the mid-point of $\overline{BC}$. Then $ADB \leftrightarrow ADC$ is an SSS correspondence. By the SSS Postulate, $\triangle ADB \cong \triangle ADC$. Therefore $\angle BAD \cong \angle CAD$, because these are corresponding angles. Hence $\angle A$ has a bisector.

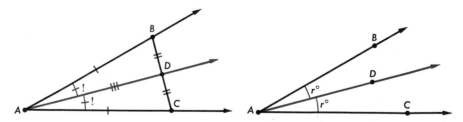

(2) Suppose that $\overrightarrow{AD}$ bisects $\angle BAC$ as shown on the right above. Let $r = m\angle DAC$. Then $r = m\angle DAB$, because these angles are congruent. By Postulate 13, $r + r = m\angle BAC$, and so $r = \frac{1}{2}m\angle BAC$. But we also know that $D$ is on the same side of $\overleftrightarrow{AC}$ as $B$. (Why?) By the Angle Construction Postulate, there is only one ray which "lies on the right side of $\overleftrightarrow{AC}$" and "gives an angle with the right measure."

## Problem Set 5–5

1. Are the following statements true or false? Explain your answers.

   (a) The bisector of an angle lies entirely in the interior of the angle.

   (b) The bisector of an angle forms two acute angles with the sides of the angle.

2. Given that $\overrightarrow{AP}$ bisects $\angle BAC$ and $AC = AB$. Prove that $PC = PB$.

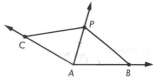

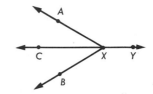

3. Points $A$ and $B$ are on opposite sides of $\overleftrightarrow{CY}$, $C$ is in the interior of $\angle AXB$, and $C$-$X$-$Y$. If $\angle AXY \cong \angle BXY$, prove that $\overrightarrow{XC}$ bisects $\angle AXB$.

4. Given two angles that form a linear pair. Prove that their bisectors are perpendicular.

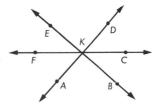

5. Given: $\overleftrightarrow{AD}$, $\overleftrightarrow{BE}$, and $\overleftrightarrow{CF}$ intersect one another at $K$, and $\overrightarrow{KC}$ bisects $\angle DKB$.

   Prove: $\overrightarrow{KF}$ bisects $\angle AKE$.

* 6. $\overleftrightarrow{MN}$ and $\overleftrightarrow{PQ}$ intersect at $O$, with $M$-$O$-$N$ and $P$-$O$-$Q$. $S$ and $T$ are points in the interior of $\angle QON$ such that $\angle TOQ \cong \angle TON$ and $\angle SOQ \cong \angle SON$. $\overrightarrow{OR}$ bisects $\angle POM$. Prove that $R$, $S$, and $T$ are collinear.

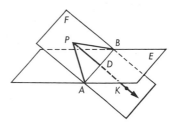

7. In the figure, planes $E$ and $F$ intersect in line $\overleftrightarrow{AB}$. $\overrightarrow{PK}$ is in plane $F$ and intersects $\overleftrightarrow{AB}$ at $D$. $PA = PB$, $\angle PAB \cong \angle PBA$, and $D$ is the mid-point of $\overline{AB}$. Prove that $\overrightarrow{PK}$ bisects $\angle APB$.

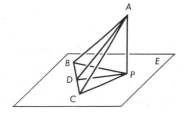

* 8. In the figure, $P$, $B$, $D$, and $C$ are points in plane $E$, and $A$ is not in plane $E$. $\triangle ABC$ and $\triangle PBC$ are isosceles, with $AB = AC$ and $PB = PC$, respectively. If $\overrightarrow{AD}$ bisects $\angle BAC$, prove that $\overrightarrow{PD}$ bisects $\angle BPC$.

## 5–6    ISOSCELES AND EQUILATERAL TRIANGLES

At the end of Section 5–1, we mentioned the case of matching up the vertices of a triangle $\triangle ABC$ in which at least two sides of the triangle are of the same length. This, in fact, is the case that we deal with in our first congruence theorem.

**Theorem 5–3.**    The Isosceles Triangle Theorem

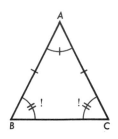

If two sides of a triangle are congruent, then the angles opposite these sides are congruent.

**Restatement.**    Given $\triangle ABC$. If $\overline{AB} \cong \overline{AC}$, then $\angle B \cong \angle C$.

**Proof.**    Consider the correspondence

$$ABC \leftrightarrow ACB$$

between $\triangle ABC$ and itself. Under this correspondence, we see that

$$\overline{AB} \leftrightarrow \overline{AC},$$
$$\overline{AC} \leftrightarrow \overline{AB},$$
$$\angle A \leftrightarrow \angle A.$$

Since this is an SAS correspondence, it follows by the SAS Postulate that

$$\triangle ABC \cong \triangle ACB,$$

that is, the correspondence $ABC \leftrightarrow ACB$ is a congruence. By the definition of a congruence between triangles all pairs of corresponding parts are congruent. Therefore $\angle B \cong \angle C$ because these angles are corresponding parts.

We now show how the above proof looks in two-column form. The same restatement and figure are used.

**Proof**

| STATEMENTS | REASONS |
|---|---|
| 1.  $\overline{AB} \cong \overline{AC}$.    $\overline{AC} \cong \overline{AB}$. | Given. |
| 2.  $\angle A \cong \angle A$. | Identity congruence. |
| 3.  $\triangle ABC \cong \triangle ACB$. | Steps 1 and 2 and SAS. |
| 4.  $\angle B \cong \angle C$. | Definition of a congruence between triangles. |

**Definitions**

> A triangle with two congruent sides is called *isosceles*. The remaining side is the *base*. The two angles that include the base are *base angles*. The angle opposite the base is the *vertex angle*.

In these terms, we can state Theorem 5–3 in the following form: "The base angles of an isosceles triangle are congruent."

**Definitions**

> A triangle whose three sides are congruent is called *equilateral*.
> A triangle no two of whose sides are congruent is called *scalene*.
> A triangle is *equiangular* if all three of its angles are congruent.

Using the terms *equilateral* and *equiangular*, we state a theorem which readily follows from Theorem 5–3. We denote this theorem as Corollary 5–3.1. A *corollary* is a theorem which is an easy consequence of another theorem.

**Corollary 5–3.1**

> Every equilateral triangle is equiangular.

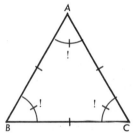

**Restatement.** Given △*ABC*. If *BC* = *AC* = *AB*, then ∠*A* ≅ ∠*B* ≅ ∠*C*.

To prove this, we apply Theorem 5–3 twice. The details are left to you.

The following theorem may look like Theorem 5–3, but in fact it is different. A look at the restatements shows this quite clearly. Notice also the difference in the markings of the figures.

**Theorem 5–4**

> If two angles of a triangle are congruent, then the sides opposite them are congruent.

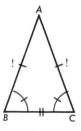

**Restatement.** Given △*ABC*. If ∠*B* ≅ ∠*C*, then *AB* = *AC*.

**Proof.** Since $\angle B \cong \angle C$, $\overline{BC} \cong \overline{CB}$, and $\angle C \cong \angle B$, the correspondence

$$ABC \leftrightarrow ACB$$

is an ASA correspondence. Therefore it is a congruence, and

$$\triangle ABC \cong \triangle ACB.$$

Therefore $AB = AC$, because corresponding sides are congruent.

**Corollary 5–4.1**

Every equiangular triangle is equilateral.

You should be able to write a restatement and a proof.

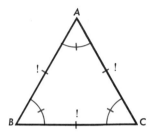

## Problem Set 5–6

1. Select the choice which correctly completes each sentence.
   (a) An angle bisector is a
      (i) segment.      (ii) ray.      (iii) plane.
   (b) An equilateral triangle is
      (i) isosceles.      (ii) scalene.      (iii) not isosceles.
   (c) A corollary is a
      (i) definition.      (ii) postulate.      (iii) theorem.
   (d) If two angles of a triangle are congruent, we can conclude that it has two congruent sides according to a
      (i) definition.      (ii) corollary.      (iii) theorem.

2. In the figure, $\triangle PRS$ is isosceles with $PR = PS$. Prove that $\angle x \cong \angle y$.

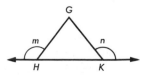

3. If, in the figure, $\angle m \cong \angle n$, prove that $\triangle GHK$ is isosceles.

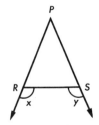

**4.** Given: The plane figure $ADBC$ with $AD = BD$ and $AC = BC$.
Prove: $\angle CAD \cong \angle CBD$.

**5.** Given: The plane figure $ADBC$ with $AC = BC$ and $\angle CAD \cong \angle CBD$.
Prove: $AD = BD$.

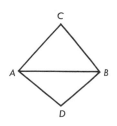

**6.** In Problems 4 and 5, does the hypothesis have to specify that the figure is a plane figure? Explain.

Figure for Problems 4, 5, 6

**7.** Prove Corollary 5–4.1:

Every equiangular triangle is equilateral.

**8.** Given the figure as marked, prove that $\triangle MNK$ is isosceles.

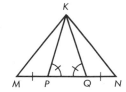

**9.** Given $\triangle ABC$ in which the correspondence $ABC \leftrightarrow ACB$ is a congruence, then we can conclude that $\triangle ABC$ is

(a) scalene.       (b) isosceles.       (c) equilateral.

**10.** Given $\triangle ABC$ in which the correspondence $ABC \leftrightarrow CAB$ is a congruence, then $\triangle ABC$ is

(a) scalene.       (b) isosceles.       (c) equilateral.

**11.** Prove: The bisector of the angle opposite the base of an isosceles triangle bisects the base and is perpendicular to the base.

**12.** In the figure, $AC = BC$, $\angle A \cong \angle y$, and $\angle B \cong \angle x$. Prove that $\triangle CDE$ is isosceles.

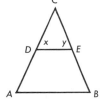

* **13.** In a plane, points $C$ and $D$ are on opposite sides of $\overleftrightarrow{AB}$ such that $\triangle ABC$ is an equilateral triangle and $\triangle ABD$ is an equiangular triangle. Prove that $\angle C \cong \angle D$.

**14.** Given that in the figure $\overline{PQ} \perp \overline{MQ}$, $\overline{PQ} \perp \overline{NQ}$, and $MQ = NQ$, prove that $\triangle MNP$ is isosceles.

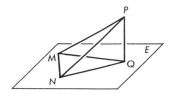

**15.** If, in the figure, $\angle PMN \cong \angle PNM$ and $\angle MPQ \cong \angle NPQ$, prove that $\angle PMQ \cong \angle PNQ$.

Figure for Problems 14 and 15

## 5–7.  OVERLAPPING TRIANGLES.  USE OF FIGURES TO CONVEY INFORMATION

Frequently in geometric figures, the triangles that we need to work with are not entirely separate but overlap, like $\triangle AFM$ and $\triangle FAH$ in the figure on the right.

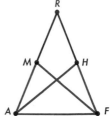

To avoid confusion and mistakes in dealing with such cases, it is especially important to write our congruences correctly:

$$\triangle AFM \cong \triangle FAH.$$

We check that the correspondence $AFM \leftrightarrow FAH$ really is a congruence, and then we refer back to the congruence $\triangle AFM \cong \triangle FAH$ when we wish to conclude that two corresponding sides (or corresponding angles) are congruent.  Looking only at the congruence $\triangle AFM \cong \triangle FAH$, and *not* at the figure, we know that

$$AF = FA, \qquad FM = AH, \qquad AM = FH$$

because these are corresponding sides, under the correspondence

This approach is much more reliable than twisting your head to look at a figure sidewise in the hope that you won't get confused.

Let us now consider a case in which this problem comes up in the proof of a theorem.

*Given: HA = HF; HM = HQ.*
*To prove: FM = AQ.*

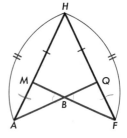

A very common way of proving that two segments are congruent is to show that the segments are corresponding sides of congruent triangles. If this method can be used successfully here, then we must first of all locate the triangles which contain $\overline{FM}$ and $\overline{AQ}$. These are $\triangle HMF$ and $\triangle HQA$, and these triangles overlap quite a bit. Now the problem becomes one of proving that the triangles really are congruent. The proof, written in the double-column form, is given below.

## Proof

| STATEMENTS | REASONS |
|---|---|
| 1.  $HA = HF$. | Given. |
| 2.  $\angle H \cong \angle H$. | An angle is congruent to itself. |
| 3.  $HM = HQ$. | Why? |
| 4.  $\triangle HMF \cong \triangle HQA$. | Why? |
| 5.  $FM = AQ$. | Why? |

A strictly logical proof must not depend on a figure but must follow from the postulates, the definitions, and the previously proved theorems. But geometers use figures very freely as a shorthand in explaining what the problem was in the first place. In this spirit, we stated Example 1 at the beginning of Section 5–4 as follows.

*Given:* $\overline{AR}$ and $\overline{BH}$ bisect each other at $F$.

*To prove:* $\overline{AB} \cong \overline{RH}$.

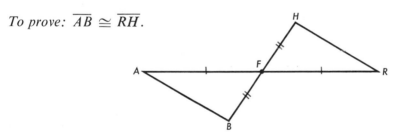

We explained later that the whole theorem could be conveyed by additional marks on the figure, without using words at all, like this:

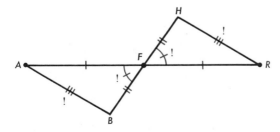

To get along without a figure, we would have to restate Example 1 in the following form.

*Example 1*

Let *A*, *B*, *F*, *H*, and *R* be five noncollinear points lying in a plane. If (1) *F* is between *A* and *R*, (2) *F* is between *B* and *H*, (3) *AF = FR*, and (4) *BF = FH*, then (5) *AB = RH*.

The first two statements of the example, using figures, are surely easier to read than the third statement, and they are just as exact, once you understand how figures are used as shorthand.  We shall use figures to indicate collinearity of points, the order of points on a line, the location of points in the interiors of angles, and, in general, the relative positions of points, lines, and planes.  On the other hand, you should *not* infer that segments are congruent, or that angles are congruent, merely because they look as if they were.  To convey this kind of information by a figure, we have to *mark* the figure in the usual way.

For example, the figure on the right tells us that $\overline{DE} \cong \overline{EF}$, but the figure on the left does not tell us that $\overline{AB} \cong \overline{BC}$, even though careful measurement suggests that this ought to be the case.

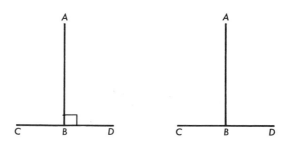

Similarly, the figure on the left above tells us that $\overline{AB} \perp \overline{CD}$, but the figure on the right does not.

## Problem Set 5–7

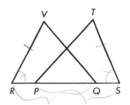

1. In the figure, $RV = ST$, $RQ = SP$, and $\angle VRQ \cong \angle TSP$. Complete the proof that $QV = PT$.

### Proof

| STATEMENTS | REASONS |
|---|---|
| 1. $RV = ST$. | _____. |
| 2. $\angle VRQ \cong \angle TSP$. | _____. |
| 3. _____. | Given. |
| 4. $\triangle RQV \cong$ _____. | _____. |
| 5. _____. | _____. |

2. If, in the figure, $\overline{KG} \perp \overline{GH}$, $\overline{LH} \perp \overline{GH}$, and $\angle KHG \cong \angle LGH$, prove that $\overline{KH} \cong \overline{LG}$.

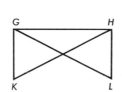

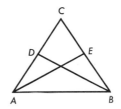

3. Given $AC = BC$ and $\angle CAE \cong \angle CBD$, prove that $\triangle ACE \cong \triangle BCD$.

4. In the figure $AC = BC$, $DC = EC$, and $AD = BE$. Complete the proof that

$$\angle ACE \cong \angle BCD.$$

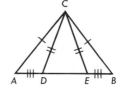

### Proof

| STATEMENTS | REASONS |
|---|---|
| 1. $AC = BC$. <br> $\quad DC = EC$. | Given. |
| 2. $AD = BE$. | _____. |
| 3. $DE = DE$. | _____. |
| 4. $AD + DE = BE + DE$. | Addition Property of Equality. |
| 5. $AE = BD$. | Definition of "between" and Step 4. |
| 6. _____. | _____. |
| 7. $\angle ACE \cong \angle BCD$. | _____. |

**5.** In the figure, $PM = QN$, $PS = QR$, and $MR = NS$. Prove that

$$\angle PSN \cong \angle QRM.$$

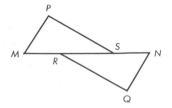

**6.** If, in the figure, $AF = BG$, $\angle A \cong \angle B$, and $AE = BD$, prove that $EF = DG$.

* **7.** If, in the figure, $\angle A \cong \angle B$, $AD = BE$, and $\angle ADG \cong \angle BEF$, prove that $\angle CFE \cong \angle CGD$.

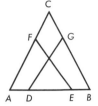

Figure for Problems 6 and 7

* **8.** In the figure on the left, $AD = BC$, $AC = BD$, $AK = BN$, and $AG = BH$. Prove that $KG = NH$.

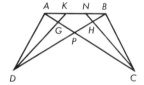
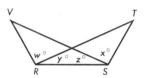

**9.** Given the plane figure with $w = x$ and $y = z$, prove that $RV = ST$.

**10.** Given that in the figure $\angle x \cong \angle y$ and $\angle m \cong \angle n$, prove that $AC = BC$.

* **11.** If, in the figure, $DF = EF$ and $\angle x \cong \angle y$, prove that $\triangle AFB$ is isosceles.

* **12.** If, in the figure, $AC = BC$ and $DC = EC$, prove that $DF = EF$.

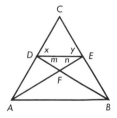

Figure for Problems 10, 11, 12

**13.** If, in the figure, $MK = MQ$, $ML = MP$, and $KL = QP$, find the angle congruent to $\angle KML$. Prove your answer.

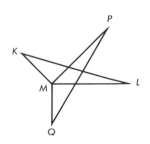

* **14.** If, in the figure, $MK = MQ$, $\angle K \cong \angle Q$, $\overline{PM} \perp \overline{MK}$, and $\overline{LM} \perp \overline{MQ}$, prove that $\angle L \cong \angle P$.

Figure for Problems 13 and 14

**15.** On the sides of $\angle A$ the points $B$ and $C$ are taken such that $AB = AC$. A line through $B$ is perpendicular to $\overrightarrow{AC}$ at $D$. Similarly, a line through $C$ is perpendicular to $\overrightarrow{AB}$ at $E$. If $AD = AE$, prove that $BD = CE$.

**\* 16.** Line $L$ is perpendicular to $\overline{XY}$ and bisects $\overline{XY}$ at $S$. Points $R$ and $T$ are the mid-points of $\overline{XS}$ and $\overline{YS}$, respectively. Points $A$ and $B$ are taken on $L$ on opposite sides of $\overleftrightarrow{XY}$ such that $AX = BY$ and $AT = BR$. Prove that $AS = BS$.

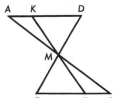

**\* 17.** Prove that if $\angle D \cong \angle DKM$ and $KM = CM = TM$, then $AD = BC$.

**18.** In the figure, $B$, $D$, $H$ are in plane $E$, and $A$ and $C$ are not in plane $E$. If $\overline{AB} \perp \overline{BD}$, $\overline{CD} \perp \overline{HD}$, $AB = HD$, and $CD = BD$, prove that $AD = HC$.

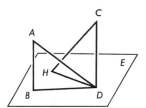

**19.** (a) Prove that if, in the figure, $X$ is the mid-point of $\overline{MN}$, $MZ = NY$, and $XZ = XY$, then $\angle Y \cong \angle Z$.

    (b) Is it necessary that $M$, $N$, $X$, $Y$, and $Z$ be coplanar?

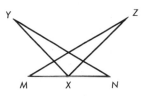

**\* 20.** (a) In the figure, if $M$, $N$, $X$, $Y$, and $Z$ are coplanar, $X$ is the mid-point of $\overline{MN}$, $\angle M \cong \angle N$, and $\angle MXY \cong \angle NXZ$, prove that $\angle Y \cong \angle Z$.

Figure for Problems 19 and 20

    (b) Is it necessary that $M$, $N$, $X$, $Y$, and $Z$ be coplanar? Explain.

## 5–8. QUADRILATERALS, SQUARES, AND RECTANGLES

A quadrilateral is a four-sided figure. Examples are:

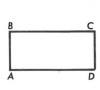

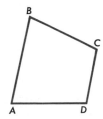

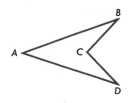

A figure like the one on the left below is *not* a quadrilateral.

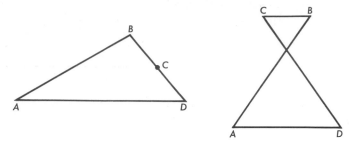

Also, the sides of a quadrilateral are not allowed to cross each other. The figure on the right above is *not* a quadrilateral.

The following definitions are stated so as to include the cases we want to include and rule out the cases that we want to rule out.

## Definitions

Let *A*, *B*, *C*, and *D* be four coplanar points. If no three of these points are collinear, and the segments $\overline{AB}$, $\overline{BC}$, $\overline{CD}$, and $\overline{DA}$ intersect only at their end points, then the union of the four segments is called a *quadrilateral*. The four segments are called its *sides*, and the points *A*, *B*, *C*, and *D* are called its *vertices*. The angles ∠*DAB*, ∠*ABC*, ∠*BCD*, and ∠*CDA* are called its *angles*, and may be denoted briefly as ∠*A*, ∠*B*, ∠*C*, and ∠*D*.

If all four angles of a quadrilateral are right angles, then the quadrilateral is a *rectangle*.

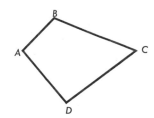

If all four of the angles are right angles, and all four sides are congruent, then the quadrilateral is a *square*.

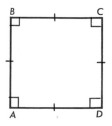

The quadrilateral itself is denoted by □*ABCD*.

In this figure, the marks tell us that $\overline{AD}$ is a *median* of $\triangle ABC$. This can be formally stated as follows.

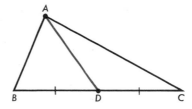

**Definition**

> A *median* of a triangle is a segment whose end points are a vertex of the triangle and the mid-point of the opposite side.

Every triangle has three medians—one for each vertex.

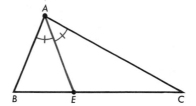

The marks on this figure indicate that $\overline{AE}$ is an *angle bisector* of $\triangle ABC$.

**Definition**

> A segment is an *angle bisector* of a triangle if (1) it lies in the ray which bisects an angle of the triangle, and (2) its end points are the vertex of this angle and a point of the opposite side.

## Problem Set 5–8

1. Construct a large scalene triangle. Construct its three medians. Construct its three angle bisectors.

2. Given: $\triangle ABC$ with median $\overline{AD}$ perpendicular to side $\overline{BC}$.

   Prove: $\overline{AD}$ bisects $\angle BAC$ and $\triangle ABC$ is isosceles.

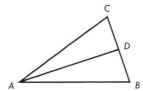

3. Prove: The median to the base of an isosceles triangle is perpendicular to the base and bisects the angle opposite the base.

4. Given that $\square MOPQ$ is a square with $R$ the mid-point of $\overline{MQ}$. Prove that $\triangle ROP$ is isosceles.

**5.** In $\square GKHM$, $\angle G$ and $\angle H$ are right angles, $GK = MH$, and $GH = MK$. $G$ and $H$ are on opposite sides of $\overleftrightarrow{MK}$. Prove that $\square GKHM$ is a rectangle.

**6.** In $\square ABCD$, $\overline{AC} \perp \overline{BD}$ at $F$, $AC = BD$, and $FD = FC$. Prove that $\triangle ACD \cong \triangle BDC$.

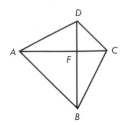

**7.** Prove: The medians to the congruent sides of an isosceles triangle are congruent.

**8.** Prove: In an isosceles triangle, the bisectors of the base angles are congruent.

**9.** $\square ABCD$ is a square and $P$, $Q$, $R$, and $S$ are the mid-points of $\overline{AB}$, $\overline{BC}$, $\overline{CD}$, and $\overline{DA}$, respectively. Prove that $\angle PQR \cong \angle PSR$.

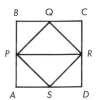

**10.** $\square ABFH$ is a square. $X$ is a point on $\overrightarrow{AH}$, and $Y$ is a point on $\overrightarrow{BF}$ such that $AX = BY$. Prove that $AY = BX$.

**11.** $\overrightarrow{AP}$ bisects $\angle BAC$. $D$ is a point on $\overrightarrow{AB}$, and $E$ is a point on $\overrightarrow{AC}$ such that $AD = AE$. Prove that $PD = PE$.

**\* 12.** Given the figure with $\overrightarrow{KM}$ bisecting both $\angle HKG$ and $\angle HSG$. Prove that $\overrightarrow{KM} \perp \overline{HG}$.

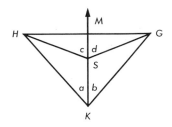

**\* 13.** If, in the figure, $XU = XV$ and

$$\angle 1 \cong \angle 2 \cong \angle 3 \cong \angle 4,$$

prove that

$$\angle 5 \cong \angle 6 \text{ and } \angle 7 \cong \angle 8.$$

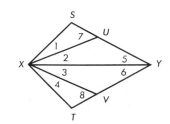

## HONORS PROBLEM

(a) On the basis of theorems proved so far, can you prove that if $\overline{AC} \cong \overline{MP}$, $\overline{BC} \cong \overline{NP}$, and median $\overline{AD} \cong$ median $\overline{MQ}$, then $\triangle ABC \cong \triangle MNP$? If so, do so. If not, why not?

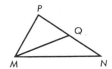

(b) On the basis of theorems proved so far, can you prove that if $\overline{AC} \cong \overline{MP}$, $\overline{AB} \cong \overline{MN}$, and median $\overline{AD} \cong$ median $\overline{MQ}$, then $\triangle ABC \cong \triangle MNP$? If so, do so.

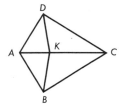

## Supplementary Problems

1. Given: $DC = BC$ and
   $DK = BK.$
   Prove: $AD = AB.$

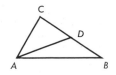

2. Given two congruent triangles, the median to a side of one triangle is congruent to the median to the corresponding side of the other triangle.

3. If, in the figure, $MQ = PQ = PR = NR$, prove that $\triangle MNP$ is isosceles.

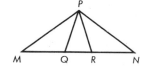

4. Given $\triangle RST$ with $S$-$X$-$T$ such that $SX = SR$. $Q$ is a point such that $R$-$Q$-$T$ and $\overrightarrow{SQ}$ bisects $\angle RST$. Draw $\overline{QX}$. Which angle is congruent to $\angle R$? Prove the congruence.

5. In the figure, $XW = ZY$, $AX = BY$, and $AZ = BW$. Which angle is congruent to $\angle A$? Prove the congruence.

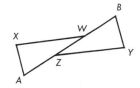

6. Given the figure, in which $\overline{QS}$ and $\overline{RT}$ bisect each other at $P$, prove that $AP = BP$.

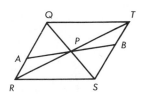

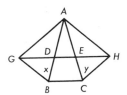

7. If, in the figure, $AB = AC$, $AD = AE$, and $\angle x \cong \angle y$, then $AG = AH$.

8. Prove that the angle bisector of each angle of an equilateral triangle is a median of the triangle.

9. (a) In the figure $AD = BC$, $AB = DC$, and $\overline{MN}$ bisects $\overline{AC}$ at $K$. Does $\overline{AC}$ bisect $\overline{MN}$? Prove your answer.

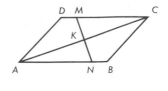

   (b) Must all points of the figure be coplanar?

10. (a) In the figure, $NK = ML$ and $MK = NL$. Prove that $\angle MNK \cong \angle NML$.

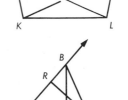

   (b) Must $KM$ and $NL$ intersect?

11. Given: The figure with $AB = AC$ and

$$\angle RCB \cong \angle TBC.$$

Prove: $RC = BT$.

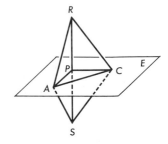

12. Prove that, given two congruent triangles, the angle bisector of an angle of one triangle is congruent to the angle bisector of the corresponding angle of the other triangle.

* 13. In the figure, $A$, $P$, and $C$ lie in plane $E$, and $R$ and $S$ are on opposite sides of $E$. If $\overline{AP} \perp \overline{RS}$, $RP = SP$, and $RC = SC$, prove that

   (a) $\overline{CP} \perp \overline{RS}$,

   (b) $\angle ACR \cong \angle ACS$.

* 14. On $\overleftrightarrow{AB}$, $A$-$C$-$B$ and $\overleftrightarrow{CD} \perp \overleftrightarrow{AB}$. Point $P$ is in the interior of $\angle ACD$ and point $Q$ is in the interior of $\angle BCD$ such that $\angle PCA \cong \angle QCB$. If $\overleftrightarrow{CD} \perp \overrightarrow{PQ}$, then $PC = QC$.

* 15. Let $\overline{AP}$ and $\overline{BC}$ bisect each other at $N$, and $\overline{AC}$ and $\overline{BQ}$ bisect each other at $K$. Show that $QC = PC$.

* 16. Given $\triangle ABC$ with $AB = BC$. Let $D$ be a point on the side of $\overleftrightarrow{AB}$ opposite to $C$ such that $\triangle ABD$ is equilateral. Let $E$ be a point on the side of $\overleftrightarrow{BC}$ opposite to $A$ such that $\triangle BCE$ is equilateral. Prove that $AE = CD$.

* 17. Given $\square ABCD$ as in the figure with $AB = DC$ and $AD = BC$, prove that $\overline{AC}$ and $\overline{BD}$ bisect each other.

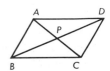

* **18.** In the figure, points $G$ and $B$ trisect $\overline{MR}$, and points $G$ and $P$ trisect $\overline{AC}$. If $AG = BG$ show that $\angle R \cong \angle C$. [*Note: Trisect* means to separate into three congruent parts.]

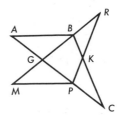

+ **19.** Write out a careful definition of what is meant by "$C$ and $D$ trisect $\overline{AB}$."

*+ **20.** If $\overleftrightarrow{XY}$ is perpendicular to each of three different rays $\overrightarrow{XA}$, $\overrightarrow{XB}$, $\overrightarrow{XC}$ and $XA = XB = XC$, prove that $AY = BY = CY$.

* **21.** Given: $\triangle KVL$ is isosceles with $KV = LV$, and $\overrightarrow{MP}$ contains median $\overline{VP}$ of $\triangle KVL$.

Prove: $ST = RT$.

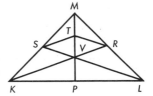

*+ **22.** (a) Let $\overline{AB}$ and $\overline{CD}$ bisect each other at $K$. Prove that $AC = BD$ and $AD = BC$.

(b) Now let $\overline{EF}$ also be bisected at $K$. Can you find six pairs of congruent segments none of which contains $K$?

(c) If $\overline{EF}$ does not lie in the same plane with $\overline{AB}$ and $\overline{CD}$, how do your conclusions in part (b) change? Try to visualize the figure, or sketch a picture, or make a model.

+ **23.** Given $\angle BAC$ such that $AB = AC$; $R$ is on $\overrightarrow{AB}$ and $T$ is on $\overrightarrow{AC}$ such that $RC = TB$. On the basis of this information, can you prove that $AR = AT$? If so, do so. If not, explain why not.

*+ **24.** Let $\triangle PAB$ and $\triangle QAB$ lie in different planes but have a common side $\overline{AB}$. If $\triangle PAB \cong \triangle QAB$ and if $X$ is any point in $\overline{AB}$, then $\angle XPQ \cong \angle XQP$.

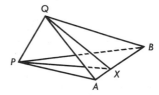

*+ **25.** Complete Euclid's proof of the theorem that the base angles of an isosceles triangle are congruent. Given: $\angle BAC$ with $AB = AC$.

Prove: $\angle ACB \cong \angle ABC$.

[*Hint:* First take a point $E$ such that $A$-$B$-$E$ and a point $F$ such that $A$-$C$-$F$ so that $AE = AF$. Draw $\overline{BF}$ and $\overline{CE}$.]

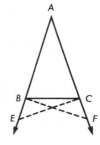

## Chapter Review

1. Indicate whether each statement is true or false.

    (a) If in the correspondence $ABC \leftrightarrow KLM$, $\overline{AC} \cong \overline{KM}$, $\overline{AB} \cong \overline{KL}$, and $\angle A \cong \angle K$, then the correspondence is a congruence.

    (b) If $\overline{AC} = \overline{BD}$, we can conclude that either $A = B$ and $C = D$ or that $A = D$ and $B = C$.

    (c) Two triangles are congruent if the three angles of one triangle are congruent to the three angles of the other triangle.

    (d) If, in $\triangle DEF$, $m \angle D = m \angle E = m \angle F$, then $\triangle DEF$ is equilateral.

    (e) A median of a triangle bisects an angle of the triangle.

    (f) If $\triangle XYZ \cong \triangle BAC$, then $\angle X \cong \angle A$.

    (g) In $\triangle ABC$, if $\angle A \cong \angle C$, then $AB = AC$.

    (h) If $\triangle XYZ \cong \triangle ZXY$, then $\triangle XYZ$ is equilateral.

    (i) Two triangles are congruent if two sides and an angle of one are congruent to two sides and an angle of the other.

    (j) There is no $\triangle ABC$ in which $\angle A = \angle B$.

2. Define "congruent segments."

3. Define "bisector of an angle."

4. Define "angle bisector of a triangle."

5. Complete: If an angle bisector of a triangle is also a median, then the triangle is _____.

6. Complete: A quadrilateral which has four right angles is called a _____.

7. Complete: In $\triangle PRQ$, $\angle Q$ is included by _____ and _____, and $\angle P$ and $\angle R$ include _____.

8. $\triangle ABC$ and $\triangle PQR$ each have two sides whose lengths are 7 and an angle whose measure is 40. Are the triangles congruent? Why or why not?

9. If in the figure, $AB = AC$ and $\overrightarrow{AR}$ bisects $\angle BAC$, prove that

    (a) $RB = RC$,

    (b) $\overrightarrow{AR}$ contains the bisector of $\angle BRC$.

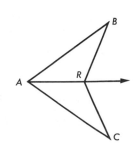

10. Prove: If $\triangle ABC$ is equilateral, then $\triangle ABC \cong \triangle CAB \cong \triangle ACB$.

11. Write out an hypothesis and a conclusion for the figure as marked.

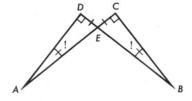

12. Write the theorem suggested by the figure on the left below.

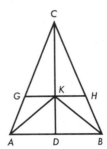

13. In the plane figure on the right above, $AC = BC$ and $AK = BK$. Make a list of all the conclusions that follow. (You should be able to prove each one.)

\* 14. In an isosceles triangle, $\triangle PQR$, the bisector of a base angle $\angle Q$ intersects the opposite side at $S$. $T$ is a point of base $\overline{PQ}$ such that $ST = PT$. $\overline{SV}$ bisects $\angle PST$. Prove that $\angle TSV \cong \angle RQS$.

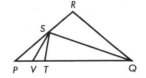

\* 15. In the figure, $A$, $B$, $C$, and $D$ are noncoplanar and $AB = AC = AD = BC = BD = CD$. $Q$ and $R$ are mid-points of $\overline{AC}$ and $\overline{AD}$, respectively, and $P$ is any point of $\overline{AB}$. Prove that $\triangle PQR$ is isosceles.

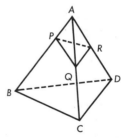

\*+ 16. Let $L$ be the edge of two half-planes, $H_1$ and $H_2$. $A$ and $B$ are two points of $L$, $M$ is a point in $H_1$, and $R$ is a point in $H_2$ such that $\angle MAB \cong \angle RAB$ and $AM = AR$.

(a) Prove that $\triangle MRB$ is isosceles.

(b) Must $\overline{MR}$ intersect $L$?

(c) Does the answer to (a) require that $H_1$ and $H_2$ be coplanar?

# 6 | A Closer Look at Proof

## 6–1.  HOW A DEDUCTIVE SYSTEM WORKS

In Chapter 1 we tried to explain in general terms how our study of geometry was going to work. After the experience that you have gained since then, you ought to be in a much better position to understand the explanation.

The idea of a set, the methods of algebra, and the process of logical reasoning are things that we have been working *with*. The geometry itself is what we have been working *on*. We started with *point, line,* and *plane* as undefined terms; and so far, we have used seventeen postulates. Sometimes, new terms have been defined by an appeal to postulates. (For example, the distance *PQ* was defined to be the positive number given by the Distance Postulate.) Sometimes definitions have been based only on the undefined terms. (For example, a set of points is *collinear* if all points of the set lie on the same *line*.) But at every point we have built our definitions with terms that were, in some way, previously known. By now we have piled definitions on top of one another so often that the list is very long; and, in fact, the length of the list is one of the main reasons we had to be careful, at the outset, to keep the record straight.

Similarly, all the statements that we make about geometry are ultimately based on the postulates. So far we have sometimes proved theorems directly from postulates, and sometimes we have based our proofs on theorems that were already proved. But in every case, the chain of reasoning can be traced back to the postulates.

You might find it a good idea, at this point, to reread the second half of Chapter 1. It will seem much clearer to you now than it did the first time. It is much easier to look back, and understand what you have done, than to understand an explanation of what you are about to do.

## 6–2.  INDIRECT PROOFS

We remarked in Chapter 1 that the best way to learn about logical reasoning is to do some of it. In general, this is true. But there is one kind of proof that calls for special discussion. For Theorem 3–1, we used what is called an *indirect proof*. The theorem and its proof were as follows.

### Theorem 3–1

If two different lines intersect, their intersection contains only one point.

**Proof.**   If two different lines intersected at two different points $P$ and $Q$, then there would be two lines containing $P$ and $Q$. The Line Postulate tells us that this never happens.

Possibly you have seen this sort of reasoning used before. You may already know the proof that $\sqrt{2}$ is an irrational number, and this proof is indirect. In any case you must have heard statements of this sort many times, in ordinary conversation. Both of the following remarks are examples of indirect proofs.

## *Example 1*

> "It must not be raining outside.
>
> If it were raining, then those people coming in the door would be wet, but they aren't."

## *Example 2*

> "Today must not be the right day for the football game.
>
> If the game were being played today, then by now the stadium would be full of people, but you and I are the only ones here."

In each case, the speaker wants to show that a certain statement is true. He starts his proof by supposing that the statement that he wants to prove is false; he then observes that this leads to a conclusion which contradicts a known fact. In the first case, the speaker starts by supposing that it is raining; this leads to the conclusion that the people coming in the door would be wet; and this contradicts the known fact that the people are dry. Similarly, in the second case the speaker begins by supposing that the football game is to be played today; and this leads to a contradiction of the fact that the stadium contains only two people.

In the proof of Theorem 3–1, we start by supposing that some two different lines intersect in two different points. This contradicts the Line Postulate. Therefore the supposition is wrong, and this means that the theorem is right.

Very often, our indirect proofs in geometry will be as short and simple as this; they will amount merely to common-sense observations. But such common-sense observations are part of the ABC's of mathematical reasoning, and it would be hard to get along without them.

## Problem Set 6–2

1. For the sake of argument accept each of the following hypotheses and then give a logical completion for each conclusion.

   (a) *Hypothesis:* All boys like to play football. My brother is fourteen years old.

   *Conclusion:* My brother_____.

   (b) *Hypothesis:* Only careless people make mistakes. I am never careless.

   *Conclusion:* I_____.

   (c) *Hypothesis:* Jack always laughs when he tells a joke. Jack is telling a joke.

   *Conclusion:* Jack_____.

   (d) *Hypothesis:* In any isosceles triangle, the base angles are congruent. In $\triangle ABC$, $AC = BC$.

   *Conclusion:* _____.

2. Which of the following arguments are examples of indirect reasoning?

   (a) The outside temperature must be below 32°F. If it were not below 32°F, the window panes would not be frosted. But they are frosted. Therefore the outside temperature is below 32°F.

   (b) It must be time to eat lunch. If it were not time for lunch, I would not be hungry. But I am very hungry. Therefore it must be time for lunch.

   (c) The concert must be finished. Many people leave the concert hall only when the concert is over. Many people are leaving the concert hall. Therefore the concert is finished.·

3. The time must be later than 4 p.m. If the time were not later than 4 p.m., I would hear the noise of the construction men at work. I do not hear any noise.

   In this example of indirect proof, identify

   (a) the statement to be proved,

   (b) the supposition made,

   (c) the conclusion resulting from the supposition, and

   (d) the known fact contradictory to (c).

4. Mrs. Adams purchased a set of kitchen utensils advertised as a stainless-steel product. After using the set a few weeks, she discovered that some of the utensils were beginning to rust. She thereupon decided that the set was not stainless steel and returned it for a refund.
   Follow the directions of Problem 3.

**5.** Prove that the bisector of any angle of a scalene triangle cannot be perpendicular to the opposite side.

**6.** Prove that no two angles of a scalene triangle are congruent.

+ **7.** What conclusions can you draw from the following hypothesis in which $p$, $q$, and $r$ stand for different statements?

> If $p$ is true, then $q$ is true.
>
> If $q$ is true, then $r$ is true.
>
> $p$ is true.

+ **8.** What conclusions can you draw from the following hypothesis?

> If $p$ is true, then $q$ is true.
>
> If $r$ is true, then $s$ is not true.
>
> If $q$ is true, then $s$ is true.
>
> $p$ is true.

Did you use indirect reasoning at any point? Explain.

+ **9.**
> If $K$ is blue, then $M$ is red.
>
> If $K$ is green, then $M$ is yellow.
>
> If $M$ is red, then $J$ is blue.

(a) $K$ is blue, so $M$ is _____ and $J$ is _____.

(b) $M$ is yellow. Is it possible to draw a conclusion concerning $K$? If so, what conclusion?

(c) $J$ is not blue. Is it possible to draw a conclusion concerning $K$? If so, what conclusion?

+ **10.** What conclusion follows from the following data?

(a) Nobody is allowed to join the swimming club unless he can play the piccolo.

(b) No turtle can play the piccolo.

(c) Nobody is allowed to wear striped trunks in the club pool unless he is a member of the swimming club.

(d) I always wear striped trunks in the club pool.

[*Hint:* Convert each statement to an "if . . . then" form and diagram the argument as in Problems 7 and 8. For example, let $p$ be "someone is a member of the swimming club," etc.]

+ **11.** What conclusion follows from the following hypothesis?

> Tame lions have sharp teeth.
>
> Lions that eat people never get sick.
>
> Lions that never eat people have dull teeth.
>
> My pet lion has pneumonia.

Did you use indirect reasoning? Explain.

## 6–3.  THEOREMS ON LINES AND PLANES

It is now rather easy to prove the other theorems of Chapter 3. For convenience, we first restate the postulates on which the proofs are based.

**POSTULATE 4.**  The Line Postulate

> *For every two points there is exactly one line that contains both points.*

**POSTULATE 5**

> *(a) Every plane contains at least three noncollinear points.*
>
> *(b) Space contains at least four noncoplanar points.*

**POSTULATE 6**

> *If two points of a line lie in a plane, then the line lies in the same plane.*

**POSTULATE 7.**  The Plane Postulate

> *Any three points lie in at least one plane, and any three noncollinear points lie in exactly one plane.*

We shall now prove the following theorem.

**Theorem 3–2**

> If a line intersects a plane not containing it, then the intersection contains only one point.

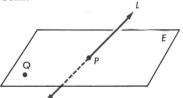

**Proof.**  We are given a line $L$ and a plane $E$.  By hypothesis, we have

(1) $L$ intersects $E$ in at least one point $P$, and

(2) $E$ does not contain $L$.

We shall give an indirect proof, and we therefore start by supposing that

(3) $L$ intersects $E$ in some other point $Q$.

We need to show that (3) leads to a contradiction of a known fact— and it does: If $P$ and $Q$ lie in $E$, then it follows by Postulate 6 that $L$ lies in $E$.  This contradicts (2).  Therefore (3) is false.  Therefore Theorem 3–2 is true.

Of course, the figure for this proof looks rather peculiar. We have indicated a point $Q$, merely to remind ourselves of the notation of the proof. The proof itself shows that no such point can possibly exist. In fact, the figures for indirect proofs will always look ridiculous, for the excellent reason that they describe impossible situations. If we had drawn a figure for Theorem 3–1, it might have looked even worse:

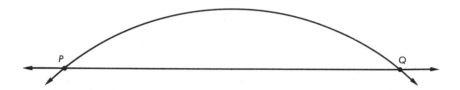

This figure suggests an impossible situation in which two lines intersect in two different points.

### Theorem 3–3

Given a line and a point not on the line, there is exactly one plane containing both of them.

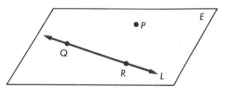

Let $L$ be the given line, and let $P$ be the given point. To prove the theorem, we need to show two things:

(1) there is a plane $E$, containing $P$ and $L$;

(2) there is only one plane $E$, containing $P$ and $L$.

Statements (1) and (2), taken together, tell us that there is *exactly* one plane containing $P$ and $L$.

**Proof of (1).**  Let $Q$ and $R$ be any two points of $L$. By Postulate 7 there is a plane $E$, containing $P$, $Q$, and $R$. By Postulate 6, $E$ contains $L$. Thus $E$ contains $P$ and $L$.

**Proof of (2).**  This proof will be indirect. *Suppose* that there is another plane $E'$ which contains $P$ and $L$. Then $E'$ contains $P$, $Q$, and $R$.
But $P$, $Q$, and $R$ are noncollinear. The reason is that $L$ is the only line that contains $Q$ and $R$ (why?), and $L$ does not contain $P$.
Thus we have two different planes, $E$ and $E'$, containing the noncollinear points $P$, $Q$, and $R$. This contradicts Postulate 7.

Note that this theorem and its proof split up naturally into two parts. This illustrates the distinction between *existence* and *uniqueness*. The first half of the proof shows the *existence* of a plane $E$ containing $P$ and $L$. The second half shows the *uniqueness* of the plane containing $P$ and $L$. When we prove existence, we show that there is *at least one* object of a certain kind. When we prove uniqueness, we show that there is *at most one*. If it happens that we can prove both, then we know that there is *exactly one*.

However, existence and uniqueness do not always go together, by any means; in many cases, we may have one without the other, and often we have neither. For example, for the fleas on a stray dog, we can usually prove existence but not uniqueness. (It is a lucky dog indeed that has only one flea.) Similarly, if $x$ is rational, then there *exist* integers $p$ and $q$ such that

$$x = \frac{p}{q}.$$

But these integers are not unique, because we also have

$$x = \frac{2p}{2q} = \frac{3p}{3q},$$

and so on. For the eldest daughters of a given mother, we obviously have uniqueness, but not necessarily existence; in some families, all of the children are boys. For the points common to two different segments, we don't necessarily have either existence or uniqueness; the intersection may contain a whole segment, or exactly one point, or no points at all:

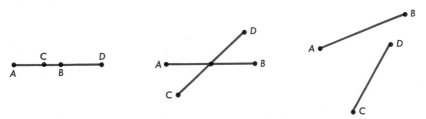

The phrase "one and only one" is often used instead of "exactly one," to emphasize the double value of the statement.

Our next theorem splits into two parts, in the same way as the preceding one.

### Theorem 3–4

Given two intersecting lines, there is exactly one plane containing them.

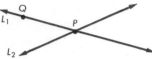

We are given the lines $L_1$ and $L_2$ intersecting in the point $P$. We need to show two things:

(1) *Existence.* There is a plane $E$ containing $L_1$ and $L_2$.

(2) *Uniqueness.* There is only one plane $E$ which contains $L_1$ and $L_2$.

We give the proofs in double-column form.

**Proof of (1)**

| STATEMENTS | REASONS |
|---|---|
| 1. $L_1$ contains a point $Q$ different from P. | By the Ruler Postulate, every line contains infinitely many points. |
| 2. $Q$ is not on $L_2$. | By Theorem 3–1, $L_1$ intersects $L_2$ only at $P$. |
| 3. There is a plane $E$ containing $Q$ and $L_2$. | Theorem 3–3. |
| 4. $E$ contains $L_1$. | By Postulate 6, since $E$ contains $P$ and $Q$. |

**Proof of (2)**

| STATEMENTS | REASONS |
|---|---|
| 5. *Suppose* that another plane, $E'$, contains $L_1$ and $L_2$. | Beginning of indirect proof. |
| 6. $E'$ contains $Q$. | $Q$ is on $L_1$. |
| 7. Both $E$ and $E'$ contain $Q$ and $L_2$. | Steps 3, 4, 5 and 6. |
| 8. $E$ is the only plane containing $L_1$ and $L_2$. | Step 7 contradicts Theorem 3–3. |

Note that the proof of (2) supplies you with a pattern for writing up indirect proofs in the double-column form. Strictly speaking, of course, the phrase "Beginning of indirect proof" is not a "reason"; it is merely an explanation of what we had in mind when we wrote down step 5.

## Problem Set 6–3

1. Which theorem may be restated as "Two intersecting lines determine a plane"?

2. If the three lines in the figure on the left below are not all coplanar, how many planes do they determine? List each plane by naming the lines which determine it.

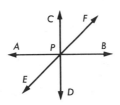
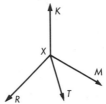

3. In the figure on the right above, no three of the rays are coplanar. How many planes do they determine? Name each plane by the points which determine it.

4. Which postulate or theorem stated in Section 6–3 asserts uniqueness of a point for which existence cannot be asserted?

5. As indicated in the figure, points $A$ and $B$ lie in plane $E$, and point $P$ lies above plane $E$. Which postulate or theorem asserts that $\overleftrightarrow{AB}$ is contained in $E$? There is a second plane implicit in the figure. Name it. What is its intersection with $E$? If a fourth point, $Q$, lies below plane $E$ but is not collinear with $P$ and $A$ or $P$ and $B$, name the planes thereby determined. Draw the figure.

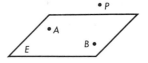

6. Explain the use of the phrase "one and only one."

7. Suppose you wish to prove that in a plane, at a given point of a given line, there is at most one line perpendicular to the given line. Would you be proving existence or uniqueness? If your proof is indirect, what supposition would you make to begin your reasoning?

## 6–4.  PERPENDICULARS

Using a ruler and a protractor, it is easy to draw the perpendicular to a given line at a given point of the line. We simply lay off a 90°-angle, as in the figure, with vertex at the given point $P$, one side $\overrightarrow{PX}$ on the given

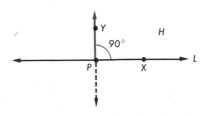

line $L$, and the other side in one of the half-planes determined by $L$. The perpendicular ought to be unique because there is only one 90°-mark on the protractor.

We shall now describe this situation in a theorem, and prove it on the basis of our postulates.

### Theorem 6–1

In a given plane, through a given point of a given line, there is one and only one line perpendicular to the given line.

**Restatement.** Let $E$ be a plane, let $L$ be a line in $E$, and let $P$ be a point of $L$. Then

(1) there is a line $M$ in $E$ such that $M$ contains $P$ and $M \perp L$; and

(2) there is only one such line $M$.

**Proof of (1).** Let $H$ be one of the two half-planes in $E$, determined by $L$, and let $X$ be any point of $L$, other than $P$. (See the figure above.) By the Angle Construction Postulate, there is a ray $\overrightarrow{PY}$, with $Y$ in $H$, such that $m \angle YPX = 90$. Let $M = \overleftrightarrow{PY}$. Then $M \perp L$ at $P$.

**Proof of (2).** Suppose now that both $M_1$ and $M_2$ are perpendicular to $L$ at $P$. We shall show that $M_1 = M_2$.

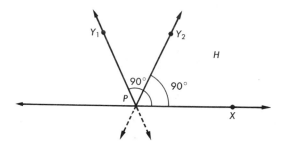

Now $M_1$ and $M_2$ contain rays $\overrightarrow{PY}_1$ and $\overrightarrow{PY}_2$, with $Y_1$ and $Y_2$ in $H$. By the definition of "perpendicular" and Theorem 4–8, both of the angles $\angle Y_1PX$ and $\angle Y_2PX$ are right angles, as indicated in the figure. By the Angle Construction Postulate, this means that $\overrightarrow{PY}_1$ and $\overrightarrow{PY}_2$ are the same ray. Since $M_1$ and $M_2$ have more than one point in common, they cannot be different lines. Therefore $M_1 = M_2$.

Note that to prove the uniqueness of the perpendiculars to $L$ at $P$, we had to restrict ourselves to a given plane. In space, every line has infinitely many perpendiculars at each of its points. Thus, on a wagon, all spokes of a wheel are perpendicular to the axle.

The markings on the following figure indicate that $L$ is the *perpendicular bisector* of $\overline{AB}$.

### Definition

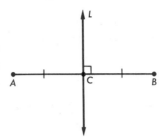

In a given plane, the *perpendicular bisec-tor* of a segment is the line which is perpendicular to the segment at its mid-point.

Every segment $\overline{AB}$ has one and only one mid-point $C$; and through $C$ there is one and only one line perpendicular to $\overleftrightarrow{AB}$. Therefore the perpendicular bisector exists and is unique.

The following theorem gives another description of the perpendicular bisector.

### Theorem 6–2. The Perpendicular Bisector Theorem

The perpendicular bisector of a segment, in a plane, is the set of all points of the plane that are equidistant from the end-points of the segment.

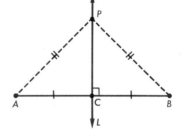

**Restatement.** Let $L$ be the perpendicular bisector of $\overline{AB}$ in the plane $E$. Then

(1) if $P$ is on $L$, then $PA = PB$, and

(2) if $PA = PB$, then $P$ is on $L$.

This is an example of what is called a *characterization* theorem. To *characterize* a set of points, we state a condition which (1) is satis-fied by the points of the given set, and (2) is not satisfied by any other points. In this case, the set of points is the perpendicular bisector of $\overline{AB}$, and the condition is $PA = PB$. Therefore the restatement of the theorem naturally splits into two parts, and so does the proof.

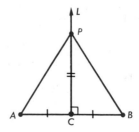

**Proof of (1).** Let $C$ be the mid-point of $\overline{AB}$, and let $P$ be any point of $L$. If $P = C$, then obviously $PA = PB$. Suppose, then, that $P$ is different from $C$, so that $P$ is not on $\overleftrightarrow{AB}$. We have $PC = PC$ by identity; $\angle PCA \cong \angle PCB$ because both are right angles; and $CA = CB$ because $C$ is the mid-point. By SAS, we have $\triangle PCA \cong \triangle PCB$. Therefore $PA = PB$.

**Proof of (2).** Given that $P$ is in the plane $E$, and $PA = PB$. If $P$ is on $\overleftrightarrow{AB}$, then $P = C$, because $\overline{AB}$ has only one mid-point. If $P$ is not on $\overleftrightarrow{AB}$, let $L'$ be the line $\overleftrightarrow{PC}$. Then $PC = PC$, $CA = CB$ and $PA = PB$. (Why?) By SSS, we have

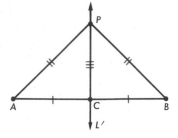

$$\triangle PCA \cong \triangle PCB,$$

as before. Therefore, by definition, $\angle PCB$ is a right angle, and so $L' \perp \overline{AB}$ at $C$. By Theorem 6–1, perpendiculars are unique. Therefore $L' = L$. Therefore $P$ is on $L$, which was to be proved.

### Corollary 6–2.1

Given a segment $\overline{AB}$ and a line $L$ in the same plane. If two points of $L$ are each equidistant from $A$ and $B$, then $L$ is the perpendicular bisector of $\overline{AB}$.

**Proof.** By Theorem 6–2, $L$ contains two points of the perpendicular bisector of $\overline{AB}$. Since two points determine a line, this means that $L$ is the perpendicular bisector of $\overline{AB}$.

We have found that there was really no problem in constructing the perpendicular to a line through a point *on* the line: we merely lay off a 90°-angle. If the point is *not* on the line, the construction requires an idea.

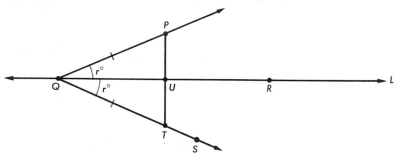

Given a line $L$, and a point $P$, not on $L$. We wish to construct a line through $P$, perpendicular to $L$. (We are working, of course, in a plane $E$ containing $L$ and $P$.)

Let $Q$ and $R$ be any two points of $L$. To get the perpendicular, we first draw the ray $\overrightarrow{QP}$ and measure $\angle PQR$. We then draw a ray $\overrightarrow{QS}$, with $S$ on the opposite side of $L$ from $P$, as indicated in the figure, such that

$$\angle SQR \cong \angle PQR.$$

(What postulate allows this?)  We then plot a point $T$ on $\overrightarrow{QS}$ such that $TQ = PQ$. Then $\overline{TP}$ intersects $L$ in a point $U$. (Why?)  Now $QU = QU$, $\angle PQU \cong \angle TQU$, and $TQ = PQ$. Therefore, by SAS, $\triangle PQU \cong \triangle TQU$, and $\angle PUQ$ and $\angle TUQ$ are right angles. Therefore $\overleftrightarrow{TP} \perp L$, and we have drawn the perpendicular to $L$ through $P$.

On the basis of this discussion, you ought to be able to complete the proof of the following theorem in double-column form.

### Theorem 6–3

Through a given external point there is at least one line perpendicular to a given line.

**Restatement.**  Let $L$ be a line, and let $P$ be a point not on $L$.  Then there is a line which is perpendicular to $L$ and contains $P$.

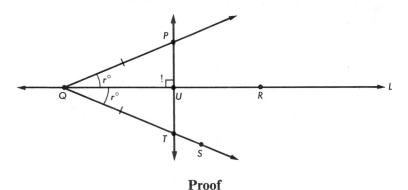

**Proof**

| Statements | Reasons |
|---|---|
| 1. $L$ contains two points $Q$ and $R$. | The Ruler Postulate. |
| 2. There is a ray $\overrightarrow{QS}$, with $S$ on the opposite side of $L$ from $P$, such that $\angle SQR \cong \angle PQR$. | ? |
| 3. There is a point $T$ of $\overrightarrow{QS}$ such that $TQ = PQ$. | ? |
| 4. $T$ and $P$ are on opposite sides of $L$. | $P$ and $S$ are on opposite sides of $L$, and $S$ and $T$ are on the same side of $L$. |
| 5. $\overline{TP}$ intersects $L$ in a point $U$. | ? |
| 6. $\triangle PQU \cong \triangle TQU$. | ? |
| 7. $\angle PUQ$ is a right angle. | ? |
| 8. $\overleftrightarrow{PU} \perp L$. | ? |

This proof, as we have written it, does not allow for the possibility $Q = U$. When we pick the point $Q$ at random, on $L$, it conceivably may happen that $\overleftrightarrow{PQ} \perp L$. But of course if this happens there is nothing to prove, because we already have our perpendicular, namely, the line $\overleftrightarrow{PQ}$.

Thus the perpendicular to a line, through an external point, *exists*. We show next that the perpendicular is *unique*.

### Theorem 6–4

Through a given external point there is at most one line perpendicular to a given line.

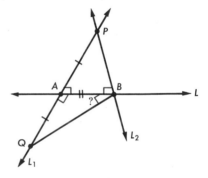

**Proof.** The proof is indirect, like most uniqueness proofs. Suppose that $L_1$ and $L_2$ are two different lines through $P$, each perpendicular to $L$. Let $A$ and $B$ be the points where $L_1$ and $L_2$ intersect $L$. Let $Q$ be the point, on the ray opposite to $\overrightarrow{AP}$, for which $AQ = AP$. (By the Point-Plotting Theorem.) By SAS, we have

$$\triangle PAB \cong \triangle QAB.$$

(It doesn't look that way in the figure, but remember that the figure is a picture of an impossible situation; our job, in the proof, is to show that the situation pictured is impossible.)

Therefore $\angle PBA \cong \angle QBA$, because they are corresponding angles. Therefore $\overleftrightarrow{BQ} \perp L$ at $B$. Therefore there are two lines, $L_2$ and $\overleftrightarrow{BQ}$, which are perpendicular to $L$ at $B$. This contradicts Theorem 6–1, which says that there is only one line perpendicular to a given line through a point of the line, in a given plane. Hence our assumption, that there were two perpendiculars to $L$ through $P$, is false.

### Corollary 6–4.1

No triangle has two right angles.

**Proof.** In $\triangle ABC$, if both $\angle A$ and $\angle B$ were right angles, then there would be two perpendiculars to $\overleftrightarrow{AB}$ through $C$. By Theorem 6–4, this is impossible.

## Definitions

A *right triangle* is a triangle one of whose angles is a right angle. The side opposite the right angle is called the *hypotenuse,* and the other two sides are called the *legs.*

The preceding theorem, of course, is what gives us the right to speak of *the* right angle of a right triangle.

## Problem Set 6–4

1. If, in a plane $M$, with point $A$ on line $L$, $\overrightarrow{AT} \perp L$ and $\overrightarrow{AQ} \perp L$, what conclusion can you draw regarding $\overrightarrow{AQ}$ and $\overleftrightarrow{AT}$? Why?

2. What theorem tells us that the vertex opposite the base of an isosceles triangle lies on the perpendicular bisector of the base?

3. In the figure, $L$ is the perpendicular bisector of $\overline{AB}$. If the lengths of segments are as indicated, find $x$, $y$, and $z$.

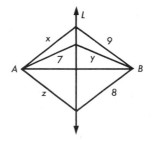

4. If $D$ is the mid-point of $\overline{BC}$ and $\overleftrightarrow{AD} \perp \overline{BC}$, prove that $\triangle ABC$ is isosceles. Do *not* use congruent triangles in your proof.

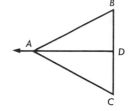

5. In a plane, $GE = KE$, $GM = KM$, and $H$ lies on $\overleftrightarrow{EM}$. Prove that $GH = KH$, *without* using congruent triangles.

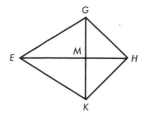

6. Line $L$ is the perpendicular bisector of $\overline{QT}$. $P$ is a point on the same side of line $L$ as $Q$. $\overline{PT}$ intersects $L$ at $R$. Prove that $PT = PR + RQ$.

7. (a) In a plane, how many perpendiculars are there to a given line at a point of the line?

(b) In space, how many perpendiculars are there to a given line at a point of the line?

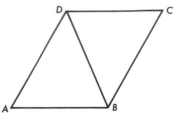

8. Copy the figure.   Using ruler and protractor construct  perpendiculars through $A$ and $C$ to $\overleftrightarrow{DB}$.  Construct the perpendicular through $B$ to $\overleftrightarrow{DC}$ and the perpendicular through $A$ to $\overleftrightarrow{BC}$.

9. Which theorem allows us to say,

   "*the* perpendicular to a line through a given external point"?

10. (a) In $\triangle PQR$, if $\angle R$ is a right angle, then $\overline{PQ}$ is called the _____, and $\overline{RQ}$ and $\overline{RP}$ are called the _____.

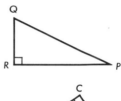

(b) In $\triangle ABC$, if $\angle C$ is a right angle, the hypotenuse is _____, and the legs are _____ and _____.

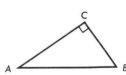

11. Prove that if the median to the hypotenuse of a right triangle is perpendicular to the hypotenuse, then the right triangle is isosceles.

* 12. Given $\triangle ABC$ with $AC = BC$.  The bisectors of the base angles, $\angle A$ and $\angle B$, intersect each other at $F$.  Prove that $\overleftrightarrow{CF}$ is perpendicular to $\overline{AB}$. (It is not necessary to use any congruent triangles in your proof.)

* 13. One diagonal of a quadrilateral bisects two angles of the quadrilateral. Prove that it bisects the other diagonal.

* 14. $A$, $B$, and $C$ lie in plane $E$.  $P$ and $Q$ are on opposite sides of $E$.  Given that $PB = QB$, $A$ is the mid-point of $\overline{PQ}$, and $\angle PBC \cong \angle QBC$, prove that $\overline{PQ} \perp \overline{AC}$.

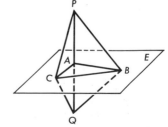

## 6–5.   INTRODUCING AUXILIARY SETS INTO PROOFS. THE USE OF THE WORD "LET"

You have probably noted that in some of our proofs, we have introduced points and lines that were not given in the statement of the theorem.   Recall, for example, the place in Section 6–4 where we wanted to show that there is always a perpendicular to a given line, through a given external point.

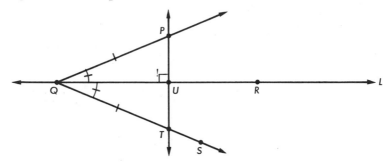

Only the line $L$ and the point $P$ were given, but to get the perpendicular $\overleftrightarrow{TP}$, we had to introduce the points $Q$ and $R$, the rays $\overrightarrow{QP}$ and $\overrightarrow{QS}$, and the point $T$.

In each step of the double-column proof of this theorem (Theorem 6–3), the statements assert that there really are points and rays of the sort that we want to talk about.  And if you filled in the reasons correctly, then at each step you referred to a postulate (or perhaps a theorem) which justified the statement.

Most of the time, however, the reasons in such cases are very simple; and in writing paragraph proofs, we often use more informal language. In the discussion preceding Theorem 6–3, you have seen an example of this.  We said:

> "*Let* $Q$ and $R$ be any two points of $L$.  To get the perpendicular, we first *draw* the ray $\overrightarrow{QP}$ . . . ."

Mathematicians often talk in this fashion, and there is no reason why they shouldn't.  But if you are not keeping careful track of what is going on, this sort of language may easily lead to misunderstandings. Sometimes it may seem that mathematicians simply "let" things be whatever way they want them to be.  This, of course, is not what they are doing.  When we say, "let $Q$ and $R$ be any two points of $L$," we are claiming that $L$ contains two points, and we are claiming to know why.  Once we have proved Theorems 6–3 and 6–4, we know

that perpendiculars exist and are unique. We therefore have the right
to say, "let $L'$ be the perpendicular to $L$ through $P$." This is an abbreviated way of referring to both these theorems at once. [*Query:* If we
knew Theorem 6–3, but not Theorem 6–4, what sort of abbreviated
statement would we have the right to make?]

In formal double-column proofs, when we introduce auxiliary sets,
we need to refer to postulates and theorems as reasons. A list of the
postulates and theorems that we shall refer to for this purpose follows.
These are the statements that tell us that some point, line, or plane
exists, or is unique, or both.

### POSTULATE 4.    The Line Postulate

*For every two points there is exactly one line that contains both
points.*

### POSTULATE 5

(*a*) *Every plane contains at least three noncollinear points.*

(*b*) *Space contains at least four noncoplanar points.*

### Theorem 2–1.    The Point-Plotting Theorem

Let $\overrightarrow{AB}$ be a ray, and let $x$ be a positive number. Then there is
exactly one point $P$ of $\overrightarrow{AB}$ such that $AP = x$.

### Theorem 2–2

Every segment has exactly one mid-point.

### Theorem 3–1

If two different lines intersect, their intersection contains only one
point.

### Theorem 3–2

If a line intersects a plane not containing it, then the intersection
contains only one point.

### POSTULATE 7.    The Plane Postulate

*Any three points lie in at least one plane, and any three noncollinear
points lie in exactly one plane.*

### Theorem 3–3

Given a line and a point not on the line, there is exactly one
plane containing both.

## Theorem 3–4

Given two intersecting lines, there is exactly one plane containing both.

## POSTULATE 12. The Angle Construction Postulate

*Let $\overrightarrow{AB}$ be a ray on the edge of the half-plane H. For every number r between 0 and 180 there is exactly one ray $\overrightarrow{AP}$, with P in H, such that $m\angle PAB = r$.*

## Theorem 5–2

Every angle has exactly one bisector.

## Theorem 6–1

In a given plane, through a given point of a given line, there is one and only one line perpendicular to the given line.

## Theorem 6–3

Through a given external point there is at least one line perpendicular to a given line.

## Theorem 6–4

Through a given external point there is at most one line perpendicular to a given line.

Among the theorems and postulates that we have presented so far, these are the ones that we shall use when we introduce auxiliary sets. But these surely aren't going to do us any good in proving new theorems for ourselves, unless we can think of a set that is *useful* to introduce. In fact, thinking of *useful* sets to introduce is both the difficult and the most interesting part of our job; the theorem citations are merely a way of making sure that our work is orderly.

There are no fixed rules for devising proofs; we learn by practice. Let us look at some examples.

### Example 1

*Given:* The plane figure with $AD = AE$ and $CD = CE$.

*To prove:* $\angle D \cong \angle E$.

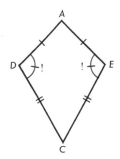

Since all our postulates and theorems concerning congruence have dealt with triangles, it seems reasonable that our figure should show some triangles. We can accomplish this easily by introducing either $\overline{AC}$ or $\overline{DE}$.

Suppose we introduce $\overline{DE}$ so that our figure looks like the one on the right. This allows us to complete the proof, since $m\angle ADE = m\angle AED$ and $m\angle CDE = m\angle CED$ give us $m\angle ADC = m\angle AEC$ by the Angle Addition Postulate.

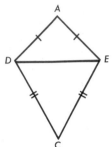

*A word of warning:* Before you "introduce" something, make sure that it exists. Nothing is easier than to describe imaginary objects by laying words hastily end to end. Consider, for example, the following "theorem" and its "proof."

## "Theorem"

In any triangle $\triangle ABC$, we have $\angle B \cong \angle C$.

**"Proof."** Let $D$ be a point between $B$ and $C$, such that $BD = DC$ and $\overline{AD} \perp \overline{BC}$. Then $\angle ADB \cong \angle ADC$, because both are right angles. Therefore $ADB \leftrightarrow ADC$ is an SAS correspondence. Therefore $\triangle ADB \cong \triangle ADC$, and $\angle B \cong \angle C$.

This "theorem" is ridiculous, and so its proof must be wrong. And it is not hard to see that the proof goes astray at its very start, with a light-hearted use of the word "let." Unless it happens that $\angle B \cong \angle C$, the mid-point of $\overline{BC}$ and the foot of the perpendicular from $A$ are two different points. Therefore, in most cases, the point $D$ that we were "letting" exist does

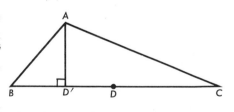

not really exist at all. Note that this would have been quite obvious if the author of the wrong proof had been willing to use a scalene triangle in his figure. Good figures are no guarantee against errors, but they are a big help.

## Problem Set 6–5

**1.** Prove the theorem stated in Example 1 on p. 171 by introducing $\overline{AC}$.

**2.** Given the figure as marked.   Prove that $\angle M \cong \angle P$.

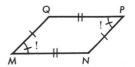

**3.** Given the figure with

$$AD = CB \quad \text{and} \quad AB = CD.$$

Prove that $AK = CK$.

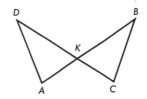

**4.** Make a list on your paper of the postulates and theorems given on pp. 170 and 171, using 4 for Postulate 4, 2–1 for Theorem 2–1, and so on. If a postulate or theorem asserts existence, put E after its number on your list; if uniqueness, put U; if both existence and uniqueness, put EU.   For example, Postulate 4 should appear on your list as "4EU."

**5.** Given points $A$ and $B$ in plane $E$, and points $P$ and $Q$ on opposite sides of plane $E$ such that $PA = QA$ and $\overleftrightarrow{AB} \perp \overleftrightarrow{PQ}$. Prove that $B$ is equidistant from $P$ and $Q$.   How does Theorem 3–4 enter your proof?

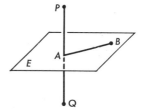

**6.** Given: $Q, R, S$, and $T$ are coplanar. $QR = QT$.

$$m \angle R = m \angle T.$$

Prove: $SR = ST$.
    Does your proof hold if $Q, R, S$, and $T$ are not coplanar?

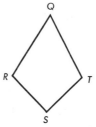

**7.** Find the error in the following "proof." On the sides of $\angle A$, points $B$ and $C$ are taken so that $AB = AC$. $D$ is any point in the interior of $\angle A$. Introduce the ray which bisects $\angle A$ and contains $D$.   Introduce $\overline{DC}$ and $\overline{DB}$.   By the definition of angle bisector, $\angle DAC \cong \angle DAB$.   $AD = AD$ by identity.    Therefore $\triangle ADC \cong \triangle ADB$ by $SAS$, and $DB = DC$. Thus $D$ is equidistant from $B$ and $C$.

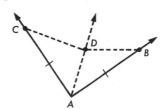

**8.** Given: $AB = PQ$ and
$\qquad BP = AQ.$
Prove: (a) $\angle A \cong \angle P,$
$\qquad$ (b) $\triangle ABM \cong \triangle PQM.$

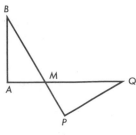

* **9.** Given: $AH = RD,$ $\angle A \cong \angle R,$ and $H,$ $A,$ $R,$ and $D$ are coplanar.
Prove: $\angle H \cong \angle D.$

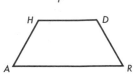

* **10.** Outline a second solution to Problem 9 by introducing auxiliary segments different from the ones you used before.

* **11.** Devise two proofs for the following and state which proof does not depend on the requirement that the points $A,$ $B,$ $C,$ and $D$ be coplanar.
Given: $AB = AC$ and $BD = CD$ in the figure.
Prove: $\angle ABD \cong \angle ACD.$

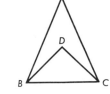

* **12.** In the figure, planes $R$ and $T$ intersect in $\overleftrightarrow{MN}.$ $E$ is in $T,$ $S$ is in $R,$ and $\overleftrightarrow{MN}$ contains $A$ and $Y.$ If $EY = EA$ and $SY = SA,$ prove that $\angle EAS \cong \angle EYS.$

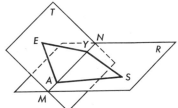

## 6–6.  HOW TO DO WITHOUT THE ASA POSTULATE

In the preceding chapter, we based our study of triangle congruences on the three postulates SAS, ASA, and SSS.  In fact, the only one of these that we really needed to accept as a postulate was SAS; if we assume only SAS, the other two can be proved.  Let us first consider the case of ASA.

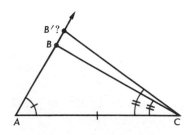
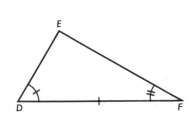

Given an ASA correspondence

$$ABC \leftrightarrow DEF,$$

as indicated in the figure, so that

$$\angle A \cong \angle D,$$

(1)    $AC = DF,$

$$\angle C \cong \angle F.$$

We need to show that $\triangle ABC \cong \triangle DEF.$

**Proof**

| STATEMENTS | REASONS |
|---|---|
| 2. $\overrightarrow{AB}$ contains a point $B'$ such that $AB' = DE.$ | The Point-Plotting Theorem. |
| 3. $AB'C \leftrightarrow DEF$ is an SAS correspondence. | Steps 1 and 2. |
| 4. $\triangle AB'C \cong \triangle DEF.$ | SAS. |
| 5. $\angle ACB' \cong \angle DFE.$ | Corresponding angles. |
| 6. $\overrightarrow{CB'} = \overrightarrow{CB}.$ | The Angle Construction Postulate. |
| 7. $B' = B.$ | Two different lines intersect in at most one point. |
| 8. $\triangle ABC \cong \triangle DEF.$ | Steps 4 and 7. |

## 6–7.   HOW TO DO WITHOUT THE SSS POSTULATE

We shall now show that SSS can also be proved as a theorem.

First we recall that in proving the Isosceles Triangle Theorem, all that we used was SAS. Since $ABC \leftrightarrow ACB$ is an SAS correspondence, we know that $\triangle ABC \cong \triangle ACB$, and so

$$\angle B \cong \angle C.$$

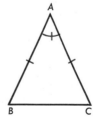

We can therefore use the Isosceles Triangle Theorem in proving SSS, without committing the error of reasoning in a circle.

Now suppose we have given an SSS correspondence

$$ABC \leftrightarrow DEF.$$

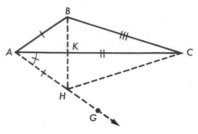 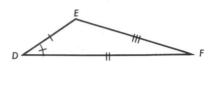

**Proof**

| STATEMENTS | REASONS |
|---|---|
| 1.  $AB = DE$,   $AC = DF$, $BC = EF$. | Given. |
| 2.  There is a point $G$ on the opposite side of $\overleftrightarrow{AC}$ from $B$ such that $\angle CAG \cong \angle D$. | The Angle Construction Postulate. |
| 3.  There is a point $H$ of $\overrightarrow{AG}$ such that $AH = DE$. | The Point-Plotting Theorem. |
| 4.  $AHC \leftrightarrow DEF$ is an SAS correspondence. | Steps 1, 2, and 3. |
| 5.  $\triangle AHC \cong \triangle DEF$. | SAS. |

Thus we have a congruent copy of $\triangle DEF$, on the under side of $\triangle ABC$. This finishes the first half of the proof. In the second half, we are going to show that $\triangle ABC \cong \triangle AHC$. The following proof applies to the case shown in the figure, in which $\overline{BH}$ intersects $\overleftrightarrow{AC}$ in a point between $A$ and $C$.

**Proof** (*cont.*)

| STATEMENTS | REASONS |
|---|---|
| 6.  $\angle ABH \cong \angle AHB$. | Isosceles Triangle Theorem. |
| 7.  $\angle HBC \cong \angle CHB$. | Isosceles Triangle Theorem. |
| 8.  $\angle ABC \cong \angle AHC$. | Angle Addition Postulate. |
| 9.  $ABC \leftrightarrow AHC$ is an SAS correspondence. | Steps 1, and 5, 8. |
| 10.  $\triangle ABC \cong \triangle AHC$. | SAS. |
| 11.  $\triangle ABC \cong \triangle DEF$. | Steps 5 and 10. |

Of course, there are two other cases to consider:

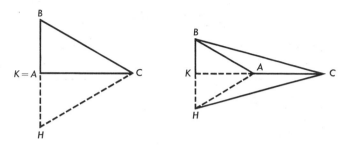

The proofs in these cases are left to you.

## 6–8. BETWEENNESS AND SEPARATION

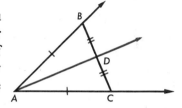

If you were watching very carefully, you may have noticed places where two of our proofs were not complete. In the proof of Theorem 5–2, we really needed to know that the mid-point $D$ of $\overline{BC}$ was in the interior of $\angle BAC$.

We needed this information in order to know that $\overrightarrow{AD}$ satisfied the definition of an angle bisector.

Similarly, in the proof of SSS, in the preceding section, to use angle addition in step 8, we needed to know that the point $K$ was in the interior of $\angle AHC$.

Strictly speaking, these statements call for proofs. But the proofs are omitted in nearly all books, including Euclid and most textbooks. This is not necessarily bad. Geometry is quite rightly guided by common sense; it is common sense that tells us that our postulates were reasonable in the first place. And the study of geometry was over two thousand years old before people managed to write postulates that were really adequate for the proofs of geometric theorems.

Once we have the postulates, however, and once we have learned to use them, we may as well get our work into better order by stating and proving the theorems that we need.

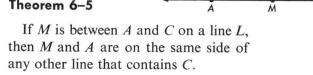

**Theorem 6–5**

If $M$ is between $A$ and $C$ on a line $L$, then $M$ and $A$ are on the same side of any other line that contains $C$.

**Proof.** Let $L'$ be another line, containing $C$, and suppose that $A$ and $M$ are on opposite sides of $L'$. Then $\overline{AM}$ contains a point $D$ of $L'$. But $\overline{AM}$ lies on $L$, and $L$ intersects $L'$ only at $C$. Therefore $C = D$. Therefore, by definition of a segment, $C$ is between $A$ and $M$. This is impossible, because $M$ is between $A$ and $C$. [See Statement (2) on p. 41.]

This easily leads to the theorem that we needed in the proofs of Theorem 5–2 and SSS:

### Theorem 6–6

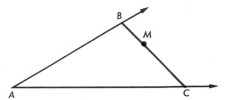

If $M$ is between $B$ and $C$, and $A$ is any point not on $\overleftrightarrow{BC}$, then $M$ is in the interior of $\angle BAC$.

**Proof.** By the preceding theorem we know that (1) $M$ and $B$ are on the same side of $\overleftrightarrow{AC}$. By another application of the preceding theorem we know that (2) $M$ and $C$ are on the same side of $\overleftrightarrow{AB}$. By definition of the interior of an angle, this means that $M$ is in the interior of $\angle BAC$.

## Problem Set 6–8

[*Note:* In this problem set, no information is to be read from any figure.]

+ 1. Draw a figure for the following statement and justify its validity: In any triangle, each point of a side of the triangle other than the end points lies in the interior of the angle opposite the side.

+ 2. Given line $\overleftrightarrow{AC}$, with a point $R$ such that $R$-$A$-$C$, a point $B$ not on $\overleftrightarrow{AC}$, and points $P$ and $Q$ on $\overline{BC}$ and $\overline{BA}$ such that $B$-$P$-$C$ and $B$-$Q$-$A$. Complete each of the following statements and be prepared to justify your answers.

   (a) $P$ lies in the interior of $\angle$ _____.

   (b) $Q$ and $B$ lie on the _____ side of $\overleftrightarrow{AC}$.

   (c) $P$ and $B$ lie on _____ of $\overleftrightarrow{AC}$.

   (d) $Q$ and $P$ lie on _____ of $\overleftrightarrow{AC}$.

   (e) $R$ and $P$ lie on _____ of $\overleftrightarrow{AB}$.

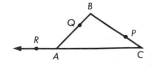

+ 3. Prove: If $M$ is between $A$ and $C$ on a line $L$, then $A$ and $C$ are on opposite sides of any other line that contains $M$.

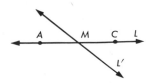

+ **4.** Given the coplanar points $A$, $B$, $C$, $D$, $E$, and $H$ such that $A$, $B$, and $C$ are non-collinear, $B$-$C$-$D$, $A$-$E$-$C$, and $B$-$E$-$H$, prove that $A$ and $H$ are on the same side of $\overleftrightarrow{BD}$.

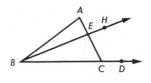

*+ **5.** Prove: In a plane, if a line intersects a side of a triangle at a point not a vertex, then it must intersect at least one other side of the triangle.

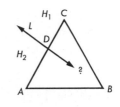

[*Hint:* Let $H_1$ and $H_2$ be the half-planes with edge $L$, with $C$ in $H_1$. There are three cases to consider: $B$ is on $L$, $B$ is in $H_1$, and $B$ is in $H_2$.]

*+ **6.** Given the coplanar points $A$, $B$, $C$, $D$, $E$, and $H$ such that $A$, $B$, and $C$ are noncollinear, $B$-$C$-$D$, $A$-$E$-$C$, and $B$-$E$-$H$, prove that $H$ is in the interior of $\angle ACD$. [*Hint:*

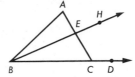

By the definition of interior of an angle, you must show that $A$ and $H$ are on the same side of $\overleftrightarrow{CD}$ (see Problem 4) and that $D$ and $H$ are on the same side of $\overleftrightarrow{AC}$.]

*+ **7.** The following theorem, whose truth seems so obvious, is frequently accepted without proof.

If $K$ is a point in the interior of $\angle ABC$, then $\overrightarrow{BK}$ intersects $\overline{AC}$.

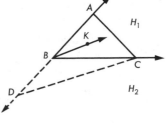

You should be able to supply a proof after answering the questions below. You may use other problems of this problem set to justify your reasoning.

(a) Let $H_1$ and $H_2$ be the half-planes having edge $\overleftrightarrow{BC}$, with $A$ in $H_1$. Take any point $D$ on the ray opposite to $\overrightarrow{BA}$. Draw $\overline{DC}$ forming $\triangle DAC$. Why is $D$ in $H_2$?

(b) Why is $K$ in $H_1$? What theorem shows that each point of $\overrightarrow{BK}$ except $B$ is in $H_1$?

(c) Why is each point of $\overline{DC}$ other than $C$ in $H_2$?

(d) Why does $\overline{DC}$ not intersect $\overrightarrow{BK}$?

(e) Why does $\overline{DC}$ not intersect the ray opposite to $\overrightarrow{BK}$?

(f) Why does $\overline{DC}$ not intersect $\overleftrightarrow{BK}$?

(g) Why must $\overleftrightarrow{BK}$ intersect $\overline{AC}$?

(h) Why does the ray opposite to $\overrightarrow{BK}$ not intersect $\overline{AC}$?

(i) Why does $\overrightarrow{BK}$ intersect $\overline{AC}$?

## HONORS PROBLEM

The following faulty argument which attempts to demonstrate that an obtuse angle is congruent to a right angle emphasizes the importance of knowing the side of a line on which a point lies. Suppose that $\square ABCD$ is a rectangle and that the side $\overline{BC}$ is swung outward so that $BC' = BC$ and $\angle ABC'$ is obtuse. Let the perpendicular bisector of $\overline{AB}$ intersect the perpendicular bisector of $\overline{DC'}$ at $X$. If $X$ is below $\overleftrightarrow{AB}$ as shown, we have

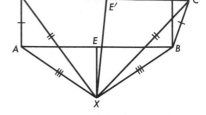

$$\triangle AXD \cong \triangle BXC'$$

by the SSS Theorem, and hence

$$m\angle DAX = m\angle C'BX.$$

Also, $\triangle EAX \cong \triangle EBX$ by SSS, and so $m\angle EAX = m\angle EBX$. It follows by subtraction that $m\angle DAE = m\angle C'BE$. If $X$ lies above $\overleftrightarrow{AB}$, as in the second figure, we get, exactly as before, $m\angle DAX = m\angle C'BX, m\angle EAX = m\angle EBX$, and the desired equality, $m\angle DAE = m\angle C'BE$, follows by addition. What is wrong with the above argument?

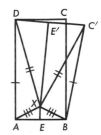

[*Hint:* Try drawing an exact figure for the case in which $m\angle ABC$ is only a little less than 180. How much of the "proof" is valid in this case?]

## Chapter Review

1. Assume that you are going to try to prove each statement below by the indirect method. What is the supposition, for each statement, with which you would begin?

   (a) If a triangle has no two angles congruent, then it is not isosceles.

   (b) Given a line and a point not on the line, there is at most one line through the point and perpendicular to the given line.

   (c) If a point is equidistant from the ends of a segment, it lies on the perpendicular bisector of the segment.

   (d) If two coplanar lines are perpendicular to the same line, they are parallel.

   (e) In a plane, there is at most one line perpendicular to a given line at a given point of the line.

   (f) $\sqrt{2}$ is not a rational number.

   (g) Zero has no reciprocal.

2. Define "perpendicular bisector of a segment."

3. State the Perpendicular Bisector Theorem.

4. Copy each triangle, making certain each is scalene. Construct the perpendicular bisector of each side of each triangle. Do any of the perpendicular bisectors bisect an angle of one of the triangles?

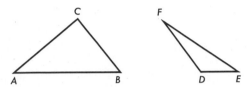

5. Indicate for each statement below whether it is true or false.

   (a) In a plane there are at most two perpendiculars to a line at a point of the line.

   (b) Proving that "there is exactly one" means proving both existence and uniqueness.

   (c) The longest side of any triangle is called the hypotenuse.

   (d) In a right triangle, the side opposite the right angle is called the hypothesis.

6. In the figure, $AE = BC$, $ED = CD$, $G$ is the mid-point of $\overline{AB}$ and $\angle E \cong \angle C$. Prove that
$$\overline{DG} \perp \overline{AB}.$$

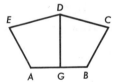

* 7. Line $L$ is the perpendicular bisector of $\overline{BC}$, with $A$ the mid-point of $\overline{BC}$. Points $K$ and $G$ are on the same side of $\overleftrightarrow{BC}$. $K$ is on the same side of $L$ as $B$, and $G$ is on the same side of $L$ as $C$ such that $\angle BAK \cong \angle CAG$. The perpendicular to $\overline{BC}$ at $B$ intersects $\overrightarrow{AK}$ at $D$, and the perpendicular to $\overline{BC}$ at $C$ intersects $\overrightarrow{AG}$ at $E$. Prove that $\overline{BE}$ and $\overline{CD}$ intersect on $L$.

* 8. $\overline{AB}$ and $\overline{CD}$ are coplanar and congruent. The perpendicular bisector of $\overline{AD}$ and the perpendicular bisector of $\overline{BC}$ intersect at $X$. Prove that $\triangle ABX \cong \triangle DCX$.

# 7 | Geometric Inequalities

# 7-1. MAKING REASONABLE CONJECTURES

Up to now, in our study of the geometry of the triangle, we have been dealing only with conditions under which we can say that two segments are of equal length, or two angles are of equal measure. We will now proceed to study conditions under which we can say that one segment is longer than another (that is, has a greater length), or one angle is larger than another (that is, has a greater measure).

We shall not start, however, by proving theorems. Let us start, rather, by making some reasonable conjectures about the sort of statements that ought to be true. (These statements should not be called theorems unless and until they are proved.)

Let us look at the following example: Given a triangle with two sides of unequal length, what can we say about the angles opposite these sides? Note that this problem is naturally suggested by Theorem 5-3, which says that if two sides of a triangle have the same length, then the angles opposite them have the same measure.

You can investigate this situation by sketching a triangle with two sides of obviously unequal lengths:

Here $BC$ is greater than $AB$, and $m \angle A$ is greater than $m \angle C$. After sketching a few more triangles, you will probably be convinced that the following statement ought to be true.

> *If two sides of a triangle are of unequal length, then the angles opposite them are of unequal measure, and the larger angle is opposite the longer side.*

Now try the same sort of procedure with the following problems.

## Problem Set 7-1

1. In each of these triangles, $m \angle A > m \angle B$. What conjecture can you make about the sides opposite $\angle A$ and $\angle B$?

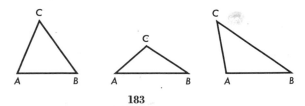

**2.** Consider any three triangles. Label each with $A$, $B$, and $C$. Does $AB + BC > AC$ seem to be true? How does $BC + AC$ compare with $AB$? How about $BC$ and $AC + AB$? What general statement do your answers suggest?

**3.** Consider several scalene triangles of varying shapes. For each triangle list the longest side and the greatest angle. What conjecture ought to be true? Do your examples prove that it is true?

**4.** Draw $\triangle RST$ and $\triangle ABC$ such that

$$RS = AB, \qquad ST = BC, \qquad \text{and} \qquad m \angle RST > m \angle ABC.$$

Compare $RT$ and $AC$.

**5.**

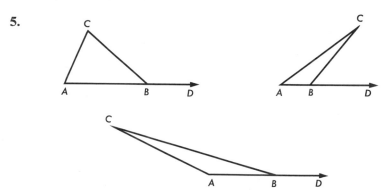

What conjecture concerning $m \angle CBD$ and $m \angle BAC$ is suggested by the triangles shown here? In the third figure, if the vertex $C$ were moved very far to the left of $A$ and $B$, do you think your conjecture would still hold? Can you think of a way to prove it?

**6.** Draw any triangle, $\triangle MOP$. Let $K$ be a point between $M$ and the midpoint of $\overline{MP}$, and draw $\overline{KO}$. For the $\triangle MOP$ and $\triangle KOP$ we have $PO = PO$, $\angle P \cong \angle P$, and $MP > KP$. A hasty person might conjecture that $MO > KO$. Show that this does not always hold.

**7.** Given a line, $L$, and a point, $P$, not on $L$. Let $Q$ be the foot of the perpendicular from $P$ to $L$ and let $A$ be any other point of $L$. What conjecture involving $PQ$ and $PA$ seems to be valid?

**+ 8.** Does the following procedure describe a valid way of trisecting any angle? Make some drawings to help you decide.

On the sides of any angle, $\angle A$, take points $B$ and $C$ so that $AB = AC$. Draw $\overline{BC}$ and trisect $\overline{BC}$ with points $D$ and $E$ so that $BD = DE = EC$. Draw $\overline{AD}$ and $\overline{AE}$. Then $\overrightarrow{AD}$ and $\overrightarrow{AE}$ are trisectors of $\angle A$.

+  9. $\overline{QC}$ and $\overline{QB}$ are noncollinear segments in plane $E$.  $P$ is a point not in $E$ such that $\angle PQB$ and $\angle PQC$ are right angles; $QC <$ $QB$.  Write a proposition whose conclusion concerns $PB$ and $PC$, and which you think is true.

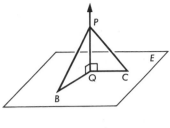

*+ 10. $A$ is a point in plane $E$, $\overrightarrow{AB}$ is a ray not lying in $E$, and $\overrightarrow{AC}$ is a ray lying in $E$.  Considering different positions of $\overrightarrow{AC}$, describe as accurately as you can the position of $\overrightarrow{AC}$ which makes $m \angle BAC$ as large as possible; as small as possible.  No proof is expected, but you are asked to guess the answer on the basis of your knowledge of space.

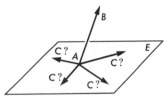

## 7–2.  INEQUALITIES FOR NUMBERS, SEGMENTS, AND ANGLES

Inequalities between segments and angles are defined in terms of the numbers that measure the segments and angles.

**Definition**

$\overline{AB} < \overline{CD}$   if   $AB < CD$.

In words: One segment is *less than* (or *shorter than*) another if its length is less.  Similarly,

**Definition**

$\angle A < \angle B$   if   $m\angle A < m\angle B$.

Before proceeding to the study of inequalities between segments and angles, we should therefore recall, from Section 2–2, the laws which govern inequalities between numbers.

### O-1.  Trichotomy

For every $x$ and $y$, one and only one of the following conditions holds: $x < y$, $x = y$, $x > y$.

### O-2.  Transitivity

If $x < y$ and $y < z$, then $x < z$.

### O-3.    The Addition Law

If    $a < b$    and    $x \leq y$,    then    $a + x < b + y$.

### O-4.    The Multiplication Law

If    $x < y$    and    $a > 0$,    then    $ax < ay$.

The algebra that we shall use in dealing with geometric inequalities will be very simple. We shall not even need O-4. We shall, however, need the following theorem.

### Theorem 7–1

If $a = b + c$ and $c > 0$, then $a > b$.

**Proof.** Since $a - b = c$, we have $a - b > 0$. Therefore

$$(a - b) + b > 0 + b    \quad \text{and} \quad    a > b.$$

## Problem Set 7–2

**1.** For each of the following examples, identify the order property it illustrates.

(a) If $m > 7$ and $n < 7$, then $n < m$.

(b) If $4 < 6$, then $14 < 21$.

(c) If $AB < 13$, then $AB \neq 13$.

(d) If $x - y = 7$ and $y < 3$, then $x < 10$.

(e) If $\angle A < \angle C$ and $\angle B > \angle C$, then $\angle A < \angle B$.

(f) If $RS < GH$ and $ST < HK$, then $RS + ST < GH + HK$.

**2.** In the figure,

$$AB < GB    \quad \text{and} \quad    BC < BH.$$

Prove that $AC \neq GH$.

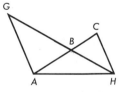

**3.** Given that $A$, $B$, and $C$ are collinear and that $G$, $H$, and $K$ are collinear. The points are spaced such that $AB < GH$ and $BC < HK$. Does it follow that $AC < GK$? Why or why not?

**4.** Given: The figure with

$$\angle DAB < \angle DBA    \quad \text{and} \quad    \angle DAC < \angle DBC.$$

Prove: $\angle CAB < \angle CBA$.

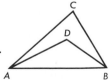

5. Explain carefully why Theorem 7–1 has the following consequence:

   If $D$ is a point in the interior of $\angle ABC$, then $\angle ABC > \angle ABD$ and $\angle ABC > \angle CBD$.

6. In the figure, $BD = CD$. Prove that

   $$\angle ABC > \angle DCB.$$

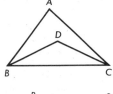

7. Given the figure with $M$ the mid-point of both $\overline{PS}$ and $\overline{RQ}$. Prove that $\angle RQT > \angle R$.

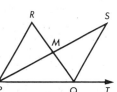

* 8. Use Property O-2 to prove that any negative number is less than any positive number.

* 9. Suppose that Property O-3 had been stated simply as:

   For every $a$, $b$, and $x$, if $a < b$, then $a + x < b + x$.

   Show that the other part of O-3 would follow as a theorem:

   For every $a$, $b$, $x$, and $y$, if $a < b$ and $x < y$, then $a + x < b + y$.

   [*Hint:* Get $a + x < b + x$ and $x + b < y + b$, and use O-2.]

*+ 10. Refer to the figure for Problem 7 but assume only the following hypothesis: $S$ and $P$ are on opposite sides of $\overleftrightarrow{RQ}$, $P$-$Q$-$T$, and $S$ and $R$ are on the same side of $\overleftrightarrow{PT}$. Prove that $S$ is in the interior of $\angle RQT$.

## 7–3. THE EXTERIOR ANGLE THEOREM

In the figures below, $\angle 1$ is called an *exterior angle* of $\triangle ABC$:

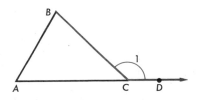
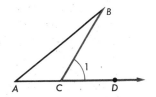

**Definition**

If $C$ is between $A$ and $D$, then $\angle BCD$ is an *exterior* angle of $\triangle ABC$.

Every triangle has six exterior angles, as shown in the figure below.

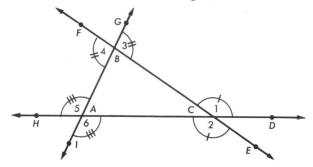

These form three pairs of vertical angles; and the angles in each vertical pair are congruent, as indicated in the figure.

Every exterior angle of a triangle forms a linear pair with one of the angles of the triangle itself. For example, in the figure, $\angle 1$ and $\angle C$ of $\triangle ABC$ form a linear pair. The other two angles of the triangle are called the *remote interior* angles.

**Definition**

$\angle A$ and $\angle B$ of $\triangle ABC$ are called the *remote* interior angles of the exterior angles $\angle BCD$ and $\angle ACE$.

Similarly, $\angle A$ and $\angle C$ are the remote interior angles of $\angle ABF$ and $\angle CBG$.

The following theorem is the key to the study of geometric inequalities.

**Theorem 7–2.**   The Exterior Angle Theorem

An exterior angle of a triangle is greater than each of its remote interior angles.

**Restatement.**  Given $\triangle ABC$. If $C$ is between $A$ and $D$, then

$$\angle BCD > \angle B.$$

First we observe that the restatement really does convey the whole content of the theorem. The restatement tells us that $\angle 1 > \angle B$. By a change of notation (interchanging $A$ and $B$), we conclude that $\angle 2 > \angle A$. Since $\angle 1 \cong \angle 2$, it follows that $\angle 1 > \angle A$. Therefore $\angle 1$ is greater than each of its remote interior angles.

We proceed to prove the restatement.

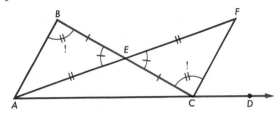

## Proof

| STATEMENTS | REASONS |
|---|---|
| 1.  Let $E$ be the mid-point of $\overline{BC}$. | ? |
| 2.  Let $F$ be a point of the ray opposite to $\overrightarrow{EA}$, such that $EF = EA$. | ? |
| 3.  $\angle BEA \cong \angle CEF$. | ? |
| 4.  $\triangle BEA \cong \triangle CEF$. | ? |
| 5.  $m\angle B = m\angle ECF$. | ? |
| 6.  $m\angle BCD = m\angle ECF + m\angle FCD$. | The Angle Addition Postulate. |
| 7.  $m\angle BCD = m\angle B + m\angle FCD$. | Statements 5 and 6. |
| 8.  $m\angle BCD > m\angle B$. | Theorem 7–1. |
| 9.  $\angle BCD > \angle B$. | Definition of $>$ for angles. |

The Exterior Angle Theorem has an easy corollary.

**Corollary 7–2.1**

> If a triangle has one right angle, then its other angles are acute.

(If $\angle C$ is a right angle, then so is $\angle 1$. The Exterior Angle Theorem tells us that $\angle 1 > \angle B$ and $\angle 1 > \angle A$. Therefore $m\angle B < 90$ and $m\angle A < 90$.)

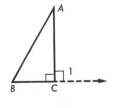

If we had known about the Exterior Angle Theorem, in the last chapter, we could have concluded more easily that the perpendicular to a line from an external point is unique. If there were two perpendiculars from $P$ to $L$, then $\angle 1$ would be congruent to $\angle PQR$, which is impossible: $\angle 1$ is an exterior angle of $\triangle PQR$, and $\angle PQR$ is one of its remote interior angles.

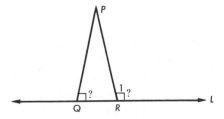

## Problem Set 7–3

1. (a) Name the remote interior angles of $\angle ABE$ in the figure.

   (b) Which exterior angle has $\angle ABC$ and $\angle BAC$ as its remote interior angles?

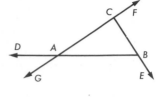

2. (a) In the figure, which angles are exterior angles of the triangle?

   (b) What is the relation of $m\angle DAC$ to $m\angle B$? Why?

   (c) What is the relationship of $m\angle DAC$ to $m\angle BAE$? Why?

   (d) What is the relationship of $m\angle DAC$ to $m\angle BAC$? Why?

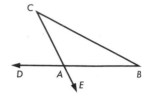

3. Use the figure only to explain notation, and complete each statement on the basis of theorems that you have seen proved:

   (a) If $x = 40$ and $y = 30$, then $w > $ _____.

   (b) If $x = 72$ and $y = 73$, then $w$ _____.

   (c) If $y = 54$ and $z = 68$, then $w$ _____.

   (d) If $w = 112$, then $x$ _____.

   (e) If $w = 150$, then $z$ _____.

   (f) If $x = 25$ and $z = 90$, then $w$ _____.

   (g) If $z = 90$ then $x$ _____ and $y$ _____.

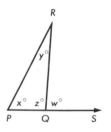

4. Given the figure on the left below prove that $\angle CAK > \angle G$.

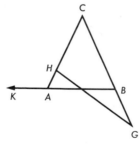

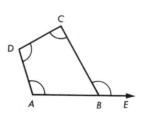

5. The figure on the right above is one illustration of this statement: An exterior angle of a quadrilateral is greater than each remote interior angle.

   Is this a true statement? Explain.

6. (a) In the figure, $\overrightarrow{PS}$ bisects $\angle RPM$. Prove that $\angle SCM > \angle SPM$.

   (b) Prove that if $\angle SCV \cong \angle PRV$, then $\angle PRT > \angle S$.

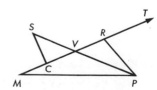

7. Given any two segments, $\overline{AB}$ and $\overline{DE}$. Can we make a statement relating $AB$ and $DE$ that will always be true? What is it? Give a reason for your answer.

8. Explain why the markings on the figure indicate an impossible situation.

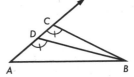

+  9. Prove the following theorem.

The sum of the measures of any two angles of a triangle is less than 180.

**Restatement.** If the angles of a triangle have measures as indicated in the figure, then

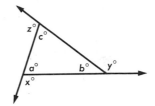

$$a + b < 180,$$
$$b + c < 180,$$
$$a + c < 180.$$

+ 10. Prove the following theorem.

The base angles of any isosceles triangle are acute.

[*Hint:* Use the theorem of Problem 9.]

## 7–4.  CONGRUENCE THEOREMS BASED ON THE EXTERIOR ANGLE THEOREM

### Definition

Given a correspondence $ABC \leftrightarrow DEF$ between two triangles:

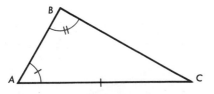  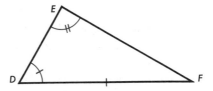

If a pair of corresponding sides are congruent, and two pairs of corresponding angles are congruent, then the correspondence is called an *SAA correspondence*. (Here, of course, SAA stands for Side Angle Angle.)

**Theorem 7–3.**   The SAA Theorem

Every SAA correspondence is a congruence.

If the congruent sides are included between the congruent angles, then we already know by ASA that the correspondence is a congruence. We may therefore assume, in the restatement, that we have the sort of correspondence suggested by the figure above.

**Restatement.**   Given $\triangle ABC$ and $\triangle DEF$. If

$$\angle A \cong \angle D, \qquad \angle B \cong \angle E, \qquad \text{and} \qquad \overline{AC} \cong \overline{DF},$$

then

$$\triangle ABC \cong \triangle DEF.$$

**Proof.**   There are three possibilities for $AB$ and $DE$:

$$\begin{aligned} &(1) \qquad AB = DE, \\ &(2) \qquad AB < DE, \\ &(3) \qquad AB > DE. \end{aligned}$$

If (1) holds, then the theorem follows, because in this case $ABC \leftrightarrow DEF$ is an SAS correspondence. We shall show that (2) and (3) are impossible.

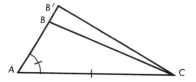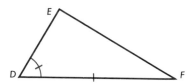

Suppose that (2) holds: $AB < DE$. Let $B'$ be the point of $\overrightarrow{AB}$ such that $AB' = DE$. Then $\triangle AB'C \cong \triangle DEF$, by SAS. Therefore $\angle AB'C \cong \angle DEF$. Therefore $\angle ABC \cong \angle AB'C$. (Why?) But this is impossible, because the Exterior Angle Theorem tells us that $\angle ABC > \angle AB'C$.

In a very similar way, we can show that (3) $AB > DE$ is impossible. You should be able to supply the details.

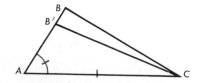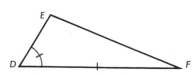

Since (2) and (3) are impossible, (1) must hold, and $\triangle ABC \cong \triangle DEF$ by SAS. This completes the proof.

We found, in the last chapter, that there is no such thing as an SSA Theorem. That is, an SSA correspondence is not necessarily a congruence. For the case of *right* triangles, however, we can prove a theorem of this kind.

**Theorem 7–4.** The Hypotenuse-Leg Theorem

Given a correspondence between two right triangles. If the hypotenuse and one leg of one of the triangles are congruent to the corresponding parts of the second triangle, then the correspondence is a congruence.

**Restatement.** Given $\triangle ABC$ and $\triangle DEF$, such that

$$m \angle A = m \angle D = 90,$$

$$AB = DE, \quad BC = EF.$$

Then

$$\triangle ABC \cong \triangle DEF.$$

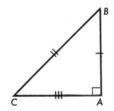 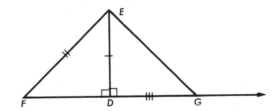

**Proof**

| STATEMENTS | REASONS |
|---|---|
| 1. There is a point $G$, on the ray opposite to $\overrightarrow{DF}$, such that $DG = AC$. | ? |
| 2. $\triangle DEG \cong \triangle ABC$. | ? |
| 3. $EG = BC$. | ? |
| 4. $\angle G \cong \angle C$. | ? |
| 5. $EG = EF$. | Step 3 and given. |
| 6. $\angle F \cong \angle G$. | ? |
| 7. $\triangle DEF \cong \triangle DEG$. | Steps 5 and 6, and SAA. |
| 8. $\triangle ABC \cong \triangle DEF$. | Steps 2 and 7. |

## Problem Set 7–4

**1.** Summarize all the methods that you now know for proving that triangles are congruent.

**2.** Given: $\overline{PT} \perp \overline{RT}$,    $\overline{SV} \perp \overline{QV}$,
        $RT = QV$,    $PQ = SR$.

Prove: $PT = SV$.

**3.** In the figure, $\overleftrightarrow{CD}$ bisects $\overline{AB}$ and $\angle C \cong \angle D$. Prove that $\overline{AB}$ bisects $\overline{CD}$.

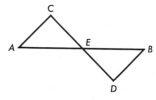
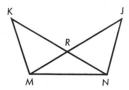

**4.** Given: $\angle K \cong \angle J$ and $MR = NR$. Prove: $MK = NJ$.

**5.** From the mid-point of one side of a triangle, segments are drawn perpendicular to the other two sides. Prove that if the segments are congruent, the triangle is isosceles.

**6.** Given: $E$ is the mid-point of $\overline{AB}$, $\overline{AD} \perp \overline{AB}$, $\overline{BC} \perp \overline{AB}$, and $\angle ADE \cong \angle BCE$.

Prove: $\angle EDC \cong \angle ECD$.

**7.** Points $K$ and $M$ trisect $\overline{GH}$, with G-K-M. Points $J$ and $I$, on the same side of $\overleftrightarrow{GH}$, are on the perpendiculars to $\overline{GH}$ at $G$ and $H$, respectively, such that $JM = IK$. $\overline{JM}$ and $\overline{IK}$ intersect at $P$. Prove that $\triangle PKM$ is isosceles.

* **8.** Given the figure with $\angle D$ and $\angle C$ right angles and $\triangle APR \cong \triangle BQT$. Prove that $\triangle ADF \cong \triangle BCE$.

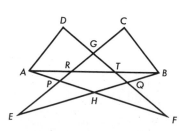
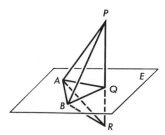

*+ **9.** $A$, $B$, and $Q$ are in plane $E$, $\overline{AQ} \perp \overline{PR}$, $\overline{BQ} \perp \overline{PR}$, and $\angle PAB \cong \angle PBA$. Prove that $\angle PAR \cong \angle PBR$.

## 7-5.    INEQUALITIES IN A SINGLE TRIANGLE

We shall now proceed to prove some of the theorems that we con-
jectured at the beginning of the chapter.

**Theorem 7-5**

If two sides of a triangle are not congruent, then the angles opposite them are not congruent, and the larger angle is opposite the
longer side.

**Restatement.**    In any triangle $\triangle ABC$, if $AB > AC$, then $\angle C > \angle B$.

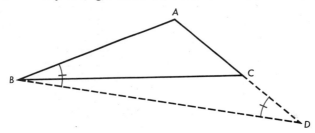

**Proof.**    Let $D$ be a point of $\overrightarrow{AC}$, such that $AD = AB$.    Then
$\angle ABD \cong \angle D$, because the base angles of an isosceles triangle are
congruent.    Since $AD = AB > AC$, $C$ must be between $A$ and $D$.
Therefore, by the Angle Addition Postulate,

$$m\angle ABD = m\angle ABC + m\angle CBD.$$

Therefore

$$m\angle ABC < m\angle ABD.$$

(Why?)    We are now through using measures of angles, and so we
rewrite the above simply as

$$\angle ABC < \angle ABD.$$

Since $\angle ABD \cong \angle D$, it follows that

$$\angle ABC < \angle D.$$

But we know by the Exterior Angle Theorem that

$$\angle D < \angle ACB.$$

Therefore,

$$\angle ABC < \angle ACB.$$

Therefore, in $\triangle ABC$ we have $\angle B < \angle C$, which is what we wanted.

### Theorem 7–6

If two angles of a triangle are not congruent, then the sides opposite them are not congruent, and the longer side is opposite the larger angle.

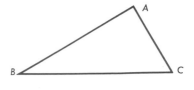

**Restatement.**    In any triangle $\triangle ABC$, if $\angle C > \angle B$, then $AB > AC$.

**Proof.**    There are three possibilities for the numbers $AB$ and $AC$:

$$(1) \ AB < AC,$$
$$(2) \ AB = AC,$$
$$(3) \ AB > AC.$$

If (1) were true, then it would follow by the preceding theorem that $\angle C < \angle B$, and this is false.  Therefore (1) is impossible.

If (2) were true, then $\angle B$ and $\angle C$ would be the base angles of an isosceles triangle.  This would give $\angle B \cong \angle C$, which is false.  Therefore (2) is impossible.

The only remaining possibility is (3), which is what we wanted to prove.

The above is merely a convenient way of writing an indirect proof. We might have said the same thing, more formally, as follows:

"Suppose that the theorem is false.  Then either $AB = AC$ or $AB < AC$.  $AB = AC$ is impossible, because .... $AB < AC$ is impossible, because ....   Therefore the theorem is not false.  Therefore the theorem is true."

But the scheme that we used the first time is probably easier to follow, and we shall be using it again.  The idea is to list all of the "possibilities" in a given situation, and then to show that only one of them is really possible.

## Problem Set 7–5

1. In $\triangle ABC$, $AB = 12$, $BC = 7$, $AC = 9$.  Name the largest angle; the smallest angle.

2. In $\triangle PQR$, $m\angle P = 72$, $m\angle Q = 37$, $m\angle R = 71$.  Name the longest side; the shortest side.

**3.** In the figure, $\angle ABD > \angle DBC$. Prove that $AD > BD$.

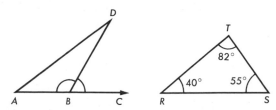

**4.** Name the sides of the figure on the right above in order of increasing length.

**5.** Given the figure on the left below with angle measures as marked. Prove that $\overline{PR}$ is the longest segment.

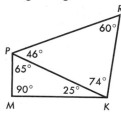
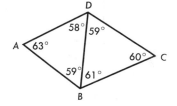

**6.** In the figure on the right above, if the angles have the indicated measures, which segment is longest?

**7.** If the angles have the indicated measures, which segment is shortest?

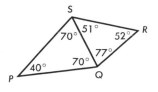
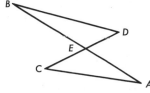

**8.** $\overline{AB}$ and $\overline{CD}$ intersect at $E$, $\angle C > \angle A$ and $\angle D > \angle B$. Prove that $AB > CD$.

* **9.** In isosceles $\triangle KGH$, $KG = KH$; $P$ is any point of $\overleftrightarrow{GH}$ not in $\overline{GH}$. Prove that $PK$ is always greater than either $KG$ or $KH$.

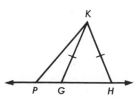
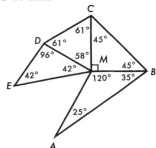

* **10.** If the angles in the figure on the right have the indicated measures, which segment is shortest?

## 7–6.  CONVERSES

Theorems 7–5 and 7–6 are related in a special way; they are called *converses* of each other.  The relation between them is more readily seen if we restate them as follows.

### Theorem 7–5′

Given $\triangle ABC$.  If $AB > AC$, then $\angle C > \angle B$.

### Theorem 7–6′

Given $\triangle ABC$.  If $\angle C > \angle B$, then $AB > AC$.

We have had many examples of this before.  For example:

### Theorem 5–3

If two sides of a triangle are congruent, then the angles opposite these sides are congruent.

### Theorem 5–4

If two angles of a triangle are congruent, then the sides opposite them are congruent.

Here also, the relation becomes clearer if we restate the theorems.

### Theorem 5–3′

Given $\triangle ABC$.  If $AB = AC$, then $\angle C \cong \angle B$.

### Theorem 5–4′

Given $\triangle ABC$.  If $\angle C \cong \angle B$, then $AB = AC$.

When we have proved a theorem which has a simple "if . . . , then . . ." form, it is usually a good idea to investigate the converse. We *need* to make a separate investigation in each case, because it can easily happen that the converse of a true theorem is not true at all. For example, we know that if two angles are vertical, then they are congruent.  The converse would say that if two angles are congruent, then they are vertical; and this is not only false, but ridiculous.  Similarly, if $x = y$, then $x^2 = y^2$.  The converse would say that if $x^2 = y^2$, then $x = y$.  Thus the converse is false: it fails to allow for the possibility $x = -y$.

If it happens that a theorem and its converse are both true, then we can combine them into a single theorem, using the phrase, "*if and only if*."  For example, we can combine Theorems 7–5 and 7–6 like this.

**Theorem**

Given $\triangle ABC$. $AB > AC$ if and only if $\angle C > \angle B$.

And we can combine Theorems 5–3 and 5–4 as follows.

**Theorem**

Two angles of a triangle are congruent if and only if the sides opposite them are congruent.

## Problem Set 7–6

1. Write the converse of each statement. Try to decide whether each statement, and each converse, is true or false.

   (a) If you are over 20 years old, then you have the right to vote.

   (b) You see lions and elephants if you are in Africa.

   (c) Anyone having scarlet fever is seriously ill.

2. Follow the directions of Problem 1.

   (a) If two angles are congruent, they are right angles.

   (b) If two angles form a linear pair, then they are supplementary.

   (c) A point on the perpendicular bisector of a segment is equidistant from the ends of the segment.

   (d) Two angles are each acute if they are complementary.

3. When asked to give the converse of the statement, "If I hold a lighted match too long, I will be burned," John said, "I will be burned if I hold a lighted match too long." Was John's sentence the converse of the original statement? Discuss.

4. (a) Is a converse of every true statement true? Justify your answer.

   (b) May a converse of a false statement be true? Justify your answer.

5. Combine the following into one theorem, using "if and only if."

   > Every equilateral triangle is equiangular.
   >
   > Every equiangular triangle is equilateral.

6. Separate the following theorem into two theorems in the "if . . . then" form:

   > A triangle is equilateral if and only if the bisector of each angle of the triangle is the perpendicular bisector of the opposite side.

   Which of the two theorems is the "only if" part of the theorem stated here?

## 7–7.  THE DISTANCE BETWEEN A LINE AND A POINT. THE TRIANGLE INEQUALITY

**Theorem 7–7.**  The First Minimum Theorem

The shortest segment joining a point to a line is the perpendicular segment.

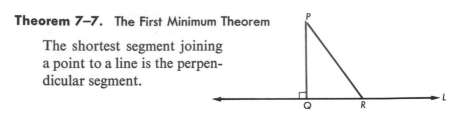

**Restatement.**  Given a line $L$ and an external point $P$.  If $\overline{PQ} \perp L$ at $Q$, and $R$ is any other point of $L$, then $PQ < PR$.

**Proof.**  By hypothesis, $m\angle Q = 90$.  By Corollary 7–2.1, $\angle R$ is acute.  Thus $m\angle R < m\angle Q$.  By Theorem 7–6, $PR > PQ$.

The distance between a point $P$ and a line $L$ ought to be the *minimum* distance between $P$ and the points of $L$.  In the light of the preceding theorem, we know that there is such a minimum distance, and we know where it occurs.  We can therefore write our definition as follows.

### Definition

The *distance* between a line and an external point is the length of the perpendicular segment from the point to the line.  The distance between a line and a point on the line is defined to be zero.

The following theorem tells us, not surprisingly, that no detour is a shortcut.

**Theorem 7–8.**  The Triangle Inequality

The sum of the lengths of any two sides of a triangle is greater than the length of the third side.

**Restatement.**  In any triangle $\triangle ABC$, we have

$$AB + BC > AC.$$

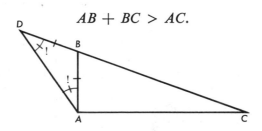

**Proof.** Let $D$ be a point of the ray opposite to $\overrightarrow{BC}$, such that $BD = BA$, as indicated in the figure. Then

$$DC = DB + BC$$

because $B$ is between $D$ and $C$. Therefore

$$(1) \qquad DC = AB + BC.$$

Now

$$m\angle DAC = m\angle DAB + m\angle BAC$$

because $B$ is in the interior of $\angle DAC$. Therefore

$$m\angle DAC > m\angle DAB.$$

But

$$m\angle D = m\angle DAB$$

because $BD = BA$. Therefore

$$(2) \qquad m\angle DAC > m\angle D.$$

Applying Theorem 7–6 to $\triangle ADC$, we get

$$(3) \qquad DC > AC.$$

Combining (1) and (3), we get $AB + BC > AC$, which was to be proved.


## Problem Set 7–7

1. For the figure on the left below, we can assert that $CD <$ \_\_\_\_ and $CD <$ \_\_\_\_, and that $BE <$ \_\_\_\_ and $BE <$ \_\_\_\_. State the theorem involved.

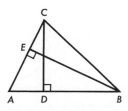 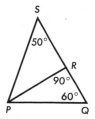

2. Using the angle measures shown in the figure, place $PS$, $PR$, and $PQ$ in the correct order.  \_\_\_\_ $<$ \_\_\_\_ $<$ \_\_\_\_.  Quote theorems to support your conclusion.

**3.** Prove that the sum of the lengths of the diagonals of a quadrilateral is less than the perimeter of the quadrilateral.

**4.** Given the figure, prove that

$$EP + PM + MK > EK.$$

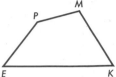

**5.** You can answer this problem by experimenting or, perhaps, by reasoning. Suppose that you are to draw a triangle having two sides of length 3 in. and 7 in. The third side must have a length less than _____, and greater than _____.

**6.** Two sides of a triangle have lengths $j$ and $k$. If $j < k$, what are the restrictions on $x$, the length of the third side?

**7.** Given a line $L$ and two points, $P$ and $Q$, on the same side of $L$. Find the point $R$ on $L$ for which $PR + RQ$ is as small as possible. [*Hint:* This should be easy if you did Problem 6 of Problem Set 6–4.]

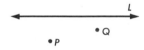

**8.** Given two segments, $\overline{AC}$ and $\overline{BD}$, intersecting at $P$. Prove that if $X$ is any point of the plane of $\overline{AC}$ and $\overline{BD}$ other than $P$, then

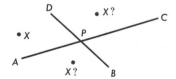

$$XA + XB + XC + XD$$
$$> PA + PB + PC + PD.$$

Will this result hold if $X$ is not in the plane of $\overline{AC}$ and $\overline{BD}$?

*+   **9.** Let $A$, $B$, and $C$ be points, not necessarily different. Prove that $AB + BC \geq AC$. (There are several cases to consider.)

*+  **10.** Prove that the shortest polygonal path from one point to another is the segment joining them.

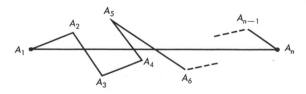

**Restatement:** Given $n$ points $A_1, A_2, \ldots, A_n$, prove that
$$A_1A_2 + A_2A_3 + \ldots + A_{n-1}A_n \geq A_1A_n.$$

## 7–8.  THE HINGE THEOREM AND ITS CONVERSE

Consider two sticks, connected by
a hinge at $A$, with the other ends $B$ and
$C$ joined by a rubber band.

As the hinge is opened wider, the
rubber band ought to be stretched
longer.

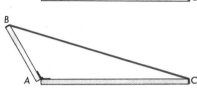

Putting this in geometric language, we get the following theorem.
(You may find that the restatement is easier to read than the theorem
itself.)

**Theorem 7–9.**  The Hinge Theorem

If two sides of one triangle are congruent, respectively, to two
sides of a second triangle, and the included angle of the first
triangle is larger than the included angle of the second, then the
third side of the first triangle is longer than the third side of the
second

**Restatement.**  Given  $\triangle ABC$  and  $\triangle DEF$, with  $AB = DE$  and
$AC = DF$. If $\angle A > \angle D$, then $BC > EF$.

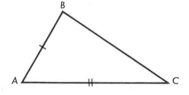

**Proof.**  *Step 1.*  First we construct
$\triangle AKC$, with $K$ in the interior of
$\angle BAC$, such that $\triangle AKC \cong \triangle DEF$:

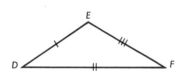

To do this, we first take $\overrightarrow{AQ}$, with $Q$ on the same side of $\overleftrightarrow{AC}$ as $B$, such
that $\angle QAC \cong \angle D$ (by the Angle Construction Postulate). Then we
take a point $K$ of $\overrightarrow{AQ}$ such that $AK = DE$ (by the Point-Plotting
Theorem). By SAS, we have $\triangle AKC \cong \triangle DEF$, which is what we
wanted.

*Step 2.*   Now we bisect $\angle BAK$, and let $M$ be the point where the bisector crosses $\overline{BC}$.

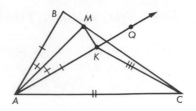

We are now almost done.  By SAS, we have

$$\triangle AMB \cong \triangle AMK.$$

Therefore $MB = MK$.  Applying the Triangle Inequality (Theorem 7–8) to $\triangle CKM$, we get

$$CK < CM + MK.$$

Therefore

$$CK < CM + MB$$

because $MB = MK$.  Since

$$CK = EF \text{ and } CM + MB = BC,$$

we have

$$EF < BC,$$

which is what we wanted.

The converse of the Hinge Theorem is also true.

### Theorem 7–10.   The Converse Hinge Theorem

If two sides of one triangle are congruent respectively to two sides of a second triangle, and the third side of the first triangle is longer than the third side of the second, then the included angle of the first triangle is larger than the included angle of the second.

**Restatement.**   Given $\triangle ABC$ and $\triangle DEF$, with $AB = DE$ and $AC = DF$.  If $BC > EF$, then $\angle A > \angle D$.

To derive this theorem from the Hinge Theorem, we use the same method that we used to derive Theorem 7–6 from Theorem 7–5.  That is, we show that $\angle A < \angle D$ and $\angle A \cong \angle D$ are impossible, so that the only remaining possibility is $\angle A > \angle D$.  For the first half of the proof we need the Hinge Theorem; and for the second half we need SAS.  You should fill in the details for yourself.

## Problem Set 7–8

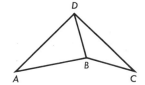

**1.** In the figure,

   $AD = CD$    and    $\angle ADB > \angle CDB$.

   Prove that $AB > BC$.

**2.** In isosceles triangle $\triangle PQR$, $S$ is a point of the base other than the mid-point.   Prove that $\overline{PS}$ does not bisect $\angle RPQ$.

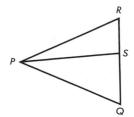

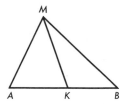

**3.** Given: $\triangle ABM$ with median $\overline{MK}$ and $\angle MKB > \angle MKA$.

   Prove: $AM < MB$.

**4.** $\triangle ABC$ and $\triangle ABD$ have a common side $\overline{AB}$, and $AC = AD$.   If $C$ is in the interior of $\angle DAB$, prove that $BD > BC$.

**5.** In $\triangle RST$, $RT > ST$ and $M$ is the mid-point of $\overline{RS}$.   Is $\angle TMR$ acute or obtuse?   Explain.

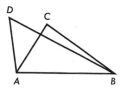

**6.** Given the figure as marked.   Prove that

   $$\angle W > \angle U.$$

**7.** In this figure, $FH = AQ$ and $AH > FQ$.

   Prove that $AB > FB$.

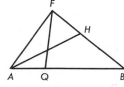

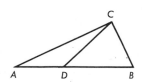

**8.** Given the figure with $AD = BC$, prove that $AC > DB$.

**9.** In $\triangle ABC$, $A$-$F$-$C$ and $A$-$D$-$B$ such that $FC = DB$.   If $AB > AC$, prove that $FB > CD$.

## 7–9.  ALTITUDES OF TRIANGLES

In each of the figures below, the segment $\overline{BD}$ is an *altitude* of $\triangle ABC$:

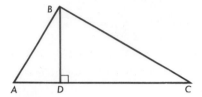 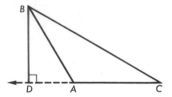

In each case, $\overline{BD}$ is the perpendicular from $B$ to $\overleftrightarrow{AC}$, and is called the *altitude* from $B$ to $\overleftrightarrow{AC}$.  Note that the foot of this perpendicular does not necessarily lie on the segment $\overline{AC}$.  But all cases are allowed for in the following definition.

**Definition**

> An *altitude* of a triangle is a perpendicular segment from a vertex of the triangle to the line containing the opposite side.

[*Query:* Is it possible for an altitude of a triangle to be a *side* of the triangle?  If so, under what conditions does this happen?]

Of course, every triangle has three altitudes, one from each vertex, like this:

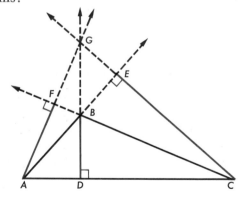

Here $\overline{BD}$ is the altitude from $B$, $\overline{AF}$ is the altitude from $A$, and $\overline{CE}$ is the altitude from $C$.  Note that in this particular case, although no two of the segments $\overline{BD}$, $\overline{AF}$, and $\overline{CE}$ have a point in common, the lines containing them all seem to intersect in a point $G$.

Unfortunately, the same word "altitude" is used in two other ways.

(1) Sometimes the *length* of an altitude is also called an altitude. Thus, if the distance $BD$ is 6, we may say that the altitude from $B$ is 6.

(2) A *line containing* an altitude is also called an altitude. Thus, in the figure above, the lines $\overleftrightarrow{BD}$, $\overleftrightarrow{AF}$, and $\overleftrightarrow{CE}$ may be referred to as altitudes. This is the way we shall be using the word, in Chapter 15, when we show that the three "altitudes" of a triangle always intersect at one point. If an altitude had to be a segment, this theorem would of course be false, as the above figure shows.

This triple use of a single word might easily lead to trouble, but it usually doesn't, because in most cases we can tell from the context what meaning is intended.

## Problem Set 7–9

1. Copy △*ABC*. Note that it is scalene. Draw the angle bisector of ∠*C*. Next put in the median from *C* to $\overline{AB}$. Finally, draw the altitude from *C* to $\overline{AB}$. If you have worked carefully, you should see that these segments are distinct. In what kind of triangle would the angle bisector, median, and altitude be the same segment?

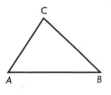

2. Copy the obtuse triangle, △*PQR*, and draw its three altitudes.

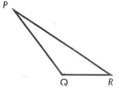

3. Prove that the altitude to the base of an isosceles triangle is also a median.

4. Prove the following theorem.

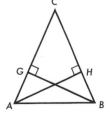

> The altitudes to the congruent sides of an isosceles triangle are congruent.

(The figure shows the case for $m \angle C < 90$. Consider also $m \angle C = 90$ and $m \angle C > 90$.)

5. Prove: The altitudes of an equilateral triangle are congruent.

6. Prove the converse of the theorem of Problem 4:

   If two altitudes of a triangle are congruent, the triangle is isosceles.

**7.** Prove the following theorem.

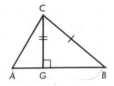

Given a correspondence $ABC \leftrightarrow DEF$. If $AB = DE$, $BC = EF$, and the altitude from $C$ is congruent to the altitude from $F$, then the correspondence is a congruence.

**Restatement.**

Given: $AB = DE$ and $BC = EF$. Altitudes $\overline{CG}$ and $\overline{FH}$. $CG = FH$.

Prove: $\triangle ABC \cong \triangle DEF$.

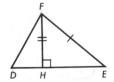

**8.** Prove that the perimeter of a triangle is greater than the sum of the three altitudes.

## Chapter Review

**1.** For each example, identify the order property it illustrates.
  (a) If $r > 6$ and $6 > t$, then $t < r$.
  (b) If $MP = 3$ and $RS = 7$, then $MP + RS = 10$.
  (c) If $DK \geq 11$ and $DK \leq 11$, then $DK = 11$.

**2.** If $D$ is a point in the interior of $\angle ABC$, explain why $\angle ABC > \angle DBC$.

**3.** If $a = 20$, then $x$ _____.
  If $b = 65$, then $x$ _____.
  If $c = 100$, then $x$ _____.

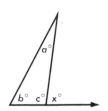

**4.** Define distance between a point and a line. Define altitude of a triangle.

**5.** Prove: If a median of a triangle is not perpendicular to the side it bisects, then at least two sides of the triangle are not congruent.

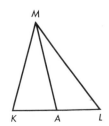

**6.** Three guy wires of equal length support a newly planted tree on level ground. If they are all fastened to the tree at the same height, will they be pegged to the ground at equal distances from the foot of the tree? Why?

**7.** In an equilateral triangle a median, an angle bisector, and an altitude are drawn at different vertices. How do their lengths compare?

**8.** Given the figure, prove that $\angle ADB > \angle C$.

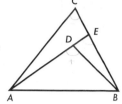

**9.** In $\triangle ABC$, $AC > AB$. Prove that if $D$ is any point between $B$ and $C$, then $AD < AC$.

**10.** Prove the following theorem.

Any point on the bisector of an angle is equidistant from the sides of the angle.

Given: $\overrightarrow{AP}$ bisects $\angle BAC$,

$\overline{PE} \perp \overrightarrow{AB}$,

$\overline{PF} \perp \overrightarrow{AC}$.

Prove: $PE = PF$.

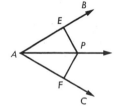

**11.** With measures of angles as indicated, which segment is the shortest? Explain your reasoning.

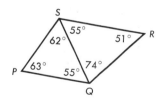

**12.** Planes $E$ and $F$ intersect in $\overleftrightarrow{AB}$. $C$ is in $F$; $D$ is in $E$. $CB = AD$. $\overline{CA} \perp \overline{AB}$ and $\overline{DB} \perp \overline{AB}$. Prove that $CA = DB$.

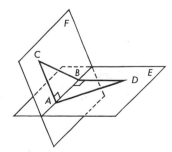

**13.** Segments drawn from a point in the interior of a triangle to the three vertices have lengths $r$, $s$, $t$. Prove that $r + s + t$ is greater than one-half the perimeter of the triangle.

**14.** Prove: If $\overline{AM}$ is a median of $\triangle ABC$, then segments from $B$ and $C$ perpendicular to $\overleftrightarrow{AM}$ are congruent.

**15.** In the figure, $PT = TR = RQ$. Prove that

$$PR > RQ.$$

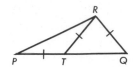

* **16.** Prove the following theorem.

> If two oblique (nonperpendicular) segments are drawn to a line from any point on a perpendicular to the line, the segment whose end point in the line is more remote from the foot of the perpendicular is the longer segment.

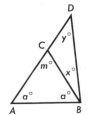

* **17.** Given that $AC = BC$, $AB < AC$, and $A$-$C$-$D$. Prove that $\triangle ABD$ is scalene.

* **18.** Prove: The sum of the distances from a point in the interior of a triangle to the ends of one side is less than the sum of the lengths of the other two sides; that is, prove that $a + b > c + d$.

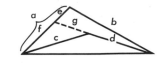

* **19.** In $\triangle ABC$, $\angle C$ is a right angle. If $m \angle B = 2m \angle A$, then $AB = 2BC$. [*Hint:* Introduce the bisector of $\angle B$.]

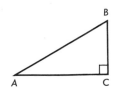

* **20.** (a) Given $\triangle ABC$ with $BC = a$, $AC = b$, and $AB = c$. Prove that

$$|a - b| < c.$$

(b) State, in words, the generalization of part (a) as a theorem.

*+ **21.** The sum of the measures of the angles of a triangle is less than 270.

+ **22.** On the basis of the postulates we have stated and the theorems we have proved so far in this book it is impossible to prove that the sum of the measures of the three angles of a triangle is 180 (a fact with which you have been familiar for some time). However, we can easily construct a special triangle and prove that the sum of the measures of its angles is less than 181. Let $\angle BAC$ have measure 1 (Angle Construction Postulate). On $\overrightarrow{AB}$ and $\overrightarrow{AC}$ take points $K$ and $M$ such that $AK = AM$. The sum of the measures of the angles of $\triangle AKM$ is less than 181. Why? If we made $m\angle A = \frac{1}{2}$, what could we say of the angle sum?

**HONORS PROBLEM**

Let $\overleftrightarrow{BD}$ intersect $\overleftrightarrow{AC}$ at $B$, between $A$ and $C$. Perpendiculars from $A$ and $C$ to $\overleftrightarrow{BD}$ meet $\overleftrightarrow{BD}$ at $P$ and $Q$, respectively. Prove that $P$ and $Q$ are not on the same side of $\overleftrightarrow{AC}$.

# 8 | Perpendicular Lines and Planes in Space

## 8-1. THE DEFINITION OF PERPENDICULARITY FOR LINES AND PLANES

In this chapter, we shall be concerned with figures that do not lie in a single plane. Therefore, before you start reading this chapter, it would be worthwhile to review Chapter 3, in which the basic ideas of space geometry were introduced.

Perpendicularity between lines and planes is defined as follows.

**Definition**

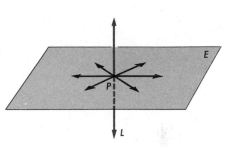

A line and a plane are *perpendicular* if they intersect and if every line lying in the plane and passing through the point of intersection is perpendicular to the given line. If the line $L$ and the plane $E$ are perpendicular, then we write $L \perp E$ or $E \perp L$. If $P$ is their point of intersection, then we say that $L \perp E$ at $P$.

In the figure, we have shown three lines in $E$, passing through $P$. According to our definition, all three are supposed to be perpendicular to $L$ at $P$, although they may not look that way. (In a perspective drawing, perpendicular lines don't necessarily look perpendicular.) Note that if we had required merely that *one* line in $E$ be perpendicular to $L$, this wouldn't have meant a thing: you can easily convince yourself that *every* plane through $P$ contains such a line. On the other hand, it will turn out that if $E$ contains *two* lines which are perpendicular to $L$ at $P$, then $L \perp E$ at $P$. We shall pursue this idea in the next section.

## Problem Set 8-1

1. The figure at the right represents plane $E$.
   (a) Do any points outside the figure belong to $E$?
   (b) Is plane $E$ intended to include every point outside the figure?

2. (a) Sketch a plane perpendicular to a vertical line.
   (b) Sketch a plane perpendicular to a horizontal line.
   (c) In each plane in parts (a) and (b) sketch three lines which pass through the point of intersection with the original line. State for each case, the relationship of each of the three lines to the original line.

3. Reread the definition of perpendicularity of a line and a plane and decide whether the following is true on the basis of that definition:

> If a line is perpendicular to a plane, then it is perpendicular to every line in the plane passing through the point of intersection.

4. If $\angle KPM$ is a right angle and $\overrightarrow{PM}$ is in $E$, can you conclude that $E$ is perpendicular to $\overleftrightarrow{PK}$? Why or why not?

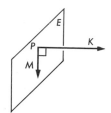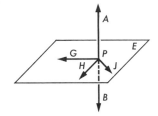

5. Given that $G$, $H$, $J$, and $P$ are in plane $E$ and $\overleftrightarrow{AB} \perp E$ at $P$. Which of the following must be right angles?

$$\angle APJ, \quad \angle HPJ, \quad \angle GPH, \quad \angle GPB, \quad \angle HPB, \quad \angle HPA.$$

6. In the figure, $H$, $K$, and $R$ are in plane $E$ and $F$ is not in $E$.

(a) Name the planes determined by the points of the figure.

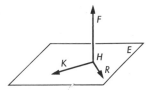

(b) If $\overrightarrow{HR}$ is perpendicular to plane $HKF$, which angles in the figure must be right angles?

7. Points $A$, $B$, $C$, $D$, and $G$ lie in the vertical plane, $E$, and $\overrightarrow{AP} \perp E$. Name all angles which must be right angles.

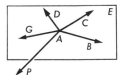

8. Given the figure with $A$, $B$, and $C$ in plane $E$. $\overline{PA} \perp E$ and $PC = PB$. Prove that $AC = AB$.

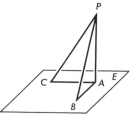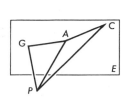

9. Points $A$, $G$, and $C$ lie in vertical plane $E$, and $P$ is a point "in front" of $E$. If $\overline{PA} \perp E$ and $AG = AC$, prove that $PG = PC$.

10. Collinear points $A$, $B$, and $X$ are in plane $E$, and points $P$ and $Q$ are on the same side of $E$. If $PB = QB$ and $PA = QA$, prove that $PX = QX$. Will your proof hold if $P$ and $Q$ are on opposite sides of $E$? if $P$ and $Q$ are in $E$?

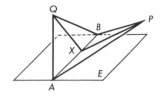

## 8–2.   A LEMMA

At the end of the preceding section, we said that if $E$ contains two lines which are perpendicular to $L$ at $P$, then $E \perp L$ at $P$. The proof of this theorem is rather long. To make it seem a little easier, we shall first prove a preliminary theorem, to help us in the main proof. Such "helping theorems" are called *lemmas*. This term comes from a Greek word meaning *branch*. Thus a lemma is a branch of a long proof.

Our lemma is easy to prove.

### Theorem 8–1

If $B$ and $C$ are equidistant from $P$ and $Q$, then every point between $B$ and $C$ is equidistant from $P$ and $Q$.

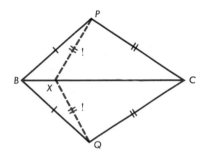

The restatement is conveyed by the figure. Note that $P$, $B$, $X$ and $C$ must lie in a single plane, because $X$ lies on $\overleftrightarrow{BC}$ and some plane contains $\overleftrightarrow{BC}$ and $P$. But it can easily happen that $\triangle BPC$ and $\triangle BQC$ lie in different planes, and in fact this is exactly the case in which we are going to need the theorem.

**Proof.**  (1) We have given $BP = BQ$, and $CP = CQ$ as indicated in the figure. By SSS it follows that $\triangle BPC \cong \triangle BQC$.

(2) Therefore $\angle PBC \cong \angle QBC$.

(3) By SAS, it follows that $\triangle PBX \cong \triangle QBX$.

(4) Therefore $PX = QX$, and $X$ is equidistant from $P$ and $Q$, which was to be proved.

We shall also need Corollary 6–2.1 from Chapter 6.

**Corollary 6–2.1**

Given a segment $\overline{AB}$ and a line $L$ in the same plane. If two points of $L$ are equidistant from $A$ and $B$, then $L$ is the perpendicular bisector of $\overline{AB}$.

We shall need this corollary only in the special case conveyed by the following figure:

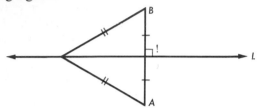

## 8–3.   THE BASIC THEOREM ON PERPENDICULARS

**Theorem 8–2**

If a line is perpendicular to each of two intersecting lines at their point of intersection, then it is perpendicular to the plane that contains them.

**Restatement.**   Let $L_1$ and $L_2$ be two lines in a plane $E$, intersecting at $A$. Let $L$ be a line which is perpendicular to both $L_1$ and $L_2$ at $A$. Then $L$ is perpendicular to every line $L_3$ which lies in $E$ and contains $A$.

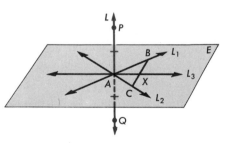

**Proof.**   (1) Let $P$ and $Q$ be two points of $L$ which are equidistant from $A$. Then *$L_1$ and $L_2$ are perpendicular bisectors of $\overline{PQ}$* (in two different planes, of course).

(2) Each of the lines $L_1$ and $L_2$ contains points on each side of $L_3$ in $E$. Let $B$ and $C$ be points of $L_1$ and $L_2$, lying on opposite sides of $L_3$ in $E$. Then line $L_3$ *contains a point $X$, lying between $B$ and $C$.*

(3) By (1) and Theorem 6–2, *each of the points $B$ and $C$ is equidistant from $P$ and $Q$.*

(4) By Theorem 8–1, *$X$ is equidistant from $P$ and $Q$.*

(5) Thus $L_3$ contains the mid-point of $\overline{PQ}$, and contains another point $X$ which is equidistant from $P$ and $Q$. By Corollary 6–2.1, $L_3 \perp L$, which was to be proved.

## Problem Set 8–3

1. Given points $A$, $G$, $H$, $K$, $J$, and $M$ in plane $E$. $\overleftrightarrow{AP} \perp \overleftrightarrow{AG}$, $\overleftrightarrow{AP} \perp \overleftrightarrow{AJ}$, and $A$, $G$, and $J$ are noncollinear. Prove that $\overleftrightarrow{AP}$ is perpendicular to $\overleftrightarrow{AK}$ and to $\overleftrightarrow{AM}$.

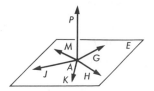

2. What is the relationship between $L$, the line of intersection of two walls of your classroom, and $F$, the plane of the floor? Explain. Is $L$ perpendicular to every line in $F$? How many lines in $F$ are perpendicular to $L$?

3. In the figure, $\overline{AB} \perp \overline{BC}$, $\overline{DB} \perp \overline{BC}$, and $AB = DB$. Prove that $\triangle ABC \cong \triangle DBC$. Is $\overline{AB} \perp E$? Why or why not?

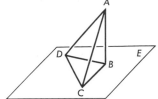

4. Square $\square ABCD$ is in plane $E$. $P$ is a point not in $E$ such that $\overline{PA} \perp \overline{AB}$.

   (a) Name all the planes determined by pairs of segments.

   (b) At least one of the segments is perpendicular to one of the planes asked for in part (a). Which segment? Which plane? How does Theorem 8–2 help you to give a correct answer?

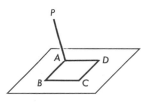

5. In Problem 3, which segment is perpendicular to which plane?

6. Given that $K$ is the mid-point of $\overline{DG}$, $AD = AG$, and $\overleftrightarrow{KP} \perp \overline{AK}$, $P$ not in the plane $ADG$. If there is a segment perpendicular to a plane, name the segment and the plane.

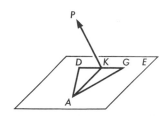

7. In the figure, $\overline{PQ} \perp \overline{MP}$, $\overline{PQ} \perp \overline{TQ}$, and $\overline{MP} \perp \overline{MT}$. Is any segment of the figure perpendicular to any plane of the figure? Name all such pairs, if any.

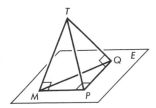

8. $\overline{AB}$ and $\overline{CD}$ are congruent segments which bisect each other at $M$. Line $L$ is perpendicular to each of $\overline{AB}$ and $\overline{CD}$ at $M$. $P$ is any point of $L$. Draw a figure and prove that $P$ is equidistant from $A$, $B$, $C$, and $D$.

* **9.** Given the cube shown here, with $BK = BM$. Prove that $H$ is equidistant from $K$ and $M$. [You may use the following properties of a cube in your proof: (a) The twelve edges of a cube are congruent. (b) Any two intersecting edges are perpendicular.]

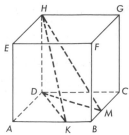

* **10.** If $A$, $B$, $C$, and $D$ are noncoplanar,

$$AD = DC, \qquad BC = BA,$$

and $\angle DBA$ is a right angle, then at least one of the segments in the figure is perpendicular to one of the planes. Which segment and which plane? Prove your answer.

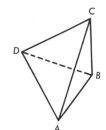

* **11.** In the figure, planes $E$ and $F$ intersect in $\overleftrightarrow{AB}$. $\overrightarrow{RQ}$ is in $F$ and $\overleftrightarrow{WX}$ is in $E$. $\overrightarrow{RQ} \perp \overleftrightarrow{AB}$ and $\overleftrightarrow{WX} \perp F$. Prove that $\overrightarrow{RQ} \perp E$.

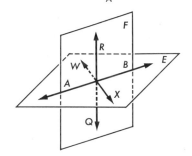

## 8–4.   EXISTENCE AND UNIQUENESS

The hard part of this chapter was over with when we proved Theorem 8–2. The other things that we need to know follow fairly easily.

### Theorem 8–3

Through a given point of a given line there passes a plane perpendicular to the given line.

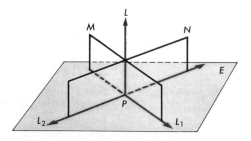

**Proof.**  Let $L$ and $P$ be the given line and point.

(1) Let $M$ and $N$ be any two different planes containing $L$.

[*Query:* How do we know that there *are* two different planes containing $L$?  Remember Postulate 5 and Theorem 3–3.]

(2) There is a line $L_1$ in $M$, perpendicular to $L$ at $P$ (Theorem 6–1).

(3) There is a line $L_2$ in $N$, perpendicular to $L$ at $P$ (Theorem 6–1).

(4) There is a plane $E$, containing $L_1$ and $L_2$ (Theorem 3–4).

(5) $E \perp L$ at $P$ [by (2), (3) and Theorem 8–2].

## Theorem 8–4

If a line and a plane are perpendicular, then the plane contains every line perpendicular to the given line at its point of intersection with the given plane.

**Restatement.**  If the line $L$ is perpendicular to the plane $E$ at the point $P$, and $L_1$ is a line perpendicular to $L$ at $P$, then $L_1$ lies in $E$.

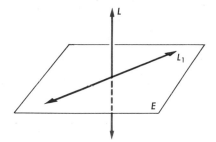
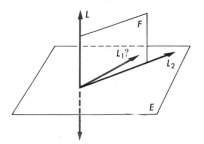

**Proof**

| STATEMENTS | REASONS |
|---|---|
| 1.  $L$ and $L_1$ lie in a plane $F$. | ? |
| 2.  The intersection of $F$ and $E$ is a line $L_2$. | ? |
| 3.  $L_2 \perp L$ at $P$. | Definition of $E \perp L$. |
| 4.  $L_1 \perp L$ at $P$. | Given. |
| 5.  $L_1$ and $L_2$ are the same line. | By Theorem 6–1, there is only one line in $F$ which is perpendicular to $L$ at $P$. |
| 6.  $L_1$ lies in $E$. | By step 2, $L_2$ lies in $E$, and by step 5, $L_1 = L_2$. |

Theorem 8–4 enables us to show that the perpendicular plane given by Theorem 8–3 is unique.

### Theorem 8–5

Through a given point of a given line there is only one plane perpendicular to the line.

**Proof.**  If there were two different perpendicular planes, then their intersection would be a single line.  This is impossible, because each of them contains *all* lines which are perpendicular to the given line at the given point.

We remember that the perpendicular bisector of a segment, in a given plane, was characterized as the set of all points of the plane that are equidistant from the end points of the segment.  For the perpendicular bisecting plane of a segment, in space, we have a characterization theorem of exactly the same kind.

### Theorem 8–6.    The Perpendicular Bisecting Plane Theorem

The perpendicular bisecting plane of a segment is the set of all points equidistant from the end points of the segment.

**Restatement.**  Let $E$ be the perpendicular bisecting plane of $\overline{AB}$. Then

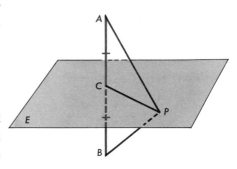

(1)   if $P$ is in $E$, then $PA = PB$;

(2)   if $PA = PB$, then $P$ is in $E$.

In the figure, $C$ is the mid-point of $\overline{AB}$.  Note that the restatement is in two parts, as we expect for a characterization theorem.

To prove (1), you need to know the definition of perpendicularity between a line and a plane, and the characterization of perpendicular bisecting lines in a plane.  To prove (2), you also need Theorem 8–5.  The details of these two proofs are left to you.

## Problem Set 8–4

**1.** (a) How many lines are perpendicular to a line at a given point of the line?

   (b) How many planes are perpendicular to a line at a given point of the line?

2. Given that $\overrightarrow{AP}$ is perpendicular to each of $\overrightarrow{AK}$, $\overrightarrow{AM}$, $\overrightarrow{AS}$, $\overrightarrow{AR}$, $\overrightarrow{AT}$. How many planes are determined by intersecting rays? Are there more than three points of the figure that are coplanar? If so, why? (Assume that no three of the given points are collinear.)

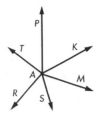

3. Planes $E$ and $F$ intersect in $\overleftrightarrow{KQ}$. $\overleftrightarrow{AB} \perp E$, with $B$ on $\overleftrightarrow{KQ}$. $R$ is in $E$ and $C$ is in $F$.

Is $\overleftrightarrow{AB} \perp \overleftrightarrow{BR}$? Why?

Is $\overleftrightarrow{AB} \perp \overleftrightarrow{KQ}$? Why?

Is $\overleftrightarrow{AB} \perp \overleftrightarrow{BC}$? Why?

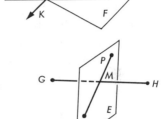

4. In the figure, $\overline{GH} \perp E$ at $M$, $MG = MH$, and $\overleftrightarrow{PQ} \perp \overline{GH}$ at $M$. Does $E$ contain $\overleftrightarrow{PQ}$? Why? With respect to $\overleftrightarrow{GH}$, what term applies to plane $E$?

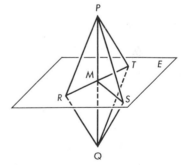

5. Two segments, $\overline{AB}$ and $\overline{CD}$, are perpendicular and bisect each other at $K$. A plane $Z$ contains $\overline{AB}$, but does not contain $\overline{CD}$. Is $Z$ the perpendicular bisecting plane of $\overline{CD}$? Draw a figure to illustrate your conclusion.

6. Plane $E$ is the perpendicular bisecting plane of $\overline{PQ}$, as shown in the figure.

(a) $PR =$ _____.

$TQ =$ _____.

$PS =$ _____.

$\angle PTM \cong$ _____.

$\triangle PTM \cong$ _____.

(b) Does $MR = MS = MT$? Explain.

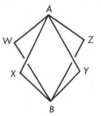

7. Given the figure with not all points coplanar.

If $AW = BW$, $AX = BX$, $AY = BY$, and $AZ = BZ$, prove that $W$, $X$, $Y$, and $Z$ are coplanar.

8. Prove Theorem 8–6.

&ast;  9. Write Theorems 8–3 and 8–5 as one theorem, using "exactly one."

&ast; 10. Write Theorem 8–6, using "if and only if."

&ast; 11. Could Theorem 8–5 have been proved before Theorem 8–3? Explain.

&ast;+ 12. Prove the following theorem.

> If $L$ is a line intersecting plane $E$ at point $M$, there is at least one line $L'$ in $E$ such that $L' \perp L$.

&ast;+ 13. Is the following statement true? Prove your answer.

> Four points, each equidistant from two fixed points, are coplanar with the two fixed points if and only if the four points are collinear.

&ast;+ 14. In the figure, $E$ is the perpendicular bisecting plane of $\overline{AB}$ at $C$. $H$ is on the same side of $E$ as $B$, and $K$ is on the same side of $E$ as $A$ such that $K$-$C$-$H$, $\overline{HB} \perp \overline{AB}$, and $\overline{KA} \perp \overline{AB}$. Prove that

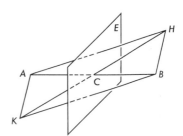

(a) $\overline{AK}$ and $\overline{BH}$ are coplanar, and

(b) $AH = BK$.

## 8–5.  PERPENDICULAR LINES AND PLANES: A SUMMARY

The following theorems are a summary of some of the basic facts about perpendicular lines and planes. Some of the proofs are easy, but some are rather long, and we shall not stop to do all of them here. We shall, however, give you a sample of the kind of reasoning that is involved, by giving lengthy hints for the proof of the following theorem.

### Theorem 8–7

Two lines perpendicular to the same plane are coplanar.

To get an idea of how the proof ought to go, let us first consider what the situation is *if* the theorem is true; that is, supposing that the two lines really do lie in a plane, *which* plane do they lie in?

We have given that $L_1 \perp E$ at $A$ and $L_2 \perp E$ at $B$; and we are *supposing* that $L_1$ and $L_2$ lie in a plane

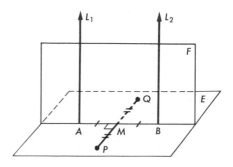

*F*. In the figure, we show the mid-point *M* of $\overline{AB}$, and we also show a segment $\overline{PQ}$ in *E*, such that $\overline{AB}$ and $\overline{PQ}$ bisect each other at right angles.

It surely looks as if $\overline{PQ} \perp F$ at *M*. If this is true, then *F is the perpendicular bisecting plane of $\overline{PQ}$.*

So far, of course, we haven't proved anything, because we have been assuming that the theorem is true. But we now have a clue to the way the proof ought to go: first we should set up $\overline{PQ}$ in *E*, such that $\overline{PQ}$ and $\overline{AB}$ bisect each other at right angles; and *then we should show that $L_1$ and $L_2$ lie in the perpendicular bisecting plane of $\overline{PQ}$.*

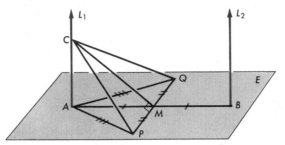

This idea works. The main steps in the proof are as follows:

(1)  $AP = AQ$ (as indicated in the figure).
(2)  $\triangle CAP \cong \triangle CAQ$.
(3)  $CP = CQ$.
(4)  *C* lies in the perpendicular bisecting plane of $\overline{PQ}$. Let this plane be *F*.
(5)  $L_1$ lies in *F*.

In exactly the same way, we conclude that

(6)  $L_2$ lies in *F*.

Therefore the plane that we were looking for is indeed the perpendicular bisecting plane of $\overline{PQ}$; this plane contains both $L_1$ and $L_2$; and therefore $L_1$ and $L_2$ are coplanar.

You may find that the discussion that led up to this proof will be worth more to you than the proof. A proof, once you get it, is logical, but the process by which you manage to think of it is very seldom logical. You have to find your way as best you can. And one of the best methods of doing this is the "method of wishful thinking" which we illustrated at the beginning of this section.

The theorems of this chapter, so far, give incomplete information about perpendicular lines and planes. The following theorems fill in the gaps.

### Theorem 8–8

Through a given point there passes one and only one *plane* perpendicular to a given *line*.

### Theorem 8–9

Through a given point there passes one and only one *line* perpendicular to a given *plane*.

These theorems convey quite a lot of information in very few words. Each of them has two cases, depending on whether the given point is on or off the given line or plane. In each of these four cases, the theorems tell us that we have both existence and uniqueness. This means that we need a total of eight proofs. Two of these have already been given in Theorems 8–3 and 8–5.

Theorem 8–9 assures us of the existence of a unique perpendicular to a given plane from an external point. Hence, we are justified in giving the following definition, analogous to the one following Theorem 7–7.

### Definition

The *distance* to a plane from an external point is the length of the perpendicular segment from the point to the plane.

### Theorem 8–10.   The Second Minimum Theorem

The shortest segment to a plane from an external point is the perpendicular segment.

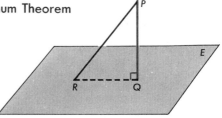

The proof is very similar to that of Theorem 7–7. Given the perpendicular segment $\overline{PQ}$, and any other segment $\overline{PR}$ from $P$ to $E$, we start the proof by passing a plane through the lines $\overleftrightarrow{PR}$ and $\overleftrightarrow{PQ}$. The rest of the proof is left to you.

## Problem Set 8–5

**1.** From a point $A$ not in a plane $E$, the shortest segment to plane $E$ is drawn, intersecting $E$ at $B$. $L$ and $L'$ are lines in $E$ such that $L$ contains $B$ and $L' \perp L$. If $L''$ is drawn so that $L'' \perp L$ and $L'' \perp L'$, show that $L''$ and $\overleftrightarrow{AB}$ are coplanar.

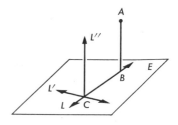

**2.** Prove the following special case of Theorem 8–9.

Through a point not in a given plane, there is at most one line perpendicular to the plane.

**\*+ 3.** *P* and *Q* are on opposite sides of plane *E* but are equidistant from plane *E*. The perpendiculars from *P* and *Q* to *E* intersect *E* at *R* and *S*, respectively. Prove that

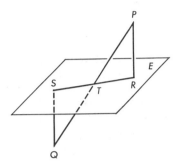

(a) $\overline{PQ}$ intersects $\overline{SR}$ at a point *T*, and

(b) *T* is the mid-point of $\overline{SR}$.

## Chapter Review

**1.** Use a figure, if necessary, to help you decide whether each statement is true or false.

(a) If two planes intersect, their intersection is a line.

(b) Three lines may intersect in a common point such that each line is perpendicular to the other two.

(c) If a line is perpendicular to each of two lines, it is perpendicular to the plane containing the two lines.

(d) The intersection of two planes may be a segment.

(e) At a point in a plane there is exactly one line perpendicular to the plane.

(f) For any four points, there is a plane containing them.

(g) If a line intersects a plane in only one point, there are at least two lines in the plane which are perpendicular to the line.

(h) Only one line can be drawn through a given point perpendicular to a given line.

(i) If three lines intersect in pairs but no point belongs to all three lines, then the three lines are coplanar.

(j) Three planes can separate space into eight regions.

**2.** Complete: The set of all points equidistant from the end points of a segment is the _____ of the segment.

**3.** Complete: The distance to a plane from a point not in the plane is _____
_____.

**4.** Complete: If a line is perpendicular to each of two _____ lines at _____, then it is perpendicular to the _____ that contains them.

**5.** In the figure, $\triangle ABC$ is equilateral in plane $E$, and $\overline{CD}$ bisects $\angle BCA$. If $\overline{HD}$ is perpendicular to $\overline{CD}$, at least one segment of the figure is perpendicular to one of the planes. Which segment? Which plane?

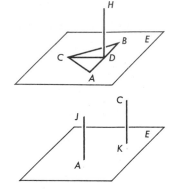

**6.** Plane $E$ contains points $A$ and $K$; $\overline{JA} \perp E$, $\overline{CK} \perp E$, but $A \neq K$. How many planes are determined by $A, K, C$, and $J$? Explain.

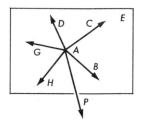

**7.** If the goal posts at one end of a football field are perpendicular to the ground, then they are coplanar even without a brace between them. Which theorem supports this conclusion? If they are not perpendicular to the ground, can they still be coplanar? Will putting a brace between them guarantee that they will always be coplanar?

**8.** $\overrightarrow{AP}$ is perpendicular to the vertical plane $E$, and $A, B, C, D, G,$ and $H$ are points in $E$. What is

$$m \angle DAP + m \angle CAP?$$

If $\angle CAB$ is a right angle, at least one ray other than $\overrightarrow{AP}$, and one plane other than $E$ are perpendicular. Name all such pairs.

**9.** $\triangle ABC$ is in plane $E$. $P$ is a point not in $E$ such that $\overline{PA} \perp \overline{AB}, \overline{PA} \perp \overline{AC}$, and $\overline{PD} \perp \overline{BC}$ with $D$ on $\overline{BC}$. Which is true: $PA > PD, PA = PD,$ or $PA < PD$? Why?

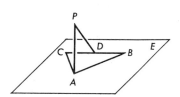

**10.** $\triangle HMT$ is in plane $E$. $HM = TM$ and $\overline{KM} \perp E$. Which is true:

$$\angle KHT > \angle KTH,$$
$$\angle KHT \cong \angle KTH,$$

or

$$\angle KHT < \angle KTH?$$

Why?

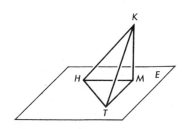

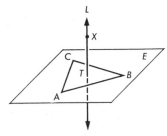

11. Given: Plane $E$ contains $\triangle ABC$.
    Line $L \perp E$ at $T$. $T$ is equidistant from $A$, $B$, and $C$. $X$ is any point on $L$.

    Prove: $X$ is equidistant from $A$, $B$, and $C$.

12. Prove that if $A$ and $B$ are each equidistant from $P$ and $Q$, then each point of $\overleftrightarrow{AB}$ is equidistant from $P$ and $Q$.

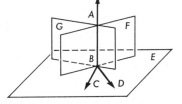

13. Given: $\overleftrightarrow{BC}$ and $\overleftrightarrow{BD}$ lie in plane $E$; plane $F \perp \overleftrightarrow{BD}$ at $B$; plane $G \perp \overleftrightarrow{BC}$ at $B$; $G$ and $F$ intersect in $\overleftrightarrow{AB}$.

    Prove: $\overleftrightarrow{AB} \perp E$.

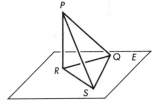

14. In the figure, $\triangle RSQ$ is in plane $E$ and $\overline{PR} \perp E$. If $\angle PQR \cong \angle PSR$, then $\angle PQS \cong \angle PSQ$.

15. In the figure, if $\overline{PR} \perp E$, $PR > RS$, $\overline{SQ} \perp \overline{RQ}$, and $\overline{SQ} \perp \overline{PQ}$, prove that $PQ > QS$.

Figure for Problems 14 and 15

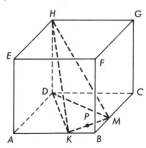

\* 16. Given the cube shown in the figure, with $BK = BM$ and $P$ the mid-point of $\overline{KM}$. Prove that plane $HDP$ is the perpendicular bisecting plane of $\overline{KM}$. [You may use the properties of a cube given in Problem 9, Problem Set 8–3.]

\* 17. Prove that each of four rays $\overrightarrow{AB}$, $\overrightarrow{AC}$, $\overrightarrow{AD}$, and $\overrightarrow{AE}$ cannot be perpendicular to the other three.

## HONORS PROBLEM

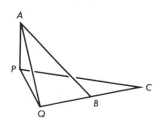

Given: $\overline{AP} \perp \overline{PQ}$, $\overline{AP} \perp \overline{PC}$, $\overline{PQ} \perp \overleftrightarrow{BC}$, $Q$-$B$-$C$.

Prove: $\overline{AQ} \perp \overleftrightarrow{BC}$.

[*Hint:* Take $R$ on $\overleftrightarrow{BC}$ so that $QR = QB$.]

# 9 | Parallel Lines in a Plane

## 9-1. CONDITIONS WHICH GUARANTEE PARALLELISM

There are three ways in which two lines can be situated in space:

(1) They may intersect in a point. In this case, Theorem 3-4 tells us that they must be coplanar.

(2) They may *fail* to intersect and *fail* to be coplanar. In this case, they are called *skew lines*. For example, consider the line $L_1$ which runs from back to front along the floor of your room and the line $L_2$ which runs from side to side along the ceiling. These are skew lines.

(3) Finally, the two lines may lie in the same plane, without intersecting one another. In this case, we say that the two lines are *parallel*.

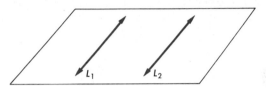

**Definition**

Two lines which are not coplanar are called *skew lines*.

**Definition**

Two lines are *parallel* if (1) they are coplanar and (2) they do not intersect.

The following theorem enables us to speak of *the* plane containing two parallel lines.

**Theorem 9-1**

Two parallel lines lie in exactly one plane.

**Proof.** If $L_1$ and $L_2$ are parallel, then we know at once from the definition that they lie in a plane $E$. We need to show that they lie in only one plane.

Let $P$ be any point of $L_2$. By Theorem 3-3 there is only one plane containing $L_1$ and $P$. Therefore there is only one plane containing $L_1$ and $L_2$, because every plane that contains $L_2$ contains $P$.

We shall write

$$L_1 \parallel L_2$$

to mean that $L_1$ and $L_2$ are parallel. If two segments $\overline{AB}$ and $\overline{CD}$ lie on parallel lines, then we shall say for short that the segments are parallel, and we shall write $\overline{AB} \parallel \overline{CD}$.

We shall speak similarly of two rays, a ray and a segment, and so on.

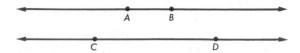

For example, given that $\overleftrightarrow{AB} \parallel \overleftrightarrow{CD}$, we may also write

$$\overrightarrow{AB} \parallel \overrightarrow{CD}, \qquad \overline{AB} \parallel \overline{CD}, \qquad \overrightarrow{BA} \parallel \overrightarrow{CD},$$

and so on, for twelve more similar cases.

On the basis of the definition, it may not seem easy to tell whether two lines are parallel. Each of the lines stretches out infinitely far in two directions, and to tell whether they intersect, it may seem that we have to look at the entire line in both cases. In some cases, however, we can tell that two lines are parallel by looking at only a short segment of each, as the following theorems show.

### Theorem 9–2

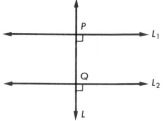

In a plane, two lines are parallel if they are both perpendicular to the same line.

**Proof.** Given that $L_1 \perp L$ at $P$ and $L_2 \perp L$ at $Q$. It is given that $L_1$ and $L_2$ are coplanar. We need to show that they do not intersect.

Suppose that $L_1$ intersects $L_2$ at a point $R$. Then there are two perpendiculars from $R$ to $L$. By Theorem 6–4, this is impossible. Therefore $L_1 \parallel L_2$. [*Query:* What method of proof is being used here?]

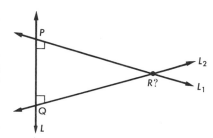

Theorem 9–2 enables us to show that parallels exist.

### Theorem 9–3

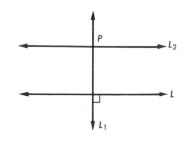

Let $L$ be a line and let $P$ be a point not on $L$. Then there is at least one line through $P$, parallel to $L$.

**Proof.**  Let $L_1$ be the perpendicular from $P$ to $L$. Let $L_2$ be the perpendicular to $L_1$ at $P$ (in the plane that contains $L$ and $P$.)  By Theorem 9–2, $L_2 \parallel L$.

It may seem natural to try to prove next that the parallel given by Theorem 9–3 is unique. That is, we might try to prove the following.

*Through a given external point there is only one line parallel to a given line.*

It is a fact, however, that this statement cannot be proved as a theorem, on the basis of the postulates that we have so far. It must be taken as a new postulate. This postulate has a long and interesting history. For well over two thousand years, the standard textbook of geometry was Euclid's *Elements,* written in about 300 B.C.  In the *Elements,* Euclid used a postulate which says that parallels are unique. Usually, mathematicians like to assume as little as they can get by with, and prove as much as they can manage to prove. For this reason, many of them tried to turn Euclid's Parallel Postulate into a theorem. All of them failed. Finally, in the nineteenth century, it was discovered that the Parallel Postulate *cannot* be proved on the basis of the other postulates.

We shall return to this question later. Meanwhile, let us investigate a little further the conditions under which we can say that two lines are parallel.

In the figure on the left below, the line $T$ is a *transversal* of the coplanar lines $L_1$ and $L_2$.

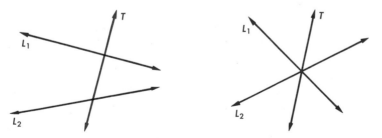

In the figure on the right, $T$ is *not* a transversal. More precisely:

## Definition

A *transversal* of two coplanar lines is a line which intersects them in two different points.

In each of the following figures, $\angle 1$ and $\angle 2$ are *alternate interior angles.*

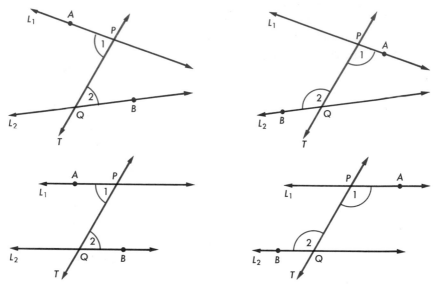

Note that the lines cut by the transversal may or may not be parallel. The labels in the figures suggest how we should describe alternate interior angles in a definition.

### Definition

Given two lines $L_1$ and $L_2$, cut by a transversal $T$ at points $P$ and $Q$. Let $A$ be a point of $L_1$ and let $B$ be a point of $L_2$, such that $A$ and $B$ lie on opposite sides of $T$. Then $\angle APQ$ and $\angle PQB$ are *alternate interior angles.*

### Theorem 9–4

If two lines are cut by a transversal, and one pair of alternate interior angles are congruent, then the other pair of alternate interior angles are also congruent.

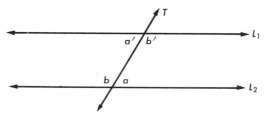

That is, if $\angle a \cong \angle a'$, then $\angle b \cong \angle b'$. And if $\angle b \cong \angle b'$, then $\angle a \cong \angle a'$. The proof is left to you.

The following theorem is a generalization of Theorem 9–2. That is, it includes Theorem 9–2 as a special case. Since it applies in more cases than Theorem 9–2, it is more useful. The letters AIP in the name of this theorem stand for "Alternate Interior Parallel." The converse of Theorem 9–5, which will be Theorem 9–8, will similarly be called "The PAI Theorem."

**Theorem 9–5.** The AIP Theorem

Given two lines cut by a transversal. If a pair of alternate interior angles are congruent, then the lines are parallel.

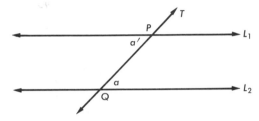

**Proof.** Let $T$ be a transversal, intersecting $L_1$ and $L_2$ at $P$ and $Q$. We have given that a pair of alternate interior angles are congruent. By the preceding theorem, we have

(1) *both* pairs of alternate interior angles are congruent.

Now suppose that $L_1$ intersects $L_2$ at a point $R$. We shall show that this leads to a contradiction of (1).

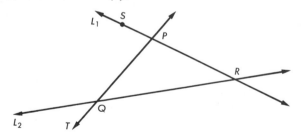

Let $S$ be a point of $L_1$, on the side of $T$ opposite to $R$. Then $\angle SPQ$ is an exterior angle of $\triangle PQR$, and $\angle PQR$ is one of its remote interior angles. By the Exterior Angle Theorem,

(2) $\angle SPQ > \angle PQR$.

This contradicts (1), because these are alternate interior angles. Therefore $L_1$ does not intersect $L_2$, and $L_1 \parallel L_2$, which was to be proved.

## Problem Set 9–1

[*Note:* In the problem sets of this chapter when problems are stated by means of figures, the figures are supposed to be planar unless otherwise designated.]

1. Which of the following statements are true?

   (a) If two lines do not lie in the same plane, they may be parallel.

   (b) The definition of parallel lines states that the lines must remain the same distance apart.

   (c) If two lines are perpendicular to the same line at different points of the line, they are parallel.

   (d) If two lines in a plane are intersected by a transversal, the alternate interior angles are congruent.

2. Given: $\overrightarrow{AD}$ bisects $\angle CAB$ and $CA = CD$.

   Prove: $\overleftrightarrow{CD} \parallel \overleftrightarrow{AB}$.

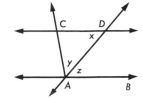

3. Would it follow that $L_1 \parallel L_2$ if

   (a) $m\angle q = 100$ and       (b) $m\angle p = 80$ and
   $\quad m\angle r = 100$?            $\quad m\angle r = 100$?

   (c) $m\angle s = 120$ and       (d) $m\angle r = 90$ and
   $\quad m\angle p = 60$?            $\quad m\angle p = 90$?

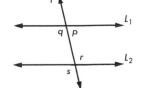

4. Is it possible to find two lines in space which are neither parallel nor intersecting?

5. Prove the following theorem.

   If two lines are cut by a transversal, and a pair of interior angles which contain points on the same side of the transversal are supplementary, the lines are parallel.

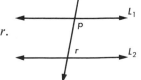

   Given: $L_1, L_2$, and $T$.  $\angle p$ is supplementary to $\angle r$.

   Prove: $L_1 \parallel L_2$.

6. Given a line $L$ and a point $P$ not on $L$, show how a protractor and a ruler can be used to draw a line through $P$ parallel to $L$.

7. In the figure, $P$, $Q$, and $R$ are three noncollinear points in plane $E$, $\overrightarrow{PK} \perp E$ and $\overrightarrow{RM} \perp E$. Prove that $\overleftrightarrow{PK} \parallel \overleftrightarrow{RM}$.

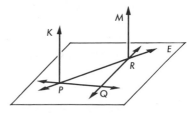

8. $\overline{AB}$ and $\overline{CD}$ bisect each other at $E$. Prove that

$$\overline{AD} \parallel \overline{CB}.$$

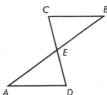

9. Given the quadrilateral $\square ABCD$ with right angles $\angle A$ and $\angle B$ and $AD = BC$. Prove that $\angle D \cong \angle C$. [*Hint:* Draw $\overline{AC}$ and $\overline{BD}$.]

Can you also prove that $\angle D$ and $\angle C$ are right angles?

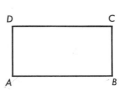

10. In the figure, $A$, $B$, and $C$ are collinear, $AP = AQ$, $BP = BQ$, $BX = BY$, and $CX = CY$. Prove that $\overline{PQ} \parallel \overline{XY}$.

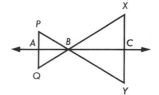

* 11. Given: $\square ABCD$ with $H$ the mid-point of $\overline{AB}$, $G$ the mid-point of $\overline{DC}$, $AD = BC$, and $\angle A \cong \angle B$.

Prove: $\overleftrightarrow{GH} \perp \overline{DC}$,
$\overleftrightarrow{GH} \perp \overline{AB}$,
$\overline{AB} \parallel \overline{DC}$.

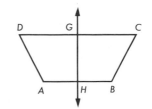

* 12. Given: $\triangle ABC$ in which

$$AP = PB = RQ,$$
$$BQ = QC = PR,$$
$$AR = RC = PQ.$$

Prove: $m\angle A + m\angle B + m\angle C = 180$.

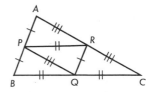

Why does this *not* prove that the sum of the measures of the angles of any triangle is 180?

## HONORS PROBLEM

Suppose that the following two definitions are agreed upon.

A *vertical line* is a line containing the center of the earth.

A *horizontal line* is a line perpendicular to some vertical line.

(a) Could two horizontal lines be parallel?

(b) Could two vertical lines be parallel?

(c) Could two vertical lines be perpendicular?

(d) Could two horizontal lines be perpendicular?

(e) Would every vertical line be a horizontal line?

(f) Would every horizontal line be a vertical line?

(g) Could a horizontal line be parallel to a vertical line?

(h) Would every line be horizontal?

## 9–2.  CORRESPONDING ANGLES

In the figure below, the angles marked $a$ and $a'$ are called *corresponding angles*.

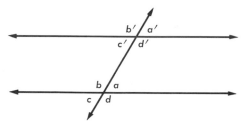

Similarly, $b$ and $b'$ are corresponding angles; and the pairs $c$, $c'$ and $d$, $d'$ are also corresponding angles.  To be exact:

**Definition**

If two lines are cut by a transversal, if $\angle x$ and $\angle y$ are alternate interior angles, and if $\angle y$ and $\angle z$ are vertical angles, then $\angle x$ and $\angle z$ are *corresponding angles*.

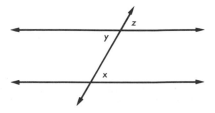

You should prove the following two theorems.

### Theorem 9–6

Given two lines cut by a transversal.  If a pair of corresponding angles are congruent, then a pair of alternate interior angles are congruent.

(Remember the Vertical Angle Theorem.)

### Theorem 9–7

Given two lines cut by a transversal.  If a pair of corresponding angles are congruent, then the lines are parallel.

It looks as if the converses of Theorems 9–5 and 9–7 ought to be true.  That is, when two parallel lines are cut by a transversal, then alternate interior angles ought to be congruent, and corresponding angles ought to be congruent.  The proof of these converses, however, requires the Parallel Postulate.  We shall therefore state this postulate in the following section, and use it hereafter.

## Problem Set 9–2

**1.** In the figure, $AC = BC$ and $\angle DCE \cong \angle B$.  Prove that $\overrightarrow{CE} \parallel \overline{AB}$.

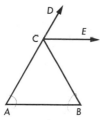
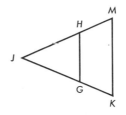

**2.** Given: $\triangle KMJ$ with $KJ = MJ$, $GJ = HJ$, and $\angle HGJ \cong \angle HMK$.
Prove: $\overline{GH} \parallel \overline{KM}$.

**3.** In the figure, $\angle B$ and $\angle D$ are right angles, and $DC = AB$.  Prove that $\overline{AD} \parallel \overline{BC}$.

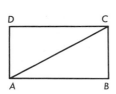
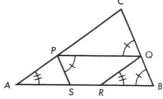

**4.** In the figure as marked, why is $\overline{PQ} \parallel \overline{AB}$?  $\overline{AC} \parallel \overline{QR}$?  $\overline{PS} \parallel \overline{BC}$?

## 9–3.  THE PARALLEL POSTULATE

**POSTULATE 18.**   The Parallel Postulate

> ***Through a given external point there is only one parallel to a given line.***

Note that since we have proved that parallels *exist*, the postulate needs to say only that they are unique. It is the uniqueness of parallels that gives us the converses of the theorems in the preceding section. We start with the converse of Theorem 9–5.

**Theorem 9–8.**   The PAI Theorem

> If two parallel lines are cut by a transversal, then alternate interior angles are congruent.

**Proof.**  We have given parallel lines $L_1$ and $L_2$, and a transversal $T$, intersecting them in $P$ and $Q$.

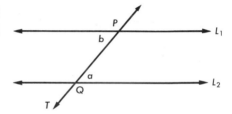

Suppose that $\angle a$ and $\angle b$ are *not* congruent. Let $L$ be the line through $P$ for which alternate interior angles *are* congruent. That is, in the figure below, $\angle a \cong \angle c$. By the Angle Construction Postulate, there is exactly one such line $L$; and this means also that $L \neq L_1$.

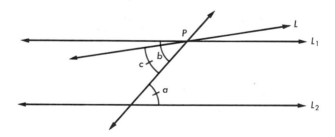

Then $L \parallel L_2$, by Theorem 9–5. Since $L \neq L_1$, it follows that there are two lines through $P$, parallel to $L_2$. This contradicts the Parallel Postulate. Therefore

$$\angle a \cong \angle b,$$

which was to be proved.

The proofs of the following four theorems are short and fairly easy, and so we leave them to you.

## Theorem 9–9

If two parallel lines are cut by a transversal, each pair of corresponding angles are congruent.

## Theorem 9–10

If two parallel lines are cut by a transversal, the interior angles on the same side of the transversal are supplementary.

**Restatement.** Given $L_1 \parallel L_2$, with a transversal $T$. Then $\angle b$ and $\angle d$ are supplementary and $\angle a$ and $\angle c$ are supplementary.

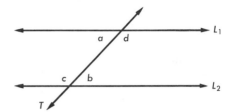

## Theorem 9–11

In a plane, if two lines are each parallel to a third line, then they are parallel to each other.

The same theorem holds for the case in which the three lines are not coplanar. (See Corollary 10–4.2.) But the theorem cannot be proved in the general case by the methods of this chapter.

## Theorem 9–12

In a plane, if a line is perpendicular to one of two parallel lines it is perpendicular to the other.

A quick proof of this theorem is suggested by the figure on the right. (An angle is a right angle if and only if it is congruent to an angle with which it forms a linear pair.)

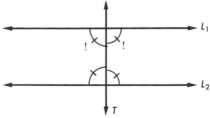

A final remark: If you used an indirect proof for Theorem 9–9, you were working too hard. See the definition of corresponding angles, and remember the Vertical Angle Theorem.

## Problem Set 9–3

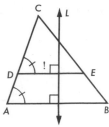

1. Given the figure with $\angle CDE \cong \angle A$ and $L \perp \overleftrightarrow{AB}$. Prove that $L \perp \overleftrightarrow{DE}$.

2. Given: Quadrilateral $\square EASY$ with right angles $\angle E$, $\angle A$, and $\angle S$.

   Prove: $\overline{EY} \perp \overline{SY}$.

3. Prove that a line parallel to the base of an isosceles triangle and intersecting the other two sides of the triangle at different points forms another isosceles triangle.

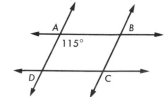

4. If $\overleftrightarrow{AB} \parallel \overleftrightarrow{DC}$ and $m \angle BAD = 115$, what is $m \angle ADC$? If also $\overleftrightarrow{AD} \parallel \overleftrightarrow{BC}$, what is $m \angle BCD$?

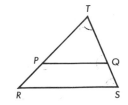

5. Given: In the figure, $RT = RS$, $\overleftrightarrow{PQ} \parallel \overleftrightarrow{RS}$.

   Prove: $PQ = PT$.

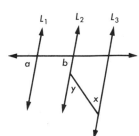

6. In the figure, $\angle x \cong \angle y$ and $\angle a \cong \angle b$. Prove that $L_1 \parallel L_3$.

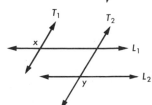

7. Given the figure with $L_1 \parallel L_2$ and $T_1 \parallel T_2$. Prove that $\angle x \cong \angle y$.

8. Given that $\overline{AC}$ and $\overline{DB}$ intersect at $E$, with $A$-$E$-$C$ and $D$-$E$-$B$, such that $AD = BC$ and $\overline{AD} \parallel \overline{BC}$. Prove that $\overline{AC}$ and $\overline{DB}$ bisect each other at $E$.

9. Given $\triangle PMN$, $\overrightarrow{MX}$ bisects $\angle M$, $\overrightarrow{NX}$ bisects $\angle N$, and $\overline{QR}$, through $X$, is parallel to $\overline{MN}$.

   Prove that $\triangle QMX$ and $\triangle RXN$ are isosceles.

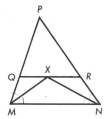

+ 10. Prove the following theorem by an indirect method.

   Given two parallel lines, $L_1$ and $L_2$. If, in the same plane, a third line, $L_3$, intersects one of the parallels, say $L_2$, then it intersects the other parallel, $L_1$.

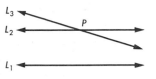

11. If two parallel lines are cut by a transversal, then the bisectors of any two corresponding angles are parallel.

12. Prove the following theorem.

   In a plane, if the sides of an angle are parallel to the sides of another angle, the two angles are either (a) congruent or (b) supplementary.

   [*Note:* The figure shows only two cases, but similar, easy proofs may be given for all other cases. For a hint, see Problem 7 of this problem set.]

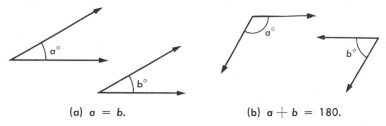

   (a) $a = b$.              (b) $a + b = 180$.

* 13. In $\triangle ABC$ the bisector of $\angle A$ intersects $\overline{BC}$ at $D$. The perpendicular bisector of $\overline{AD}$ intersects $\overline{AC}$ at $G$. Prove that $\overline{GD} \parallel \overline{AB}$.

* 14. In $\triangle FGH$ the bisector of $\angle F$ and the bisector of $\angle G$ intersect at $C$. The line through $C$ and parallel to $\overline{FG}$ intersects $\overline{FH}$ at $A$ and $\overline{GH}$ at $B$. Prove that the perimeter of $\triangle ABH$ equals the sum of $FH$ and $GH$.

* 15. Given $\triangle ABC$. Prove that if $A$ lies on a line parallel to $\overline{BC}$, then $m \angle A + m \angle B + m \angle C = 180$.

+ **16.** If Theorem 9–8 is taken as a postulate instead of the Parallel Postulate, then the Parallel Postulate can be proved as a theorem.

> Given a line $L$ and a point $P$ not on $L$. Then there is at most one line, $L_1$, containing $P$ and parallel to $L$.

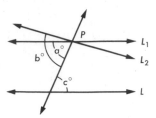

[*Hint:* Does $a = c = b$?]

+ **17.** Show that if Theorem 9–12 is taken as a postulate, the Parallel Postulate follows as a theorem.

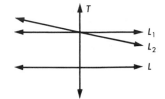

## 9–4.   TRIANGLES

### Theorem 9–13

For every triangle, the sum of the measures of the angles is 180.

**Proof.**   Given $\triangle ABC$, let $L$ be the line through $B$, parallel to $\overline{AC}$. Let $\angle x$, $\angle x'$, $\angle y$, $\angle y'$, and $\angle z$ be as shown in the figure.

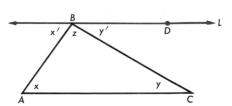

| STATEMENTS | REASONS |
|---|---|
| 1. $m\angle x = m\angle x'$. | These are alternate interior angles. |
| 2. $m\angle y = m\angle y'$. | Same as for Step 1. |
| 3. $m\angle ABD = m\angle z + m\angle y'$. | Angle Addition Postulate. |
| 4. $m\angle x' + m\angle ABD = 180$. | Supplement Postulate. |
| 5. $m\angle x' + m\angle z + m\angle y' = 180$. | Steps 3 and 4. |
| 6. $m\angle x + m\angle z + m\angle y = 180$. | Steps 1, 2 and 5. |

From this theorem we get some very important corollaries.

### Corollary 9–13.1

Given a correspondence between two triangles. If two pairs of corresponding angles are congruent, then the third pair of corresponding angles are also congruent.

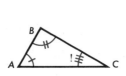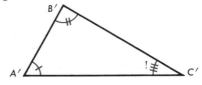

### Corollary 9–13.2

The acute angles of a right triangle are complementary.

### Corollary 9–13.3

For any triangle, the measure of an exterior angle is the sum of the measures of the two remote interior angles.

Obviously, we used the Parallel Postulate to prove Theorem 9–13. This was not just a matter of convenience; in fact, the theorem *cannot* be proved without using the Parallel Postulate. It was discovered in the nineteenth century that there is a kind of geometry (now called *hyperbolic* geometry) in which Euclid's Parallel Postulate fails to hold. Hyperbolic geometry is not only a respectable branch of mathematics but a useful one in physics. In hyperbolic geometry, Theorem 9–13 is not only unprovable but actually *false*. And many other peculiar things happen. For example, in hyperbolic geometry, scale models are impossible, because no two figures ever have exactly the same shape unless they have exactly the same size.

Euclidean geometry is, however, an excellent approximation of physical space; and it is, of course, the kind of geometry that everybody should study first.

## Problem Set 9–4

1. If two angles of a triangle have the following measures, what is the measure of the third angle?

   (a) 64 and 59.        (b) 26 and 134.        (c) $k$ and $2k$.

   (d) $u$ and $v$.        (e) 90 and $n$.        (f) $60 + a$ and $60 - a$.

2. The measures of the angles of a triangle are in the ratio of $1 : 2 : 3$. Find the measure of each angle.

3. The measure of one angle of a triangle is 25 more than that of a second angle, and the measure of the third angle is 9 less than twice the measure of the second angle. Find each measure.

4. On a figure like the one shown, determine the measure of each angle.

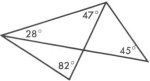

5. Given that $\angle A \cong \angle D$ and $\angle B \cong \angle E$, explain why you can or cannot conclude that
   (a) $\angle C \cong \angle F$.
   (b) $\overline{AB} \cong \overline{DE}$.

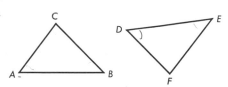

6. The measure of one angle of a triangle is five times that of a second angle, and the measure of an exterior angle at the third vertex is 120. Find the measure of each angle of the triangle.

7. In the figure, $\overline{PR} \perp \overline{RQ}$, $\overline{ST} \perp \overline{RQ}$, and $\overline{SQ} \perp \overline{PS}$. Prove that $\angle P \cong \angle Q$.

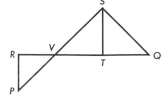

8. In $\triangle ABC$, $\angle ACB$ is a right angle and $\overline{CD} \perp \overline{AB}$. Prove that $\angle A \cong \angle BCD$.

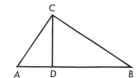

9. Prove: If the bisector of an exterior angle of a triangle is parallel to a side of the triangle, the triangle is isosceles.

10. Prove: If a line containing a vertex of an isosceles triangle is parallel to the base of the triangle, it bisects each exterior angle at the vertex.

11. Why is the Parallel Postulate essential to the proof of Theorem 9–13?

12. Given: The figure.

   Prove: $a + b = x + y$.

   [*Hint:* Draw $\overline{MH}$.]

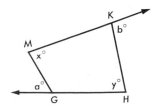

* 13. In $\triangle ABC$, $\angle C$ is a right angle, and $M$ is a point of the hypotenuse such that $AM = CM$. Prove that $M$ is equidistant from $A$, $B$, and $C$.

* **14.** Given: In $\triangle PQR$, $\angle R$ is a right angle,

    $QT = QV$, and $PS = PV$.

    Prove: $x = 45$.

    [*Hint:* Let $m \angle P = a$. Write formulas for other angle measures.]

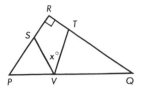

* **15.**

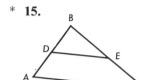 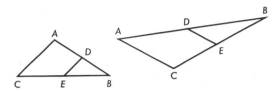

Consider the three triangles shown here. What seems to be true for $\overline{DE}$ and $\overline{AC}$ in each case? How does $DE$ compare with $AC$ in each case? What are $D$ and $E$? Do your answers so far suggest an important property of triangles? Write a conjecture concerning $\overline{DE}$ and $\overline{AC}$ and $DE$ and $AC$. Can you find an example to prove the conjecture false? Can you prove that it is true?

* **16.** In $\triangle ABC$, $AC = BC$. $D$ is a point of $\overleftrightarrow{BC}$ with $C$-$B$-$D$, and $E$ is a point of $\overline{AB}$ with $A$-$E$-$B$ such that $BD = BE$. $\overleftrightarrow{DE}$ intersects $\overline{AC}$ at $F$. Prove that $m \angle CFE = 3(m \angle D)$.

## 9–5.   QUADRILATERALS IN A PLANE

We recall, from Section 5–8, the definition of a quadrilateral.

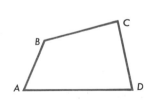 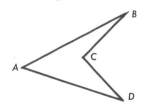

**Definition**

Let $A$, $B$, $C$, and $D$ be four points of the same plane. If no three of these points are collinear, and the segments $\overline{AB}$, $\overline{BC}$, $\overline{CD}$, and $\overline{DA}$ intersect only at their end points, then the union of these four segments is called a *quadrilateral*. The four segments are called its *sides*, and the points $A$, $B$, $C$, and $D$ are called its *vertices*. The angles $\angle DAB$, $\angle ABC$, $\angle BCD$, and $\angle CDA$ are called its *angles*.

The quadrilateral itself is denoted by $\square ABCD$. The angles of $\square ABCD$ may be denoted for short by $\angle A$, $\angle B$, $\angle C$, and $\angle D$.

In the figure above, the quadrilateral on the left is called *convex*, but the figure on the right is not. To see how the difference between these quadrilaterals can be described, we draw the lines that contain the sides of each of them.

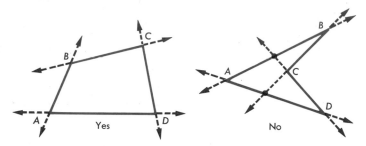

The following definition describes the property of convexity.

## Definition

A quadrilateral is *convex* if no two of its vertices lie on opposite sides of a line containing a side of the quadrilateral.

The figure on the left above satisfies this condition. The one on the right does not. (Why? What do you need to point out, to show that a quadrilateral is *not* convex?)

## Definitions

Two sides of a quadrilateral are *opposite* if they do not intersect. Two of its angles are *opposite* if they do not have a side of the quadrilateral in common. Two sides are *consecutive* if they have a common end point. Two angles are *consecutive* if they have a side of the quadrilateral in common. A *diagonal* of a quadrilateral is a segment joining two nonconsecutive vertices.

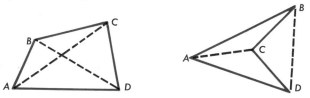

Thus, in $\square ABCD$, the following pairs of sides and angles are opposite: $\overline{AB}$ and $\overline{CD}$; $\overline{BC}$ and $\overline{AD}$; $\angle A$ and $\angle C$; $\angle B$ and $\angle D$. A few of the consecutive pairs are: $\overline{AB}$ and $\overline{BC}$, $\overline{BC}$ and $\overline{CD}$, $\angle D$ and $\angle A$; $\angle A$ and $\angle B$. The diagonals of $\square ABCD$ are $\overline{AC}$ and $\overline{BD}$.

**Definition**

A *trapezoid* is a quadrilateral which has two parallel sides.

Note that this definition allows the possibility that *both* pairs of opposite sides are parallel. If this happens, we have a *parallelogram*.

**Definition**

A *parallelogram* is a quadrilateral in which both pairs of opposite sides are parallel.

The proofs of the following theorems are straightforward.

**Theorem 9–14**

Each diagonal separates a parallelogram into two congruent triangles.

That is, if $\square ABCD$ is a parallelogram, then $\triangle ABC \cong \triangle CDA$.

**Theorem 9–15**

In a parallelogram, any two opposite sides are congruent.

**Corollary 9–15.1**

If two lines are parallel, then all points of each line are equidistant from the other line.

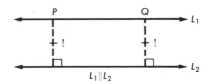

We recall, from Section 7–7, that the distance between a line and an external point is defined to be the length of the perpendicular segment from the point to the line. We sometimes refer to Corollary 9–15.1 by saying that "parallel lines are everywhere equidistant."

**Definition**

The *distance between two parallel lines* is the distance from any point of one to the other.

**Theorem 9–16**

In a parallelogram, any two opposite angles are congruent.

### Theorem 9–17

In a parallelogram, any two consecutive angles are supplementary.

### Theorem 9–18

The diagonals of a parallelogram bisect each other.

Given that $\square ABCD$ is a parallelogram, the preceding theorems enable us to draw various conclusions about its properties. We now consider the *converse* problem: what do we need to know about $\square ABCD$ to conclude that it is a parallelogram?

### Theorem 9–19

Given a quadrilateral in which both pairs of opposite sides are congruent. Then the quadrilateral is a parallelogram.

### Theorem 9–20

If two sides of a quadrilateral are parallel and congruent, then the quadrilateral is a parallelogram.

### Theorem 9–21

If the diagonals of a quadrilateral bisect each other, then the quadrilateral is a parallelogram.

The following theorem is not obvious, and neither is its proof. We shall give the proof in full.

### Theorem 9–22

The segment between the mid-points of two sides of a triangle is parallel to the third side and half as long.

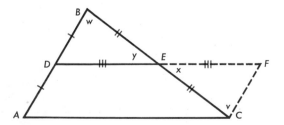

**Restatement.** Given $\triangle ABC$. If $D$ and $E$ are the mid-points of $\overline{AB}$ and $\overline{BC}$, then $\overline{DE} \parallel \overline{AC}$ and $DE = \frac{1}{2}AC$.

**Proof.** Let $F$ be the point, on the ray opposite to $\overrightarrow{ED}$, such that $EF = DE$. We now have the situation described by the marks in the figure. The notation of the proof below is that of the figure.

| STATEMENTS | REASONS |
|---|---|
| 1. $EF = DE$. | Definition of $F$. |
| 2. $EB = EC$. | Definition of mid-point. |
| 3. $\angle x \cong \angle y$. | Vertical Angle Theorem. |
| 4. $\triangle EFC \cong \triangle EDB$. | SAS. |
| 5. $\angle v \cong \angle w$. | Corresponding angles. |
| 6. $\overleftrightarrow{AB} \parallel \overleftrightarrow{CF}$. | AIP (Theorem 9–5). |
| 7. $DB = FC$. | Corresponding sides. |
| 8. $AD = DB$. | Definition of mid-point. |
| 9. $AD = FC$. | Steps 7 and 8. |
| 10. $\square ADFC$ is a parallelogram. | Theorem 9–20. |
| 11. $\overline{DE} \parallel \overline{AC}$. | Definition of a parallelogram. |
| 12. $DE = \frac{1}{2}DF$. | Step 1. |
| 13. $DE = \frac{1}{2}AC$. | Step 12 and Theorem 9–15. |

## Problem Set 9–5

**1.** The measure of one angle of a parallelogram is 45. What are the measures of the other angles?

**2.** Two consecutive angles of a parallelogram have measures $(x + 30)$ and $(2x - 60)$, respectively. Determine the numerical measure of each angle of the parallelogram.

**3.** In the figure, $\square ABCD$ and $\square AKRS$ are parallelograms. What is the relationship of $\angle D$ to $\angle R$? of $\angle R$ to $\angle C$? Prove your answer.

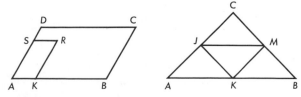

**4.** In the figure $\square AKMJ$ and $\square BMJK$ are parallelograms. If $KJ = KM$, then $\triangle ABC$ is isosceles.

5. Given a parallelogram and one diagonal. Prove that if segments from opposite vertices are perpendicular to the diagonal, the segments are parallel and congruent.

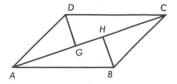

6. $\square PQRS$ is a parallelogram.

$$PW = PS \quad \text{and} \quad RU = RQ.$$

Prove that $\square SWQU$ is a parallelogram.

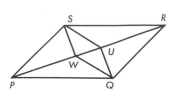

7. Given an isosceles triangle and a point, $P$, of the base, other than its end points. If through $P$ a parallel to each congruent side is drawn, then (1) a parallelogram is formed, and (2) the perimeter of the parallelogram equals the sum of the lengths of the triangle's congruent sides.

8. Is the following statement true? Explain.

A trapezoid is a parallelogram if and only if its diagonals bisect each other.

9. In the plane figure, $\square ABCD$ and $\square BEFC$ are parallelograms. Prove that $\square AEFD$ is a parallelogram.

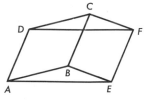

10. In $\triangle PQR$, $A$ and $B$ are mid-points of $\overline{PQ}$ and $\overline{RQ}$, respectively. If $RP = 16$, $m \angle P = 58$, and $m \angle Q = 38$, what are $AB$ and $m \angle ABR$?

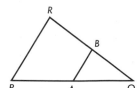

11. Given any triangle, $\triangle ABC$, and the mid-point of each side, $P$, $Q$, and $R$. Prove that the perimeter of $\triangle PQR$ is one-half the perimeter of $\triangle ABC$.

12. (a) Do the diagonals of a quadrilateral always intersect each other?

(b) Sketch a quadrilateral $\square ABCD$ in which $B$ and $D$ are on the same side of diagonal $\overline{AC}$.

13. The diagonals $\overline{AC}$ and $\overline{BD}$ of parallelogram $\square ABCD$ intersect at $M$. Prove that if points $X$ and $Y$ are on opposite sides of the parallelogram such that $\overline{XY}$ contains $M$, then $M$ bisects $\overline{XY}$.

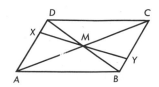

14. State and prove a theorem suggested by the figures given, where *P*, *Q*, *R*, and *S* are mid-points. [*Hint:* Introduce a diagonal of ☐*ABCD*.]

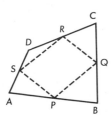 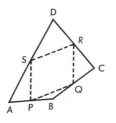 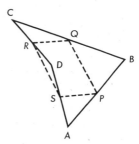

15. Prove: The segments joining the mid-points of opposite sides of any quadrilateral bisect each other. [*Hint:* See Problem 14.]

16. In the figure, ☐*ABCD* is a trapezoid, with *DC* < *AB*. Prove that if *AD* = *BC*, then ∠*A* ≅ ∠*B*. [*Hint:* See Corollary 9–15.1.]

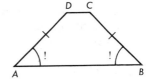

17. A trapezoid having at least one pair of opposite sides congruent is called an *isosceles trapezoid*. Prove that every parallelogram is an isosceles trapezoid. Is the converse true?

18. Prove: If two consecutive angles of a trapezoid are congruent, but not supplementary, the trapezoid is isosceles.

 + 19. Prove that if ☐*ABCD* is a parallelogram, then *D* is in the interior of ∠*ABC*.

*+ 20. Prove that the diagonals of a parallelogram intersect each other. [*Hint:* Use Problem 19 above and Problem 7 of Problem Set 6–8.]

## 9–6.   RHOMBUS, RECTANGLE, AND SQUARE

### Definitions

A *rhombus* is a parallelogram all of whose sides are congruent.

A *rectangle* is a parallelogram all of whose angles are right angles.

A *square* is a rectangle all of whose sides are congruent.

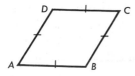 

As before, we leave the proofs of the following theorems to you.

### Theorem 9–23

If a parallelogram has one right angle, then it has four right angles, and the parallelogram is a rectangle.

### Theorem 9–24

In a rhombus, the diagonals are perpendicular to one another.

[*Hint:* See Corollary 6–2.1.]

### Theorem 9–25

If the diagonals of a quadrilateral bisect each other and are perpendicular, then the quadrilateral is a rhombus.

## Problem Set 9–6

1. For each of the statements below, indicate whether it is true or false.
   (a) A rectangle is a trapezoid.          (b) A square is a parallelogram.
   (c) A rhombus is a square.               (d) A rectangle is a square.
   (e) A square is a rectangle.             (f)  A square is a rhombus.
   (g) The diagonals of a rhombus bisect each other.
   (h) The diagonals of a rectangle are perpendicular to each other.
   (i)  The diagonals of a square are perpendicular and bisect each other.
   (j)  If the diagonals of a quadrilateral are perpendicular, the quadrilateral is a rhombus.

2. Prove: The diagonals of a rectangle are congruent.

3. Prove: The diagonals of a rhombus bisect the angles of the rhombus.

4. Given: $\triangle ABC$ with $AC = BC$; $P$, $Q$, and $R$ are mid-points.
   Prove: $\square PQCR$ is a rhombus.

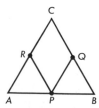
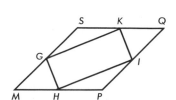

5. Given: Rhombus $\square MPQS$. $G$, $H$, $I$, and $K$ are mid-points.
   Prove: $\square GHIK$ is a rectangle.

6. For which of the four quadrilaterals—parallelogram, rectangle, rhombus, square—can each of the following properties be proved?

(a) The diagonals bisect each other.

(b) The diagonals are congruent.

(c) Consecutive angles are congruent.

(d) The diagonals bisect the angles of the quadrilateral.

(e) The diagonals are perpendicular.

(f) Opposite angles are congruent.

(g) The diagonals are congruent and perpendicular.

7. Would the following conditions for a quadrilateral be sufficient to prove that it is a parallelogram? a rectangle? a rhombus? a square? Consider each item separately.

(a) It has two pairs of parallel sides.

(b) Three of its angles are right angles.

(c) It is equilateral.

(d) Its diagonals are congruent and perpendicular.

(e) Each pair of consecutive angles is supplementary.

(f) Two sides are parallel.

(g) Its diagonals bisect each other.

(h) Its diagonals are congruent, are perpendicular, and bisect each other.

\* 8. Prove: If in $\square ABCD$, $\angle A \cong \angle C$ and $\angle B \cong \angle D$, then $\square ABCD$ is a parallelogram. [*Hint:* Introduce a diagonal. Use Theorem 9–13 and Problem 7 of Problem Set 9–1.]

\* 9. Given parallelogram $\square ABCD$ with $AD > AB$. The bisector of $\angle A$ intersects $\overline{BC}$ at $G$, and the bisector of $\angle B$ intersects $\overline{AD}$ at $H$. Prove that $\square ABGH$ is a rhombus.

10. Given: $\square PQRS$ is a square. $J$, $K$, $L$, $M$ separate the sides into segments, as in the figure, of lengths $a$ and $b$.

Prove: $\square JKLM$ is a square.

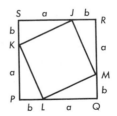

\* 11. A quadrilateral in which exactly one diagonal is the perpendicular bisector of the other diagonal is called a *kite*. Prove that a kite has two pairs of congruent sides, but that its opposite sides are not congruent.

\*+ 12. In the convex quadrilateral $\square ABCD$, $\overline{AD}$ is the shortest side and $\overline{BC}$ is the longest side. Prove that $\angle D > \angle B$. [*Hint:* Draw a diagonal.] Is this theorem true if $\square ABCD$ is not required to be convex?

## 9–7.  SOME THEOREMS ON RIGHT TRIANGLES

Our knowledge of quadrilaterals gives us some information about right triangles.

**Theorem 9–26**

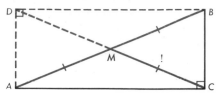

The median to the hypotenuse of a right triangle is half as long as the hypotenuse.

**Proof.**  Given $\triangle ABC$, with $\angle C$ a right angle and $M$ the mid-point of $\overline{AB}$.  Take a point $D$ on $\overrightarrow{CM}$ such that $\square ADBC$ is a parallelogram. (How do you find such a point?)  Then $\square ADBC$ is a rectangle. (Why?) Then $CD = AB$.  (Why?)  Therefore $CM = \frac{1}{2}AB$, which is what we wanted.

The theorem below tells us something about the shapes of certain special triangles.

**Theorem 9–27.**  The 30-60-90 Triangle Theorem

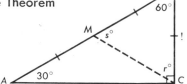

If an acute angle of a right triangle has measure 30, then the opposite side is half as long as the hypotenuse.

**Proof.**  Given $\triangle ABC$, with a right angle at $C$ and with $m\angle A = 30$. Let $M$ be the mid-point of the hypotenuse $\overline{AB}$.  Then by Theorem 9–26 we know that

$$AM = MB = MC,$$

as indicated in the figure.

Now $m\angle B = 60$.  (Why?)  Therefore $r = 60$, by the Isosceles Triangle Theorem.

But

$$r + s + 60 = 180.$$

Therefore $s = 60$, and $\triangle MBC$ is equiangular.  Therefore $\triangle MBC$ is equilateral.  Therefore

$$BC = MC = \frac{1}{2}AB,$$

which was to be proved.

We sometimes refer to this theorem by saying that "in a 30-60-90 triangle, the hypotenuse is twice as long as the shorter leg."

The converse of this theorem is also true.

**Theorem 9–28**

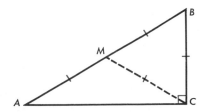

If one leg of a right triangle is half as long as the hypotenuse, then the opposite angle has measure 30.

**Proof.** Given $\triangle ABC$, with a right angle at $C$, and $BC = \frac{1}{2}AB$. Let $M$ be the mid-point of $\overline{AB}$. Then $AM = MB = BC$. By Theorem 9–26, $MC = MB$. (We have now justified all the marks in the figure.)

Since $\triangle MBC$ is equilateral, it is equiangular. Therefore $m \angle B = 60$. By Corollary 9–13.2, $m \angle A = 30$, which was to be proved.

## Problem Set 9–7

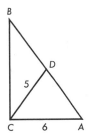

1. In $\triangle ABC$, $\angle C$ is a right angle, $AC = 6$, and the length of median $\overline{CD}$ is 5. What is $AB$?

2. In the figure, $RQ = 2RP$. Then $m \angle R = $ ?

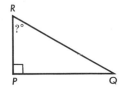

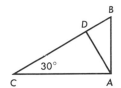

3. In the figure, $\overline{AC} \perp \overline{AB}$ and $\overline{AD} \perp \overline{BC}$. If $BC = 12$, find $DB$.

4. In an equilateral triangle $\triangle GHK$, the altitude $\overline{GM}$ has length 9. Through $M$, perpendiculars are drawn to the other two sides. Prove that these perpendicular segments are congruent, and find their length.

5. Prove the converse of Theorem 9–26:

In a triangle, if a median is half as long as the side which it bisects, then the triangle is a right triangle and the side is its hypotenuse.

Given: $\triangle ABC$, median $\overline{AD}$, $AD = \frac{1}{2}BC$.

Prove: $\triangle ABC$ is a right triangle, and $\overline{BC}$ is its hypotenuse.

[*Hint:* Prove $x + y = 90$.]

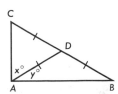

6. In the figure, $F$ is the mid-point of $\overline{AE}$, and $\angle ABE$, $\angle ACE$, and $\angle ADE$ are right angles. Prove that $F$ is equidistant from $A$, $B$, $C$, $D$, and $E$.

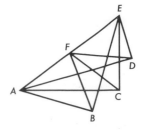

7. $\triangle PQR$ is isosceles, with $PR = QR = a$. $L$ is any line through $R$, but not containing $P$ or $Q$. $X$ and $Y$ are two points of $L$ at distance $a$ from $R$. Prove that $\overline{XP} \perp \overline{YP}$ and $\overline{XQ} \perp \overline{YQ}$.

8. In any right triangle, the altitude to the hypotenuse separates the hypotenuse into two segments. Prove that in a 30-60-90 triangle, the lengths of these segments are in the ratio 1 : 3.

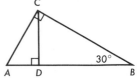

9. Given an equilateral triangle, $\triangle ABC$. On the ray opposite to $\overrightarrow{BA}$, take $D$ such that $BD = AC$. Prove that $m\angle BCD = 30$.

10. In the figure, $\triangle ABC$ is equilateral, $\overline{AD} \perp E$, and $P$ and $Q$ are the mid-points of $\overline{AC}$ and $\overline{AB}$, respectively. Prove that $\triangle PDQ$ is equilateral.

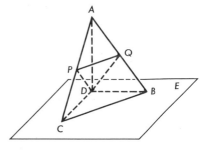

## 9–8.  TRANSVERSALS TO MANY PARALLEL LINES

### Definitions

If a transversal intersects two lines $L_1$, $L_2$ in points $A$ and $B$, then we say that $L_1$ and $L_2$ *intercept* the segment $\overline{AB}$ on the transversal.

Suppose that we have given three lines $L_1$, $L_2$, $L_3$ and a transversal intersecting them in points $A$, $B$, and $C$. If $AB = BC$, then we say that the three lines *intercept congruent segments* on the transversal.

We shall show that if three parallel lines intercept congruent segments on one transversal, then they intercept congruent segments on any other transversal. Our first step is to prove the following theorem.

### Theorem 9–29

If three parallel lines intercept congruent segments on one transversal $T$, then they intercept congruent segments on every transversal $T'$ which is parallel to $T$.

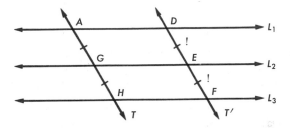

**Proof.** First we observe that $\square AGED$ and $\square GHFE$ are parallelograms. (Why?) We have given $AG = GH$. By Theorem 9–15, $AG = DE$ and $GH = EF$. Therefore $DE = EF$.

We can now prove the theorem in the general case.

### Theorem 9–30

If three parallel lines intercept congruent segments on one transversal, then they intercept congruent segments on any other transversal.

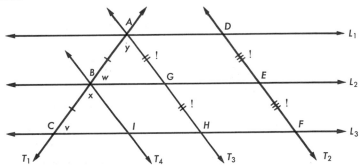

**Proof.** Let $L_1$, $L_2$ and $L_3$ be the three parallel lines, and let $T_1$ and $T_2$ be the two transversals. In the notation of the figure, we have given $AB = BC$, and we want to prove that $DE = EF$. We already know that this holds if $T_1 \parallel T_2$. We may therefore assume that $T_1$ and $T_2$ are *not* parallel.

Let $T_3$ be the parallel to $T_2$ through $A$, and let $T_4$ be the parallel to $T_2$ through $B$. (Remember Theorem 9–11.)

| STATEMENTS | REASONS |
|---|---|
| 1. $AB = BC$. | Given. |
| 2. $\angle x \cong \angle y$. | Theorem 9–9. |
| 3. $\angle v \cong \angle w$. | Theorem 9–9. |
| 4. $\triangle ABG \cong \triangle BCI$. | ASA. |
| 5. $AG = BI$. | Corresponding sides. |
| 6. $BI = GH$. | Opposite sides of a parallelogram are congruent. |
| 7. $AG = GH$. | Steps 5 and 6. |
| 8. $DE = EF$. | Theorem 9–29. |

For any number of parallel lines, the same conclusion holds.

### Corollary 9–30.1

If three or more parallel lines intercept congruent segments on one transversal, then they intercept congruent segments on any other transversal.

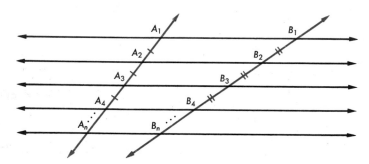

That is, given that

$$A_1A_2 = A_2A_3 = A_3A_4 = \cdots,$$

it follows that

$$B_1B_2 = B_2B_3 = B_3B_4 = \cdots,$$

and so on. This follows by repeated applications of the theorem that we have just proved.

## Problem Set 9–8

**1.** Given: $AB = BC$,

$$\overrightarrow{AP} \parallel \overrightarrow{BQ} \parallel \overrightarrow{CR},$$

$$\overrightarrow{PX} \parallel \overrightarrow{QY} \parallel \overrightarrow{RZ}.$$

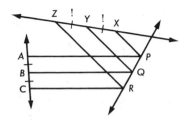

Prove: $XY = YZ$.

Must $\overleftrightarrow{AC}$ and $\overleftrightarrow{XZ}$ be coplanar for the proof to hold?

**2.** Prove the following theorem.

If a line bisects one side of a triangle and is parallel to a second side, then it bisects the third side.

**3.** In the figure,

$$\overleftrightarrow{DE} \parallel \overleftrightarrow{AB}, \qquad \overleftrightarrow{EF} \parallel \overleftrightarrow{AC},$$

and $D$ is the mid-point of $\overline{AC}$. Prove that

$$\triangle CDE \cong \triangle EFB.$$

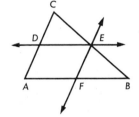

**4.** If a transversal cuts parallels $L_1$ and $L_2$ at $D$ and $A$, and another transversal cuts $L_1$ and $L_2$ at $C$ and $B$, then $\square ABCD$ is a trapezoid. Given that $L_3 \parallel L_1$, why is $L_3$ also parallel to $L_2$? If $L_3$ contains $E$, the mid-point of $\overline{AD}$, why does $L_3$ contain $F$, the mid-point of $\overline{BC}$? Does $L_3$ contain $\overline{EF}$? Why? The segment $\overline{EF}$ is called the *median* of trapezoid $\square ABCD$, and the parallel sides $\overline{AB}$ and $\overline{CD}$ are called *bases* of the trapezoid.

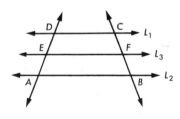

(a) Prove that the median of a trapezoid bisects both diagonals.

(b) Prove that the length of the median of a trapezoid is one-half the sum of the lengths of the bases; that is, prove that

$$EF = \tfrac{1}{2}(AB + CD).$$

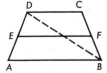

[*Hint:* Use one diagonal and Theorem 9–22.]

**5.** $\square ABCD$ is a trapezoid with $\overline{AB} \parallel \overline{DC}$. $\overline{EF}$ is the median (see Problem 4).

(a) If $AB = 12$ and $DC = 7$, then $EF = $ ?

(b) If $AB = 14$ and $DC = 14$, then $EF = $ ?

(c) If $DC = 6$ and $EF = 14$, then $AB = $ ?

(d) If $AB = 27$ and $EF = 18$, then $DC = $ ?

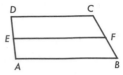

**6.** Prove that in a parallelogram, the two segments joining a pair of opposite vertices to the mid-points of a pair of opposite sides trisect a diagonal.

Given: $\square ABCD$ is a parallelogram.

   $P$ and $Q$ are mid-points.

Prove: $AR = RS = SC$.

[*Hint:* Is $\overline{DQ}$ parallel to $\overline{RB}$?]

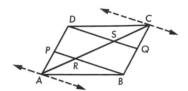

**+ 7.** In Problem 6, if $K$ is the mid-point of $\overline{DC}$ and $M$ is the mid-point of $\overline{AB}$, will $\overline{BK}$ and $\overline{DM}$ contain the points $S$ and $R$? Why?

**+ 8.** In Problem 6, if $\overrightarrow{DB}$ and $\overrightarrow{AC}$ intersect at $E$, prove that $ES = \frac{1}{6}AC$.

**\*+ 9.** In the figure, the parallel lines are equally spaced and divide $\overline{AC}$ into 7 congruent segments. Given $AB = 2$ and $BC = 1\frac{1}{2}$, 7 is the smallest number of congruent segments into which any set of parallels will divide $\overline{AC}$, if the parallels are to include $\overleftrightarrow{AG}$, $\overleftrightarrow{BH}$, and $\overleftrightarrow{CK}$. Under these same conditions, what will be the smallest number of congruent segments if

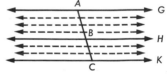

(a) $AB = 4$,    $BC = 1$?

(b) $AB = 3.5$,    $BC = 1$?

(c) $AB = 15$,    $BC = 3$?

(d) $AB = 1.3$,    $BC = 0.8$?

(e) $AB = 1.414$,    $BC = 1$?

(f) $AB = \sqrt{2}$,    $BC = 1$?

(g) $AB = \sqrt{3}$,    $BC = 2\sqrt{3}$?

(h) $AB = \sqrt{2}$,    $BC = \sqrt{3}$?

## HONORS PROBLEM

Use the figure as a hint to help you prove the following theorem.

The medians of a triangle intersect in a common point whose distance from any vertex is two-thirds the length of the median from that vertex.

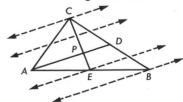

## 9–9.  HOW ERATOSTHENES MEASURED THE EARTH

The circumference of the earth, at the equator, is about 24,900 miles. In the fifteenth century, people thought that it was much smaller than this.  Hence, when Columbus set out for India and landed on one of the Bahama Islands, he thought that he was already in India.  Thus his margin of error was greater than the width of the United States, plus that of the Pacific Ocean.

In the third century B.C., however, the Greeks knew better.  At that time a Greek mathematician, Eratosthenes, measured the circumference of the earth, and his result was in error by only one or two percent. He devised the following method.

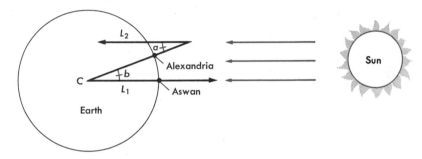

It was observed that at Aswan (then called Syene) on the Nile, at noon on the summer solstice, the sun was exactly overhead.  That is, at noon of this particular day, a vertical pole cast no shadow at all, and the bottom of a deep well was completely lit up.

In the figure, $C$ is the center of the earth.  At noon on the summer solstice, in Alexandria, Eratosthenes measured the angle marked $\angle a$ on the figure, that is, the angle between a vertical pole and the ray from the top of the pole through the tip of its shadow.  He found that this was an angle of about 7° 12′, or about $\frac{1}{50}$ of a complete circumference.

Now the sun's rays, observed on earth, are very close to being parallel.  Assuming that they are actually parallel, it follows that when the lines $L_1$ and $L_2$ in the figure are cut by a transversal, alternate interior angles are congruent.  Therefore $\angle a \cong \angle b$.  Therefore the distance from Aswan to Alexandria must be about $\frac{1}{50}$ of the circumference of the earth.

The distance from Aswan to Alexandria was known to be about 5000 Greek stadia.  (A *stadium* was an ancient unit of distance.) Eratosthenes concluded that the circumference of the earth must be about 250,000 stadia.  Converting to miles, according to what ancient sources tell us about the length of a stadium, we obtain 24,662 miles.

Thus Eratosthenes' error was well under two percent.    Later, he changed his estimate to an even closer one, 252,000 stadia, but nobody seems to know why he made the change.    On the basis of the evidence, some historians believe that he was not only very clever and careful, but also very lucky.

From the earliest times, geometry has played a leading part in applied mathematics.    The Egyptians needed it badly, because the Nile overflowed every year, wiped out small landmarks, and thus created difficult surveying problems.    Hence the word *geometry*, from two Greek words meaning *earth* and *measurement*.    Later it turned out that "geometry" could be used not just to measure things *on* the earth, but literally to measure the *earth* itself.    This illustrates a general rule: when good mathematics has been developed for one reason, it usually turns out to be good for other, unexpected reasons.

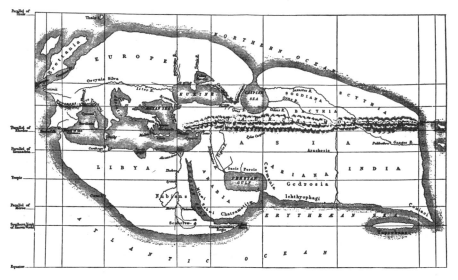

ERATOSTHENES (276–194 B.C.)

Very little is known about the work of Eratosthenes.    We have some fragments of his books, in the form of quotations by other ancient authors, but none of his own books have survived.    The records indicate, however, that he wrote on nearly everything: geometry, astronomy, the theory of numbers, history, and comedy.    He was also a poet.    The Greeks called him *Beta* (the second letter of their alphabet) on the ground that he was the second best in everything, although not the very best in any one thing.

His achievement in measuring the earth, however, was so spectacular that it was fully reported by others, and rightly credited to him.

The illustration shows a map of the world based on the ideas of Eratosthenes.

# Chapter Review

## Set A

1. Indicate whether each statement is true or false.

    (a) In a plane, if a line is parallel to one of two parallels, it is parallel to the other.

    (b) The diagonals of a rhombus bisect the angles of the rhombus.

    (c) If the median to the hypotenuse of a right triangle is 7 in. long, the hypotenuse is 14 in. long.

    (d) A parallelogram is a trapezoid.

    (e) If two lines are cut by a transversal, the corresponding angles are congruent.

    (f) Either diagonal of a parallelogram forms, with the sides, two congruent triangles.

    (g) The diagonals of a rhombus are congruent.

    (h) If one leg of a 30-60-90 triangle is 8 in. long, the hypotenuse is 16 in. long.

    (i) Two lines are either parallel or intersecting.

    (j) In a plane, if a line intersects one of two parallel lines, it intersects the other.

2. Complete each statement.

    (a) If two parallel lines are cut by a transversal, the interior angles on the same side of the transversal are _____  _____.

    (b) If two angles of a triangle are congruent to two angles of another triangle, then _____.

    (c) The acute angles of a right triangle are _____.

    (d) The hypotenuse of a 30-60-90 triangle is of length 13.  The leg opposite the _____ angle is congruent to the _____ to the hypotenuse, and the length of each is _____.

    (e) If three or more parallels intercept _____ segments on one transversal, then _____.

    (f) The Parallel Postulate establishes the _____ of a line which contains a point and which is _____ to a line which does not contain the point.

3. For each example, select the one choice which makes the statement true.

    (a) If the diagonals of a quadrilateral bisect each other, the quadrilateral is a

      (i) rhombus,    (ii) square,    (iii) parallelogram,    (iv) rectangle.

   (b) The figure formed by joining the consecutive mid-points of the sides
       of any quadrilateral is
       (i) a rectangle,                    (ii) a parallelogram,
       (iii) a rhombus,                    (iv) none of these.
   (c) The bisectors of the opposite angles of a nonrhombic parallelogram
       are
       (i) parallel,    (ii) collinear,    (iii) perpendicular,    (iv) skew.
   (d) The bisectors of the interior angles on the same side of a transversal
       to two parallel lines are
       (i) parallel,                              (ii) perpendicular,
       (iii) intersecting, but not perpendicular,    (iv) skew.

4. Would the following conditions about a quadrilateral be sufficient to
   prove it a trapezoid? a parallelogram? a rectangle? a rhombus? a square?
   Consider each item separately.
   (a) All four sides are congruent.    (b) Two sides are parallel.
   (c) Two sides are congruent.         (d) Its diagonals bisect each other.
   (e) Its diagonals are congruent and bisect each other.
   (f) It is equiangular.
   (g) Its diagonals are congruent and perpendicular.
   (h) It is equilateral and equiangular.
   (i) Every two opposite angles are congruent.
   (j) Each diagonal bisects two of its angles.

5. Indicate, using the letter A, S, or N, whether each statement is true in ALL
   cases, true in SOME cases and false in others, or NOT true in any case.
   (a) Line segments in the same plane which do not intersect are parallel.
   (b) If two lines are cut by a transversal, the rays bisecting a pair of
       alternate interior angles are parallel.
   (c) The diagonals of a rhombus bisect each other.
   (d) The diagonals of a quadrilateral are parallel.
   (e) The opposite angles of a parallelogram are supplementary.
   (f) A square is a rectangle.
   (g) If a diagonal of a quadrilateral forms with the sides two congruent
       triangles, the quadrilateral is a parallelogram.
   (h) If a median of a triangle is half as long as the side it bisects, the
       triangle is a right triangle.
   (i) If two opposite sides of a quadrilateral are parallel and the other
       two sides are congruent, the quadrilateral is a parallelogram.
   (j) If two opposite angles of a quadrilateral are right angles, the quad-
       rilateral is a rectangle.

## Set B

1. Given the figure with $D$ and $E$ the mid-points of $\overline{AB}$ and $\overline{AC}$.

   (a) If $m\angle A = 33$ and $m\angle C = 45$, what are $m\angle CBF$ and $m\angle CED$?

   (b) If $BC = 6$, then $DE = $ ?

   (c) $\square DBCE$ is a _____.

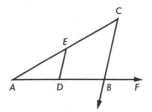

2. If in $\triangle ABC$, $AB = 12$, $BC = 9$, and $AC = 13$, and $P$, $Q$, and $R$ are the mid-points of the sides, what is the perimeter of $\triangle PQR$?

3. Given: $\square GHKM$ is a parallelogram and

$$MQ = HP.$$

   Prove: $\overline{GK}$ and $\overline{PQ}$ bisect each other.

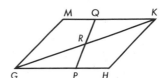

4. In the figure, $\square DEBF$ is a parallelogram and $AE = CF$. Prove that $\square ABCD$ is a parallelogram.

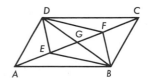

5. Prove: If the bisectors of two consecutive angles of a parallelogram intersect, they are perpendicular.

6. Given $\overleftrightarrow{AC} \parallel \overleftrightarrow{BD}$. The bisectors of $\angle CAB$ and $\angle DBA$ intersect at $P$, and

$$AB = 2PB.$$

   Find $x$ and $y$.

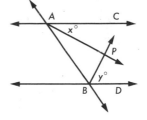

7. Why is the following reasoning invalid?
   By Theorem 9–11 we know that in a plane, two lines parallel to the same line are parallel to each other. Therefore, if $\overleftrightarrow{AP} \parallel L$ and $\overleftrightarrow{BP} \parallel L$ and $\overleftrightarrow{AP}$, $\overleftrightarrow{BP}$, and $L$ are coplanar, then $\overleftrightarrow{AP} \parallel \overleftrightarrow{BP}$. This proves that two intersecting lines may, in fact, be parallel!

8. In a figure like the one given here, determine the measure of each angle.

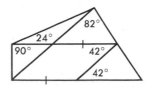

9. Prove: In a plane, if a line is perpendicular to one of two intersecting lines, it is not perpendicular to the other line.

10. Given: $\angle a \cong \angle b$,

    $\qquad \angle p \cong \angle q$.

    Prove: $\angle x$ is a right angle.

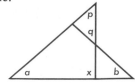

11. In $\triangle MPK$, $\angle K$ is a right angle and $m \angle P = 30$. If $\overline{KH} \perp \overline{MP}$, $\overline{HR} \perp \overline{MK}$, $\overline{RQ} \perp \overline{MP}$, and $MP = 80$, find $MQ$.

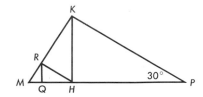

12. Prove: If a trapezoid has two nonparallel sides each congruent to one of the parallel sides, then the diagonals bisect the angles at the other parallel side.

13. When a beam of light is reflected from a smooth surface, the angle formed by the incoming beam with the surface is congruent to the angle formed by the reflected beam and the surface.
    In the figure, $m \angle ABC = 90$, $m \angle BCD = 75$, and the beam of light makes an angle of 35° with $\overrightarrow{RA}$. Copy the figure and complete the path of the light beam as it reflects from $\overrightarrow{AB}$, from $\overrightarrow{BC}$, from $\overrightarrow{DC}$, and from $\overrightarrow{AB}$ again. At what angle does the beam reflect from $\overrightarrow{AB}$ the second time?

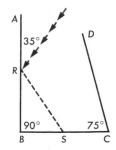

14. Prove either the truth or falsity of the following statement.

    If a quadrilateral has one pair of parallel sides and one pair of congruent sides, the quadrilateral is a parallelogram.

15. In the figure, $\overline{ED} \parallel \overline{BC}$, $ED = BC$, and $P$, $Q$, and $R$ are mid-points. Prove that $\overline{QD}$ bisects $\overline{PR}$. [*Hint:* Introduce $\overline{PQ}$ and $\overline{EB}$.]

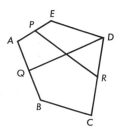

* **16.** Prove either the truth or falsity of this statement.

    If the diagonals of a quadrilateral are congruent and perpendicular, the quadrilateral is a square.

* **17.** Prove either the truth or falsity of the following statement.

    If the diagonals of a quadrilateral are congruent and bisect each other, the quadrilateral is a rectangle.

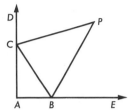

* **18.** In the figure, $\overrightarrow{AC} \perp \overrightarrow{AE}$, and the bisectors of $\angle DCB$ and $\angle EBC$ intersect at $P$.    Find $m \angle P$ and show your reasoning.

* **19.** Prove: If each diagonal of a quadrilateral bisects two angles of the quadrilateral, the quadrilateral is a rhombus.

* **20.** The diagonals of $\square ABCD$ are perpendicular at $M$, and $P$, $Q$, $R$, $S$ are mid-points of the sides.  Prove that twice the sum $MP + MQ + MR + MS$ equals the perimeter of $\square ABCD$.

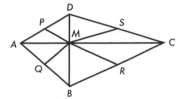

* **21.** Prove: The sum of the lengths of the perpendiculars from any point in the base of an isosceles triangle to the congruent sides equals the altitude to either congruent side. [*Hint:* Let a parallel to $\overline{AC}$ through $P$ meet $\overline{BT}$ at $Q$.  Show $RP + PS = BT$.]

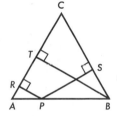

* **22.** Let $\triangle MPQ$ be isosceles, with $MP = MQ$.  Through any point $A$ between $M$ and $Q$ draw a perpendicular to $\overrightarrow{PQ}$, meeting $\overrightarrow{PQ}$ at $B$ and meeting $\overrightarrow{PM}$ at $C$.  Prove that $\triangle MCA$ is isosceles.

* **23.** In any triangle $\triangle ABC$, a line through $A$ is perpendicular to the bisector of $\angle B$ at $K$.  Another line through $K$ is parallel to $\overline{BC}$ and intersects $\overrightarrow{AB}$ at $M$.  Prove that $M$ is the mid-point of $\overline{AB}$.  Can you also prove that $\overleftrightarrow{MK}$ bisects $\overline{AC}$?

* **24.** $\triangle ABC$ is any triangle with $G$ and $H$ the mid-points of $\overline{AC}$ and $\overline{BC}$.  On the ray opposite to $\overrightarrow{HA}$ take $R$ such that $HR = HA$.  Similarly, on the ray opposite to $\overrightarrow{GB}$ take $S$ such that $GS = GB$. Prove that $R$, $C$, and $S$ are collinear and that $CR = CS$.

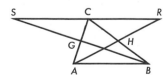

# 10 | Parallel Lines and Planes

## 10–1. BASIC FACTS ABOUT PARALLEL PLANES

### Definition

Two planes, or a plane and a line, are *parallel* if they do not intersect.

If the planes $E_1$ and $E_2$ are parallel, we write $E_1 \parallel E_2$. If the line $L$ and the plane $E$ are parallel, we write $L \parallel E$ or $E \parallel L$.

As we shall see, parallels in space behave in much the same way as parallel lines in a plane. There are, however, important differences. For one thing, there is no such thing as a pair of skew planes: every two planes in space either intersect or are parallel. Furthermore, if two lines lie in parallel planes, it does not follow that the lines are parallel. (See the figure on the left below.) Also, if two lines are parallel, we can always find two planes containing them which are not parallel. (See the figure on the right below.)

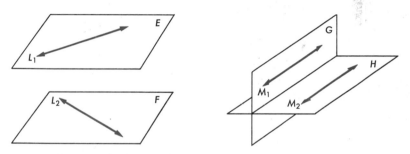

The following theorem describes a common situation in which parallel planes and parallel lines occur in the same figure.

### Theorem 10–1

If a plane intersects two parallel planes, then it intersects them in two parallel lines.

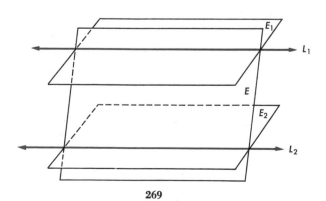

**Proof.**    Given a plane $E$, intersecting two parallel planes $E_1$ and $E_2$. By Postulate 8 (p. 60), we have

(1)    $E$ intersects $E_1$ in a line $L_1$, and

(2)    $E$ intersects $E_2$ in a line $L_2$.

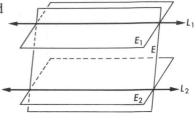

Obviously

(3)    $L_1$ and $L_2$ are coplanar

(because both of them lie in $E$).    And

(4)    $L_1$ and $L_2$ have no point in common

(because $E_1$ and $E_2$ have no point in common).    Statements (3) and (4) tell us that

(5)    $L_1 \parallel L_2$.


**Theorem 10–2**

If a line is perpendicular to one of two parallel planes it is perpendicular to the other.


**Proof.**    We have given $E_2 \parallel E_1$ and $L \perp E_1$.    Let $A$ be any point which lies in $E_2$ but not on $L$.    Then

(1)    $L$ and $A$ lie in a plane $E$. (Why?)

(2)    $E$ intersects $E_1$ and $E_2$ in lines $L_1$ and $L_2$.  (Why?)

(3)    $L_1 \parallel L_2$   (by Theorem 10–1).

(4)    $L \perp L_1$   (because $L \perp E_1$).

(5)    $L \perp L_2$   (by Theorem 9–12).

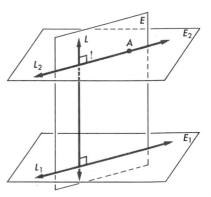

Thus we have a line in $E_2$ which is perpendicular to $L$.   Repeating the whole process, starting with another point $B$, we get another line in $E_2$, perpendicular to $L$.   We now have $L \perp E_2$, by Theorem 8–2.

The following theorem is analogous to Theorem 9–2.

### Theorem 10–3

Two planes perpendicular to the same line are parallel.

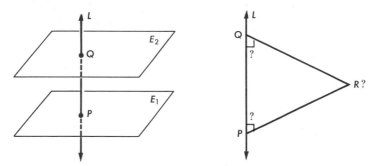

**Proof.**  We have given $E_1 \perp L$ at $P$ and $E_2 \perp L$ at $Q$. We want to show that $E_1 \parallel E_2$. If this is not true, then $E_1$ intersects $E_2$ in at least one point, $R$.

Now $\overleftrightarrow{RP} \perp L$ and $\overleftrightarrow{RQ} \perp L$, because $L$ is perpendicular to every line in $E_1$ through $P$ and also to every line in $E_2$ through $Q$. This gives us two perpendiculars from $R$ to $L$, which is impossible. (See Theorem 6–4.)   Therefore $E_1$ and $E_2$ are parallel.

### Corollary 10–3.1

If each of two planes is parallel to a third plane, they are parallel to each other.

(You should be able to follow the proof without a figure.  Try it!)

**Proof.**  Given $E_1 \parallel E_3$, $E_2 \parallel E_3$.  Let $L$ be a line perpendicular to $E_3$.  Then

   (1)  $L \perp E_1$  (by Theorem 10–2).
   (2)  $L \perp E_2$  (by Theorem 10–2).
   (3)  $E_1 \parallel E_2$  (by Theorem 10–3).

### Theorem 10–4

Two lines perpendicular to the same plane are parallel.

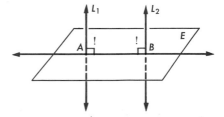

**Proof.**  Given $L_1 \perp E$ at $A$ and $L_2 \perp E$ at $B$. By Theorem 8–7, $L_1$ and $L_2$ are coplanar.  Since $L_1 \perp E, L_1 \perp \overleftrightarrow{AB}$. Since $L_2 \perp E, L_2 \perp \overleftrightarrow{AB}$. By Theorem 9–2, $L_1 \parallel L_2$.

### Corollary 10–4.1

A plane perpendicular to one of two parallel lines is perpendicular to the other.

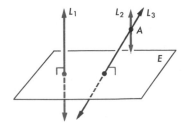

**Proof.** Given $L_1 \parallel L_2$ and $L_1 \perp E$. Let $L_3$ be a line through any point $A$ of $L_2$, perpendicular to $E$. $L_3$ exists by Theorem 8–9. Then by Theorem 10–4, $L_1 \parallel L_3$. By the Parallel Postulate, $L_3 = L_2$. That is, $L_3$ and $L_2$ must be the same line. Since $L_3 \perp E$, we have $L_2 \perp E$.

### Corollary 10–4.2

If each of two lines is parallel to a third line, then they are parallel to each other.

**Proof.** Given that $L_1 \parallel L_3$ and $L_2 \parallel L_3$. We want to show that $L_1 \parallel L_2$.

Let $E$ be a plane perpendicular to $L_3$. By the preceding corollary, $L_1 \perp E$ and $L_2 \perp E$. By Theorem 10–4, $L_1 \parallel L_2$.

### Theorem 10–5

Parallel planes are everywhere equidistant.

**Restatement.** If $E_1 \parallel E_2$, then all points of $E_1$ are equidistant from $E_2$.

We recall that the distance between a point $P$ and a plane $E$ is the length of the perpendicular segment from $P$ to $E$.

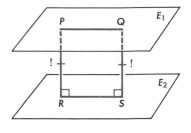

**Proof.** Let $P$ and $Q$ be any two points of $E_1$, and let $\overline{PR}$ and $\overline{QS}$ be the perpendicular segments from $P$ and $Q$ to $E_2$. Then

(1) $\overleftrightarrow{PR} \parallel \overleftrightarrow{QS}$  (by Theorem 10–4).

(2) $P, Q, R,$ and $S$ are coplanar, because these points lie on two parallel lines.

(3) $\overleftrightarrow{PQ} \parallel \overleftrightarrow{RS}$  (by Theorem 10–1).

(4) $\square PQSR$ is a parallelogram, by (1), (2), and (3).

(5) $PR = QS$, because opposite sides of a parallelogram are congruent.

We know by Theorem 10–2 that the segments from $E_1$, perpendicular to $E_2$, are precisely the segments from $E_2$, perpendicular to $E_1$. We therefore know more than our restatement actually says; that is, we know the following: *If two planes are parallel, then all perpendicular segments from one of the planes to the other have the same length.* Hereafter, we shall interpret Theorem 10–5 to mean this.

Note that $\square PQSR$ is, in fact, a rectangle. But this fact is not needed in the proof.

## Problem Set 10–1

1. Given: Planes $E$ and $F$ are parallel,

    $E$ contains $\overleftrightarrow{AB}$,  $F$ contains $\overleftrightarrow{CD}$,

    $\overline{AC} \perp F$,   and   $\overline{BD} \perp F$.

    Prove: $\overline{AD}$ and $\overline{BC}$ bisect each other.

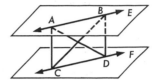

2. If plane $K \perp L$ at $P$ and plane $M \perp L$ at $T$, what can you conclude about $K$ and $M$? Why?

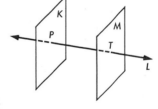

3. Prove the following statement true or false.

    If $E$ and $F$ are parallel planes and $E$ contains line $L_1$ and $F$ contains line $L_2$, then $L_1 \parallel L_2$.

4. Plane $G$ contains points $A$, $B$, $C$, and plane $H$ contains points $D$, $E$, $F$, such that $\overline{AD} \perp G$, $\overline{AD} \perp H$, and $AB = DF$. Which of the following statements must be true?

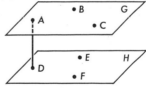

    (a) $AF = BD$.      (b) $\overline{BC} \parallel \overline{EF}$.         (c) $\triangle ABC \cong \triangle DFE$.

    (d) $G \parallel H$.         (e) $\overline{AC} \perp \overline{AD}$.         (f) $\angle AFD \cong \angle DBA$.

    (g) $\overline{AF}$ and $\overline{BD}$ bisect each other.         (h) $\overline{AC} \parallel \overline{DF}$.

5. In the figure, $\square ABCD$, $\square ADEK$, and $\square BCEK$ are parallelograms. Prove that

    (a) $\overline{EK} \parallel \overline{AD} \parallel \overline{BC}$, and

    (b) $\angle KAB \cong \angle EDC$.

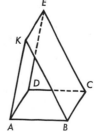

**6.** Given plane $M$ parallel to plane $K$. $A$ and $C$ are points in $M$, $B$ and $D$ are points in $K$, such that $\overline{AD} \perp K$ and $\overline{BC} \perp M$. Prove that $AB = CD$.

**7.** Prove the following.

   If two parallel lines are intersected by two parallel planes, then the planes intercept congruent segments on the two lines.

**8.** In the figure, skew lines $L_1$ and $L_2$ intersect the parallel planes $E$, $F$, $G$, and $\overline{AR}$ intersects $F$ at $K$. If $AB = BC$, prove that $PQ = QR$.

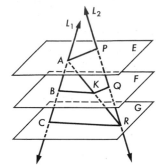

**9.** In Problem 8, prove also that

$$BQ < \tfrac{1}{2}(AP + CR).$$

**10.** In the figure, planes $M$ and $N$ intersect in $\overleftrightarrow{AB}$, and $M$ and $N$ intersect the parallel planes $E$ and $F$ in $\overleftrightarrow{AD}$, $\overleftrightarrow{BC}$, $\overleftrightarrow{AH}$, and $\overleftrightarrow{BG}$. If $AD = BC$ and $AH = BG$, prove that

$$\angle DAH \cong \angle CBG.$$

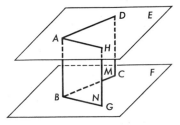

**11.** Indicate whether each statement is true or false. Draw a small sketch to illustrate each statement if it is true, or provide a sketch of a counterexample if it is false.

   (a) If a line lies in a plane, a line parallel to the line is parallel to the plane.

   (b) If a line and a plane are parallel, every line in the plane is parallel to the given line.

   (c) Two lines parallel to the same plane may be perpendicular to each other.

   (d) If two lines are parallel, every plane containing only one of the lines is parallel to the other line.

   (e) If a plane intersects two parallel planes, the lines of intersection are parallel.

   (f) If a plane intersects two intersecting planes, the lines of intersection may be parallel.

**12.** Show how to determine a plane which contains one of two given skew lines and is parallel to the other line. Prove your construction.

* **13.** Given: $\overline{PM}$ and $\overline{PS}$ lie in plane $E$. $P$, $M$, and $S$ are noncollinear. $\overline{KM} \perp \overline{PM}$, $\overline{QS} \perp \overline{PS}$, and $\overline{KM} \parallel \overline{QS}$.

Prove: $\overline{KM} \perp E$ and $\overline{QS} \perp E$.
[*Hint:* Introduce another parallel.]

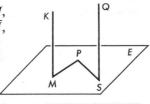

* **14.** $F$ and $E$ are parallel planes. $A$, $B$, $C$ are in $E$, $P$ is in $F$, and $\overline{PA} \perp F$. $R$, $T$, $V$ are mid-points of $\overline{PB}$, $\overline{PA}$, and $\overline{PC}$, respectively. Prove that the plane $RTV$ is parallel to $F$.

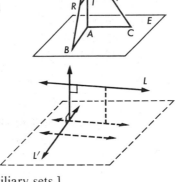

*+ **15.** Prove the following theorem.

There is one, and only one, line which is perpendicular to each of two given skew lines.

[*Hint:* The figure indicates how to obtain the common perpendicular. Dashed lines and segments indicate auxiliary sets.]

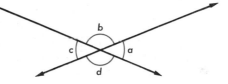

## 10–2 DIHEDRAL ANGLES. PERPENDICULAR PLANES

We know that when two lines in a plane intersect, they form four angles:

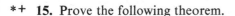

Consider now two planes in space, intersecting in a line as in the figure on the left below.

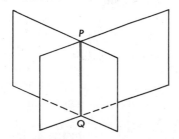

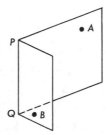

They form four figures, each of which looks like the figure on the right above. Such a figure is called a *dihedral angle*, and the line $\overleftrightarrow{PQ}$ shown in the figure is called its *edge*.

**Definitions**

If two half-planes have the same edge, but do not lie in the same plane, then the union of the two half-planes and their common edge is a *dihedral angle*. The line which is their common edge is called the *edge* of the dihedral angle. The union of the edge and either of the two half-planes is called a *side*, or a *face*, of the dihedral angle.

To describe a particular dihedral angle, we need to say what line is its edge, and what its sides are. We usually do this by naming two points $P$ and $Q$ of the edge, and two points $A$ and $B$ lying in the two sides. (See the figure above.) We then denote the dihedral angle by $\angle A$-$PQ$-$B$.

We may speak of the *interior* and *exterior* of a dihedral angle; and we may also speak of *vertical* dihedral angles. The ideas here are very similar to familiar ideas about angles in a plane, and you ought to be able to furnish your own definitions for them.

It would be nice to be able to say that vertical dihedral angles are congruent. But first we need to explain what is meant by the *measure* of a dihedral angle. We do this in the following way.

**Definition**

Given a dihedral angle, and a plane perpendicular to its edge. The intersection of the perpendicular plane with the dihedral angle is called a *plane angle* of the dihedral angle.

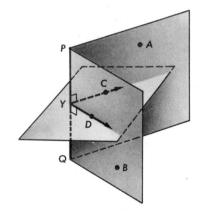

In the figure, the marks indicate that $\angle PYC$ and $\angle PYD$ are right angles. This means that the plane containing $\angle CYD$ is perpendicular to $\overleftrightarrow{PQ}$ at $Y$. Under the definition that we have just given, this means that $\angle CYD$ really is a plane angle of $\angle A$-$PQ$-$B$.

It seems natural to define the measure of $\angle A$-$PQ$-$B$ as the measure of $\angle CYD$. But this would hardly make sense if different plane angles of the same dihedral angle had different measures. We therefore need to prove the following theorem.

**Theorem 10–6**

All plane angles of the same dihedral angle are congruent.

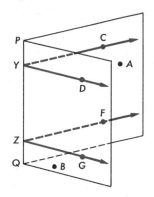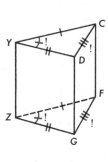

**Proof.** Given two plane angles of $\angle A\text{-}PQ\text{-}B$, with vertices at $Y$ and $Z$. We take points $C$, $D$, $F$, and $G$, on the sides of the angles, so that $YC = ZF$ and $YD = ZG$, as indicated in the figure on the right. We now have

(1)  $\square YCFZ$ is a parallelogram. ($\overline{YC}$ and $\overline{FZ}$ are congruent. And they are parallel, because they lie in the same plane and are perpendicular to the same line. See Theorem 9–20.)

In exactly the same way, we obtain

(2)  $\square YDGZ$ is a parallelogram.

Therefore

(3)  $\overline{DG} \parallel \overline{CF}$. (They are both parallel to $\overline{YZ}$.)

(4)  $DG = CF$ (because $DG = YZ = CF$).

(5)  $\square DGFC$ is a parallelogram (because $\overline{DG}$ and $\overline{CF}$ are congruent and parallel).

(6)  $DC = GF$.  (Why?)

(7)  $\triangle CYD \cong \triangle FZG$  (by $SSS$).

(8)  $\angle CYD \cong \angle FZG$.

Of course, (8) is what we wanted.

We can now make the following definitions.

**Definitions**

The *measure* of a dihedral angle is the real number which is the measure of each of its plane angles. A *right* dihedral angle is one whose plane angles are right angles. Two planes are *perpendicular* if they contain a right dihedral angle.

The following theorems are easy to prove, on the basis of the definitions.

### Theorem 10–7

If a line is perpendicular to a plane, then every plane containing the line is perpendicular to the given plane.

**Restatement.**  Let $L$ be a line, perpendicular to the plane $E$ at the point $A$, and let $F$ be any plane containing $L$.  Then $F \perp E$.

[*Hint for the proof:* Let $\overleftrightarrow{PQ}$ be the line in which $F$ intersects $E$. Take $\overleftrightarrow{AB} \perp \overleftrightarrow{PQ}$ in $E$.  Now remember the definitions of the statements $L \perp E$ and $F \perp E$, and show that $F$ and $E$ really are perpendicular.]

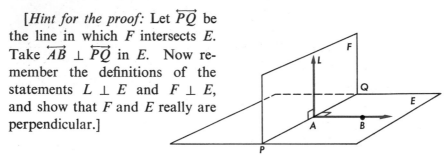

### Theorem 10–8

If two planes are perpendicular, then any line in one of them, perpendicular to their line of intersection, is perpendicular to the other plane.

You can use the same figure as for the preceding theorem.  Let $L$ be the given line, perpendicular to $\overleftrightarrow{PQ}$ at $A$, and take $\overleftrightarrow{AB} \perp \overleftrightarrow{PQ}$ as before.  This time $E \perp F$ is given, and we want to prove that $L \perp E$.

## Problem Set 10–2

**1.** Name all the dihedral angles in the figure on the left below.

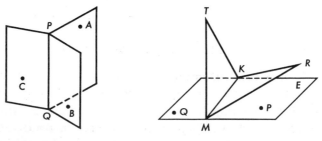

**2.** Name all the dihedral angles in the figure on the right above.  (There are more than three.  Note that $E$ is the name of a plane, not of a point.)

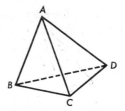

3. Name the six dihedral angles in this tetra-hedron.

4. Prove the following theorem.

   Vertical dihedral angles are congruent.

5. Prove the following theorem.

   If two parallel planes are intersected by a third plane, the alternate interior dihedral angles are congruent.

   [*Hint:* Introduce another plane.]

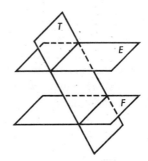

6. In the figure, $\overrightarrow{AM} \parallel \overrightarrow{BK}$ and $\overrightarrow{BK} \perp E$. $D$ is the mid-point of $\overline{BC}$ and

$$AC = AD.$$

   Find the measure of each angle of the figure.

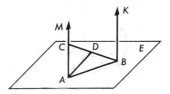

7. In the figure for Problem 2, if $T$ and $R$ are in the perpendicular bisecting plane of $\overline{MK}$, $S$ is the mid-point of $\overline{MK}$, and $m \angle RST = 110$, what is $m \angle T\text{-}MK\text{-}R$?  What is $m \angle T\text{-}MK\text{-}Q + m \angle R\text{-}MK\text{-}P$?

8. Each of $\overline{AP}$, $\overline{BP}$, and $\overline{CP}$ is perpendicular to the other two.  $AC = BC$ and $D$, $E$, $F$ are mid-points.  Prove that

$$\angle DEF \cong \angle PAB$$

   and find their measure.

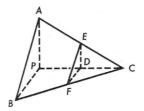

9. Define the interior of a dihedral angle.

10. Indicate whether each statement is true or false.  You should draw a small sketch to illustrate each statement if it is true, or sketch a counter-example if it is false.

   (a) Each side of a dihedral angle contains the common edge.

   (b) Two dihedral angles are congruent if a plane angle of one is congruent to a plane angle of the other.

(c) If a plane and a line are perpendicular, every plane which contains the line is perpendicular to the plane.

(d) Two planes perpendicular to the same plane are parallel to each other.

11. Given the cube shown here. Find

$$m \angle DHE, \qquad m \angle DEH,$$
$$m \angle HGD, \qquad m \angle EGD.$$

[You may use the following properties of a cube: (1) the twelve edges are congruent; (2) any two intersecting edges are perpendicular.]

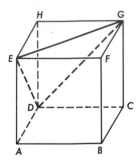

12. If $A$, $B$, $C$, and $D$ are four non-coplanar points, no three of which are collinear, the union of $\overline{AB}$, $\overline{BC}$, $\overline{CD}$, and $\overline{DA}$ is called a *skew quadrilateral*. Prove that the figure formed by joining consecutively the midpoints of the sides of a skew quadrilateral is a parallelogram.

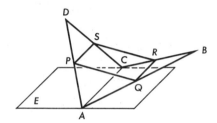

* 13. Prove the following.

If two intersecting planes are each perpendicular to a third plane, their intersection is perpendicular to the third plane.

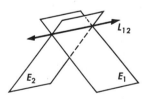

[*Hint:* In plane $E$, draw $\overrightarrow{PA} \perp \overleftrightarrow{MK}$ and $\overrightarrow{QA} \perp \overleftrightarrow{RS}$.   Use Theorems 10–8 and 8–2.]

*+ 14. Prove the following.

If three planes $E_1$, $E_2$, and $E_3$ intersect in the three lines $L_{12}$, $L_{23}$, $L_{13}$, then either the three lines intersect in a common point or each line is parallel to the other two lines.

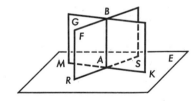

[*Hint:* The figure shows $E_1$ and $E_2$ intersecting in $L_{12}$. Consider the two possibilities for $E_3$: (1) $E_3 \parallel L_{12}$; (2) $E_3$ intersects $L_{12}$.]

# HONORS PROBLEM

## Desargues' Theorem

Given two triangles lying in nonparallel planes such that the lines joining their corresponding vertices intersect in a common point. If the lines containing corresponding sides of the triangles intersect, the points of intersection are collinear.

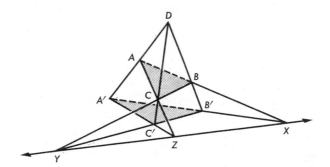

**Restatement:** Given $\triangle ABC$ and $\triangle A'B'C'$ in nonparallel planes such that $\overleftrightarrow{AA'}$, $\overleftrightarrow{BB'}$, and $\overleftrightarrow{CC'}$ intersect at $D$. If $\overleftrightarrow{AB}$ and $\overleftrightarrow{A'B'}$ intersect at $X$, $\overleftrightarrow{BC}$ and $\overleftrightarrow{B'C'}$ intersect at $Y$, and $\overleftrightarrow{AC}$ and $\overleftrightarrow{A'C'}$ intersect at $Z$, then $X$, $Y$, and $Z$ are collinear.

# 10–3.  PROJECTIONS

## Definition

The *projection* of a point into a plane is the foot of the perpendicular from the point to the plane.

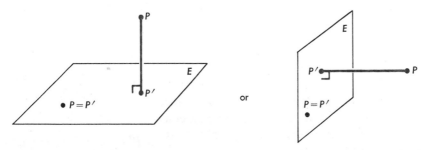

or

By Theorem 8–9, there is one and only one such perpendicular. In each of the figures, $P'$ is the projection of $P$ into $E$. We allow the possibility that $P$ lies in $E$. In this case, the projection of $P$ is $P$ itself.

**Definition**

The *projection* of a line into a plane is the set of all points of the plane which are projections of points of the line.

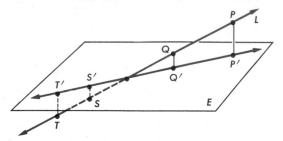

In the figure, $P'$ is the projection of $P$, $Q'$ is the projection of $Q$, $S'$ is the projection of $S$, and so on. The figure suggests that the projection of a line is always a line; and, in fact, this is what always happens, except when the line and the plane are perpendicular, as in the figure on the right. Here $A$ is the projection of *every* point $P$ of the line, and therefore $A$ is the projection of the whole line. To get a true theorem, we need to rule out this possibility.

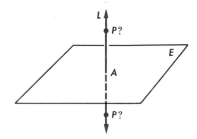

**Theorem 10–9**

If a line and a plane are not perpendicular, then the projection of the line into the plane is a line.

**Proof.** Given that the line $L$ is not perpendicular to the plane $E$.

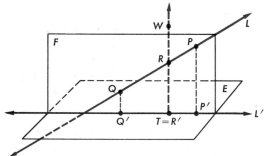

Let $P$ and $Q$ be any two points of $L$, and let $P'$ and $Q'$ be their projections. Then $P' \neq Q'$. (Why?) And $\overrightarrow{PP'}$ and $\overleftrightarrow{QQ'}$ are coplanar, because they are both perpendicular to the same plane (Theorem 8–7). Let $F$ be the plane which contains $\overrightarrow{PP'}$ and $\overleftrightarrow{QQ'}$; and let $L'$ be the line in which $F$ intersects $E$. Now $L$ lies in $F$, because $F$ contains two points of $L$. We are going to prove that $L'$ is the projection of $L$ into $E$. Since $L'$ is a line, this will complete the proof of the theorem.

Now $F \perp E$. This is true for two reasons: every plane containing $\overleftrightarrow{PP'}$ is perpendicular to $E$, and so also is every plane containing $\overleftrightarrow{QQ'}$ (Theorem 10–7).

We shall prove two things:

(1)  If $R$ is a point of $L$, then the projection $R'$ lies in $L'$.

(2)  If $T$ is a point of $L'$, then $T$ is the projection of some point of $L$.

**Proof of (1).**  Let $T$ be the foot of the perpendicular from $R$ to $L'$ in the plane $F$. By Theorem 10–8, $\overleftrightarrow{RT} \perp E$. Therefore $T = R'$, because perpendiculars are unique. Therefore $R'$ lies in $L'$.

**Proof of (2).**  Given a point $T$ of $L'$, let $\overleftrightarrow{TW}$ be the perpendicular to $L'$ at $T$, in the plane $F$. By Theorem 10–8, $\overleftrightarrow{TW} \perp E$. Therefore $\overleftrightarrow{TW}$ and $L$ are not parallel. (Why?) Let $R$ be the point at which $\overleftrightarrow{TW}$ intersects $L$. Then $T = R'$.

We have shown that every point of the projection is in $L'$, and every point of $L'$ is in the projection. Therefore $L'$ and the projection are exactly the same set of points. Therefore the projection is a line, which was to be proved.

The idea of a projection can be defined more generally, for *any* set of points.

### Definition

If $A$ is any set of points in space, and $E$ is a plane, then the *projection of A into E* is the set of all points which are projections of points of $A$ into $E$.

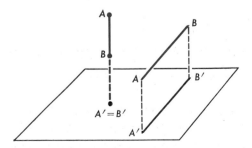

For example, the projection of a segment is usually a segment, although in some cases it may be a point. Similarly, the projection of a triangle is usually a triangle, although it may turn out to be a segment.

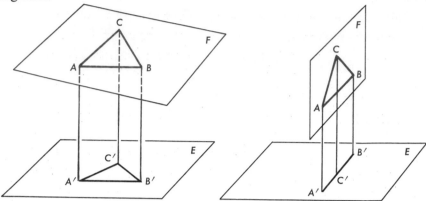

The second possibility arises whenever the plane of the triangle is perpendicular to $E$, as in the figure on the right.

## Problem Set 10–3

1. In the figure, plane $F$ is perpendicular to plane $E$ at $\overleftrightarrow{AB}$, $C$ is in $F$, and $\overline{CD} \perp \overline{AB}$. What is the projection of $\overline{AC}$? of $\overline{BC}$? of $\triangle ABC$?

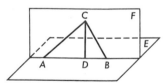

2. If one diagonal of a rhombus is perpendicular to a plane at an end point, what sort of figure is the projection of the rhombus into the plane?

3. In the figure, planes $E$ and $F$ intersect in $\overleftrightarrow{PQ}$. $\overline{AB}$, in $F$, is twice as long as its projection, $\overline{BC}$. $\overleftrightarrow{PQ} \perp$ plane $ABC$. Find $m \angle A\text{-}PQ\text{-}C$.

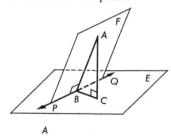

4. $P$, $Q$, $R$, and $S$ are projections of $A$, $B$, $C$, and $D$ into plane $E$. If $B$ and $C$ trisect $\overline{AD}$, why do $Q$ and $R$ trisect $\overline{PS}$?

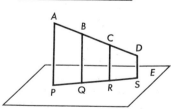

5. Be prepared to justify your answers to the following questions.
   (a) Is the projection of a point always a point?
   (b) Is the projection of a segment always a segment?

(c) Can the projection of an angle be a ray? a line? a segment? an angle?

(d) Can the projection of an acute angle be an obtuse angle?

(e) Is the projection of a right angle ever a right angle?

(f) Can the projection of a segment be longer than the segment? shorter than the segment?

6. Answer as in Problem 5.

(a) Can the projection of two intersecting lines ever be two parallel lines?

(b) Can the projection of two skew lines ever be two parallel lines?

(c) Can the projection of two skew lines ever be two intersecting lines?

(d) Is the projection of two parallel lines always two parallel lines?

7. One face of an acute dihedral angle contains a square. What sort of figure is the projection of the square into the other face?

8. Given two parallel planes, $E$ and $F$. $\triangle ABC$ is in $F$. Prove that the projection of $\triangle ABC$ into $E$ is a triangle congruent to $\triangle ABC$.

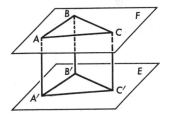

+  9. The figure on the left is a tetrahedron. The figure on the right is the projection of the tetrahedron into the plane $BCD$. Sketch the projections into the planes $ABC$ and $ACD$.

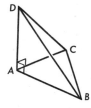
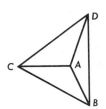

+ 10. If a diagonal of a cube is perpendicular to a plane, sketch the projection into the plane of all the edges of the cube.

* 11. In plane $E$, $M$ is the mid-point of $\overline{AB}$. $C$ is a point not in $E$, but its projection, $D$, is on the perpendicular bisector of $\overline{AB}$. Prove that $\triangle ABC$ is isosceles.

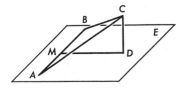

+ **12.** In mechanical drawing, the top view, or "plan," of a solid may be considered to be the projection of the various segments of the solid into a horizontal plane above the solid, as illustrated below on the left. The top view as it would actually be drawn is shown on the right. (No attempt is made here to obtain true scale.)

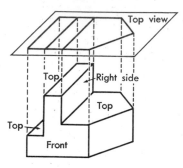

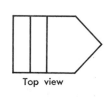

(a) Sketch a front view of the solid; that is, sketch the projection of the segments of the solid into a plane parallel to the front face.

(b) Sketch the right side view of the solid.

* **13.** Given: $\overrightarrow{RS}$ is in plane $E$.

$\angle PRS$ is a right angle.

$Q$ is the projection of $P$.

Prove: $\angle QRS$ is a right angle.
[*Hint:* Introduce $\overrightarrow{RT}$, the perpendicular to $E$ at $R$.]

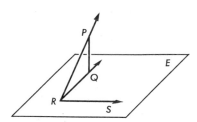

+ **14.** Given: $\overrightarrow{AQ}$ is the projection of $\overrightarrow{AR}$ into plane $E$.

$\overrightarrow{AP}$ is any other ray from $A$ in $E$.

Prove: $m\angle QAR < m\angle PAR$.

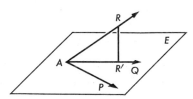

[*Hint:* On $\overrightarrow{AP}$, introduce point $K$ such that $AK = AR'$. Draw $\overline{KR'}$ and $\overline{KR}$.]

## Chapter Review

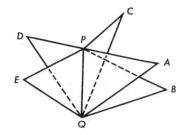

**1.** Name the dihedral angles in this figure, assuming that no two of the indicated triangles are coplanar.

2. Given: $E \perp \overline{AC}$, $F \perp \overline{AC}$, $F \perp \overline{BD}$.

   Prove: $E \perp \overline{BD}$ and $\overline{AC} \parallel \overline{BD}$.

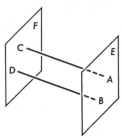 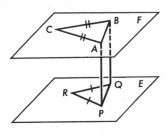

3. Given the figure (on the right above) as marked. $\triangle ABC$ is in plane $F$; $\triangle PQR$ is in plane $E$; $\square ABQP$ is a rectangle and $\overline{AP} \perp E$. Which of the following statements are true?

   (a) $\overline{BQ} \perp E$.         (b) $AQ = BP$.         (c) $F \parallel E$.

   (d) $\overline{PQ}$ is the projection of $\overline{AB}$ into $E$.         (e) $\triangle ABC \cong \triangle PQR$.

   (f) $PC = QC$.         (g) $\overline{BC} \parallel \overline{RQ}$.         (h) $\triangle PAC \cong \triangle RBC$.

4. Indicate, by A, S, or N, whether each statement is true in ALL cases, true in SOME cases and false in others, or true in NO cases.

   (a) Two lines parallel to the same plane are perpendicular to each other.

   (b) If a plane intersects each of two parallel planes, the lines of intersection are skew.

   (c) If two planes are parallel to the same line, they are parallel to each other.

   (d) The intersection of a plane with the faces of a dihedral angle is a plane angle of the dihedral angle.

   (e) If two lines are perpendicular to the same plane, the lines are parallel.

   (f) If two lines are parallel to the same plane, the lines are parallel.

   (g) If a line is perpendicular to a plane, every plane containing the line is perpendicular to the plane.

   (h) The projection of an angle may be a point.

   (i) Two lines are parallel if each is perpendicular to the same line.

   (j) If each of two intersecting planes is perpendicular to a third plane, their line of intersection is perpendicular to the third plane.

5. $\overleftrightarrow{AB}$ is the edge of $\angle S\text{-}AB\text{-}T$ and $P$ is on $\overline{AB}$. If $m \angle SPT = 90$, is $\angle S\text{-}AB\text{-}T$ a right dihedral angle? Explain.

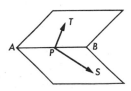

**6.** Planes $E$ and $F$ intersect in $\overleftrightarrow{KM}$; $\overrightarrow{AB}$ and $\overrightarrow{PQ}$ are in $E$; $\overrightarrow{AC}$ and $\overrightarrow{PR}$ are in $F$. If $m\angle MAB = 90$ and $m\angle KAC = 90$, is $\angle BAC$ a plane angle of $\angle B\text{-}KM\text{-}C$? If $m\angle RPQ = 90$, is $\overrightarrow{PQ} \parallel \overrightarrow{AB}$?

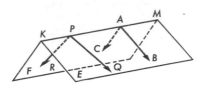

**7.** In the figure, $PQ = \frac{1}{2}PC = \frac{1}{2}PA$, $AB = BC$, and $\overrightarrow{PQ} \perp E$. Which of the following is true?

$$m\angle P\text{-}AC\text{-}Q < 30,$$

$$m\angle P\text{-}AC\text{-}Q = 30,$$

$$m\angle P\text{-}AC\text{-}Q > 30.$$

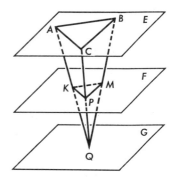

**8.** Given: Parallel planes $E$, $F$, and $G$, with $Q$ in $G$, $\triangle KMP$ in $F$, and $\triangle ABC$ in $E$. $AK = KQ$.

Prove: The perimeter of $\triangle ABC$ is twice the perimeter of $\triangle KMP$.

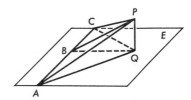

\*    **9.** In the figure, parallelogram $\square ABCD$ is not parallel to plane $E$. $K$, $L$, $M$, $N$ are the projections into $E$ of the vertices $A$, $B$, $C$, $D$, respectively. Prove that

$$AK + CM = BL + DN.$$

[*Hint:* Let $Q$ be the projection of $P$ into $E$. Draw $\overline{PQ}$.]

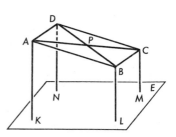

\*+  **10.** Sketch a figure showing the intersection of a plane with all six faces of a cube. Then imagine the intersection projected into a plane parallel to the first plane but not intersecting the cube and draw the result.

NIKOLAI IVANOVITCH LOBACHEVSKY (1793–1856)

Early in the nineteenth century, non-Euclidean geometry was discovered by three men, working independently in three different countries. These men were C. F. Gauss in Germany, János Bolyai in Hungary, and Nikolai Ivanovitch Lobachevsky in Russia.

Until then, everybody had believed that the uniqueness of parallels was simply a fact, both of geometry and of physics. These three men tried assuming the contrary: they assumed that through a given external point there is *more than one* parallel to a given line. This led to a new kind of geometry, which was mathematically just as good as the familiar geometry of Euclid. And this new geometry turned out to be useful in physics—after the discovery of relativity theory by Albert Einstein.

Lobachevsky is usually given most of the credit for non-Euclidean geometry. He carried the theory further than Bolyai did. And unlike Gauss, he had the courage to publish his work. Gauss seems to have been afraid of looking foolish. He was considered to be the greatest mathematician of his time, and so he would have had a long way to fall.

# 11 | Polygonal Regions and Their Areas

## 11–1.  POLYGONAL REGIONS

**Definition**

A *triangular region* is the union of a triangle and its interior.

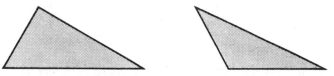

A *polygonal region* is a plane figure formed by fitting together a finite number of triangular regions:

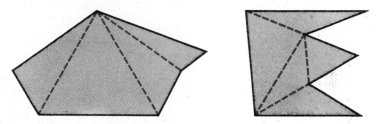

Hereafter we shall not use shading in pictures of regions in cases where it is plain what region is being described.

**Definition**

A *polygonal region* is the union of a finite number of triangular regions, in a plane, such that if two of these intersect, their intersection is either a point or a segment.

The dashed lines in the figures above show how each of the two polygonal regions can be expressed as such a union. Some more examples are shown below.

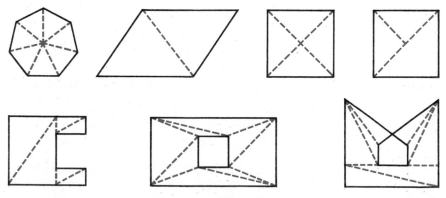

In the last two examples,

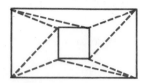 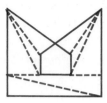

the regions have "holes" in them. This is allowed by the definition, and these last two figures are perfectly good polygonal regions.

The shaded region shown below is in fact a polygonal region.

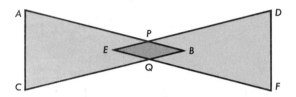

Note, however, that you can't prove this by mentioning the triangular regions determined by $\triangle ABC$ and $\triangle DEF$. The trouble is that the intersection of these two triangular regions is not a point or a segment, as the definition says it should be. The intersection is the little diamond-shaped region in the middle of the figure.

On the other hand, it is easy to cut up this region differently, so as to show that it is a polygonal region.

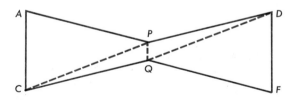

If a figure can be cut up into triangular regions at all, then this can be done in many ways. For example, a parallelogram plus its interior can be cut up in at least the three ways shown below.

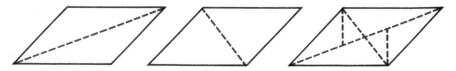

And it is easy to see that there are infinitely many other ways of cutting up such a figure.

In this chapter, we shall study the areas of polygonal regions, and learn to compute them.   For this purpose, we shall use four new postulates.

### POSTULATE 19.   The Area Postulate

> *To every polygonal region there corresponds a unique positive real number.*

### Definition

The *area* of a polygonal region is the number assigned to it by Postulate 19.   The area of the region $R$ is denoted by $aR$.   This is pronounced *area of R*.

Hereafter in this chapter, when we speak of a *region*, we shall always mean a polygonal region.

Surely the area of a region ought to depend only on the size and shape of the region; it ought not to depend on the place where the region happens to be located in space.   We state this fact as a postulate, for the case of triangular regions.

### POSTULATE 20.   The Congruence Postulate

> *If two triangles are congruent, then the triangular regions determined by them have the same area.*

If we cut a region into two pieces, then the area of the region ought to be the sum of the areas of the two pieces.

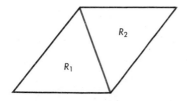 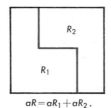 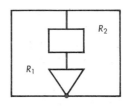

$$aR = aR_1 + aR_2.$$

In each of these figures, the total region $R$ is the union of two regions $R_1$ and $R_2$.   In each case, $R_1$ and $R_2$ intersect in at most a finite number of segments and points.   Under these conditions, we can find $aR$ by addition.

**POSTULATE 21.** The Area Addition Postulate

*Suppose that the region R is the union of two regions $R_1$ and $R_2$. Suppose that $R_1$ and $R_2$ intersect in at most a finite number of segments and points. Then $aR = aR_1 + aR_2$.*

There are simple cases where one region is the union of two others, but where the above formula does not hold at all. If $R_1$ and $R_2$ are triangular regions as in the figure, and $R$ is their union, then $aR$ is less than $aR_1 + aR_2$. (When we add, the area of the diamond-shaped region in the middle is counted twice.) Hence we needed the second "Suppose . . ." in the hypothesis of the Addition Postulate.

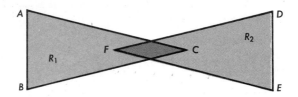

We remember from Chapter 2 that the unit of distance could be chosen at will. The same is true of the unit of area. But we ought to be consistent in choosing our units: if we are measuring distance in feet, then we ought to measure area in square feet; if we use yards, then we should use square yards; and so on. This is the idea behind the following postulate.

**POSTULATE 22.** The Unit Postulate

*The area of a square region is the square of the length of its edge.*

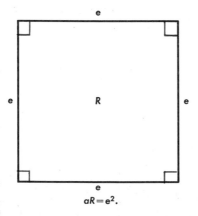

$$aR = e^2.$$

Hereafter, for short, we shall speak of the area of a square, the area of a triangle, and so on. In each case we mean, of course, the area of the corresponding region. We shall also speak of the base and altitude of a rectangle, meaning the length of the base and the length of the altitude. This is convenient, and, in each case, you ought to be able to tell from the context whether we are talking about a segment or about the number which measures its length.

By a simple trick, we shall now find the area of a rectangle.

**Theorem 11–1**

The area of a rectangle is the product of its base and its altitude.

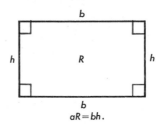

**Proof.** Consider the figure on the right.

Here $A$ denotes the unknown area of our rectangle. The areas of our two squares are $b^2$ and $h^2$, by Postulate 22; and the area of the total figure is $(b + h)^2$. Therefore, by repeated applications of the Area Addition Postulate,

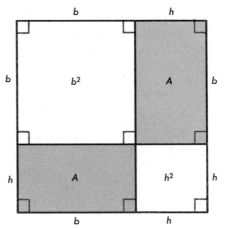

$$b^2 + 2A + h^2 = (b + h)^2$$
$$= b^2 + 2bh + h^2,$$

and

$$A = bh,$$

which is what we wanted.

If you wonder how we knew from our postulates that the two rectangles in the figure have the same area, you should examine the figure on the right. All four triangles are congruent, and so have the same area; and the area of each rectangle is twice the area of each triangle.

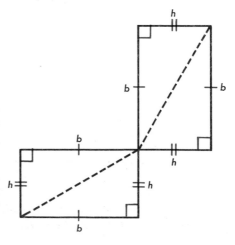

## Problem Set 11–1

1. Show that each region below is polygonal by triangulating each one according to the definition of polygonal region. Try to find the smallest number of triangular regions in each case.

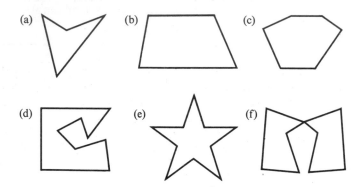

2. If, in the figure on the left below, $aR_1 = 50$, $aR_2 = 25$, and $R$ is the union of $R_1$ and $R_2$, what is $aR$? Quote a postulate or theorem to support your conclusion.

3. If, in the figure on the right above, $aR_1 = 30$, $aR_2 = 30$, and $R$ is the union of $R_1$ and $R_2$, is $aR = 60$? Quote a postulate or theorem to support your conclusion.

4. Find the area of a rectangle 16 ft long by 10 ft 3 in. wide.

5. A square and a rectangle have equal areas. If the rectangle is 25 in. by 16 in., what is a side of the square?

6. How is the area of a square changed if a side is doubled? tripled? halved?

7. (a) If the altitude of a rectangle is doubled while the base stays the same, how is the area changed?

   (b) If the base of a rectangle is doubled while the altitude stays the same, how is the area changed?

   (c) If both the base and the altitude of a rectangle are doubled, how is the area changed?

8. How many tiles, each 4 in. square (i.e., 4 in. to a side) are needed to cover a rectangular wall 15 ft 8 in. by 7 ft?

9. Prove: If two rectangles have the same base, $b$, then the ratio of their areas equals the ratio of their altitudes.

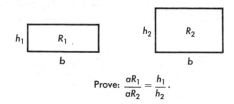

Prove: $\dfrac{aR_1}{aR_2} = \dfrac{h_1}{h_2}$.

10. A rectangular plot of land is to be planted with grass seed. The dimensions of the plot are 22 yd by 28 yd. If one 2-lb bag of grass seed is needed for each 750 sq. ft of land, how many bags must be provided?

11. The figure is the face of a certain machine part. To compute the cost of painting a number of these parts, one must know the area of a face. The shaded regions are not to be painted. Find the area of the region to be painted. What postulates and theorems do you use in computing the area?

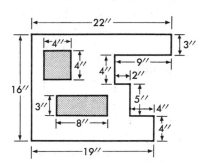

12. Compute the area of a rectangle having base $b$ and altitude $h$, given that
   (a) $b = 17$   and   $h = 12$.   (b) $b = 1\frac{1}{3}$   and   $h = 5\frac{3}{4}$.
   (c) $b = 3$   and   $h = \sqrt{5}$.   (d) $b = \sqrt{10}$   and   $h = \sqrt{15}$.

13. Compute the area of a square having side $s$, given that
   (a) $s = 24$.   (b) $s = 3\frac{3}{5}$.   (c) $s = \sqrt{7}$.   (d) $s = 4\sqrt{6}$.

14. Indicate whether each statement is true or false. Support your answers with reasons.
   (a) A square is a polygonal region.
   (b) To every positive number there corresponds a unique polygonal region.
   (c) If two triangles are congruent, then the triangular regions have equal areas.
   (d) A triangular region does not include the triangle.
   (e) The area of the union of two polygonal regions is the sum of their areas.
   (f) A triangular region is a polygonal region.
   (g) There exists a square with area $\sqrt{17}$.
   (h) There exists a rectangle with area $4\sqrt{5}$ whose base is a rational number.

+ **15.** In the figure below, $A$, $B$, $C$, $D$, $E$, $F$, and $G$
are called *vertices*, $\overline{AB}$, $\overline{BC}$, $\overline{CD}$, $\overline{DE}$, $\overline{EG}$,
$\overline{GA}$, $\overline{EF}$, $\overline{FD}$, and $\overline{FB}$ are called *edges*, and
the polygonal regions $ABE$, $FED$, and
$BCDF$ are called *faces*. The exterior of the
figure is also considered a face. Let the num-
ber of faces be $f$, the number of vertices be $v$, and the number of edges
be $e$. A theorem originated by a famous mathematician, Euler, relates
$f$, $v$, and $e$ in the formula $f - e + v$. It refers to a large class of
figures of which the above is one possibility. Let us compute $f - e + v$
for the figure above: $f = 4$, $e = 9$, and $v = 7$; hence, $4 - 9 + 7 = 2$.

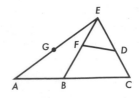

(a) Compute $f - e + v$ for each of the two figures below. Note that
the edges are not necessarily segments. The figure on the right could
be a section of a map showing counties.

(b) What pattern do you observe in the results of the three computations?

(c) In the figure on the left take a point in the interior of the quadrilateral and draw segments from each of its vertices to the point.
How does this affect the computation of $f - e + v$? Can you
explain why?

(d) Take a point in the exterior of either figure and join it to the
nearest two vertices. How does this affect the computation?

(e) If you are interested in this problem and would like to pursue it
further, you will find it discussed in *The Enjoyment of Mathematics*
by Rademacher and Toeplitz and in *Fundamental Concepts of
Geometry* by Meserve.

## 11–2. AREAS OF TRIANGLES AND QUADRILATERALS

Let us now get some more area formulas, on the basis of our
postulates.

**Theorem 11–2**

The area of a right triangle is half the
product of its legs.

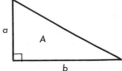

**Proof.** Given a right triangle with legs $a$ and $b$. Let its area be $A$. We form a rectangle $\square UVWX$ (as on the right) having the legs of our right triangle as two of its sides. Then

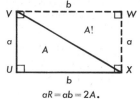

(1)  $\triangle VUX \cong \triangle XWV$,

(2)  $a \triangle XWV = A$,

(3)  $A + A = ab$,

(4)  $A = \frac{1}{2}ab$.

$aR = ab = 2A.$

Reasons? (You may need more than one reason for some of the steps.)

From this theorem we can get a formula for the area of any triangle. As soon as we have done this, we shall have no further need for Theorem 11-2, because our general theorem will include it as a special case.

## Theorem 11-3

The area of a triangle is half the product of any base and the corresponding altitude.

**Proof.** Let the given base and altitude be $b$ and $h$, and let the area be $A$. There are three cases to consider.

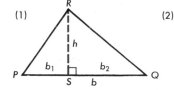  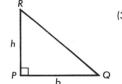  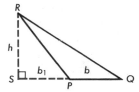

(1) If the foot of the altitude is between the end points of the base, then the altitude cuts our triangle into two triangles with bases $b_1$ and $b_2$, and $b_1 + b_2 = b$. By the preceding theorem, the areas of these triangles are $\frac{1}{2}b_1 h$ and $\frac{1}{2}b_2 h$. By the Area Addition Postulate,

$$A = \tfrac{1}{2}b_1 h + \tfrac{1}{2}b_2 h.$$

Therefore

$$A = \tfrac{1}{2}(b_1 + b_2)h = \tfrac{1}{2}bh,$$

which is what we wanted.

(2) If the foot of the altitude is an end point of the base, then our triangle is a right triangle, and $A = \frac{1}{2}bh$, by the preceding theorem.

(3) If the foot of the altitude misses the base, as in the third figure, we have

$$\tfrac{1}{2}b_1 h + A = \tfrac{1}{2}(b_1 + b)h,$$

and

$$A = \tfrac{1}{2}bh,$$

as before. (Reasons?)

Note that Theorem 11–3 can be applied to any triangle in three ways: we can choose any of the three sides as base, multiply by the corresponding altitude, and divide by 2. Note that

$$\tfrac{1}{2}b_1 h_1, \quad \tfrac{1}{2}b_2 h_2, \quad \text{and} \quad \tfrac{1}{2}b_3 h_3$$

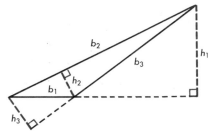

must be the same number, because each of them is the right answer to the same problem.

Now that we know how to find areas of triangles, the rest is simple: to find the area of a polygonal region, we cut it up into triangles and add. This procedure is especially easy for trapezoids.

### Theorem 11–4

The area of a trapezoid is half the product of its altitude and the sum of its bases.

**Proof.** Let $A$ be the area of the trapezoid. Either diagonal divides the trapezoid into two triangles, with bases $b_1$ and $b_2$ and the same altitude $h$. (Why is $PV = TR$?) By the Area Addition Postulate,

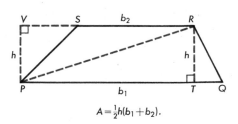

$$A = \tfrac{1}{2}h(b_1 + b_2).$$

$$A = \tfrac{1}{2}b_1 h + \tfrac{1}{2}b_2 h$$

$$= \tfrac{1}{2}h(b_1 + b_2),$$

which is what we wanted.

This immediately gives us an area formula for parallelograms.

### Theorem 11–5

The area of a parallelogram is the product of any base and the corresponding altitude.

**Proof.** Let $A$ be the area of the parallelogram. Every parallelogram is a trapezoid, with $b_1 = b_2 = b$. Therefore

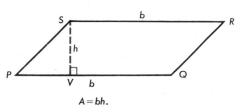

$A = bh.$

$$A = \tfrac{1}{2}h(b + b)$$
$$= bh.$$

The area formula for triangles has two easy but useful consequences.

### Theorem 11–6

If two triangles have the same base $b$ and the same altitude $h$, then they have the same area.

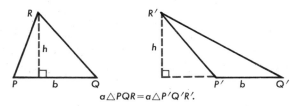

$a\triangle PQR = a\triangle P'Q'R'.$

This is obvious, because the area of each of them is $\tfrac{1}{2}bh$.

### Theorem 11–7

If two triangles have the same altitude $h$, then the ratio of their areas is equal to the ratio of their bases.

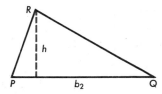

**Proof.** Let the bases be $b_1$ and $b_2$.

Then
$$\frac{a\triangle ABC}{a\triangle PQR} = \frac{\tfrac{1}{2}b_1 h}{\tfrac{1}{2}b_2 h} = \frac{b_1}{b_2}.$$

## Problem Set 11–2

1. In $\triangle ABC$, $AC = 8$, and the altitude to $\overline{AC}$ is 3. In $\triangle DEF$, $EF = 6$.
   If $a\triangle ABC = a\triangle DEF$, find the altitude to $\overline{EF}$.

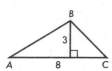 

2. In $\triangle PQR$, $\angle P$ is a right angle, $PR = 16$, $PQ = 12$, and $RQ = 20$.
   (a) Find the area of $\triangle PQR$.    (b) Find the altitude to the hypotenuse.

3. In the figure, $B$ is the mid-point of $\overline{AC}$
   and $\overline{ED} \parallel \overline{AC}$.  Prove that $a\triangle ABE = a\triangle BCD$.

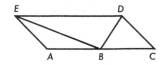

4. $\square KMPR$ is a parallelogram.  Given
   that $m \angle K = 30$, $KM = 11$, and
   $KR = 8$, find $a\square KMPR$.

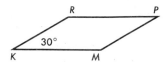

5. A rhombus has a side of 12 and the measure of one angle is 150.  Find
   the area of the rhombus.

6. One right triangle has legs 18 in. and 14 in.  Another right triangle has
   legs 14 in. and 24 in.  What is the ratio of the areas of the two triangles?

7. Two sides of a triangle are 15 in. and 20 in. long, and the altitude to the
   15-in. side is 8 in.  How long is the altitude to the 20-in. side?

8. In $\triangle ABC$, $\overline{CD}$ is the altitude to $\overleftrightarrow{AB}$, and $\overline{AE}$ is the altitude to $\overleftrightarrow{BC}$.

   (a) If $AB = 8$, $CD = 9$, $AE = 6$, find $BC$.

   (b) If $AB = 11$, $AE = 5$, $BC = 15$, find $CD$.

   (c) If $CD = h$, $AB = c$, $BC = a$, find $AE$.

   (d) If $AB = 15$, $CD = 14$, $BC = 21$, find $AE$.

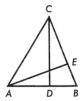

9. The hypotenuse of a right triangle is 50 in. long, one leg is 14 in. long, and
   the area of the triangle is 336 sq. in.  How long is the altitude to the
   hypotenuse?  How long is the altitude to the given leg?

10. A triangle and a parallelogram have equal areas and equal bases.  How
    do their altitudes compare?

**11.** $\square ABCD$ is a parallelogram, $\overleftrightarrow{EH} \perp \overleftrightarrow{DC}$, $\overleftrightarrow{CF} \perp \overleftrightarrow{AB}$, and $\overleftrightarrow{BG} \perp \overleftrightarrow{DA}$.

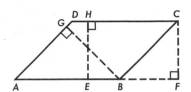

(a) If $AB = 18$, $EH = 10$, and $BG = 15$, what is $AD$?

(b) If $AD = 22$, $BG = 7$ and $EH = 14$, what is $DC$?

(c) If $CF = 12$, $BG = 16$, $BC = 17$, then $AB = $ ?

(d) If $BG = 24$, $AD = 28$, $AB = 32$, then $EH = $ ?

(e) If $AB = \sqrt{50}$, $CF = 6$, $GB = \sqrt{18}$, then $BC = $ ?

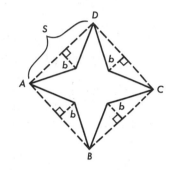

**12.** In the figure, $\square ABCD$ is a square, and the segments forming the boundary of the star are congruent. Find the area of the star in terms of $s$ and $b$.

**13.** Prove: The two regions into which a median of a triangle separates the triangular region have equal areas.

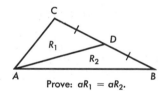

Prove: $aR_1 = aR_2$.

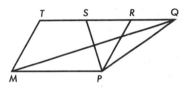

**14.** In the figure, $\square MPRT$ is a parallelogram and $TS = SR = RQ$. What is the ratio of

(a) $a\triangle PRS$ and $a\triangle PRQ$?     (b) $a\triangle PMQ$ and $a\square MPRT$?

(c) $a\triangle PMQ$ and $a\triangle PQS$?     (d) $a\triangle PQR$ and $a\square MPST$?

**15.** $\square ABCD$ is a trapezoid with parallel sides $\overline{AB}$ and $\overline{CD}$.

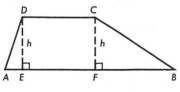

(a) If $AB = 18$, $DC = 12$, $h = 9$, then $a\square ABCD = $ ?

(b) If $a\square ABCD = 84$, $AB = 17$, $CD = 11$, then $h = $ ?

(c) If $a\square ABCD = 375$, $h = 15$, $AB = 38$, then $CD = $ ?

(d) If $AB = 15$, $DC = 8$, $BC = 10$, and $m \angle B = 30$, then $a\square ABCD = $ ?

(e) If $AB = 13$, $h = 5$, $a\square ABCD = 65$, then $CD = $ ?

**16.** What is the area of a trapezoid if its altitude is 6 and its median is 12?
[*Hint:* Refer to Problem 4 of Problem Set 9–8.]

**17.** A surveyor was to determine the area
of the plot of land *ABCDE* diagramed
here. He located the north-south line
through *E* and the east-west lines
through *A*, *B*, *C*, and *D*. He found
that $AO = 37$ ft, $BR = 47$ ft, $CQ =$
42 ft, $DP = 28$ ft, $PQ = 13$ ft, $QE =$
7 ft, $ER = 19$ ft, and $RO = 18$ ft. He
then computed the required area. Find
the required area to the nearest square
yard.

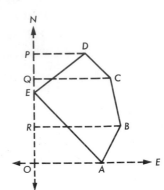

**18.** Prove the following theorem.

If the diagonals of a convex quadrilateral are perpendicular to each
other, then the area of the quadrilateral equals one-half the
product of the lengths of the
diagonals.

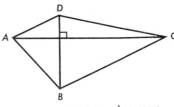

Prove: $a \square ABCD = \frac{1}{2}(AC)(BD)$.

Would this theorem be true if the quadrilateral were not required to
be convex?

**19.** $\square PQRS$ is convex, and $\overline{PR} \perp \overline{QS}$.

(a) If $PR = 12$ and $QS = 16$, what is
$a\square PQRS$?

(b) If $a\square PQRS = 153$ and $PR = 17$, what
is $QS$?

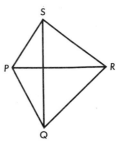

**20.** The diagonals of a rhombus are 15 and 20. What is its area? If an
altitude of the rhombus is 12, what is a side? [*Hint:* Does Problem 18
apply?]

**21.** Prove: If the diagonals of a rhombus are $d$ and $d'$, then the area of the
rhombus is $dd'/2$.

**22.** The area of a rhombus is 348 and one diagonal is 24. Find the other
diagonal.

**23.** In ☐*ABCD*, $\overleftrightarrow{AC} \perp \overleftrightarrow{BD}$.  If *AC* = 13 and *BD* = 8, can you find a☐*ABCD*?

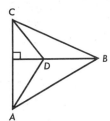 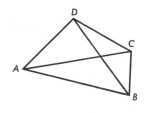

\*  **24.** In ☐*ABCD*, $\overline{AC}$ bisects $\overline{BD}$.  Prove that a△*ABC* = a△*ADC*.

\*  **25.** Given ☐*ABCD* is a parallelogram and *P*, *Q*, *R*, and *S* are the mid-points of the sides.  Prove that   a☐*PQRS* = $\frac{1}{2}$a☐*ABCD*.

\*  **26.** Given any triangle, △*MQR*, with two medians, $\overline{RS}$ and $\overline{MT}$, intersecting at *P*.  Prove that a△*PMS* = a△*PRT*.

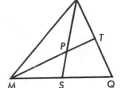

\*  **27.** ☐*ABCD* is a trapezoid with $\overline{DC} \parallel \overline{AB}$, *E* is the mid-point of $\overline{AB}$, *F* is the mid-point of $\overline{DE}$, and *G* is the mid-point of $\overline{CE}$.  Prove that a△*AFD* = a△*BGC*.

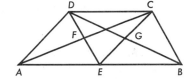

\*  **28.** Let $\overline{AB}$ be given in plane *E*.  For any positive number *k*, there is at least one point *P* such that a△*ABP* = *k*.  Is there more than one such point? How many?  Describe the set of all points *P* in plane *E* such that a△*ABP* = *k*.  Describe the set of all points *P* in space such that a△*ABP* = *k*.

\*  **29.** ☐*PQRS* is a parallelogram.  *J* is a point of $\overline{RS}$ such that *RJ* < $\frac{1}{2}$*RS*. *K* is a point of $\overline{RQ}$ such that *RK* < $\frac{1}{2}$*RQ*.  A line through *S* and parallel to $\overleftrightarrow{PK}$ intersects a line through *K* and parallel to $\overleftrightarrow{PJ}$ at *M*.  $\overleftrightarrow{PJ}$ intersects $\overline{SM}$ at *L*.  Prove that a☐*PQRS* = a☐*PKML*.  [*Hint*: Does $\overleftrightarrow{RQ}$ intersect $\overleftrightarrow{SM}$?]

\*+  **30.** Prove: If a line *L* separates a parallelogram region into two regions of equal areas, then *L* contains the point of intersection of the diagonals of the parallelogram.

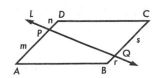

## 11–3.   THE PYTHAGOREAN THEOREM

Now that we know about areas, the Pythagorean Theorem is rather easily proved.

**Theorem 11–8.**   The Pythagorean Theorem

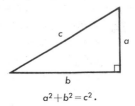

In a right triangle, the square of the hypotenuse is equal to the sum of the squares of the legs.

$a^2 + b^2 = c^2.$

**Proof.**   First we take a square with edges of length $a + b$.  In the square we draw four right triangles with legs $a$ and $b$.

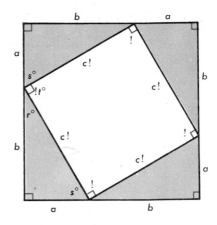

(1) By SAS, each of these four triangles is congruent to our given one.  Therefore they all have hypotenuses equal to $c$, as shown in the figure.

(2) The quadrilateral formed by the four hypotenuses is a square.  In the notation of the figure, we have

$$r + s = 90,$$

because the acute angles of a right triangle are complementary.  Since

$$r + s + t = 180,$$

it follows that $t = 90$.  Similarly for the other angles of our quadrilateral.

(3) By the Area Addition Postulate, the area of the large square is equal to the area of the small square, plus the sum of the areas of the four congruent triangles.  This gives

$$(a + b)^2 = c^2 + 4 \cdot \tfrac{1}{2}ab.$$

Therefore

$$a^2 + 2ab + b^2 = c^2 + 2ab, \quad \text{and} \quad a^2 + b^2 = c^2,$$

which was to be proved.

The converse of the Pythagorean Theorem is also true.

### Theorem 11–9

If the square of one side of a triangle is equal to the sum of the squares of the other two sides, then the triangle is a right triangle, with its right angle opposite the longest side.

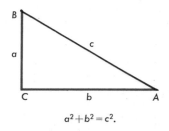

$a^2 + b^2 = c^2.$

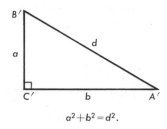

$a^2 + b^2 = d^2.$

**Proof.** Given $\triangle ABC$, with $a^2 + b^2 = c^2$, as in the figure. Let $\triangle A'B'C'$ be a *right* triangle with legs $a$ and $b$, and hypotenuse $d$. Then $c = d$, because $d^2 = a^2 + b^2 = c^2$. By SSS, $\triangle ABC \cong \angle A'B'C'$. Therefore $\angle C \cong \angle C'$. Since $\angle C'$ is a right angle, so also is $\angle C$.

PYTHAGORAS

Pythagoras is generally regarded as the first of the great Greek mathematicians, but very little is known about him as a person. He was born in about 582 B.C., and lived first on the island of Samos, in the Aegean Sea, and later in the south of Italy.

Pythagoras and his students devoted themselves to mathematics, astronomy, and philosophy. They are credited with having developed geometry into a science; they proved the Pythagorean Theorem, and they discovered the existence of irrational numbers. In astronomy they were equally good: they knew, in the sixth century B.C., that the earth is round and moves around the sun. They did not leave any written record of their work, and so nobody knows how they achieved these things, or which of their discoveries were due to Pythagoras personally.

## Problem Set 11–3

1. In right triangle, $\triangle ABC$, $c$ is the length of the hypotenuse, and $a$ and $b$ are the lengths of the legs.

   (a) If $a = 12$ and $b = 16$, then $c = $ ?

   (b) If $a = 24$ and $c = 25$, then $b = $ ?

   (c) If $a = 1$ and $b = 2$, then $c = $ ?

   (d) If $b = 18$ and $c = 20$, then $a = $ ?

   (e) If $a = 7$ and $b = 7$, then $c = $ ?

   (f) If $a = 6$ and $c = 12$, then $b = $ ?

2. A man travels 7 mi due north, then goes 3 mi due east, and then 3 mi due south. How far is he from his starting point?

3. A man travels 1 mi north, 2 mi east, 3 mi north, and 4 mi east. How far is he from his starting point?

4. In the rectangular solid, every two intersecting edges are perpendicular. If $AE = 3$, $AB = 4$, and $BC = 12$, find the length of diagonal $\overline{BE}$; of diagonal $\overline{BH}$.

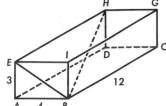

5. The hypotenuse of a right triangle is 17 and one leg is 15. Find the area of the triangle.

6. The sides of a triangle are 6 in., 9 in., and 11 in. long. Is it a right triangle? If it is, which side is the hypotenuse?

7. (a) Prove: If $m$ and $n$ are positive integers with $m > n$, then $m^2 + n^2$ will be the length of the hypotenuse of a right triangle whose legs will have lengths $m^2 - n^2$ and $2mn$. What theorem did you use?

   (b) Make a table with the following column headings:

   $$| \ m \ | \ n \ | \ m^2 - n^2 \ | \ 2mn \ | \ m^2 + n^2 \ |$$

   Use the method of part (a) to list in the table the integral lengths of the sides of right triangles having hypotenuse less than or equal to 25. There are six such "Pythagorean triples."

8. If $p$ and $q$ are lengths of the legs of a right triangle and $r$ is the length of the hypotenuse, show that for any positive number $k$, the numbers $kp$, $kq$, and $kr$ are also the lengths of the sides of a right triangle.

9. Which of the following sets of numbers could be the lengths of the sides of a right triangle?

(a) 30, 40, 60.    (b) 16, 30, 34.    (c) 10, 24, 26.

(d) $\frac{3}{4}$, 1, $1\frac{1}{4}$.    (e) 1.4, 4.8, 5.0.    (f) $1\frac{2}{3}$, $2\frac{2}{3}$, $3\frac{1}{3}$.

10. In $\triangle ABC$, $\angle C$ is a right angle, $AC = 20$, and $BC = 15$. Find

(a) $a\triangle ABC$,    (b) $AB$,

(c) the altitude to the hypotenuse.

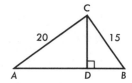

11. The hypotenuse of a triangle is 51 and another side is 24. Find the area of the triangle.

12. In the figure, $QR = 5$, $RP = 12$, $RT = h$ and $\overline{QR} \perp \overline{RP}$, $\overline{RT} \perp \overline{PQ}$. Find $h$.

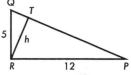

13. If the lengths of the legs of a right triangle are $a$ and $b$, find the length, $h$, of the altitude to the hypotenuse in terms of $a$ and $b$.

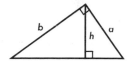

14. The legs of a right triangle are 24 and 32. Find the altitude to the hypotenuse.

15. In a rhombus, each side is 10 in. long, and one diagonal is 12 in. long. Find the area of the rhombus. Find its altitude to any side.

16. One angle of a rhombus has measure 60 and a side has length 5. Find the length of each diagonal.

17. $\Box ABCD$ is a trapezoid with $\overline{AB} \parallel \overline{DC}$. If segments have lengths as marked in the figure, find the area of the trapezoid.

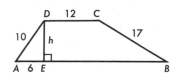

+ 18. (a) With right angles and lengths as marked in the figure, find $PB$, $PC$, and $PD$.

(b) If you continue the pattern of the figure, making $m\angle PDE = 90$ and $DE = 1$, what will $PE$ be? What would be the length of the next segment from $P$? You should discover an interesting pattern.

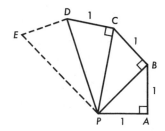

+ **19.** A proof of the Pythagorean Theorem making use of the figure on the right was discovered by General James A. Garfield several years before he became President of the United States. It appeared in about 1875 in the *New England Journal of Education.* Prove that $a^2 + b^2 = c^2$ by stating algebraically that the area of the trapezoid equals the sum of the areas of the three triangles. You must include a proof that $\angle EBA$ is a right angle.

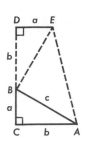

* **20.** Given trapezoid $\square ABCD$, $AB \parallel DC$, $\overline{AC} \perp \overline{BC}$, and $\overline{BD} \perp \overline{AD}$. If $AB = 25$, $AD = 15$, and $BC = 15$, what is the area of the trapezoid?

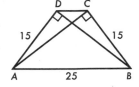

* **21.** In $\triangle ABC$ on the left below, $AC = 13$, $AB = 14$, $BC = 15$.

    (a) Find the altitude $h_c$.      (b) Find the altitude, $h_b$, to the side $\overline{AC}$.

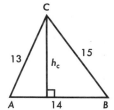
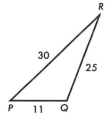

* **22.** In $\triangle PQR$ on the right above, $\angle Q$ is obtuse, $PQ = 11$, $QR = 25$, $PR = 30$. Find the altitude to $\overrightarrow{PQ}$; find $a \triangle PQR$.

* **23.** In $\triangle MOQ$, $\overline{MO} \perp \overline{OQ}$,

    $MO = OP = 1$, and $MP = PQ$.

    Find $MQ$. Find $m \angle Q$ and $m \angle QMO$.

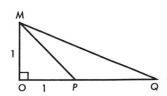

*+ **24.** Figure $ABCD$ is a tetrahedron with all of its edges congruent and each of length 2. $R$ and $S$ are mid-points of $\overline{DC}$ and $\overline{AB}$, respectively.

    (a) Prove that $\overline{RS}$ is a common perpendicular to $\overline{AB}$ and $\overline{DC}$.

    (b) Find $RS$.

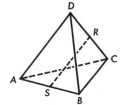

*+ **25.** The Pythagorean Theorem was known to the ancient Greeks in the following form.

> The area of the square upon the hypotenuse of a right triangle is equal to the sum of the areas of the squares upon its legs.

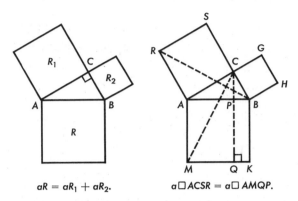

$aR = aR_1 + aR_2.$                $a\square ACSR = a\square AMQP.$

The figure on the left illustrates the theorem; the figure on the right is used in the proof. The following questions, together with your answers, suggest the method of proof.

(a) Why is $\angle RAB \cong \angle CAM$?

(b) Why is $\triangle RAB \cong \triangle CAM$?

(c) Why is $a\triangle RAB = a\triangle CAM$?

(d) Is one altitude of $\triangle RAB$ equal to $AC$?

(e) Why is $a\square ACSR = 2a\triangle RAB$?

(f) Is $a\square AMQP = 2a\triangle CAM$?

(g) Why is $a\square ACSR = a\square AMQP$?

(h) Is $a\square BHGC = a\square PQKB$?

(i) Is $a\square AMKB = a\square AMQP + a\square PQKB$? Why?

## HONORS PROBLEM

$\square ABCD$ is a square, $H$, $I$, $J$, and $K$ are mid-points of its sides, as shown, and $\square PQRS$ is a square. Determine the ratio

$$\frac{a\square PQRS}{a\square ABCD}.$$

## 11–4.  SPECIAL TRIANGLES

The Pythagorean Theorem gives us information about some special triangles.

**Theorem 11–10.**   The Isosceles Right Triangle Theorem

In an isosceles right triangle, the hypotenuse is $\sqrt{2}$ times as long as each of the legs.

You should supply a proof.

The converse is also true.

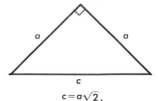

$c = a\sqrt{2}.$

**Theorem 11–11**

If the base of an isosceles triangle is $\sqrt{2}$ times as long as each of the two congruent sides, then the angle opposite the base is a right angle.

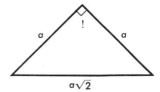

The proof begins with the observation that $a^2 + a^2 = (a\sqrt{2})^2$.

We learned in Section 9–7 that in a 30-60-90 triangle, the side opposite the 30°-angle is half as long as the hypotenuse, and we also know the converse:

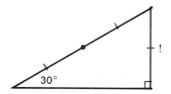
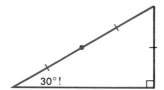

The Pythagorean Theorem now tells us the relation between the hypotenuse and the *longer* of the two legs, for 30-60-90 triangles.

**Theorem 11–12**

In a 30-60-90 triangle, the longer leg is $\sqrt{3}/2$ times as long as the hypotenuse.

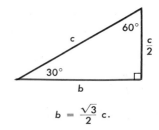

$b = \dfrac{\sqrt{3}}{2} c.$

**Proof.** Let $c$ be the length of the hypotenuse, and let $b$ be the length of the longer leg. Then the length of the shorter leg is $c/2$. By the Pythagorean Theorem,

$$\left(\frac{c}{2}\right)^2 + b^2 = c^2.$$

Now solve for $b$:

$$b = \frac{\sqrt{3}}{2}c.$$

[*Query:* Is it true that in a 30-60-90 triangle, the length of the longer leg is $\sqrt{3}$ times the length of the shorter leg?]

## Problem Set 11–4

1. How long is the diagonal of a square if its side is 6? 9? 78? $\sqrt{2}$? $\sqrt{6}$?

2. Find the longer leg of a 30-60-90 triangle if its hypotenuse is 4; 18; 98; $2\sqrt{3}$; 13.

3. $\triangle ABC$ is equilateral. If each side is 8 in. long, how long is the altitude to $\overline{AB}$? What is the area of $\triangle ABC$?

4. The acute angles of a right triangle are congruent and one of the congruent sides has length 15. How long is the third side?

5. In $\triangle PQR$, $m\angle P = 30$, $PR = 8$, $PQ = 11$. Find the altitude to $\overline{PQ}$ and the area of $\triangle PQR$.

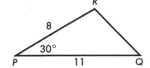

6. The measure of each base angle of an isosceles triangle is 30, and each of the two congruent sides has length 14. How long is the base? What is the area of the triangle?

7. A parallelogram has two sides of lengths 18 and 8, and the measure of one angle is 30. Find the area of the parallelogram.

8. What is the area of an isosceles triangle whose congruent sides each have length 20 and whose base angles have measures of 30? 45? 60?

9. In $\triangle ABC$, $\angle A$ is a right angle and $m\angle B = m\angle C = 45$. Given that $BC = 6$, find $AB$.

**10.** Prove: If the hypotenuse of an isosceles right triangle has length $m$, then each of the two congruent sides has length $\frac{1}{2}m\sqrt{2}$.

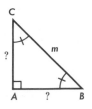

**11.** What is the area of the isosceles triangle whose congruent sides are each 12 in. long if the base angles have measures of

(a) 45?                (b) 30?                (c) 60?

**12.** What is the area of an isosceles triangle whose base is 12 if the base angles have measures of

(a) 45?                (b) 30?                (c) 60?

**13.** In trapezoid $\square ABCD$, the measures of the base angles are 45 and 30, as shown; $BC = 16$, $DC = 5$.  Find

$$a\square ABCD.$$

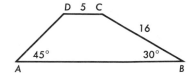

**14.** The altitude of an equilateral triangle is 12.  Find the length of a side and the area of the triangle.

**15.** Prove: The area of an equilateral triangle whose side is of length $S$ is given by $\dfrac{S^2}{4}\sqrt{3}$.

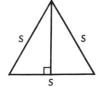

**16.** The side of one equilateral triangle equals the altitude of a second.  What is the ratio of their areas?

 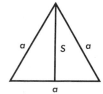

**17.** The area of an equilateral triangle is $25\sqrt{3}$.  Determine the lengths of its sides and altitudes.

**18.** A square whose area is 81 has its perimeter equal to the perimeter of an equilateral triangle.  What is the area of the triangle?

**19.** In the figure, $\triangle ABC$ lies in plane $E$ and $\overleftrightarrow{PA} \perp E$.

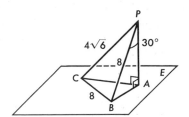

$$PB = BC = 8,$$
$$PC = 4\sqrt{6},$$
$$m\angle BPA = 30.$$

Determine the measures of as many other angles and segments as possible. Also, find $a\triangle PBC$.

**20.** In the cube, the edges are congruent and are perpendicular if they intersect. If a side has length 6, find $a\square ACGE$ and $a\triangle ACF$.

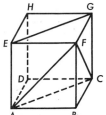

* **21.** In $\triangle ABC$, $m\angle A = 30$, $AC = 4$, $AB = 3\sqrt{3}$. Find $BC$. Is $\angle C$ a right angle? How do you know?

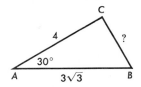

* **22.** In $\triangle PQR$, $\angle Q$ is obtuse,

$$m\angle P = 45, PR = 10, PQ = 3.$$

Find $RQ$ and $a\triangle PQR$.

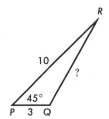

+ **23.** In the figure below, $m\angle K\text{-}PQ\text{-}M = 60$. Square $\square ABCD$ is in one face, with $\overleftrightarrow{AB} \parallel \overleftrightarrow{PQ}$, and is projected into the other face, resulting in $\square EFGH$. If $AB = \sqrt{26}$, find $a\square EFGH$.

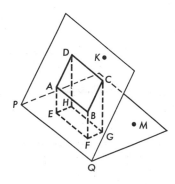

*+ **24.** In the figure on the right, $m\angle K\text{-}PQ\text{-}M = 45$. Square $\square ABCD$ is in one face, with $\overrightarrow{BD} \perp \overrightarrow{PQ}$, and is projected into the other face, resulting in $\square EFGH$. If $AB = 8$, find $a\square EFGH$.

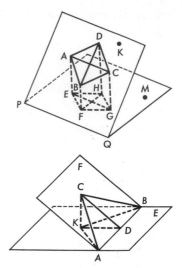

*+ **25.** Planes $E$ and $F$ intersect in $\overleftrightarrow{AB}$ forming a dihedral angle. In $F$, $\overleftrightarrow{CD}$ is the perpendicular bisector of $\overline{AB}$. $\overline{CK} \perp E$. Given that $\overline{AC} \perp \overline{BC}$, $m\angle CBK = 30$, and $BC = 6$, find $m\angle C\text{-}AB\text{-}K$ and $a\triangle ABK$.

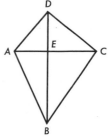

## Chapter Review

**1.** Complete: A polygonal region is the _____ of a _____ number of _____, in a plane, such that if two of these _____, their _____ is either a _____ _____ or a _____.

**2.** In the figure, $\overline{AC} \perp \overline{DB}$. If $DE = 8$ and $BE = 12$, what is the ratio of $a\triangle ACD$ to $a\triangle ABC$?

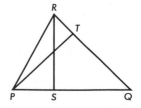

**3.** If one side of a square is three times as long as a side of a second square, the area of the first square is how many times the area of the second square? (Try to answer this one without using any area formulas at all.)

**4.** In $\triangle PQR$, $\overline{PT}$ and $\overline{RS}$ are altitudes. Given that $PR = 13$, $PS = 5$, and $m\angle Q = 45$, find $PT$.

**5.** If the diagonal of a square is 18 ft long, how long is each side? What is the area of the square?

**6.** A triangle has sides measuring 25, 25, and 48. Find its area.

**7.** An equilateral triangle has a median 15 in. long. What is its area?

**8.** $\square ABCD$ is a parallelogram. $\overline{CK} \perp \overline{AB}$ and $\angle M$ is a right angle.

   (a) If $BC = 12$, $DM = 15$, and $KC = 9$, find $DC$ and $CM$.

   (b) If $KC = \sqrt{24}$, $AK = \sqrt{18}$, and $KB = \sqrt{8}$, find $AD$ and $DM$.

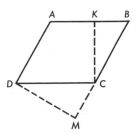

**9.** The side of a rhombus is 13 and one of its diagonals is 24. Find the area of the rhombus.

**10.** In $\triangle ABC$, $AB = 14$, the length of median $\overline{CD}$ is 8, and $m\angle ADC = 60$. What is $a\triangle ABC$?

**11.** Derive a formula for the area of this figure in terms of $a$, $b$, and $c$.

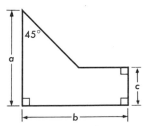

**12.** A trapezoid has parallel sides 13 in. and 21 in. long. The longer of the two nonparallel sides is 17, and the shorter is perpendicular to a parallel side. What is the area of the trapezoid?

**13.** In parallelogram $\square ABCD$, $M$ is the mid-point of $\overline{AD}$ and $K$ is the mid-point of $\overline{AB}$. Prove that

$$a\square AKCM = \tfrac{1}{2}a\square ABCD.$$

**14.** In this rectangular solid, $\overline{AG}$ and $\overline{EC}$ are diagonals. If $AB = 9$, $BF = 12$, and $AD = 8$, find $AG$ and $EC$.

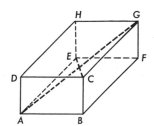

**15.** What is the length of the diagonal of a cube whose edge is 6?

**16.** In parallelogram $\square ABCD$, the bisectors of $\angle A$ and $\angle C$ meet diagonal $\overline{DB}$ at $E$ and $F$, respectively. Prove that the regions $ABCFE$ and $AEFCD$ have the same area.

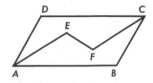

**17.** A given segment is a side of a square and also the hypotenuse of an isosceles right triangle. Prove that the area of the square is four times the area of the triangle. (Try to do this without using any area formulas at all.)

**18.** The area of an equilateral triangle is $100\sqrt{3}$. How long are its sides and altitudes?

**19.** $\square ABCD$ is a trapezoid with $\overline{AB} \parallel \overline{CD}$. $m\angle A = m\angle B = 60$ and $AB = 12$. $BC = 8$. Find $a\square ABCD$.

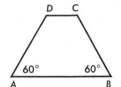

**\* 20.** $\square ABCD$ is a square. $E$ is on $\overline{AD}$ and $F$ is on $\overleftrightarrow{DC}$ so that $\overline{EB} \perp \overline{FB}$. If $a\square ABCD = 256$ and $a\triangle EBF = 200$, find $CF$.

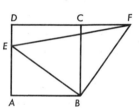

**\* 21.** $\square PQRS$ is a trapezoid, with $\overline{PQ} \parallel \overline{SR}$. $m\angle P = 45$ and $m\angle Q = 120$. If $PS = 12\sqrt{2}$ and $PQ = 27$, what is $a\square PQRS$?

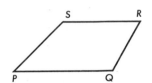

**\*+ 22.** In a triangle two sides have lengths $a$ and $b$. The altitude to the third side separates that side into segments of lengths $c$ and $d$ respectively. Prove that
$$(a + b)(a - b) = (c + d)(c - d).$$

**\*+ 23.** Given: $\square ABCD$ is a trapezoid with $\overline{AB} \parallel \overline{CD}$. $M$ and $K$ are mid-points of $\overline{AD}$ and $\overline{BC}$, respectively. $\overline{PK} \parallel \overline{AD}$.

Prove: $a\triangle APD = a\square PBCD = \frac{1}{2}a\square ABCD$.

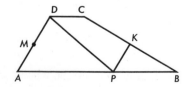

**\*+  24.** Given any two parallelograms in a plane.  Explain how a single line can be drawn which will separate each parallelogram region into two regions of equal area.

## HONORS PROBLEM

The figure at the right consists of four right triangles, four rectangles, and a square "hole" one unit on a side.

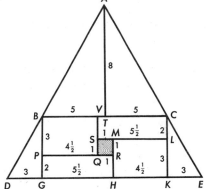

(a) Find the sum of the areas of the eight regions. (Don't count the hole!)

(b) Find the base, *DE*, and the altitude from *A* to $\overline{DE}$. Find one-half the product of these two numbers.

(c) Can you explain why the results of parts (a) and (b) are the same, in spite of the hole?

# 12 | Similarity

## 12–1. THE IDEA OF A SIMILARITY. PROPORTIONALITY

Roughly speaking, two geometric figures are similar if they have exactly the same shape, but not necessarily the same size. For example, any two circles are similar; any two squares are similar; any two equilateral triangles are similar; and any two segments are similar.

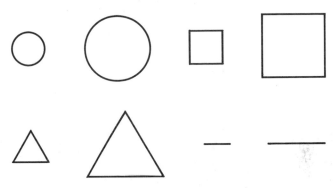

Another way of expressing this is to say that two figures are similar if one of them is an exact scale model of the other.

The marks in the figure below indicate that the two triangles ought to be similar.

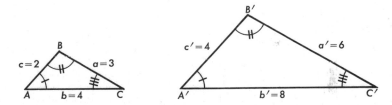

It ought to be possible to "stretch" the first triangle, doubling its size without changing its shape, so as to get the second triangle. The "stretching" scheme can be described by the correspondence

$$ABC \leftrightarrow A'B'C'.$$

Of course, this correspondence is not a congruence, because each side of the second triangle is twice as long as the corresponding side of the first. Correspondences of this kind are called *similarities*. An exact definition of a similarity will be given later in this chapter.

Similarities may shrink things instead of stretching them. For example, the correspondence

$$A'B'C' \leftrightarrow ABC$$

shrinks the second triangle onto the first.

Note that the lengths of the sides of our two triangles form two sequences of positive numbers, $a$, $b$, $c$ and $a'$, $b'$, $c'$. These sequences stand in a special relation: each number in the second sequence is exactly twice the corresponding number in the first sequence. Thus

$$a' = 2a, \qquad b' = 2b, \qquad c' = 2c.$$

Or, putting it the other way around, we can say that each number in the first sequence is exactly half of the corresponding number in the second:

$$a = \tfrac{1}{2}a', \qquad b = \tfrac{1}{2}b', \qquad c = \tfrac{1}{2}c'.$$

Thus

$$\frac{a'}{a} = \frac{b'}{b} = \frac{c'}{c},$$

because each of these fractions is equal to 2; and

$$\frac{a}{a'} = \frac{b}{b'} = \frac{c}{c'},$$

because each of these fractions is equal to $\tfrac{1}{2}$. Sequences which are related in this way are called *proportional*.

### Definition

Given two sequences $a$, $b$, $c$, ... and $p$, $q$, $r$, ... of positive numbers. If

$$\frac{a}{p} = \frac{b}{q} = \frac{c}{r} = \cdots,$$

then the sequences $a$, $b$, $c$, ... and $p$, $q$, $r$, ... are called *proportional*.

Obviously, this definition does not depend on the order in which the two sequences are named; if

$$\frac{a}{p} = \frac{b}{q} = \frac{c}{r} = \cdots,$$

then

$$\frac{p}{a} = \frac{q}{b} = \frac{r}{c} = \cdots,$$

and conversely.

We deal with proportionalities by the usual methods of algebra. The easiest proportionalities to work with are those which involve only four numbers. We often refer to such a proportionality as a *proportion*. Below are some examples of what you can conclude, given that $a, b$ and $p, q$ are proportional. Given:

$$(1) \qquad \frac{a}{p} = \frac{b}{q},$$

by definition of proportionality. Multiplying on both sides by $pq$, we obtain

$$(2) \qquad aq = bp.$$

Dividing on both sides by $bq$, we get

$$(3) \qquad \frac{a}{b} = \frac{p}{q}.$$

There is no danger of dividing by 0 here, because all the numbers in a proportionality must be positive. Next, adding 1 to both sides and simplifying, we get

$$(4) \qquad \frac{a + b}{b} = \frac{p + q}{q}.$$

Subtracting 1 from both sides of equation (3), we obtain

$$(5) \qquad \frac{a - b}{b} = \frac{p - q}{q}.$$

These are merely the most useful of the equations that can be derived from (1); there are many others. These equations need not be memorized. If you try to learn things like this by rote, then half the time you will misremember them when you need them most. What you need to remember is the type of algebraic method that we use in obtaining one equation from another.

### Definition

If $a, b, c$ are positive numbers, and

$$\frac{a}{b} = \frac{b}{c},$$

then $b$ is called the *geometric mean* between $a$ and $c$.

It is easy to calculate that $b = \sqrt{ac}$.

## Problem Set 12–1

**1.** Supply the numbers which will make each statement a proportionality.

(a) $\dfrac{2}{3} = \dfrac{?}{6} = \dfrac{?}{15} = \dfrac{2x}{?} = \dfrac{?}{1.5}$.

(b) $\dfrac{792}{3960} = \dfrac{198}{?} = \dfrac{?}{495} = \dfrac{9}{?} = \dfrac{1}{?}$.

(c) $\dfrac{?}{3} = \dfrac{6x}{?} = \dfrac{24}{18} = \dfrac{?}{6\sqrt{3}}$.

(d) $\dfrac{5}{4} = \dfrac{10}{?} = \dfrac{?}{28} = \dfrac{5\sqrt{2}}{?} = \dfrac{?}{0.04}$.

**2.** Complete each statement.

(a) If $\dfrac{5}{9} = \dfrac{15}{27}$, then $9 \cdot 15 = 5 \cdot \underline{\phantom{?}}$.

(b) If $\dfrac{a}{b} = \dfrac{3}{7}$, then $7a = \underline{\phantom{?}}$.

(c) If $\dfrac{x}{12} = \dfrac{5}{8}$, then $8x = \underline{\phantom{?}}$.

**3.** In each proportionality, solve for $x$.

(a) $\dfrac{x}{2} = \dfrac{3}{4}$.

(b) $\dfrac{5}{x} = \dfrac{4}{7}$.

(c) $\dfrac{5}{4} = \dfrac{2x}{13}$.

(d) $\dfrac{2}{3} = \dfrac{11}{x+3}$.

**4.** Complete each statement.

(a) If $\dfrac{x}{3} = \dfrac{5}{7}$, then $x = \underline{\phantom{?}} \cdot \dfrac{5}{7}$.

(b) If $\dfrac{5}{9} = \dfrac{10}{18}$, then $\dfrac{5}{10} = \dfrac{?}{18}$.

(c) If $\dfrac{3}{4} = \dfrac{12}{16}$, then $\dfrac{16}{4} = \dfrac{12}{?}$.

(d) If $\dfrac{a}{b} = \dfrac{c}{d}$, then $\dfrac{a}{c} = \underline{\phantom{?}}$.

**5.** Determine the geometric mean between 4 and 9; between 7 and 14; between 15 and 60.

**6.** Complete each statement.

(a) If $3a = 2b$, then $\dfrac{a}{b} = \underline{\phantom{?}}$ and $\dfrac{a}{2} = \underline{\phantom{?}}$.

(b) If $4m = 15$, then $\dfrac{m}{5} = \underline{\phantom{?}}$ and $\dfrac{m}{3} = \underline{\phantom{?}}$.

(c) If $6x = 5 \cdot 9$, then $\dfrac{x}{5} = \underline{\phantom{?}}$ and $\dfrac{5}{x} = \underline{\phantom{?}}$.

(d) If $\dfrac{2a}{3b} = \dfrac{7c}{5d}$, then $\dfrac{a}{b} = \underline{\phantom{?}}$ and $\dfrac{b}{a} = \underline{\phantom{?}}$.

**7.** For any two positive numbers $a$ and $c$, the geometric mean is $b = \sqrt{ac}$, and the arithmetic mean is $d = \frac{1}{2}(a + c)$. Make a table of the geometric mean and arithmetic mean for the following pairs.

(a) 2 and 8.

(b) 3 and 12.

(c) 5 and 45.

(d) 4 and 9.

(e) 9 and 16.

(f) 12 and 15.

**8.** Complete each statement.

(a) If $\dfrac{5}{12} = \dfrac{15}{36}$, then $\dfrac{5+12}{12} = \dfrac{15+?}{36}$.

(b) If $\dfrac{7}{9} = \dfrac{28}{36}$, then $\dfrac{7}{2} = \dfrac{28}{36-?}$.

(c) If $\dfrac{a}{b} = \dfrac{6}{5}$, then $\dfrac{a+b}{b} = \underline{\;\;?\;\;}$ and $\dfrac{a-b}{b} = \underline{\;\;?\;\;}$.

(d) If $\dfrac{a+c}{c} = \dfrac{11}{7}$, then $\dfrac{a}{c} = \underline{\;\;?\;\;}$ and $\dfrac{c}{a} = \underline{\;\;?\;\;}$.

**9.** Consider these three sequences.  How many pairs of sequences are proportional?

(a) 3, 8, 12, 17.  (b) 9, 24, 36, 51.  (c) $\frac{7}{2}$, $\frac{28}{3}$, 15, $\frac{119}{6}$.

It is easy to see that sequences (a) and (b) are proportional, since each number in (b) is three times the corresponding number in (a). But comparing (a) and (c) or (b) and (c) is not a simple matter.  One efficient way is to change each sequence to a proportional sequence beginning with 1, as in the following.

(a) 1, $\frac{8}{3}$, 4, $\frac{17}{3}$.

(b) 1, $\frac{24}{9}$, 4, $\frac{51}{9}$; or 1, $\frac{8}{3}$, ——, ——.

(c) 1, $\frac{8}{3}$, ——, ——.

Now answer the question.

**10.** Which pairs of the following sequences are proportional?  You may want to use the method of Problem 9 to help you decide.

(a) 5, 7, 9.  (b) 1, 2, 3.  (c) $2\frac{1}{2}$, $3\frac{1}{2}$, $4\frac{1}{2}$.  (d) 8, 15, 17.

(e) 15, 30, 45.  (f) 16, 30, 34.  (g) $\frac{1}{3}$, $\frac{2}{3}$, 1.  (h) 1.25, 1.75, 2.25.

**11.** If $x/40 = y/50 = 30/20$, solve for $x$ and $y$.

**12.** If $3/p = 5/q = r/26 = q/20$, solve for $p$, $q$, and $r$.

+ **13.** Which of the following are true for all values of the variables used, except, of course, those values which would make any term of a sequence zero?

(a) $\dfrac{5x}{6x} = \dfrac{5}{6}$.

(b) $\dfrac{a}{8b} = \dfrac{b}{8a}$.

(c) $\dfrac{r}{r^2} = \dfrac{s}{rs} = \dfrac{t}{tr}$.

(d) $\dfrac{a+b}{a^2-b^2} = \dfrac{1}{a-b}$.

(e) $\dfrac{a+b}{1} = \dfrac{a^2+b^2}{a+b}$.

(f) $\dfrac{1}{x} + \dfrac{1}{y} = \dfrac{x+y}{xy}$.

+ **14.** (a) Consider the proportionality $\frac{2}{3} = \frac{4}{6} = \frac{6}{9} = \frac{8}{12} = \frac{18}{27}$. Verify that

$$\frac{2 + 4 + 6 + 8 + 18}{3 + 6 + 9 + 12 + 27} = \frac{2}{3}.$$

Does the same procedure work for any other proportionality? Try one!

(b) Prove: If

$$\frac{a}{b} = \frac{c}{d} = \frac{e}{f} = \frac{g}{h},$$

then

$$\frac{a + c + e + g}{b + d + f + h} = \frac{a}{b}.$$

[*Hint:* Let $a/b = k$. Then $a = kb$. Also, $c = kd$, $e = kf$, $g = kh$. Does

$$\frac{a + c + e + g}{b + d + f + h} = k?]$$

## HONORS PROBLEM

Prove the following theorem.

The geometric mean of two positive numbers is always less than their arithmetic mean (i.e., average).

[*Hint:* Take $a > b > 0$. Show $\sqrt{ab} < \frac{1}{2}(a + b)$. Try assuming that the proposed inequality holds and derive from it an inequality that you *know* is true. This will show you where to begin the proof.]

## 12–2.   SIMILARITIES BETWEEN TRIANGLES

We now state the definition of a similarity between two triangles. Suppose we have given a correspondence $ABC \leftrightarrow A'B'C'$ between $\triangle ABC$ and $\triangle A'B'C'$. As usual, $a$ is the length of the side opposite $A$, $b$ is the length of the side opposite $B$, and so on. If corresponding angles are congruent and

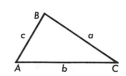

$$\frac{a}{a'} = \frac{b}{b'} = \frac{c}{c'},$$

then we say that the correspondence $ABC \leftrightarrow A'B'C'$ is a *similarity*, and we write

$$\triangle ABC \sim \triangle A'B'C'.$$

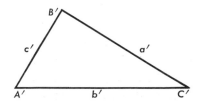

## Definition

Given a correspondence between two triangles. If corresponding angles are congruent, and corresponding sides are proportional, then the correspondence is called a *similarity*, and the triangles are said to be *similar*.

The situation here is like that for congruence: $\triangle ABC \sim \triangle A'B'C'$ means not merely that the triangles are similar, but also that the particular correspondence $ABC \leftrightarrow A'B'C'$ is a similarity. Thus, given $\triangle ABC \sim \triangle A'B'C'$, we can immediately write the proportionality

$$\frac{a}{a'} = \frac{b}{b'} = \frac{c}{c'},$$

without referring to a figure. If the lengths of the sides are not labeled, these equations take the form

$$\frac{BC}{B'C'} = \frac{AC}{A'C'} = \frac{AB}{A'B'}.$$

The definition of a similarity requires two things: (1) corresponding angles must be congruent, and (2) corresponding sides must be proportional. For triangles, it will turn out that if one of these conditions holds, then so does the other. That is, if corresponding angles are congruent, then corresponding sides are proportional, and conversely. These facts are given in the AAA Similarity Theorem and the SSS Similarity Theorem, which will be proved later in this chapter.

In requiring both (1) and (2), we were playing it safe; and this was a good plan, because triangles are the only figures for which similarity is a simple idea. Consider, for example, a square and a rectangle:

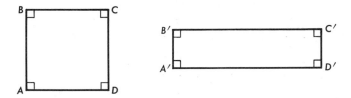

Under the correspondence $ABCD \leftrightarrow A'B'C'D'$, corresponding angles are congruent, because all the angles are right angles. But corresponding sides are not proportional, and surely neither of the two figures is a scale model of the other.

For other quadrilaterals, exactly the opposite trouble can come up. Consider a square and a rhombus:

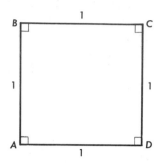 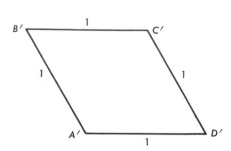

Under the correspondence $ABCD \leftrightarrow A'B'C'D'$, corresponding sides are proportional, but the figures have quite different shapes.

## Problem Set 12–2

**1.** Given $\triangle ABC \sim \triangle DEF$ and lengths of sides as marked. Find $x$ and $y$.

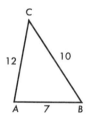 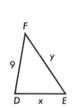 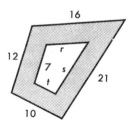

**2.** A piece of cardboard is cut, as in the figure on the right above, with the inner and outer boundaries similar quadrilaterals. If the lengths of sides are as marked, what are $r$, $s$, and $t$?

**3.** In the figure, $\triangle ABC \sim \triangle ADE$. If

$$AD = 5, \quad AE = 6, \quad BC = 12,$$

and

$$AB = 15,$$

what are $AC$ and $DE$?

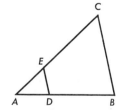

**4.** If $\triangle ABC \cong \triangle A'B'C'$, does it follow that $\triangle ABC \sim \triangle A'B'C'$? Why?

**5.** Two photographic prints of a negative are made, one a contact print and one an enlarged print. In the contact print an object has a width of 2 in. and a height of 2.3 in. In the enlargement the same object has a width of 7.5 in. What is its height in the enlargement?

6. John can get a good approximation of the height of a tall tree by the following procedure. First he stands next to the tree and notes where a point on the tree about 5 ft from the ground would be. Then he walks 40 paces (or 100 ft) from the tree. Turning toward the tree he holds a small ruler, 6 in. long, vertically in front of his eyes, until the ruler just obscures the tree above the 5-ft mark. Using a string tied through a hole in one end of the ruler, he measures in inches the distance from his eye to the ruler. He then easily computes the height of the tree by the formula

$$h = 100 \cdot \frac{6}{AB} + 5.$$

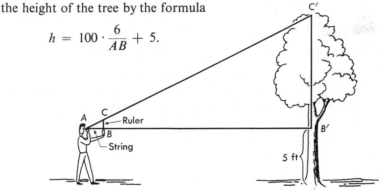

(a) Explain why this formula gives the height of the tree. What is the unit of measure?

(b) If the string measures 8 in., how tall is the tree?

7. Prove: If $D$ and $E$ are mid-points of $\overline{AC}$ and $\overline{BC}$, respectively, in $\triangle ABC$, then $\triangle CDE \sim \triangle CAB$.

8. Prove: The triangle whose vertices are the mid-points of the sides of a given triangle is similar to the given triangle.

9. Given the figure with $\triangle PMK \sim \triangle KLR$. Prove that $\angle Q \cong \angle MKL$.

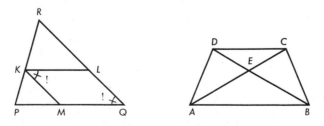

10. Given: Trapezoid $\square ABCD$ with $\overline{AB} \parallel \overline{CD}$, $\triangle AED \sim \triangle BEC$, and $\triangle AEB \sim \triangle CED$.

Prove: $AD = BC$.

## 12–3.  THE BASIC PROPORTIONALITY THEOREM AND ITS CONVERSE

Consider a triangle $\triangle ABC$, with a cross bar $\overline{DE}$, parallel to the base $\overline{BC}$. It looks as though the correspondence $ABC \leftrightarrow ADE$ ought to be a similarity. In fact, it is rather easy to prove that corresponding angles are congruent. (Proof?) To show that corresponding sides are proportional is a little more difficult. We begin with the following theorem, which says that the *sloping* sides in the figure above are proportional.

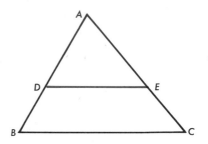

**Theorem 12–1.**  The Basic Proportionality Theorem

If a line parallel to one side of a triangle intersects the other two sides in distinct points, then it cuts off segments which are proportional to these sides.

**Restatement.**  In $\triangle ABC$ let $D$ and $E$ be points of $\overline{AB}$ and $\overline{AC}$ such that $\overline{DE} \parallel \overline{BC}$. Then

$$\frac{AB}{AD} = \frac{AC}{AE}.$$

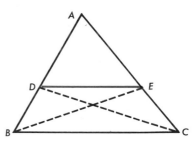

**Proof.**  In $\triangle ADE$ and $\triangle BDE$, let us regard $\overline{AD}$ and $\overline{BD}$ as the bases. Then these triangles have the same altitude. (Why?) Therefore, by Theorem 11–7, the ratio of their areas is the ratio of their bases, and we have

$$(1) \quad \frac{a\triangle BDE}{a\triangle ADE} = \frac{BD}{AD}.$$

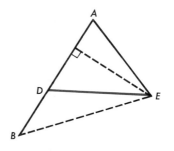

Similarly, in $\triangle ADE$ and $\triangle CDE$ let us consider $\overline{AE}$ and $\overline{CE}$ as the bases. Since these triangles have the same altitude, we conclude as before that

$$(2) \quad \frac{a\triangle CDE}{a\triangle ADE} = \frac{CE}{AE}.$$

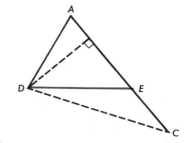

Now $\triangle BDE$ and $\triangle CDE$ have the same base $\overline{DE}$. (See the figure to the right of the restatement). And they have the same altitude, because $\overleftrightarrow{DE}$ and $\overleftrightarrow{BC}$ are parallel. Therefore, by Theorem 11–6,

(3)     $$a\triangle BDE = a\triangle CDE.$$

Fitting together the three equations (1), (2), and (3), we get

(4)     $$\frac{BD}{AD} = \frac{CE}{AE}.$$

Adding 1 to both sides of equation (4), we get

(5)     $$\frac{BD + AD}{AD} = \frac{CE + AE}{AE}, \quad \text{or} \quad \frac{AB}{AD} = \frac{AC}{AE},$$

which is what we wanted.

The converse of the Basic Proportionality Theorem is much easier to prove.

### Theorem 12–2

If a line intersects two sides of a triangle, and cuts off segments proportional to these two sides, then it is parallel to the third side.

**Restatement.** Given $\triangle ABC$. Let $D$ be a point between $A$ and $B$, and let $E$ be a point between $A$ and $C$. If

$$\frac{AB}{AD} = \frac{AC}{AE},$$

then $\overleftrightarrow{DE} \parallel \overleftrightarrow{BC}$.

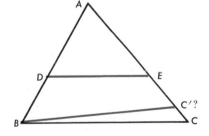

**Proof.** Let $\overleftrightarrow{BC'}$ be the line through $B$, parallel to $\overleftrightarrow{DE}$, intersecting $\overleftrightarrow{AC}$ at $C'$. By the preceding theorem,

$$\frac{AB}{AD} = \frac{AC'}{AE}.$$

Since, by hypothesis,

$$\frac{AB}{AD} = \frac{AC}{AE},$$

we have

$$\frac{AC'}{AE} = \frac{AC}{AE},$$

and $AC' = AC$. Therefore $C = C'$, and $\overleftrightarrow{DE} \parallel \overleftrightarrow{BC}$.

## Problem Set 12–3

**1.** In $\triangle ABC$, $\overline{DE} \parallel \overline{AB}$.

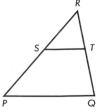

(a) Given that $AC = 12$, $CD = 4$, and $BC = 24$, find $CE$.

(b) Given $AC = 15$, $AD = 3$, and $BC = 25$. Find $BE$.

(c) Given $AD = 6$, $CD = 4$, and $CE = 7$. Find $BC$.

(d) Given $CD = 8$, $AC = 18$, and $BE = 6$. Find $CE$.

(e) Given $AD = CE$, $CD = 4$, $EB = 9$. Find $AC$.

**2.** Given $\overline{ST} \parallel \overline{PQ}$ in $\triangle PQR$, complete the following statements.

(a) $\dfrac{RP}{RS} = \dfrac{?}{?}$.

(b) $\dfrac{RS}{SP} = \dfrac{?}{?}$.

(c) $\dfrac{?}{?} = \dfrac{SP}{RP}$.

(d) $\dfrac{RT}{RQ} = \dfrac{?}{?}$.

(e) $\dfrac{RS}{RT} = \dfrac{?}{?}$.

(f) $\dfrac{RQ}{RP} = \dfrac{?}{?}$.

**3.** In each of the following triangles a segment is drawn parallel to a base, and the lengths of certain segments are marked. In each case, solve for $x$ in terms of the other letters.

(a)          (b)          (c)          (d)

**4.** In $\triangle JMK$, $m \angle M = m \angle HGK = x$.

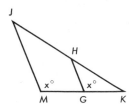

(a) Given $JH = 7$, $JK = 21$, and $GK = 10$. Find $MG$.

(b) Given $HK = MG$, $MK = 6$, and $JH = 8$. Find $GK$.

(c) Given $GK = 7$, $HK = 2MG$, and $JH = 14$. Find $JK$.

(d) Given $KJ = 24$, $HK = MK$, and $KG = 4$. Find $MK$.

**5.** If the segments in the figure on the left below have the lengths indicated, is $\overline{PQ} \parallel \overline{AB}$? Justify your answer.

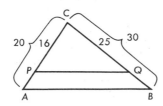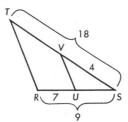

**6.** If the segments in the figure on the right above have the lengths indicated, is $\overline{UV} \parallel \overline{RT}$? Justify your answer.

**7.** Which of the following sets of lengths will make $\overline{FG} \parallel \overline{BC}$?

(a) $AB = 14$, $AF = 6$, $AC = 7$, $AG = 3$.

(b) $AB = 12$, $FB = 3$, $AC = 8$, $AG = 6$.

(c) $AF = 6$, $FB = 5$, $AG = 9$, $GC = 8$.

(d) $AC = 21$, $GC = 9$, $AB = 14$, $AF = 5$.

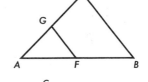

**8.** Given the figure as marked, find all values of $x$ which will make $\overline{DE} \parallel \overline{AB}$.

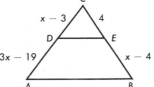

**9.** Prove the following theorem.

The bisector of an angle of a triangle separates the opposite side into segments whose lengths are proportional to the lengths of the adjacent sides.

**Restatement.** In $\triangle ABC$, if $\overrightarrow{AD}$ bisects $\angle A$ and $D$ is on $\overline{BC}$, then

$$\frac{BD}{CD} = \frac{BA}{CA}.$$

[*Hint:* Introduce $\overleftrightarrow{CE}$ parallel to $\overrightarrow{AD}$. Show that $AC = AE$.]

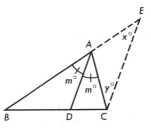

**10.** Use the theorem of Problem 9 in answering the following.

(a) The sides of a triangle are 15, 20, and 28. How long are the segments into which the bisector of the largest angle separates the opposite side? of the smallest angle?

(b) The sides of a triangle are 12, 18, and 24. Find the lengths of the segments into which the bisector of each angle separates its opposite side.

**11.** In the figure, $\overline{PS} \parallel \overline{AD}$, $\overline{SR} \parallel \overline{DC}$, and $\overline{RQ} \parallel \overline{BC}$. Prove that $\overline{PQ} \parallel \overline{AB}$.

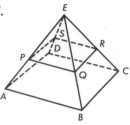

**12.** Prove the following theorem.

If three or more parallels are each cut by two transversals, the intercepted segments on the two transversals are proportional.

**Restatement.** If transversals $T_1$ and $T_2$ cut parallels $L_1$, $L_2$, and $L_3$ in $A$, $B$, $C$ and $D$, $E$, $F$, respectively, then

$$\frac{AB}{BC} = \frac{DE}{EF}.$$

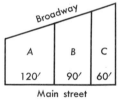

[*Hint:* Introduce $\overline{DC}$ or $\overline{AF}$.]

**13.** Three lots extend from Main Street to Broadway, as shown in the sketch. The side boundaries are perpendicular to Main Street. If the total frontage on Broadway is 360 ft, find the frontage of each lot on Broadway.

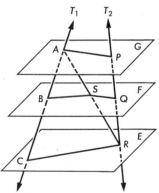

$+$ **14.** Given: Parallel planes $E$, $F$, and $G$ are intersected by transversals $T_1$ and $T_2$, as in the figure.

Prove: $\dfrac{AB}{BC} = \dfrac{PQ}{QR}.$

[*Hint:* Introduce $\overline{AR}$.]

$+$ **15.** Prove: The diagonals of a trapezoid intersect each other at a point which makes the lengths of the segments of one diagonal proportional to the lengths of the segments of the other diagonal.

+ **16.** A printer desires to make a card 6 in. long and of a width such that when folded in half, as shown, it will have the same shape as when it is unfolded. What should be the width?

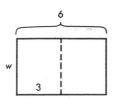

*+ **17.** Prove the following theorem.

> Given any triangle, $\triangle ABC$. If the bisectors of the interior and exterior angles at $A$ intersect $\overleftrightarrow{BC}$ at points $D$ and $D'$, respectively, then
> $$\frac{BD}{BD'} = \frac{CD}{CD'}.$$

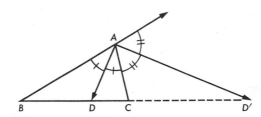

[*Hint:* Introduce $\overleftrightarrow{CE}$ parallel to $\overline{AD'}$, use Theorem 12–1 and Problem 9 of this problem set.]

*+ **18.** (a) In Problem 17, if $AC = 9$, $AB = 15$, and $BC = 16$, what are $BD$, $DC$, and $CD'$?

(b) In Problem 17, if $m \angle BAC = 90$, $AC = 6$, and $AB = 8$, what are $BD$, $DC$, and $CD'$?

*+ **19.** Does the theorem of Problem 17 hold if $AB < AC$? Illustrate and explain. How does the theorem change if $AB = AC$?

*+ **20.** A triangle has sides of 6, 12, and 16. The bisectors of the largest interior angle and the smallest exterior angle intersect the line containing the opposite side at points $X$ and $Y$, respectively. Determine the distances of $X$ and $Y$ from the vertex of the smallest angle of the triangle.

## HONORS PROBLEM

> Given $\triangle ABC$ with $AB > AC$. The bisectors of the interior and exterior angles at $A$ intersect $\overleftrightarrow{BC}$ at points $D$ and $E$, respectively. Prove that
> $$\frac{\sqrt{AD^2 + AE^2}}{CD} - \frac{\sqrt{AD^2 + AE^2}}{BD} = 2.$$

## 12–4.  THE BASIC SIMILARITY THEOREMS

**Theorem 12–3.**  The AAA Similarity Theorem

Given a correspondence between two triangles.  If corresponding angles are congruent, then the correspondence is a similarity.

**Restatement.**  Given a correspondence $ABC \leftrightarrow DEF$ between two triangles.  If  $\angle A \cong \angle D$, $\angle B \cong \angle E$,  and  $\angle C \cong \angle F$,  then $\triangle ABC \sim \triangle DEF$.

**Proof.**  Since we know by hypothesis that corresponding angles are congruent, what we need to prove is that corresponding sides are proportional.  That is, we need to show that

$$\frac{AB}{DE} = \frac{AC}{DF} = \frac{BC}{EF}.$$

We shall show that the *first* of these equations holds.  By exactly the same proof, with merely a change of notation, it will follow that the second equation also holds.

We proceed to the proof that

$$\frac{AB}{DE} = \frac{AC}{DF}.$$

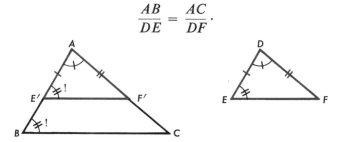

Let $E'$ and $F'$ be points of $\overrightarrow{AB}$ and $\overrightarrow{AC}$, such that $AE' = DE$ and $AF' = DF$.  By SAS we have

$$\triangle AE'F' \cong \triangle DEF.$$

Therefore $\angle AE'F' \cong \angle E$.  Since $\angle E \cong \angle B$, it follows that

$$\angle AE'F' \cong \angle B.$$

We consider two cases:

(1) If $E' = B$, then $\triangle AE'F'$ and $\triangle ABC$ are the same triangle.  In this case $\triangle ABC \cong \triangle DEF$, and

$$\frac{AB}{DE} = \frac{AC}{DF},$$

because each of these fractions is equal to 1.  (Why?)

(2) If $E'$ is different from $B$, then $\overleftrightarrow{E'F'}$ and $\overleftrightarrow{BC}$ are parallel. (Why?) By the Basic Proportionality Theorem, we have

$$\frac{AB}{AE'} = \frac{AC}{AF'}.$$

Since $AE' = DE$ and $AF' = DF$, it follows that

$$\frac{AB}{DE} = \frac{AC}{DF},$$

which was to be proved.

We recall, from Corollary 9–13.1, that if *two* pairs of corresponding angles are congruent, then the third pair must also be congruent. (The reason, of course, is that in any triangle, the sum of the measures of the angles is 180.)  This gives us the following corollary:

### Corollary 12–3.1.  The AA Corollary

Given a correspondence between two triangles.  If two pairs of corresponding angles are congruent, then the correspondence is a similarity.

We can now prove a stronger version of the Basic Proportionality Theorem, justifying the remarks made at the beginning of the preceding section, on p. 330.

### Corollary 12–3.2

If a line parallel to one side of a triangle intersects the other two sides in distinct points, then it cuts off a triangle similar to the given triangle.

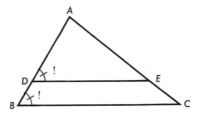

**Proof.**   When the parallel lines $\overleftrightarrow{DE}$ and $\overleftrightarrow{BC}$ are cut by the transversal $\overleftrightarrow{AB}$, corresponding angles are congruent.  Therefore $\angle ADE \cong \angle B$. Since $\angle A \cong \angle A$, it follows by the AA Corollary that

$$\triangle ADE \sim \triangle ABC.$$

## Problem Set 12–4A

**1.** Given: The figure with $\overline{AC} \parallel \overline{BD}$.
Prove: (1) $\triangle ACE \sim \triangle BDE$.
(2) $AE \cdot ED = CE \cdot EB$.

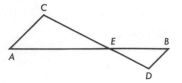

**2.** Given: $\square PQRS$ with $\overline{SR} \parallel \overline{PQ}$, diagonal $\overline{SQ}$, $U$ and $V$ are mid-points.
Prove: $US \cdot MQ = VQ \cdot MS$.

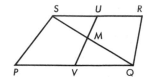

**3.** Given the figure, with $AD = 14$, $ED = 12$, $BC = 15$, and $EB = 4$.   Find $AC$, $AE$, and $AB$.

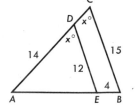

**4.** In $\triangle GHK$, $GK = HK$, $\overline{PR} \perp \overline{GK}$, and $\overline{PQ} \perp \overline{HK}$.  Prove that

$$GR \cdot PQ = PR \cdot HQ.$$

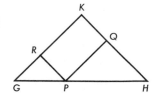

**5.** Prove the following theorem.

Any two corresponding altitudes of similar triangles have the same ratio as the corresponding sides.

**6.** In $\triangle ABC$, $\angle C$ is a right angle and $\overline{CD}$ is the altitude to the hypotenuse.

(a) Name at least one angle congruent to $\angle ACB$.

(b) Name an angle congruent to $\angle z$.

(c) Name a triangle similar to $\triangle ABC$.  Write the similarity between the two.

7. In the figure, $\overline{RQ} \perp \overline{PQ}$, $\overline{PQ} \perp \overline{PT}$, and $\overline{ST} \perp \overline{PR}$. Prove that

$$ST \cdot RQ = PS \cdot PQ.$$

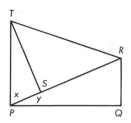

8. Given the figure, express $x$ in terms of $a$, $b$, and $c$.

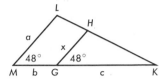

9. In the figure, $\square DEFG$ is a square and $\angle C$ is a right angle.

Prove: (1) $\triangle ADG \sim \triangle GCF$.

      (2) $\triangle ADG \sim \triangle FEB$.

      (3) $AD \cdot EB = DG \cdot FE$.

      (4) $DE = \sqrt{AD \cdot EB}$.

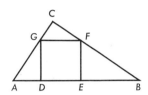

10. Prove the following theorem.

    Any two corresponding angle bisectors of similar triangles have the same ratio as the corresponding sides.

\* 11. Given the figure with $L_1 \parallel L_2$ and $\overline{AP}$, $\overline{BQ}$, $\overline{CR}$ intersecting at $K$.

    (a) Name three pairs of similar triangles and write the three similarities.

    (b) Prove that

$$\frac{AB}{PQ} = \frac{AC}{PR} = \frac{BC}{RQ}.$$

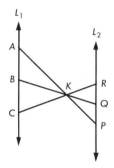

\* 12. Given the figure with perpendiculars as marked.

    (a) Prove that $\triangle BFC \sim \triangle ADC$.

    (b) Prove that

$$BF = \frac{AD \cdot BC}{AC}.$$

    (c) Prove that

$$\frac{BE}{AB} = \frac{CD}{AC} \cdot \frac{AC}{AB} + \frac{AD}{AC} \cdot \frac{BC}{AB}.$$

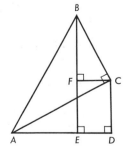

* **13.** Given a parallelogram, $\square ABCD$, with its diagonals. A line through $B$ intersects $\overline{AC}$ at $E$, $\overline{DC}$ at $G$, and $\overleftrightarrow{AD}$ at $F$. Prove that (1) $\triangle AEF \sim \triangle CEB$ and (2) $EB$ is the geometric mean of $EG$ and $EF$.

*+ **14.** In the figure, $\overline{PA}$, $\overline{QB}$, and $\overline{RC}$ are each perpendicular to $\overline{AC}$.

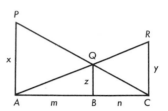

  (a) Complete:

$$\triangle PAC \sim \triangle \underline{\hspace{1.5cm}} \text{ and}$$

$$\triangle ABQ \sim \triangle \underline{\hspace{1cm}}.$$

  (b) Which is correct:

$$\frac{z}{x} = \frac{n}{m} \quad \text{or} \quad \frac{z}{x} = \frac{n}{m+n} \; ?$$

  (c) Which is correct:

$$\frac{z}{y} = \frac{m}{n} \quad \text{or} \quad \frac{z}{y} = \frac{m}{m+n} \; ?$$

  (d) Show that

$$\frac{1}{x} + \frac{1}{y} = \frac{1}{z} \cdot$$

*+ **15.** "One man can complete a job in 6 hr, and another man can complete the same job in 3 hr. If they work together, how long will it take to complete the job?" This problem can be answered by solving the equation

$$\frac{1}{6} + \frac{1}{3} = \frac{1}{n} \cdot$$

Solve this equation *geometrically*. [*Hint:* See Problem 14.]

## HONORS PROBLEM

A common problem involving electrical circuits is the following. A circuit consists of two wires in parallel, with resistances $R_1$ and $R_2$. What is the resistance of the circuit?

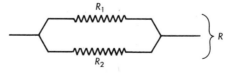

The resistance of the circuit, $R$, is given by the equation

$$\frac{1}{R} = \frac{1}{R_1} + \frac{1}{R_2} \cdot$$

Solve this equation for $R$ in terms of $R_1$ and $R_2$.

The following scheme has been used to find $R$ when $R_1$ and $R_2$ are known. Numerical scales are marked on three rays, as shown below. A straight-edge is placed so as to pass through $R_1$ and $R_2$ on the two outer scales,

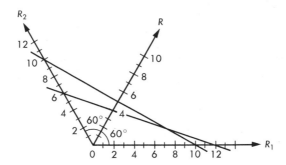

and $R$ is read on the remaining scale. For example, if $R_1 = 12$ and $R_2 = 6$, then $R = 4$; if $R_1 = 10$ and $R_2 = 10$, then $R = 5$.

(a) Find $R$, given that $R_1 = 4$ and $R_2 = 12$; $R_1 = 6$ and $R_2 = 3$; $R_1 = 7$ and $R_2 = 7$.

(b) Using the figure below, explain why the scheme described above gives solutions to the equation.

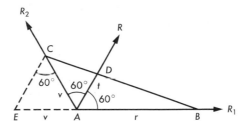

The following theorem will be convenient, and is easily proved.

**Theorem 12–4**

If $\triangle ABC \sim \triangle DEF$, and $\triangle DEF \cong \triangle GHI$, then $\triangle ABC \sim \triangle GHI$.

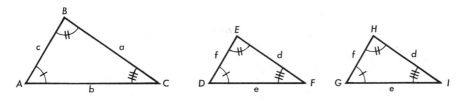

This follows immediately from the definitions of congruence and similarity.

**Theorem 12–5.**   The SAS Similarity Theorem

Given a correspondence between two triangles.  If two pairs of corresponding sides are proportional, and the included angles are congruent, then the correspondence is a similarity.

**Restatement.**   Given $\triangle ABC$, $\triangle DEF$ and the correspondence

$$ABC \leftrightarrow DEF.$$

If

$$\frac{AB}{DE} = \frac{AC}{DF}$$

and

$$\angle A \cong \angle D,$$

then

$$\triangle ABC \sim \triangle DEF.$$

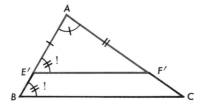 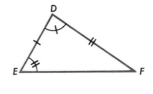

**Proof.**   (1) Let $E'$ and $F'$ be points of $\overrightarrow{AB}$ and $\overrightarrow{AC}$ such that $AE' = DE$ and $AF' = DF$.  By SAS we have

$$\triangle AE'F' \cong \triangle DEF.$$

Therefore

$$\frac{AB}{AE'} = \frac{AC}{AF'}.$$

(2) By Theorem 12–2 (the converse of the Basic Proportionality Theorem), we have $\overleftrightarrow{E'F'} \parallel \overleftrightarrow{BC}$.

(3) Therefore $\angle B \cong \angle AE'F'$.  (Why?)

(4) Since $\angle A \cong \angle A$, it follows by the AA Corollary that

$$\triangle ABC \sim \triangle AE'F'.$$

(5) But $\triangle AE'F' \cong \triangle DEF$.  Therefore, by Theorem 12–4, we have

$$\triangle ABC \sim \triangle DEF,$$

which was to be proved.

Finally, we get a sort of converse of the AAA Similarity Theorem.

**Theorem 12–6.**   The SSS Similarity Theorem

Given a correspondence between two triangles.  If corresponding sides are proportional, then the correspondence is a similarity.

**Restatement.**   Given $\triangle ABC$, $\triangle DEF$ and the correspondence

$$ABC \leftrightarrow DEF.$$

If

$$\frac{AB}{DE} = \frac{AC}{DF} = \frac{BC}{EF},$$

then

$$\triangle ABC \sim \triangle DEF.$$

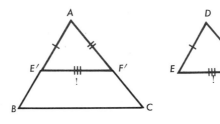

**Proof.**   As usual in this chapter, let $E'$ and $F'$ be points of $\overrightarrow{AB}$ and $\overrightarrow{AC}$ such that $AE' = DE$ and $AF' = DF$.

| STATEMENTS | REASONS |
|---|---|
| 1. $\dfrac{AB}{DE} = \dfrac{AC}{DF} = \dfrac{BC}{EF}$. | 1.  Given. |
| 2. $AE' = DE;\ AF' = DF$. | 2.  Given. |
| 3. $\dfrac{AB}{AE'} = \dfrac{AC}{AF'}$. | 3.  Substitution. |
| 4. $\angle A \cong \angle A$. | 4.  Identity. |
| 5. $\triangle ABC \sim \triangle AE'F'$. | 5.  The SAS Similarity Theorem. |
| 6. $\dfrac{E'F'}{BC} = \dfrac{AE'}{AB}$. | 6.  Definition of a similarity. |
| 7. $E'F' = BC\dfrac{AE'}{AB} = BC\dfrac{DE}{AB}$. | 7.  Statements 2 and 6. |
| 8. $EF = BC\dfrac{DE}{AB}$. | 8.  Statement 1. |
| 9. $E'F' = EF$. | 9.  Statements 7 and 8. |
| 10. $\triangle AE'F' \cong \triangle DEF$. | 10.  Statements 2 and 9 and SSS. |
| 11. $\triangle ABC \sim \triangle DEF$. | 11.  Statements 5 and 10 and Theorem 12–4. |

## Problem Set 12–4B

**1.** For each pair of triangles indicate whether the two triangles are similar and, if they are similar, according to which theorem or definition.

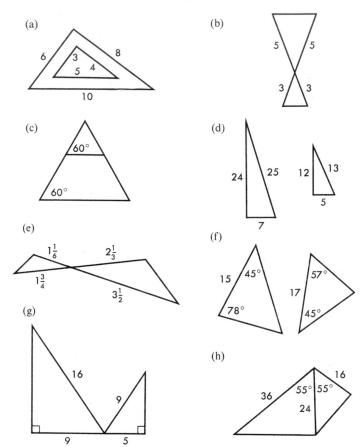

(a)

(b)

(c)

(d)

(e)

(f)

(g)

(h)

**2.** Which of these similarity theorems do not have comparable congruence theorems: SAS, SSS, AAA, AA?

**3.** Prove the following theorem.

Any two corresponding medians of similar triangles have the same ratio as the corresponding sides.

**4.** Given the figure with

$$\frac{AE}{EC} = \frac{BE}{ED}.$$

Prove: (1) $\triangle AEB \sim \triangle CED$,

(2) $\overline{AB} \parallel \overline{DC}$.

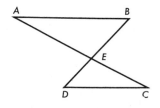

**5.** Prove: If two isosceles triangles have congruent vertex angles, the triangles are similar.

**6.** Is it possible for two triangles to be similar if

(a) two angles of one have measures 60 and 70, whereas two angles of the other have measures 50 and 80?

(b) two angles of one have measures 45 and 75, whereas two angles of the other have measures 45 and 60?

(c) one has an angle of measure 40 and two sides each of which is 5, whereas the other has an angle of measure 70 and two sides each of which is 8?

(d) one has sides which are 5, 6, and 9, whereas the other has a perimeter of 8,420,000?

**7.** Given the figure on the left, prove that $\overline{PQ} \parallel \overline{AB}$.

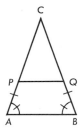

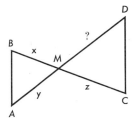

**8.** In the figure, $x$, $y$, and $z$ are lengths of $\overline{MB}$, $\overline{MA}$, and $\overline{MC}$.

(a) What must be the length of $\overline{MD}$ for the triangles to be similar?

(b) If $z = 2x$, must $m \angle D = 2m \angle A$?

**9.** In the figure, $\triangle ADC \sim \triangle PSR$, and $\overline{CD}$ and $\overline{RS}$ are medians. Prove that $\triangle ABC \sim \triangle PQR$.

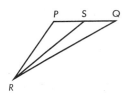

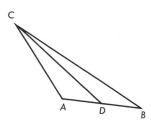

**10.** Three lines which have a common intersection at point $P$ intersect the parallel planes $E$ and $F$ at $R$ and $K$, $S$ and $M$, and $T$ and $H$, respectively. If $KP = 4$, $MP = 6$, $HP = 7$, $RP = 10$, $SP = 15$, and $TP = 17.5$, prove that $\triangle HMK \sim \triangle TSR$.

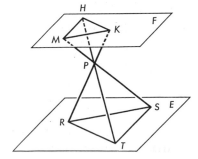

+ **11.** If the following statement is true, prove it; if it is false, provide a counter-example.

> Given a correspondence between two triangles such that the lengths of two sides of one triangle are proportional to the lengths of the corresponding sides of the other triangle, and the angle opposite one of the sides is congruent to the corresponding angle, then the triangles are similar.

+ **12.** In the figure, $PQ = PR$ and $\overline{PQ} \parallel \overline{AC}$.

Which of these statements are true?

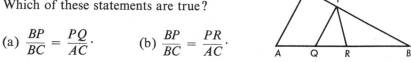

(a) $\dfrac{BP}{BC} = \dfrac{PQ}{AC}$.     (b) $\dfrac{BP}{BC} = \dfrac{PR}{AC}$.

(c) $\dfrac{BP}{BC} = \dfrac{PQ}{AC}$, $\angle PBQ \cong \angle CBA$, and $\triangle PBQ \sim \triangle CBA$.

(d) $\dfrac{BP}{BC} = \dfrac{PR}{AC}$, $\angle PBQ \cong \angle CBA$, and $\triangle PBR \sim \triangle CBA$.

## HONORS PROBLEM

> In $\triangle ABC$, $D$ is the mid-point of $\overline{AB}$ and $E$ is a point of $\overline{AC}$ such that $AE > EC$. $\overleftrightarrow{DE}$ and $\overleftrightarrow{BC}$ intersect at $F$. Prove that $FB \cdot CE = FC \cdot EA$. [*Hint:* Let the line through $C$ parallel to $\overline{AB}$ intersect $\overline{EF}$ at $P$.]

## 12–5.  SIMILARITIES IN RIGHT TRIANGLES

### Theorem 12–7

In any right triangle, the altitude to the hypotenuse separates the triangle into two triangles which are similar to each other and to the original triangle.

**Restatement.**   Let $\triangle ABC$ be a right triangle with its right angle at $C$, and let $\overline{CD}$ be the altitude from $C$ to $\overline{AB}$. Then

$$\triangle ACD \sim \triangle ABC \sim \triangle CBD.$$

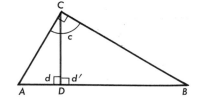

(Note that in this case the restatement tells us more than the theorem does, because it states which correspondences are similarities.

Note also that it is easy to figure out (and to remember) what these correspondences are. In the correspondence between $\triangle ACD$ and $\triangle ABC$, we must have $A \leftrightarrow A$, because $\angle A$ is common to the two triangles. We must also have $D \leftrightarrow C$, because these are the vertices where the right angles are. Finally, we must have $C \leftrightarrow B$, because at this stage $C$ has nowhere else left to go. This gives $ACD \leftrightarrow ABC$. Similarly for the second correspondence, $ABC \leftrightarrow CBD$.)

**Proof.** Obviously $\angle d \cong \angle c$ because both are right angles; and $\angle A \cong \angle A$. Therefore, under the correspondence $ACD \leftrightarrow ABC$, two pairs of corresponding angles are congruent. By the AA Corollary, we have $\triangle ACD \sim \triangle ABC$.

The proof of the other half of the theorem is exactly the same: since $\angle d' \cong \angle c$ and $\angle B \cong \angle B$, the AA Corollary gives us

$$\triangle ABC \sim \triangle CBD.$$

**Theorem 12–8**

Given a right triangle and the altitude to the hypotenuse.

(1) The altitude is the geometric mean of the segments into which it separates the hypotenuse.

(2) Each leg is the geometric mean of the hypotenuse and the segment of the hypotenuse adjacent to the leg.

**Restatement.** Let $\triangle ABC$ be a right triangle with its right angle at $C$, and let $\overline{CD}$ be the altitude to the hypotenuse $\overline{AB}$. Then

(1) $$\frac{AD}{CD} = \frac{CD}{BD}.$$

(2a) $$\frac{AD}{AC} = \frac{AC}{AB}.$$

(2b) $$\frac{BD}{BC} = \frac{BC}{BA}.$$

**Proof.** By Theorem 12–7, we have the similarities

(1)  $\triangle ACD \sim \triangle CBD,$

(2a)  $\triangle ACD \sim \triangle ABC,$

(2b)  $\triangle CBD \sim \triangle ABC.$

The equations given in the restatement describe proportionalities for pairs of corresponding sides.

## Problem Set 12–5

[*Note:* Express irrational numbers in simplified radical form.]

1. In the figure, $\overline{CD} \perp \overline{AB}$ and $\square CFDE$ is a rectangle. Write out all the similarities for the triangles similar to $\triangle ABC$. Remember that you must establish the correct correspondences.

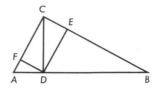

2. In the figure, $\overline{CD}$ is the altitude to the hypotenuse of $\triangle ABC$.

   (a) Given $r = 4$, $s = 9$. Find $h$.
   (b) Given $r = 7$, $s = 28$. Find $h$.
   (c) Given $r = 9$, $s = 3$. Find $a$.
   (d) Given $r = 7$, $s = 21$. Find $b$.
   (e) Given $r = \sqrt{3}$, $s = \sqrt{12}$. Find $h$, $a$, and $b$.

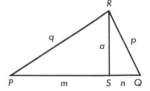

3. In the figure, $\overline{RS}$ is the altitude to the hypotenuse $\overline{PQ}$ of $\triangle PQR$.

   (a) Given $m = 27$ and $n = 3$. Find $a$, $p$, and $q$.
   (b) Given $m = 24$ and $n = 6$. Find $a$, $p$, and $q$.
   (c) Given $m = \sqrt{18}$ and $n = \sqrt{8}$. Find $a$, $p$, and $q$.
   (d) Given $p = 15$ and $n = 9$. Find $m$ and $q$.
   (e) Given $a = 8$ and $m = 16$. Find $n$, $p$, and $q$.

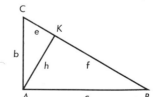

\* 4. In the figure, $\overline{AK}$ is the altitude to the hypotenuse of $\triangle ABC$.

   (a) Given $e = 5$ and $h = 15$. Find $f$, $b$, and $c$.
   (b) Given $b = 4\sqrt{3}$ and $e = 4$. Find $f$, $h$, and $c$.
   (c) Given $c = 6\sqrt{2}$ and $e = 4$. Find $f$, $b$, and $h$.
   (d) Given $b = 3\sqrt{10}$ and $f = 13$. Find $e$, $h$, and $c$.
   (e) Given $b = f = 8$. Find $e$, $h$, and $c$.

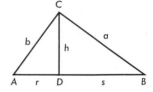

5. The altitude to the hypotenuse of a right triangle separates the hypotenuse into two segments whose lengths are $r$ and $s$. Prove that the area of the triangle is equal to the product of the geometric mean of $r$ and $s$ and the arithmetic mean of $r$ and $s$.

6. Find the area of a right triangle, given that the altitude to the hypotenuse separates the hypotenuse into segments of lengths 9 and 16; of lengths 7 and 21.

7. *The Pythagorean Theorem.* In Section 11–3 we proved the Pythagorean Theorem, using a proof based upon area formulas. Theorem 12–7 suggests another proof of this important relationship.

In the figure, $\angle ACB$ is a right angle and $\overline{CD}$ is the altitude to the hypotenuse. By Theorem 12–7 we have $a = \sqrt{cs}$ and $b = \sqrt{cr}$. With this as a beginning, complete the proof that $a^2 + b^2 = c^2$.

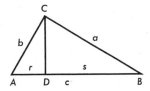

8. Given $\triangle ABC$ with $\overline{CD}$ the altitude to the hypotenuse $\overline{AB}$. Prove that

$$AC^2 - BC^2 = AD^2 - BD^2.$$

\* 9. Given the figure, in which $\square PRHQ$ is a rectangle and $\overline{HP} \perp \overline{GK}$. Prove that

$$a\square PRHQ = \sqrt{GQ \cdot QH \cdot HR \cdot RK}.$$

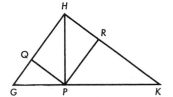

10. $\triangle ABC$ is a right triangle with $C$ the vertex of the right angle. The bisector of $\angle B$ intersects $\overline{AC}$ at $D$, and the bisector of the exterior angle at $B$ intersects $\overleftrightarrow{AC}$ at $E$. If $BD = 15$ and $BE = 20$, what arc the lengths of the sides of $\triangle ABC$.

## 12–6.  AREAS OF SIMILAR TRIANGLES

Given a square of edge $a$ and a square of edge $2a$, it is easy to see that the area of the second square is four times the area of the first: $(2a)^2 = 4a^2$. (This is also easy to see geometrically, without using any area formulas at all.)  In general, if the second square has edge $ka$, then the ratio of the areas is $k^2$, because

$$\frac{(ka)^2}{a^2} = \frac{k^2 a^2}{a^2} = k^2.$$

An analogous result holds for similar triangles.

**Theorem 12–9**

If two triangles are similar, then the ratio of their areas is the square of the ratio of any two corresponding sides.

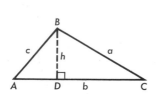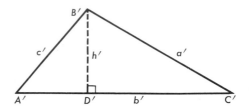

**Proof.** Given $\triangle ABC \sim \triangle A'B'C'$. Let their areas be $A_1$ and $A_2$. In the usual notation, we have

$$\frac{a'}{a} = \frac{b'}{b} = \frac{c'}{c}.$$

Let $k$ be the common value of these three fractions. We want to show that

$$\frac{A_2}{A_1} = k^2.$$

Let $\overline{BD}$ and $\overline{B'D'}$ be the altitudes from $B$ and $B'$ in the two triangles; and let $h$ and $h'$ be their lengths. Now $\angle A \cong \angle A'$, because $\triangle ABC \sim \triangle A'B'C'$. And $\angle ADB \cong \angle A'D'B'$, because both are right angles. By the AA Corollary it follows that

$$\triangle ABD \sim \triangle A'B'D'.$$

Therefore

$$\frac{b'}{b} = \frac{h'}{h} = k,$$

because corresponding sides are proportional. This gives

$$b' = kb, \qquad h' = kh.$$

But

$$A_1 = \tfrac{1}{2}bh, \qquad A_2 = \tfrac{1}{2}b'h'.$$

Therefore

$$A_2 = \tfrac{1}{2}b'h' = \tfrac{1}{2}(kb)(kh) = \tfrac{1}{2}k^2bh,$$

and

$$\frac{A_2}{A_1} = k^2,$$

which was to be proved.

## Problem Set 12–6

1. What is the ratio of the areas of two similar triangles whose longest sides are 3 in. and 4 in. long, respectively?

2. In the figure, $\angle A \cong \angle A'$ and $\angle B \cong \angle B'$. What is the ratio of the areas of the triangles if $x = 5$ and $x' = 7$? if $y = 4$ and $y' = 3\sqrt{3}$? if $x = 6$, $y = 2\sqrt{5}$, and $y' = x$?

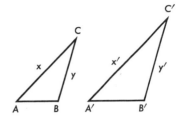

3. A side of one of two similar triangles is five times as long as the corresponding side of the other. If the area of the smaller triangle is 6 sq. in., what is the area of the larger one?

4. In $\triangle PQR$, $G$ is the mid-point of $\overline{PR}$ and $H$ is the mid-point of $\overline{QR}$. What is the ratio of $a\triangle GHR$ to $a\triangle PQR$? of $a\triangle GHR$ to $a\square PQHG$?

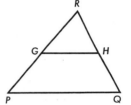

5. The areas of two similar triangles are 16 and 25. What is the ratio of a pair of corresponding sides?

6. The area of the larger of two similar triangles is 9 times the area of the smaller. If a side of the smaller triangle is 5 in. long, how long is the corresponding side of the larger triangle?

7. The areas of two similar triangles are 144 and 81. If the base of the larger triangle is 30, what is the corresponding base of the smaller triangle?

8. In $\triangle ABC$, $D$ is a point of $\overline{AC}$ such that $AD = 2CD$. $E$ is on $\overline{BC}$ such that $\overline{DE} \parallel \overline{AB}$. Compare the areas of $\triangle CDE$ and $\triangle ABC$. If $a\square ABED = 40$, what is $a\triangle ABC$?

9. $\triangle ABC$ and $\triangle A'B'C'$ are equilateral triangles. An altitude of $\triangle A'B'C'$ is of the same length as a side of $\triangle ABC$. Prove that

$$a\triangle A'B'C' = \tfrac{4}{3}a\triangle ABC.$$

10. How long must a side of an equilateral triangle be in order that its area be twice the area of an equilateral triangle whose side is 10?

**11.** Given the quadrilaterals as labeled.

$\angle x \cong \angle x'$, $\angle y \cong \angle y'$, and

$$\frac{a'}{a} = \frac{b'}{b} = \frac{c'}{c} = k.$$

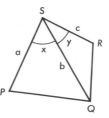
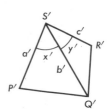

Prove: $\dfrac{a\square P'Q'R'S'}{a\square PQRS} = k^2.$

* **12.** Two pieces of wire of equal length are bent, one in the shape of a square and the other in the shape of an equilateral triangle. What is the ratio of the areas of the regions enclosed by each wire?

* **13.** In $\triangle ABC$, $\overline{CD}$ is the altitude to base $\overline{AB}$. It is desired to determine a line, $L$, parallel to $\overline{AB}$, which will cut off a triangle similar to $\triangle ABC$ but only one-half the area of $\triangle ABC$. If $L$ intersects $\overline{CD}$ at a point $M$, and if $CD = 1$, how long is $\overline{CM}$?

+ **14.** *The Pythagorean Theorem.* Theorem 12–9 provides another way of proving the Pythagorean Theorem. You are to supply reasons for the statements of the proof.

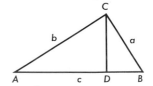

In the figure, $\angle ACB$ is a right angle and $\overline{CD}$ is the altitude to the hypotenuse.

1. $a\triangle ABC = a\triangle ACD + a\triangle CBD.$

2. $1 = \dfrac{a\triangle ACD}{a\triangle ABC} + \dfrac{a\triangle CBD}{a\triangle ABC}.$

3. $\triangle ACD \sim \triangle ABC \sim \triangle CBD.$

4. $1 = \left(\dfrac{AC}{AB}\right)^2 + \left(\dfrac{BC}{AB}\right)^2.$

5. $AB^2 = AC^2 + BC^2 \quad$ or $\quad c^2 = b^2 + a^2.$

* **15.** Given the tetrahedron $ABCD$ with base $\triangle ABC$. A plane parallel to the base intersects the faces of the tetrahedron in $\triangle RST$. $\overline{DQ}$ is the perpendicular from $D$ to the plane of $\triangle ABC$, and $\overline{DQ}$ intersects the parallel plane at $P$.

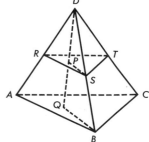

Prove: $\dfrac{a\triangle RST}{a\triangle ABC} = \left(\dfrac{DP}{DQ}\right)^2.$

## HONORS PROBLEM

A triangular lot has sides with lengths 130 ft, 140 ft, and 150 ft, as indicated in the figure. The length of the perpendicular from a corner to the 140-ft side is 120 ft. A fence is to be erected perpendicular to the 140-ft side so that the area of the lot is equally divided. How far from $A$ along $\overline{AB}$ should this perpendicular be drawn?

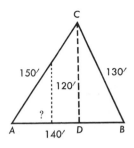

## 12–7.  THE TRIGONOMETRIC RATIOS

Consider two right triangles with a pair of congruent acute angles. By the AA Corollary, we know that $\triangle ABC \sim \triangle A'B'C'$. Therefore

$$\frac{a}{a'} = \frac{b}{b'} = \frac{c}{c'}.$$

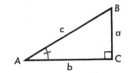

From these equations it is easy to see that

$$\frac{a}{b} = \frac{a'}{b'}, \qquad \frac{b}{c} = \frac{b'}{c'}, \qquad \frac{a}{c} = \frac{a'}{c'}.$$

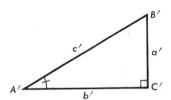

Therefore the ratios $a/c$, $b/c$, and $a/b$ do not depend on the *size* of the triangle; once we know $m\angle A$, these ratios are determined. They are called the *trigonometric ratios*. (The word *trigonometry* is from the Greek. A *trigon* is a triangle, and trigonometry is the measurement of trigons.)

The ratio $a/c$ is called the *sine* of $\angle A$; and we write

$$\sin \angle A = \frac{a}{c}.$$

If $m\angle A = r$, then we may write

$$\sin r^\circ = \frac{a}{c}.$$

This makes sense, because $a/c$ is determined if we know either $\angle A$ or $r$. Similarly, $b/c$ is called the *cosine* of $\angle A$, and we write

$$\cos \angle A = \frac{b}{c} \qquad \text{or} \qquad \cos r^\circ = \frac{b}{c}.$$

The ratio $a/b$ is called the *tangent* of $\angle A$, and we write

$$\tan \angle A = \frac{a}{b} \qquad \text{or} \qquad \tan r° = \frac{a}{b}.$$

To sum up:

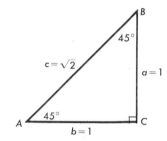

$$\sin \angle A = \sin r° = \frac{a}{c},$$

$$\cos \angle A = \cos r° = \frac{b}{c},$$

$$\tan \angle A = \tan r° = \frac{a}{b}.$$

For some angles and some numbers $r$, the trigonometric ratios are easy to calculate. Take, for example, the case $r = 45$. Since the ratios do not depend on the size of the triangle, we can use *any* right triangle $\triangle ABC$ with a 45°-angle at $A$. The triangle is then isosceles, with $a = b$. We take $a = b = 1$. By the Pythagorean Theorem, $c = \sqrt{2}$, as shown in the figure. We now have

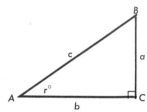

$$\sin \angle A = \sin 45° = \frac{a}{c} = \frac{1}{\sqrt{2}} = \frac{\sqrt{2}}{2},$$

$$\cos \angle A = \cos 45° = \frac{b}{c} = \frac{1}{\sqrt{2}} = \frac{\sqrt{2}}{2},$$

$$\tan \angle A = \tan 45° = \frac{a}{b} = \frac{1}{1} = 1.$$

(*Query:* If we had let $a = b = 3$, would the trigonometric ratios have changed? Why or why not?)

The case $r = 30$ is almost as easy.

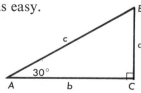

We know by Theorem 9–27 that $a = \dfrac{c}{2}$. Since the size of the triangle

does not matter, we can choose any size we like. Thus, for example, we take $c = 2$, $a = 1$, as shown in the figure. The Pythagorean Theorem gives us $b^2 = c^2 - a^2 = 4 - 1 = 3$.) We can now read off the values:

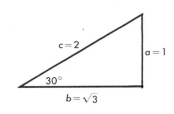

$$\sin 30° = \frac{a}{c} = \frac{1}{2},$$

$$\cos 30° = \frac{b}{c} = \frac{\sqrt{3}}{2},$$

$$\tan 30° = \frac{a}{b} = \frac{1}{\sqrt{3}} = \frac{\sqrt{3}}{3}.$$

*A word of caution:* Note that we have used the degree sign in the expressions $\sin r°$, $\cos r°$, $\tan r°$. The reason is that later you will be using another unit of measure for angles, called *radian measure*. To know what the sine of a number is, you have to know what unit is being used.

## Problem Set 12–7

**1.**

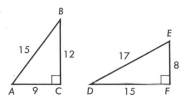
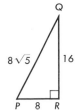

Given these right triangles with lengths of sides as indicated. Determine the following trigonometric ratios.

(a)  $\sin \angle A$      (b)  $\cos \angle A$      (c)  $\tan \angle A$      (d)  $\sin \angle D$

(e)  $\sin \angle N$      (f)  $\cos \angle D$      (g)  $\tan \angle N$      (h)  $\tan \angle P$

(i)  $\cos \angle P$      (j)  $\cos \angle N$      (k)  $\tan \angle D$      (l)  $\sin \angle E$

**2.**

Given the triangles as marked, find the following trigonometric ratios.

(a)  $\cos \angle G$      (b)  $\sin \angle H$      (c)  $\tan \angle T$      (d)  $\sin \angle W$

(e)  $\cos \angle T$      (f)  $\tan \angle G$      (g)  $\sin \angle X$      (h)  $\cos \angle Y$

**3.** In right triangle $\triangle ABC$ hypotenuse $\overline{AB}$ is 25 in. long.

(a) If $\sin \angle A = \frac{4}{5}$, how long is $\overline{BC}$?

(b) If $\cos \angle A = .60$, what is $\tan \angle A$ expressed as a decimal?

(c) If $\tan \angle A = 3\frac{3}{7}$, what are the lengths of $\overline{AC}$ and $\overline{BC}$?

**4.** In $\triangle GKM$, $GM = 30$, $GK = 50$, and $\cos \angle G = .80$. Find the altitude to $\overline{GK}$ and the area of $\triangle GKM$.

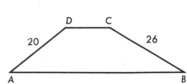

**5.** In trapezoid $\square ABCD$, $\overline{DC} \parallel \overline{AB}$, $AD = 20$, and $BC = 26$. If $\sin \angle A = .5$, what is the altitude of the trapezoid and what is $\sin \angle B$?

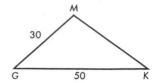

**6.** Find $\sin 60°$, $\cos 60°$, and $\tan 60°$.

**7.** Show that $\sin 30° = \cos 60°$.

**8.** What is the relationship of $\tan 60°$ and $\tan 30°$?

**9.** In $\triangle PQR$, $\sin \angle P = \frac{1}{2}\sqrt{2}$ and $\cos \angle Q = \frac{1}{2}\sqrt{3}$. Find $m \angle R$.

**10.** In $\triangle ABC$, $\tan \angle A = \sqrt{3}$ and $\tan C = \sqrt{3}/3$. Find $m \angle B$.

**11.** In $\triangle GHK$, $\tan \angle H = 2 \cos \angle G = 1$. Find $m \angle K$.

**12.** In parallelogram $\square ABCD$, diagonal $\overline{BD}$ is perpendicular to $\overline{AB}$. If $AB = 5$ and $\tan \angle A = 1$, what is $a\square ABCD$?

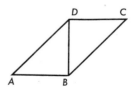

**13.** Prove the following theorem.

The sine of an acute angle is equal to the cosine of its complement.

**14.** Prove the following theorem.

The product of the tangent of an acute angle and the tangent of the complement of the angle is 1.

$+$ **15.** Show that $\tan \angle A = \dfrac{\sin \angle A}{\cos \angle A}$ for every acute angle $\angle A$.

$+$ **16.** Show that $(\sin \angle A)^2 + (\cos \angle A)^2 = 1$ for every acute angle $\angle A$.

$+$ **17.** Show that the area of an equilateral triangle with a side of length 1 is given by $(\sin 60°) (\cos 60°)$.

## HONORS PROBLEM

Prove the following theorem.

Given $\triangle ABC$ with $\angle A$ acute, then $a^2 = b^2 + c^2 - 2bc \cos \angle A$.

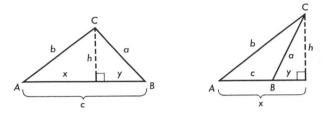

## 12–8.  NUMERICAL TRIGONOMETRY.  THE USE OF TABLES

In the preceding section, we calculated the sine, cosine, and tangent of 30°, 45° and 60°.  These were expressed in terms of $\sqrt{2}$ and $\sqrt{3}$. The decimal approximations, correct to three decimal places, are:

$$\sqrt{2} = 1.414, \qquad \frac{1}{\sqrt{2}} = \frac{\sqrt{2}}{2} = .707,$$

$$\sqrt{3} = 1.732, \qquad \frac{1}{\sqrt{3}} = \frac{\sqrt{3}}{3} = .577.$$

Therefore we have

$$\sin 30° = \tfrac{1}{2} = .500,$$

$$\cos 30° = \frac{\sqrt{3}}{2} = \frac{1.732}{2} = .866,$$

$$\tan 30° = \frac{1}{\sqrt{3}} = \frac{\sqrt{3}}{3} = .577.$$

Similarly we can calculate the trigonometric ratios for 45° and 60°. Thus we get the following table:

| Angle | Sine | Cosine | Tangent |
|-------|------|--------|---------|
| 30°   | .500 | .866   | .577    |
| 45°   | .707 | .707   | 1.000   |
| 60°   | .866 | .500   | 1.732   |

These are the trigonometric ratios that we have learned to calculate. By advanced methods it is possible to calculate the sine, cosine, and tangent of *any* angle as accurately as you want. (In fact, the ancient Greeks computed such tables because they needed them in their study of astronomy.) On p. 362 you will find a table of the values of the trigonometric ratios for angles whose measures are full degrees. The table is accurate to three decimal places, which is good enough for our present purposes.

Such tables have many important applications. Suppose, for example, that a surveyor wants to determine the distance between two points on opposite sides of a pond. He cannot measure $BC$ directly. But he can measure $AB$ and $r$. Suppose he finds that $AB = 305$ ft and $r = 32$. Now

$$\sin r^\circ = \frac{BC}{AB}.$$

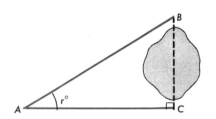

Therefore

$$BC = AB \sin r^\circ.$$

The surveyor looks in his tables and finds that $\sin 32^\circ = 0.530$. Hence

$$BC = 305 \times 0.530 = 151.65 \text{ ft.}$$

Surveyors, whose job it is to solve problems of this kind, solve them by the method described.

The tables can also be used for other types of indirect measurement. One way of measuring the height of a flagpole without climbing it would be to measure a certain distance, say 100 ft, from the base, and then measure the angle marked $\angle A$ in the figure. In the figure, $\overline{BC}$ represents the flagpole, and $m\angle A = 22$. Since

$$\tan 22^\circ = \frac{BC}{AC}.$$

we have

$$BC = AC \tan 22^\circ$$
$$= 100 \times 0.404$$
$$= 40.4 \text{ ft.}$$

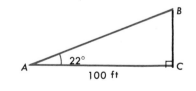

Note that in problems of this kind, we can always make sure that the arithmetic involved will be easy. We can measure off any distance we want, from the base of the pole, and so we choose a point $A$ for which $AC$ comes out to an even number of feet.

## Problem Set 12–8

1. Using the table of trigonometric ratios, give the decimal form of:
   (a) sin 12°.      (b) cos 35°.       (c) tan 20°.      (d) cos 66°.
   (e) sin 50°.      (f) cos 40°.       (g) tan 82°.      (h) sin 3°.
   (i) tan 3°.       (j) cos 60°.

2. Find $m \angle A$ given that:
   (a) sin $\angle A$ = 0.309.                  (b) cos $\angle A$ = 0.208.
   (c) tan $\angle A$ = 0.306.                  (d) cos $\angle A$ = 0.961.
   (e) tan $\angle A$ = 2.904.                  (f) sin $\angle A$ = 0.961.
   (g) sin $\angle A$ = 0.454.                  (h) cos $\angle A$ = 0.731.
   (i) tan $\angle A$ = 8.144.                  (j) tan $\angle A$ = 0.554.

3. Given that hypotenuse $\overline{AB}$ of $\triangle ABC$ is 20 ft long and $m \angle A = 38$, find $BC$ and $AC$.

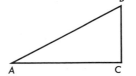

4. In $\triangle ABC$, $\angle C$ is a right angle, $m \angle A = 42$, and $AC = 7$. How long is $\overline{BC}$?

5. In $\triangle PQR, m \angle P = 54, PR = 15$, and $PQ = 18$. Find the length of the altitude to $\overline{PQ}$; to $\overline{PR}$.

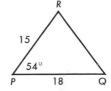

6. In $\triangle GHK, m \angle G = 70, GK = 12$, and $GH = 20$. Determine the altitude to $\overline{GH}$ and the area of $\triangle GHK$.

7. Calculate the area of $\triangle ABC$, given
   $AB = 30, \quad BC = 16, \quad$ and $\quad m \angle B = 47$.

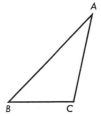

8. Determine the measures, to the nearest degree, of the acute angles of a 3-4-5 triangle.

9. Determine the measures, to the nearest degree, of the acute angles of an 8-15-17 triangle.

**10.** The base of an isosceles triangle is 8 ft long, and the angle opposite the base has measure 30°. Calculate the lengths of the three altitudes of the triangle.

**11.** In △*ABC*, ∠*C* is a right angle and *AB* = 9. Given also that tan ∠*A* = 1.111, determine *BC* and *AC*.

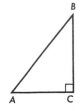

+ **12.** Examine the table of trigonometric ratios for sin 53°, sin 54°, sin 55°, sin 56°. Explain why a good estimate of sin 54°30′ is 0.814. What would be a good estimate of sin 55°30′? A good estimate of sin 54°12′ is 0.811. Why? Estimate sin 54°6′. Explain why each of the following is a good estimate:

$$\sin 30°30' = 0.508, \qquad \sin 76°30' = 0.972,$$
$$\sin 30°20' = 0.505, \qquad \sin 76°45' = 0.973.$$

This method of estimating values which do not appear explicitly in a table is called *interpolation*.

+ **13.** Interpolate in the table of trigonometric ratios to obtain estimates of the following (see Problem 12).

(a)  sin 37°30′      (b)  sin 65°30′      (c)  sin 63.5°      (d)  sin 56.3°

(e)  sin 47°20′      (f)  sin 45°40′      (g)  sin 73.4°      (h)  sin 20.5°

(i)  sin 17°30′      (j)  sin 41°15′

+ **14.** Interpolate in the table of trigonometric ratios to obtain estimates of the following (see Problem 12).

(a)  cos 33°30′      (b)  cos 36.6°      (c)  cos 18°24′      (d)  tan 31°30′

(e)  tan 42°20′      (f)  cos 61°40′      (g)  tan 58.5°      (h)  cos 67°15′

(i)  tan 66°30′      (j)  tan 63°45′

**15.** In surveying for a new highway, an engineer drove two large stakes, *A* and *B*, on opposite banks of a river, to mark the sites of bridge abutments. Then from a point *O*,

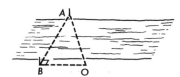

100 ft from *B* and such that $\overleftrightarrow{OB} \perp \overleftrightarrow{AB}$, he measured the angle ∠*AOB*. If *m*∠*AOB* = 73, what is the distance across the river from *A* to *B*?

**16.** A ladder on a fire truck can be extended to a maximum length of 68 ft when elevated to its maximum angle of 70°. The base of the ladder is mounted on the truck 7 ft above the ground. How high above the ground will the ladder reach?

**17.** A forest ranger watches for fires from a look-out tower built on a high hill. The site

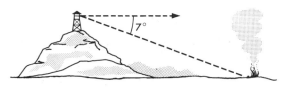

of the tower is 2420 ft above most of the surrounding land, and the tower itself is 80 ft tall. If the ranger sights a fire at an angle of 7° from the horizontal, how far, to the nearest half-mile, is the fire from the tower?

**18.** An airplane is approaching an airport at an altitude of 21,000 ft. (Assume that the airport is close to sea level.) The pilot has orders to descend at a constant angle of 6° while coming in for a landing. How far, to the nearest half-mile, from the runway should the pilot begin his descent?

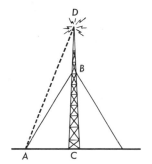

\* **19.** A tall radio tower is anchored by long cables called guy wires, such as $\overline{AB}$ in the figure. If $A$ is 250 ft from the base of the tower and if $m \angle BAC = 59$, how long is the guy wire? How far above the ground is it fastened to the tower? How tall is the tower, $\overline{DC}$, if $m \angle DAC = 71$?

## HONORS PROBLEM

In $\triangle ABC$, $\overline{CD}$ is the altitude to $\overline{AB}$ and $AB = c$.

(a) Show that the altitude $h$ is given by the formula

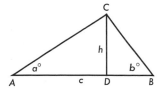

$$h = c \frac{\tan a° \tan b°}{\tan a° + \tan b°}.$$

(b) Compute $h$ given that $c = 68$, $a = 35$, and $b = 45$.

## TABLE OF TRIGONOMETRIC RATIOS

| r | sin r | cos r | tan r | r | sin r | cos r | tan r |
|---|---|---|---|---|---|---|---|
| 1° | .017 | 1.000 | .017 | 46° | .719 | .695 | 1.035 |
| 2° | .035 | .999 | .035 | 47° | .731 | .682 | 1.072 |
| 3° | .052 | .999 | .052 | 48° | .743 | .669 | 1.111 |
| 4° | .070 | .998 | .070 | 49° | .755 | .656 | 1.150 |
| 5° | .087 | .996 | .087 | 50° | .766 | .643 | 1.192 |
| 6° | .105 | .995 | .105 | 51° | .777 | .629 | 1.235 |
| 7° | .122 | .993 | .123 | 52° | .788 | .616 | 1.280 |
| 8° | .139 | .990 | .141 | 53° | .799 | .602 | 1.327 |
| 9° | .156 | .988 | .158 | 54° | .809 | .588 | 1.376 |
| 10° | .174 | .985 | .176 | 55° | .819 | .574 | 1.428 |
| 11° | .191 | .982 | .194 | 56° | .829 | .559 | 1.483 |
| 12° | .208 | .978 | .213 | 57° | .839 | .545 | 1.540 |
| 13° | .225 | .974 | .231 | 58° | .848 | .530 | 1.600 |
| 14° | .242 | .970 | .249 | 59° | .857 | .515 | 1.664 |
| 15° | .259 | .966 | .268 | 60° | .866 | .5 | 1.732 |
| 16° | .276 | .961 | .287 | 61° | .875 | .485 | 1.804 |
| 17° | .292 | .956 | .306 | 62° | .883 | .469 | 1.881 |
| 18° | .309 | .951 | .325 | 63° | .891 | .454 | 1.963 |
| 19° | .326 | .946 | .344 | 64° | .899 | .438 | 2.050 |
| 20° | .342 | .940 | .364 | 65° | .906 | .423 | 2.145 |
| 21° | .358 | .934 | .384 | 66° | .914 | .407 | 2.246 |
| 22° | .375 | .927 | .404 | 67° | .921 | .391 | 2.356 |
| 23° | .391 | .921 | .424 | 68° | .927 | .375 | 2.475 |
| 24° | .407 | .914 | .445 | 69° | .934 | .358 | 2.605 |
| 25° | .423 | .906 | .466 | 70° | .940 | .342 | 2.747 |
| 26° | .438 | .899 | .488 | 71° | .946 | .326 | 2.904 |
| 27° | .454 | .891 | .510 | 72° | .951 | .309 | 3.078 |
| 28° | .469 | .883 | .532 | 73° | .956 | .292 | 3.271 |
| 29° | .485 | .875 | .554 | 74° | .961 | .276 | 3.487 |
| 30° | .5 | .866 | .577 | 75° | .966 | .259 | 3.732 |
| 31° | .515 | .857 | .601 | 76° | .970 | .242 | 4.011 |
| 32° | .530 | .848 | .625 | 77° | .974 | .225 | 4.331 |
| 33° | .545 | .839 | .649 | 78° | .978 | .208 | 4.705 |
| 34° | .559 | .829 | .675 | 79° | .982 | .191 | 5.145 |
| 35° | .574 | .819 | .700 | 80° | .985 | .174 | 5.671 |
| 36° | .588 | .809 | .727 | 81° | .988 | .156 | 6.314 |
| 37° | .602 | .799 | .754 | 82° | .990 | .139 | 7.115 |
| 38° | .616 | .788 | .781 | 83° | .993 | .122 | 8.144 |
| 39° | .629 | .777 | .810 | 84° | .995 | .105 | 9.514 |
| 40° | .643 | .766 | .839 | 85° | .996 | .087 | 11.430 |
| 41° | .656 | .755 | .869 | 86° | .998 | .070 | 14.301 |
| 42° | .669 | .743 | .900 | 87° | .999 | .052 | 19.081 |
| 43° | .682 | .731 | .933 | 88° | .999 | .035 | 28.636 |
| 44° | .695 | .719 | .966 | 89° | 1.000 | .017 | 57.290 |
| 45° | .707 | .707 | 1 | | | | |

## 12–9.   RELATIONS AMONG THE TRIGONOMETRIC RATIOS

In a right triangle, as in the figure, we have

$$a^2 + b^2 = c^2.$$

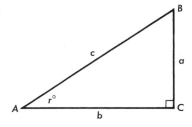

Dividing by $c^2$, we get

$$\left(\frac{a}{c}\right)^2 + \left(\frac{b}{c}\right)^2 = 1.$$

Since

$$\sin \angle A = \frac{a}{c} \quad \text{and} \quad \cos \angle A = \frac{b}{c},$$

we have the following theorem.

**Theorem 12–10**

For every $\angle A$, $(\sin \angle A)^2 + (\cos \angle A)^2 = 1$.

We usually denote the square of the sine by $\sin^2 \angle A$, which is easier to write than $(\sin A)^2$, and proceed similarly for the cosine. In this notation, the above equation takes the form

$$\sin^2 \angle A + \cos^2 \angle A = 1, \quad \text{or} \quad \sin^2 r^\circ + \cos^2 r^\circ = 1,$$

if $m \angle A = r$. All three of these equations say the same thing.

We read off from the triangle above that

$$\tan \angle A = \frac{a}{b}.$$

Since

$$\frac{a}{b} = \frac{a/c}{b/c},$$

we arrive at the following theorem.

**Theorem 12–11**

For every $\angle A$,

$$\tan \angle A = \frac{\sin \angle A}{\cos \angle A}.$$

In the notation of degree measures, the above statement says that for every $r$,

$$\tan r^\circ = \frac{\sin r^\circ}{\cos r^\circ}.$$

Finally, looking at our right triangle sidewise, we observe that

$$\sin \angle B = \frac{b}{c} = \cos \angle A$$

and

$$\cos \angle B = \frac{a}{c} = \sin \angle A.$$

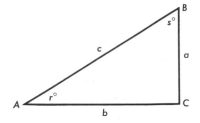

Since the acute angles of a right triangle are complementary, we have

$$s = m\angle B = 90 - r.$$

### Theorem 12–12

If $\angle A$ and $\angle B$ are complementary, then

$$\sin \angle B = \cos \angle A$$

and

$$\cos \angle B = \sin \angle A.$$

For degree measures, these equations take the form

$$\sin (90 - r)° = \cos r°,$$
$$\cos (90 - r)° = \sin r°.$$

The word *cosine* refers to these equations; it is an abbreviation of the Latin *complementi sinus*, meaning *sine of the complement*. In fact, the cosine of an angle is the sine of its complement.

## Problem Set 12–9

Use the basic relations stated in Theorems 12–10, 12–11, and 12–12 to prove the following identities.

**1.** $\dfrac{\tan r°}{\tan s°} = \dfrac{\sin r° \cos s°}{\sin s° \cos r°}.$

**2.** $\tan r° + \tan s° = \dfrac{\sin r° \cos s° + \cos r° \sin s°}{\cos r° \cos s°}.$

**3.** $\tan r° = \dfrac{\sin r°}{\sqrt{1 - \sin^2 r°}}.$

**4.** $1 - (\cos r° - \sin r°)^2 = 2 \sin r° \cos r°.$

5. The *cotangent* of an angle is the reciprocal of the tangent of that angle; that is,

$$\cot \angle A = \frac{1}{\tan \angle A}.$$

(a) Prove that $\tan (90 - r)^\circ = \cot r^\circ$.

(b) Prove that $\cot (90 - r)^\circ = \tan r^\circ$.

6. $\dfrac{1 - \sin r^\circ}{\cos r^\circ} = \dfrac{\cos r^\circ}{1 + \sin r^\circ}.$

7. $\dfrac{2 \sin r^\circ \cos r^\circ}{\cos^2 r^\circ - \sin^2 r^\circ} = \dfrac{2 \tan r^\circ}{1 - \tan^2 r^\circ}.$

8. $\dfrac{\sin r^\circ}{1 - \cos r^\circ} = \dfrac{1 + \cos r^\circ}{\sin r^\circ}.$

9. The *secant* of an angle is the reciprocal of the cosine of that angle; that is,

$$\sec \angle A = \frac{1}{\cos \angle A}.$$

Prove that $\tan r^\circ = \sin r^\circ \sec r^\circ$.

10. $1 + \tan^2 r^\circ = \sec^2 r^\circ.$  (See Problem 9.)

11. $\sec r^\circ - \cos r^\circ = \tan r^\circ \sin r^\circ.$  (See Problem 9.)

\* 12. $\dfrac{1 - \tan^2 r^\circ}{1 + \tan^2 r^\circ} = 1 - 2 \sin^2 r^\circ.$

\* 13. $\dfrac{1 - \tan r^\circ \tan s^\circ}{\tan r^\circ + \tan s^\circ} = \dfrac{\cos r^\circ \cos s^\circ - \sin r^\circ \sin s^\circ}{\sin r^\circ \cos s^\circ + \cos r^\circ \sin s^\circ}.$

\* 14. $\dfrac{\sec r^\circ}{\sin r^\circ} - \dfrac{2 \cos r^\circ}{\sin r^\circ} = \tan r^\circ - \cot r^\circ.$

# HONORS PROBLEMS

(a) Show that

$$\frac{(\cos^2 r^\circ - \sin^2 r^\circ)^2}{\cos^4 r^\circ - \sin^4 r^\circ} = \frac{1 - \tan^2 r^\circ}{1 + \tan^2 r^\circ}.$$

(b) Show that

$$\frac{\tan r^\circ}{1 - \cot r^\circ} + \frac{\cot r^\circ}{1 - \tan r^\circ} = 1 + \tan r^\circ + \cot r^\circ.$$

## Chapter Review

**1.** Complete each statement.

(a) If $5x = 8y$, then $\dfrac{y}{x} = \dfrac{?}{\phantom{?}}$.

(b) If $\dfrac{3}{4} = \dfrac{21}{28}$, then $\dfrac{7}{4} = \dfrac{?}{28}$.

(c) If $\dfrac{a+b}{a} = \dfrac{15}{12}$, then $\dfrac{b}{a} = \dfrac{?}{\phantom{?}}$.

(d) If $48 = 16k$, then $\dfrac{k}{3} = \dfrac{?}{\phantom{?}}$.

**2.** The sequences 2, $a$, 6, 5, $b$ and 5, 10, $c$, $d$, 9 are proportional. Determine $a$, $b$, $c$, and $d$.

**3.** Give the geometric mean and the arithmetic mean of each number pair listed below.

(a) 6 and 24

(b) 12 and 20

(c) $7\sqrt{3}$ and $21\sqrt{3}$

(d) $4\frac{1}{4}$ and $6\frac{3}{8}$

**4.** Sketch two figures whose corresponding sides are proportional, but which are not similar.

**5.** Sketch two figures whose corresponding angles are congruent, but which are not similar.

**6.** In $\triangle ABC$, $\overline{HK}\|\overline{AB}$.

(a) If $AH = 3$, $BK = 5$, $CK = 12$, then $CH = ?$

(b) If $AC = 14$, $AH = 6$, $CK = 12$, then $BC = ?$

(c) If $CH = 9$, $AH = 4$, $HK = 3$, then $AB = ?$

(d) If $AH = 4$, $CH = BK$, $BC = 48$, then $CH = ?$

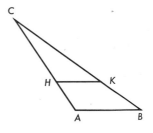

**7.** The sides of a triangle have lengths 5, 8, and 11. A similar triangle has a perimeter of 60. What are the lengths of its sides?

**8.** $\overline{AC}$ and $\overline{BD}$ intersect at $E$ such that $\overline{AB}\|\overline{CD}$ and $AB = 3CD$. If $AC = 21$, what are $AE$ and $EC$?

**9.** The sides of a triangle have lengths 7, 9, and 14. What is the perimeter of a similar triangle whose longest side is 21?

**10.** In $\triangle PQR$, $\overline{AB}\|\overline{QR}$ and $\overline{BC}\|\overline{PR}$.

(a) If $PA = 4$, $AR = 6$, and $PQ = 25$, then $BQ = ?$

(b) If $RC = 3$, $CQ = 5$, and $PQ = 24$, then $PB = ?$

(c) If $PA = 2$, $AR = 8$, and $RC = 3$, then $CQ = ?$

(d) If $PB = 4$, $BQ = 5$, $PR = 15$, and $RQ = 18$, then $PA = ?$ and $CQ = ?$

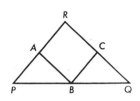

**11.** In the figure, $\square AEFD$ is a parallelogram. List all the similarities between triangles and show that

$$\frac{AE \cdot AD}{BE \cdot CD} = 1.$$

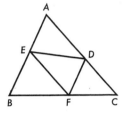

**12.** Given the figure on the left below with $\angle MGN \cong \angle HGK$, $GH = 8$, $GK = 12$, $GM = 10$, and $KN = 3$. Prove that $\angle HKG \cong \angle N$.

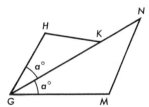

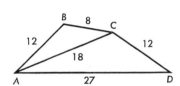

**13.** Given the figure on the right above with lengths of segments as marked. Prove that $\overrightarrow{AC}$ bisects $\angle DAB$.

**14.** The altitude to the hypotenuse of a right triangle separates the hypotenuse into segments having lengths 15 and 5. Find the length of the altitude and the lengths of the legs of the triangle.

**15.** Given the figure as marked, find $v$, $w$, $x$, $y$, and $z$.

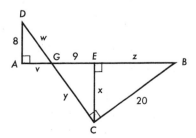

**16.** If $\triangle ABC \sim \triangle DEF$ and $\triangle DEF \sim \triangle ACB$, what kind of a triangle is $\triangle DEF$?

**17.** A tennis ball is served from a height of 7 ft and just clears a net 3 ft high. If the ball is served from a line 39 ft from the net and travels in a straight path, how far from the net does it hit the court?

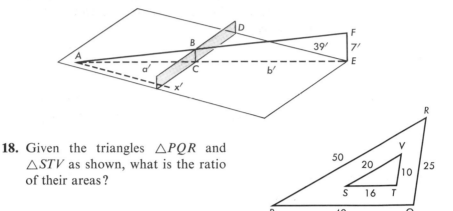

**18.** Given the triangles $\triangle PQR$ and $\triangle STV$ as shown, what is the ratio of their areas?

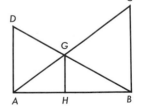

**19.** $\triangle ABC$ is an isosceles right triangle with $\angle A$ the right angle. $E$ and $D$ are points on opposite sides of $\overleftrightarrow{AC}$, with $E$ on the same side of $\overleftrightarrow{AC}$ as $B$, such that $\triangle ACD$ and $\triangle BCE$ are both equilateral. Determine the ratio of the areas of $\triangle ACD$ and $\triangle BCE$.

**20.** A side of an equilateral triangle is congruent to an altitude of another equilateral triangle. What is the ratio of the areas of the triangles?

* **21.** Given the figure with $\overline{AD}$, $\overline{HG}$, and $\overline{BC}$ each perpendicular to $\overline{AB}$. Prove:

(a) $AH \cdot GB = HB \cdot DG$.

(b) $AH \cdot GC = HB \cdot AG$.

(c) $AH \cdot BC = HB \cdot AD$.

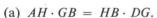

* **22.** Given that no three of the points $P,Q,R,$ and $X$ are collinear, and that $X$ is in the exterior of $\triangle PQR$. Draw segments $\overline{XP}, \overline{XQ}$ and $\overline{XR}$. Let $A$ be any point of $\overline{XR}$ and let the line through $A$ parallel to $\overleftrightarrow{PR}$ intersect $\overline{XP}$ at $B$. Let the line through $B$ parallel to $\overleftrightarrow{PQ}$ intersect $\overline{XQ}$ at $C$. Draw $\overline{AC}$. Prove that

$$\triangle ABC \sim \triangle RPQ.$$

**23.** In $\triangle ABC$ with right angle $\angle B$,

$$m \angle A = 54 \quad \text{and} \quad AC = 11.$$

Find $AB$ and $BC$.

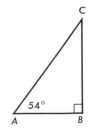

**24.** Find to the nearest degree the measures of the acute angles of a 7-24-25 triangle.

**25.** A jet plane takes off from an airport and climbs steadily at an angle of 8° until it reaches an altitude of 28,200 ft.  What is its ground distance from the airport (to the nearest mile)?

## HONORS PROBLEM

Explain how two triangles can have 5 parts (sides and angles) of one congruent to 5 parts of the other triangle and still not be congruent.

# 13 | Plane Coordinate Geometry

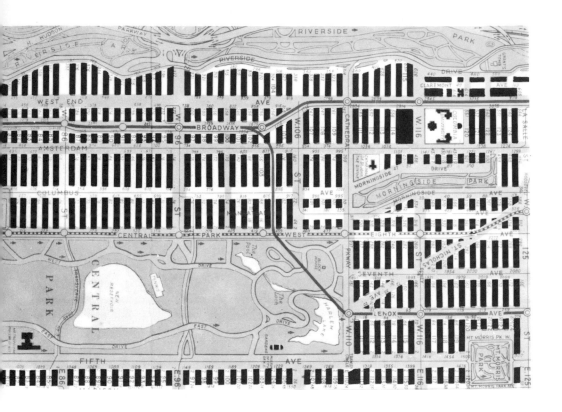

## 13–1.  INTRODUCTION

Mathematics is, in one way, quite different from the other sciences: it is the only science in which practically nothing ever has to be discarded.  Of course, mathematicians are people, and being people, they make mistakes.  But in mathematics, the mistakes of individuals are usually detected pretty quickly.  The result is that when one generation has discovered something about mathematics, the next generation can go on to discover some more, without having to stop to correct serious errors in the things that were supposed to be known.

One symptom of this situation is the fact that the geometry developed by the ancient Greeks looks just as right today as it did two thousand years ago.

The first big step forward in geometry, after the Greeks, was the development of a new method, called *coordinate geometry*.  This method was discovered in the seventeenth century by René Descartes (1596–1650).  As we shall see, what Descartes did was to explore the relations between geometry and algebra and show how each of them could throw light on the other.  In this chapter, we shall give a short introduction to coordinate geometry, so that you can see what it is and how it works.

## 13–2.  COORDINATE SYSTEMS IN A PLANE

We already know, from Chapter 2, how coordinate systems work on a line.

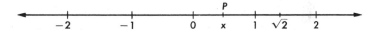

Once we have set up a coordinate system on a line, every number corresponds to a point, and every point corresponds to a number.

We shall now do the same sort of thing in a *plane*.  In a plane, a point will correspond not to a single number, but to a *pair* of numbers. The scheme works like this.  First we take a line $X$ in the plane, and set up a coordinate system on $X$. This line will be called the *x-axis*. In drawing figures, we usually put an arrowhead on the x-axis, to emphasize the positive direction on $X$.

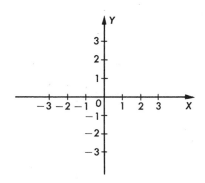

Now we let $Y$ be the perpendicular to the $x$-axis through the point with coordinate 0. On $Y$ we set up a coordinate system in such a way that the zero point on $Y$ is the zero point on $X$. (By the Ruler Placement Postulate, this can be done.) The line $Y$ will be called the *y-axis*. As before, we indicate the positive direction with an arrowhead. The point where the line $X$ intersects the line $Y$ is called the *origin*. The origin is denoted by 0, to remind us that it is the zero point on each of the axes.

We can now describe any point of the plane by a pair of numbers, as follows. Given a point $P$, we drop a perpendicular to the $x$-axis. Let the foot of the perpendicular be the point $M$. Let $x$ be the co-ordinate of $M$ on the line $X$. The number $x$ is called the *x-coordinate* of $P$. (In the figure, it looks as if $x = 2\frac{1}{2}$.)

We then drop a perpendicular to the $y$-axis. Let the foot of the perpendicular be the point $N$. Let $y$ be the coordinate of $N$ on the line $Y$. The number $y$ is called the *y-coordinate* of $P$. In the figure, it looks as if $y = 1\frac{1}{2}$. For short, we indicate that $P$ has these coordinates by writing $P(2\frac{1}{2}, 1\frac{1}{2})$.

Let us look at some more examples. From the figure, we can read off the following:

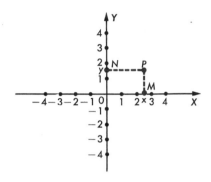

$P_1(1, 3)$,

$P_2(-2, 4)$,

$P_3(-4, 2)$,

$P_4(-3, -2)$,

$P_5(-1, -4)$,

$P_6(3, -2)$,

$P_7(3, 1)$.

Note that the order in which the coordinates are written makes a difference. The point with coordinates $(1, 3)$ is $P_1$, and this point is different from $P_7$, which has coordinates (3, 1). Thus, the coordinates of a point form an *ordered* pair of real numbers, and you can't tell where the point is unless you know which number comes first.

We sum all this up in the following definitions.

### Definitions

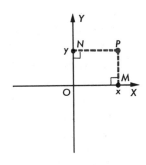

The *x-coordinate* of a point $P$ is the co-ordinate of the foot of the perpendicular from $P$ to the $x$-axis. The *y-coordinate* of $P$ is the coordinate of the foot of the perpendicular from $P$ to the $y$-axis. If $P$ has coordinates $x$ and $y$, then we write $P(x, y)$.

Just as a single line separates the plane into two pieces (each of which is a half-plane), so the two axes separate the plane into four parts, called *quadrants*. The four quadrants are identified by numbers:

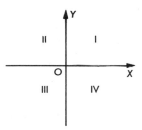

We have shown that under the scheme that we have set up, every point $P$ determines an ordered pair of real numbers. Does it work in reverse? That is, does every ordered pair $(a, b)$ of real numbers determine a point? It is easy to see that the answer is "Yes."

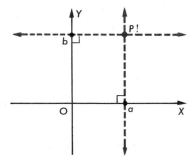

At the point of the $x$-axis with coordinate $x = a$, we set up a perpendicular. We do the same at the point of the $y$-axis with coordinate

$y = b$. The point where these perpendiculars intersect is the point with coordinates $(a, b)$.

Thus we have a one-to-one correspondence between the points of the plane and the ordered pairs of real numbers. Such a correspondence is called a *coordinate system*. To describe a coordinate system, we need to choose (1) a line $X$, to be the $x$-axis, (2) a line $Y$, to be the $y$-axis, and (3) a positive direction on each of the axes. Once we have made these three choices, the coordinate systems on both axes are determined, and they in turn determine the coordinates of all points of the plane.

In this book, we shall never be talking about two coordinate systems at the same time. So long as we stick to a single coordinate system, every point $P$ determines an ordered pair $(a, b)$, and every ordered pair $(a, b)$ determines a point. It will therefore do no harm to ignore the difference between points and number-pairs. This will enable us to use such convenient phrases as "the point $(2, 3)$" and "$P = (3, 4)$."

## Problem Set 13–2

1. (a) Give the coordinates of each point $P$ of the figure as an ordered pair of numbers.

   (b) Which three points are collinear? What are their coordinates?

   (c) Name the points in quadrant I; in quadrant IV.

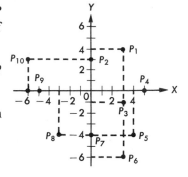

2. What are the coordinates of the origin?

3. What is the $y$-coordinate of the point $(3, -5)$? of the point $(5, -3)$? of the point $(-5, 3)$?

4. Consider the point $C(4, 7)$. What are the coordinates of its projection, $A$, into the $x$-axis? What are the coordinates of its projection, $B$, into the $y$-axis?

5. Answer the questions of Problem 4 for the point $D(-4, 7)$.

6. Name the point which is the projection of the point $(0, 6)$ into the $x$-axis.

**7.** Name the point which is the projection of the point $(-1, 0)$ into the $y$-axis.

**8.** Complete: The $x$-coordinate of every point on the $y$-axis is _____.

**9.** Complete: The $y$-coordinate of every point on the $x$-axis is _____.

**10.** Consider the points

$$A(5, 2), \quad B(4, -3), \quad C(-4, 4), \quad \text{and} \quad D(-3, -5).$$

(a) Write their names, $A$, $B$, $C$, $D$, in the order (from left to right) of their projections into the $x$-axis.

(b) Arrange them in the order (from bottom to top) of their projections into the $y$-axis.

**11.** The lines through $P(5, 7)$ which are perpendicular to the $x$-axis and to the $y$-axis form a rectangle with the two axes. Find the perimeter of the rectangle.

**12.** Find the perimeter of the rectangle formed by the axes and the perpendiculars to the axes through the point $(-4, -2)$.

**13.** Do as directed in Problem 11 for the point $P(-\frac{7}{2}, 3)$; for the point $P(-\sqrt{2}, \frac{3}{2})$; for the point $P(a, b)$, where $a$ and $b$ are any real numbers.

**14.** In which of the following pairs of points are the points closer together: $(3, 0)$ and $(7, 0)$, or $(3, 0)$ and $(-2, 0)$?

**15.** In which of the following pairs of points are the points closer together: $(2, 1)$ and $(1, 2)$, or $(2, 1)$ and $(2, 0)$?

**+ 16.** *A three-dimensional coordinate system.*
If we take a line perpendicular to the $x$-axis and to the $y$-axis at their intersection, we can set up a coordinate system in space. In this system we have a one-to-one correspondence between the points of space and ordered triples of real numbers.

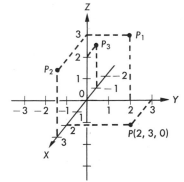

In the figure, the arrowheads indicate the positive direction on each axis and the dashed line segments are the perpendiculars which project each point $P$ into the respective axes. The projection of a point into an axis is its coordinate for that axis. Thus a point is completely described by its three coordinates, and we write $P(x, y, z)$.

In the figure (bottom of preceding page), $P$ is a point in the $xy$-plane, so that its projection into the $z$-axis (*not* indicated) is 0. Its projection into the $x$-axis is 2 and into the $y$-axis is 3. Therefore we write $P(2, 3, 0)$.

(a) $P_1$ is a point in the $yz$-plane. Write its coordinates as an ordered triple of real numbers.

(b) Points $P_2$ and $P_3$ are both in the $xz$-plane. Write their coordinates as ordered triples.

(c) Which two points are in a plane parallel to the $xy$-plane? Can you prove it? What do you observe about their coordinates?

+ **17.** If a point $P$ is described by $P(x, y, z)$, on which axis is each of the points

$$A(0, 3, 0), \qquad B(-2, 0, 0), \qquad C(0, 0, 5)?$$

+ **18.** If a point $P$ is described by $P(x, y, z)$, in which plane is each of the following points:

$$R(4, 0, 2), \qquad S(3, -2, 0), \qquad \text{and} \qquad T(0, 1, 5)?$$

*+ **19.** In representing a point in a sketch of a three-dimensional coordinate system, it is customary to consider first its projection into the $xy$-plane. In the figure $P'$ is the projection of $P(2, 3, 4)$ into the $xy$-plane. What are the coordinates of $P'$?

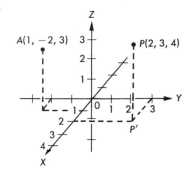

(a) What is the distance of point $P$ from the $xy$-plane? from the $xz$-plane? from the $yz$-plane?

(b) What is the distance of point $A$ from the $xy$-plane? from the $xz$-plane? from the $yz$-plane?

*+ **20.** (a) What is the distance of the point $(3, 2, -2)$ from the $xy$-plane? from the $xz$-plane? from the $yz$-plane?

(b) Answer part (a) for the point $(x, y, z)$, where $x$, $y$, $z$ are any real numbers.

RENÉ DESCARTES (1596–1650)

Descartes is a famous man in two quite separate domains: he is known among philosophers as a great philosopher and among mathematicians as a great mathematician.

His greatest contribution to mathematics was the discovery of coordinate systems and their application to problems of geometry. Ever since then algebra and geometry have worked together, to the advantage of both. To this day, coordinate systems of the sort used in this book are referred to as Cartesian coordinate systems, in honor of their inventor. The concept of coordinates was the first really fundamental contribution to geometry after the Greeks. (The word *Cartesian* comes from *Cartesius*, which is the Latin form of Descartes' name.)

Part of the credit for Descartes' discovery should go to Pierre Fermat, who had much the same ideas at about the same time. Fermat was one of the few great amateur mathematicians. He worked for the French government, and pursued mathematics in his spare time. He wrote letters to his friends about his discoveries, and never published them in any other form. But the material in Fermat's letters is now included in all the standard books on the theory of numbers.

The development of coordinate systems laid the foundation for the development of calculus, soon thereafter, by Newton and Leibniz. Thus Descartes must have been one of the men that Newton had in mind when he said that he had stood on the shoulders of giants.

## 13–3.  HOW TO DRAW PICTURES OF COORDINATE SYSTEMS ON GRAPH PAPER

In drawing pictures of coordinate systems, it is convenient to use ready-made graph paper.  On graph paper, the horizontal and vertical lines are printed, but we still have to draw everything else for ourselves.

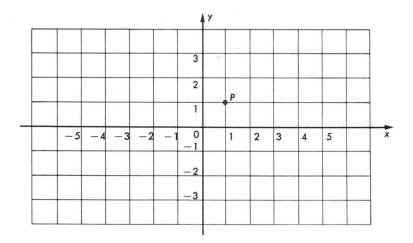

In the figure above, the red lines represent the lines that are ordinarily printed on the paper.  Everything else is drawn with a pen or pencil.  Note that the $x$-axis is labeled $x$ rather than $X$.  This is customary.  Here the symbol $x$ is not the name of anything; it is merely a reminder that the coordinates on this axis are going to be denoted by the letter $x$; and similarly for the $y$-axis.

Remember that before we started discussing coordinate systems, we were free to draw figures to any scale that we wanted.  For example, each of the following figures is a perfectly good picture of a square of edge 1.

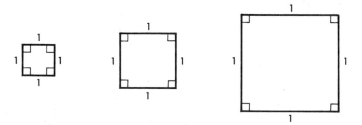

In the same way, and for the same reason, we can indicate any scale we want to on printed graph paper.  For example, we might have marked the same sheet of paper like this:

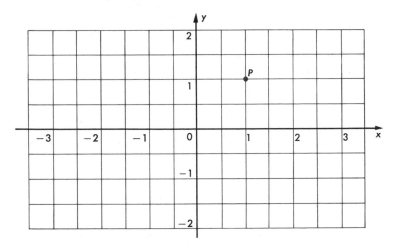

Because we have this freedom of choice, it is absolutely necessary to indicate what choice we made, by writing number labels on the axes to show the scale. If we hadn't done this in the figure above, nobody would be able to tell whether $P$ was supposed to be the point $(1, 1)$ or the point $(2, 2)$ or the point $(\pi, \pi)$.

*To repeat:* to show a coordinate system on graph paper, we draw the axes and indicate the scale.

Note that we can draw axes in any of the following (or other) positions on a sheet of paper.

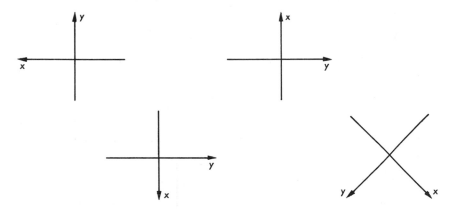

*None of these drawings are logically wrong.* But people find it much easier to read each other's graphs if they agree at the outset to draw the $x$-axis horizontally, with the coordinates increasing from left to right, and to draw the $y$-axis vertically, with coordinates increasing from bottom to top.

*A final word of caution:* You have probably seen many graphs on which the horizontal and vertical scales could be chosen independently of each other.

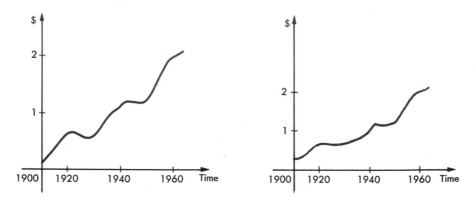

For example, if you want to draw a graph showing how the price of cheese (in dollars per pound) increased in the period from 1900 to 1960, there doesn't need to be any connection between the scales on the horizontal and vertical axes. (The scales measure different kinds of things, anyway.)

On the other hand, when you are drawing a coordinate system to do geometry, your picture will be distorted if the scales on the axes are different. The reason is that the scales will be used to measure distances.

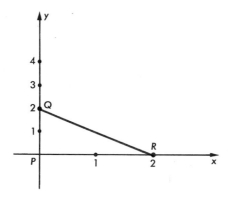

In the figure, the scales tell us that $PQ = 2$ and $PR = 2$. Therefore $\triangle PQR$ must be isosceles. But it certainly doesn't look very isosceles; and $\angle Q$ and $\angle R$ certainly don't look very congruent. This means that we have drawn a distorted picture. To avoid such distortions, we use the same scale on each axis.

## Problem Set 13–3

[*Note:* In this problem set you will find that printed graph paper will be helpful, though not essential. In Problems 1 through 12 draw one set of axes for each problem.]

1. Choose a suitable scale on a set of axes and plot each of the following points: $A(2, 3)$, $B(3, 2)$, $C(4, -3)$, $D(-3, -4)$. In which quadrant is each point?

2. Plot each of the points $A(0, 0)$, $B(5, 0)$, $C(5, 3)$, $D(0, 3)$. Find

   (a) the perimeter of $\square ABCD$.

   (b) $a\square ABCD$.

3. Plot each of the points $P(0, 0)$, $Q(3, 0)$, $R(0, 4)$. Find

   (a) the perimeter of $\triangle PQR$.

   (b) $a\triangle PQR$.

4. Plot each of the points $F(0, 0)$, $G(8, 0)$, $H(8, -6)$.

   (a) Find $a\triangle FGH$.

   (b) How long is $\overline{FH}$?

5. Given that $\triangle ABC$ has its vertices at the points $(0, 1)$, $(0, 6)$, and $(12, 1)$, find $a\triangle ABC$ and the perimeter of $\triangle ABC$.

6. Plot each of the points $A(1, 0)$, $B(7, 0)$, $C(10, 4)$, $D(4, 4)$. Find the perimeter and the area of $\square ABCD$.

7. What is the area of a triangle whose vertices are the points $(0, 5)$, $(4, 0)$, and $(-4, 0)$?

8. Plot each of the points $K(-2, 5)$, $M(-2, -3)$, $L(4, -3)$. Find $a\triangle KML$. How long is $\overline{KL}$?

9. A triangle has vertices at $(0, 0)$, $(0, 12)$, and $(10, 0)$. Find the length of the median to the shortest side.

10. Plot each of the points $A(-3, -4)$, $B(-3, 6)$, $C(4, 6)$. Find the coordinates of a point $D$ such that $\square ABCD$ is a rectangle.

11. The vertices of a triangle are the points $(1, 8)$, $(4, 1)$, and $(7, 1)$. Find the area of the triangle.

12. The ends of the base of an isosceles triangle are the points $(3, 0)$ and $(-3, 0)$. Find the coordinates of the other vertex so that the area of the triangle will be 15.

+ **13.** "When is a square not a square?" In the figures below, the scale on each x-axis is purposely different from the scale on the corresponding y-axis, in order to give a distorted picture of the figure intended. What figure was intended in each case?

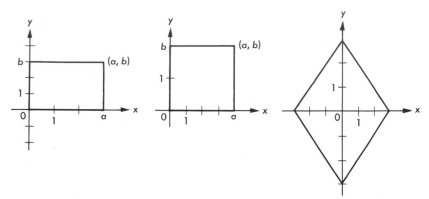

+ **14.** Given the figure on the left below, find the perimeter of ▱ABCD.

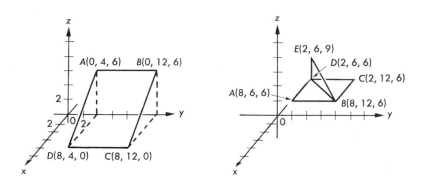

*+ **15.** In Problem 14, how long is the projection of $\overline{AC}$ into the xy-plane?

*+ **16.** Given the figure on the right above, as marked, find BE.

*+ **17.** Draw a three-dimensional coordinate system. Mark off the same scale on the y-axis and on the z-axis. On the x-axis (the one which comes "toward" you) use a scale which is about 0.7 of the scale on the other two axes. Locate the point $A(1, 3, 2)$ and the point $B(1, -3, 2)$. Draw $\overline{AB}$. How long is $\overline{AB}$?

[*Hint:* See Problem 19 of Problem Set 13–2.]

*+ **18.** Draw the figure of Problem 19 of Problem Set 13–2, but, instead of projecting P into the xy-plane first,

(a) project P into the yz-plane.        (b) project P into the xz-plane.

## 13-4.  THE SLOPE OF A NONVERTICAL LINE

The x-axis and all lines parallel to it are called *horizontal*.  The y-axis and all lines parallel to it are called *vertical*.

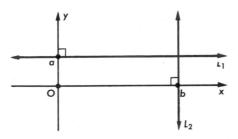

In the figure, it is easy to see that all points of the horizontal line $L_1$ have the same y-coordinate a, because the point (0, a) is the common foot of all perpendiculars to the y-axis from points of $L_1$.  Similarly, all points of the vertical line $L_2$ have the same x-coordinate b.  Of course, a segment is called horizontal if the line containing it is horizontal; and a segment is called vertical if the line containing it is vertical.

The idea of the *slope* of a segment is suggested by the following figures.

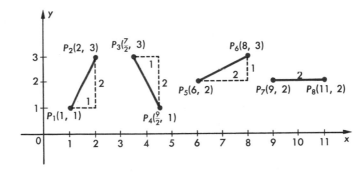

The slope of the first segment is 2; the slope of the second is $-2$; the slope of the third is $\frac{1}{2}$, and the slope of the fourth is 0.  To be exact:

**Definition**

If $P_1 = (x_1, y_1)$ and $P_2 = (x_2, y_2)$, and $\overline{P_1P_2}$ is nonvertical, then the slope of $\overline{P_1P_2}$ is

$$m = \frac{y_2 - y_1}{x_2 - x_1}.$$

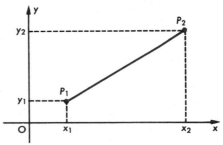

Some facts about slopes are obvious from the definition.

(1) If the points $P_1$ and $P_2$ are interchanged, the slope is the same as before, because

$$\frac{y_1 - y_2}{x_1 - x_2} = \frac{y_2 - y_1}{x_2 - x_1} = \frac{-(y_1 - y_2)}{-(x_1 - x_2)}.$$

In other words, the slope of a segment does not depend on the order in which its end points are named.

(2) On the other hand, it is important to name the coordinates in the same order in the numerator and denominator. The formula

$$\frac{y_1 - y_2}{x_2 - x_1}$$

is not a correct formula for the slope.

(3) For nonvertical segments, the slope formula always gives us a number, because the denominator $x_2 - x_1$ cannot be 0.

(4) For vertical segments, the slope formula *never* gives us a number, because in this case the denominator $x_2 - x_1$ is equal to 0. In fact, there is no such thing as the slope of a vertical segment.

(5) If a segment is horizontal, its slope is 0. (The numerator $y_2 - y_1$ is 0, and the denominator $x_2 - x_1$ is not 0.)

(6) If a segment is not horizontal (or vertical), then its slope is not 0.

(7) If a segment rises from left to right, its slope is positive. If the segment descends from left to right, its slope is negative. (See the figure on the left below.)

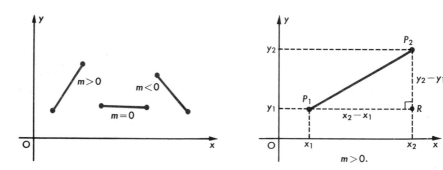

If a segment has positive slope, then its slope is the ratio of two distances as in the figure on the right above. Here, with $x_1 < x_2$ and $y_1 < y_2$, we have $P_1R = x_2 - x_1$ and $RP_2 = y_2 - y_1$. (Why?) Therefore

$$m = \frac{y_2 - y_1}{x_2 - x_1} = \frac{RP_2}{P_1R}.$$

If a segment has negative slope, then its slope is the *negative* of the ratio of two distances.

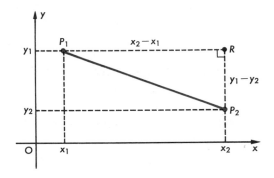

Here, with $x_1 < x_2$ and $y_2 < y_1$, we have

$$P_1R = x_2 - x_1$$

as before, but

$$RP_2 = y_1 - y_2 = -(y_2 - y_1).$$

Therefore

$$m = \frac{y_2 - y_1}{x_2 - x_1} = -\frac{RP_2}{P_1R}.$$

These ideas relate slopes to our geometry, and make it easy to see why the following theorem is true.

**Theorem 13–1**

On a nonvertical line, all segments have the same slope.

**Proof.** If the line is horizontal, this statement is obvious, because all segments on the line must have slope equal to 0. The interesting cases are indicated by the following figures:

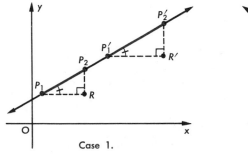

Case 1.

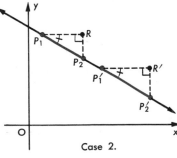

Case 2.

In Case 1, we have

$$\triangle P_1RP_2 \sim \triangle P_1'R'P_2'.$$

so that

$$\frac{RP_2}{R'P_2'} = \frac{P_1R}{P_1'R'},$$

$$\frac{RP_2}{P_1R} = \frac{R'P_2'}{P_1'R'}.$$

Therefore $\overline{P_1P_2}$ and $\overline{P_1'P_2'}$ have the same slope.

In Case 2, we also have

$$\triangle P_1RP_2 \sim \triangle P_1'R'P_2'.$$

This gives, as before,

$$\frac{RP_2}{P_1R} = \frac{R'P_2'}{P_1'R'}.$$

This result is what we wanted, because the slopes of our two segments are the *negatives* of these two ratios.

Now that we have Theorem 13–1, we can talk not only about the slopes of segments but also about the slopes of lines.

### Definition

The *slope* of a nonvertical line is the number which is the slope of every segment of the line.

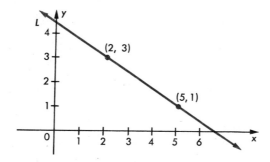

Thus, in the figure, the slope of $L$ is

$$\frac{1 - 3}{5 - 2} = -\frac{2}{3}.$$

Any other segment of the same line would give the same answer.

## Problem Set 13–4

**1.** Answer the questions below for each figure.

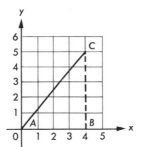 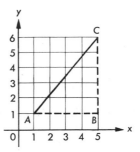

(a) What are the coordinates of *A*, *B*, and *C*?

(b) What is *BC*? What is *AB*?      (c) What is the slope of $\overline{AC}$?

**2.** Draw a set of coordinate axes. Locate four points, *A*, *B*, *C*, *D*, that have an *x*-coordinate of 3. Locate four points, *P*, *Q*, *R*, *S*, that have a *y*-coordinate of −2. Label each point with its coordinates.

**3.** Give the slope of each segment shown in the figure.

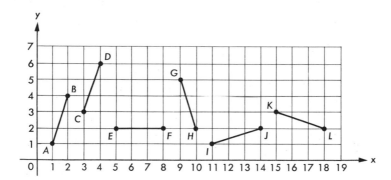

**4.** Which pairs of points given below will determine horizontal lines? Which ones vertical lines?

(a)  (5, 7)  and  (−3, 7).           (b)  (2, 4)    and  (2, −1).

(c)  (5, 2)  and  (−3, 5).           (d)  (0, −1)  and  (4, −1).

(e)  (3, 3)  and  (−3, 3).           (f)  (4, 7)    and  (−2, 6).

(g)  (0, 0)  and  (0, 5).            (h)  (0, 6)    and  (3, 0).

(i)  (*a*, *b*)  and  (*a*, *c*).           (j)  (*a*, *b*)    and  (*c*, *b*).

**5.** Find the slope of each line which contains each pair of points listed below.

(a)  (0, 0)    and  (8, 4).           (b)  (10, 5)  and  (6, 8).

(c)  $(2, -2)$  and  $(4, 2)$.      (d)  $(0, 3)$  and  $(-2, 3)$.

(e)  $(-2, 0)$  and  $(0, 6)$.      (f)  $(15, 6)$  and  $(-2, 23)$.

6. Find the slope of each line which contains each of the pairs of points listed below.

(a)  $(-5, 7)$      and  $(3, -8)$.

(b)  $(\frac{5}{2}, \frac{4}{3})$      and  $(-\frac{13}{2}, \frac{16}{3})$.

(c)  $(5\sqrt{2}, 6\sqrt{3})$  and  $(\sqrt{8}, \sqrt{12})$.

(d)  $(63, 49)$      and  $(-7, 9)$.

(e)  $(2a, 3b)$      and  $(-a, b)$.

(f)  $(0, n)$      and  $(n, 0)$.

7. The vertices of a triangle are the points $A(-2, 3)$, $B(5, -4)$, and $C(1,8)$. Find the slope of each side.

8. The vertices of a parallelogram are the points $R(1, 4)$, $S(3, 2)$, $T(4, 6)$, $V(2, 8)$. Find the slope of each side.

9. Determine the slope of each side of the quadrilateral whose vertices are $A(5, 6)$, $B(13, 6)$, $C(11, 2)$, $D(1, 2)$. Can you tell what kind of a quadrilateral it is?

10. A quadrilateral has as vertices the points $M(a, b)$, $N(c, b)$, $O(c + d, e)$, $P(a + d, e)$. Find the slope of each side.

11. $C$ is the mid-point of $\overline{AB}$, $A$ is the point $(-3, -2)$, and $B$ is the point $(2, 8)$. What is the slope of $\overline{BC}$?

12. Given the points $D(-4, 6)$, $E(1, 1)$, $F(4, -6)$. Find the slopes of $\overline{DE}$ and $\overline{EF}$. Are $D$, $E$, and $F$ collinear? Why?

13. Draw a coordinate system and plot the point $(2, 0)$. Now plot three other points whose $x$-coordinates are greater than 0 and less than 8 and which lie on a line with slope equal to 2, containing $(2, 0)$.

14. A line having a slope of $-1$ contains the point $(-2, 5)$. What is the $y$-coordinate of the point on the line whose $x$-coordinate is 8?

15. Draw a coordinate system. Draw the line through the origin which will pass through the point $(93000000, 62000000)$. Name three points of this line whose $x$-coordinates are less than 10.

* 16. Draw a coordinate system and plot the point $(-3, 1)$. Now plot three other points whose $x$-coordinates are greater than 0 and less than 10. and which lie on a line with slope equal to $-\frac{1}{3}$ and containing $(-3, 1)$.

## 13–5.   PARALLEL AND PERPENDICULAR LINES

Using slopes, we can rather easily tell whether two nonvertical lines are parallel.

(1) If two nonvertical lines are parallel, then they have the same slope.

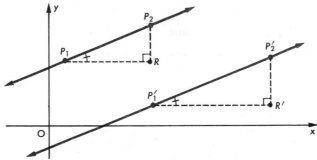

This follows from the fact that

$$\triangle P_1 R P_2 \sim \triangle P_1' R' P_2'.$$

(2) If two different nonvertical lines intersect, then their slopes are different.

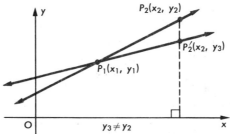

If the two lines intersect at $P_1$, as in the figure, then the slopes are

$$m = \frac{y_2 - y_1}{x_2 - x_1},$$

$$m' = \frac{y_3 - y_1}{x_2 - x_1}.$$

Here $m \neq m'$, because the denominators are the same and the numerators are different.

Combining these two statements, we get the following theorem.

### Theorem 13–2

Two nonvertical lines are parallel if and only if they have the same slope.

Suppose now that we have two perpendicular lines, intersecting at $P$. Suppose that neither of our lines is vertical.

We take a point $Q$, on one of the lines, above and to the right of $P$, and complete the right triangle $\triangle PRQ$. We then take a point $Q'$, on the other line, above and to the left of $P$, making $PQ' = PQ$. We complete the right triangle $\triangle Q'R'P$.

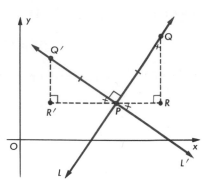

You should now check that the marks on the figure tell us that

$$\triangle PRQ \cong \triangle Q'R'P.$$

Therefore

$$\frac{RQ}{PR} = \frac{R'P}{Q'R'}.$$

But the slope of $L$ is

$$m = \frac{RQ}{PR},$$

and the slope of $L'$ is

$$m' = -\frac{Q'R'}{R'P}.$$

Therefore

$$m' = -\frac{1}{m}.$$

That is, *the slopes of perpendicular lines are negative reciprocals of each other.*

The same scheme works in reverse.

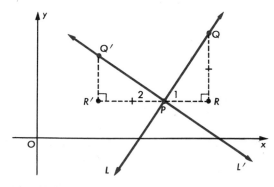

Given that $m' = -1/m$, we construct $\triangle PRQ$ as before. We then take $R'$ so that $R'P = RQ$, and we complete the right triangle

$\triangle Q'R'P$, with $Q'$ on $L'$. We then have

$$\triangle PRQ \cong \triangle Q'R'P,$$

as before. Therefore $\angle 1$ and $\angle 2$ are complementary, and $L \perp L'$. We sum up this discussion in the following theorem.

**Theorem 13–3**

Two nonvertical lines are perpendicular if and only if their slopes are negative reciprocals of each other.

Neither of the last two theorems applies to the case where one of the two given lines is vertical. But for vertical lines, the facts are plain. If $L$ is vertical, then the lines parallel to $L$ are simply the other vertical lines. And the lines perpendicular to a vertical line are simply the horizontal lines.

## Problem Set 13–5

1. Lines $L_1, L_2, L_3$, and $L_4$ have slopes $\frac{2}{3}, -4, -1\frac{1}{2}, \frac{1}{4}$, respectively. Which pairs of lines are perpendicular?

2. Consider the points $A(-1, 5)$, $B(5, 1)$, $C(6, -2)$, $D(0, 2)$. Find the slopes of $\overleftrightarrow{AB}$, $\overleftrightarrow{BC}$, $\overleftrightarrow{CD}$, and $\overleftrightarrow{AD}$. Is $\square ABCD$ a parallelogram?

3. Without plotting the points, determine which of the quadrilaterals whose vertices are given here are parallelograms.
   (a) $A(-2, -2)$, $B(4, 2)$, $C(9, 1)$, $D(3, -3)$.
   (b) $K(-5, -2)$, $L(-4, 2)$, $M(4, 6)$, $N(3, 1)$.
   (c) $P(5, 6)$, $Q(7, -3)$, $R(-2, -12)$, $S(-4, -3)$.

4. The vertices of a triangle are $A(16, 0)$, $B(9, 2)$, and $C(0, 0)$.
   (a) What are the slopes of its sides?
   (b) What are the slopes of its altitudes?

5. Given the points $E(-4, 0)$, $G(3, 5)$, and $K(8, -2)$. Show that the product of the slope of $\overleftrightarrow{EG}$ and the slope of $\overleftrightarrow{GK}$ is $-1$.

6. Prove that the quadrilateral with vertices $A(-2, 2)$, $B(2, -2)$, $C(4, 2)$ and $D(2, 4)$ is a trapezoid with perpendicular diagonals.

7. Consider the points $W(0, 3)$, $X(6, 4)$, $Y(12, -3)$, $Z(-2, -12)$. Which two lines determined by these points are perpendicular? Prove your answer.

8. Four points taken in pairs determine six segments. For each set of four points given below, find out which segments are parallel.  [*Warning!* Two *segments* which have the same slope are not necessarily parallel.]

   (a) $A(3, 6)$, $B(8, 2)$, $C(5, 9)$, $D(6, -1)$.

   (b) $P(0, -8)$, $Q(3, -2)$, $R(4, 0)$, $S(7, 6)$.

9. Prove that the triangle whose vertices are $H(-12, 1)$, $K(9, 3)$, and $M(11, -18)$ is a right triangle.

10. Show that the line through $(3n, 0)$ and $(0, 7n)$ is parallel to the line through $(0, 21n)$ and $(9n, 0)$.

11. If the line containing points $(-8, m)$ and $(2, 1)$ is parallel to the line containing points $(11, -1)$ and $(7, m + 1)$, what must be the value of $m$?

12. What values of $k$ will make the line containing points $(k, 3)$ and $(-2, 1)$ parallel to the line through $(5, k)$ and $(1, 0)$?

13. In Problem 12, what values of $k$ will make the lines perpendicular?

14. Given the points $P(1, 2)$, $Q(5, -6)$, and $R(b, b)$, determine the value of $b$ so that $\angle PQR$ is a right angle.

15. Find the slopes of the six lines determined by the points $A(-5, 4)$, $B(3, 5)$, $C(7, -2)$, $D(-1, -3)$.  Prove that $\square ABCD$ is a rhombus.

\* 16. A ray $\overrightarrow{PQ}$ makes an angle of 30° with the x-axis.  $\overrightarrow{QR} \perp \overrightarrow{PQ}$. If $P, Q, R$ are the points $P(-4, 0)$, $Q(5, 3\sqrt{3})$, and $R(x, 0)$, find the perimeter and area of $\triangle PQR$.

## 13–6.  THE DISTANCE FORMULA

If we know the coordinates of two points $P_1$ and $P_2$, then the points are determined.  Therefore the distance between them is determined (Chapter 2, the Distance Postulate).  We shall now find a way to *calculate* this distance $P_1P_2$ in terms of the coordinates $(x_1, y_1)$ and $(x_2, y_2)$.

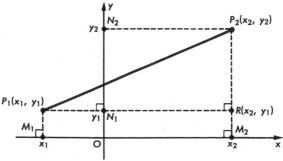

Let the feet of the perpendiculars from $P_1$ and $P_2$ be $M_1$, $N_1$, $M_2$, $N_2$, as indicated in the figure. Let $R$ be the point where the horizontal line through $P_1$ intersects the vertical line through $P_2$. Then

$$(P_1P_2)^2 = (P_1R)^2 + (RP_2)^2,$$

by the Pythagorean Theorem. $P_1R = M_1M_2$, because opposite sides of a rectangle are congruent. $RP_2 = N_1N_2$, for the same reason. Therefore, by substitution,

$$(P_1P_2)^2 = (M_1M_2)^2 + (N_1N_2)^2.$$

But we know by the Ruler Postulate that

$$M_1M_2 = |x_2 - x_1|$$

and

$$N_1N_2 = |y_2 - y_1|.$$

Therefore

$$(P_1P_2)^2 = |x_2 - x_1|^2 + |y_2 - y_1|^2.$$

Since the square of a number is the same as the square of its absolute value, this expression can be written in the form

$$(P_1P_2)^2 = (x_2 - x_1)^2 + (y_2 - y_1)^2.$$

We are now almost done. Since $P_1P_2 \geq 0$, we get

$$P_1P_2 = \sqrt{(x_2 - x_1)^2 + (y_2 - y_1)^2}.$$

This is the formula that we were looking for. In deriving it, we have proved the following theorem.

**Theorem 13–4.** The Distance Formula

The distance between the points $(x_1, y_1)$ and $(x_2, y_2)$ is

$$\sqrt{(x_2 - x_1)^2 + (y_2 - y_1)^2}.$$

For example, if $P_1 = (3, 4)$ and $P_2 = (-2, 1)$, the formula tells us that

$$P_1P_2 = \sqrt{(-2 - 3)^2 + (1 - 4)^2}$$
$$= \sqrt{(-5)^2 + (-3)^2}$$
$$= \sqrt{25 + 9}$$
$$= \sqrt{34}.$$

Note that we could have read off this result from a figure, without using the formula. We have $a = 5$, $b = 3$. By the Pythagorean Theorem,

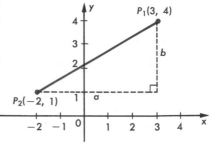

$$P_1P_2 = \sqrt{a^2 + b^2}$$

$$= \sqrt{5^2 + 3^2}$$

$$= \sqrt{34}.$$

Note, however, that to see this we have to go through the same line of reasoning that we used in deriving the formula. The whole point of deriving general formulas is that we can go through a line of reasoning only *once*, and then apply the results whenever we need them, instead of repeating the same reasoning process over and over again.

## Problem Set 13-6

1. Use the distance formula to find the distance between:
   (a)  $(0, 0)$     and  $(3, 4)$.          (b)  $(0, 0)$     and  $(3, -4)$.
   (c)  $(1, 2)$     and  $(6, 14)$.         (d)  $(8, 11)$     and  $(15, 35)$.
   (e)  $(3, 8)$     and  $(-5, -7)$.        (f)  $(-2, 3)$     and  $(-1, 4)$.
   (g)  $(5, -1)$   and  $(-3, -5)$.         (h)  $(-6, 3)$     and  $(4, -2)$.

2. Find the perimeter of a triangle whose vertices are $A(5, 7)$, $B(1, 10)$, and $C(-3, -8)$.

3. $\triangle PQR$ has vertices $P(8, 0)$, $Q(-3, 2)$, and $R(10, 2)$.
   (a) Find the length of each side.          (b) Find $a\triangle PQR$.

* 4. $\triangle KLM$ has vertices $K(-5, 18)$, $L(10, -2)$, and $M(-5, -10)$.
   (a) Find the perimeter of $\triangle KLM$.
   (b) Find $a\triangle KLM$.

5. The vertices of a quadrilateral are $D(4, -3)$, $E(7, 10)$, $F(-8, 2)$, $G(-1, -5)$. Find the length of each diagonal.

6. Prove that the triangle whose vertices are $A(2, 3)$, $B(-1, -1)$, $C(3, -4)$ is isosceles.

7. A triangle has vertices $G(0, 7)$, $H(5, -5)$, and $K(10, 7)$. Find the length of the altitude to the shortest side.

8. A triangle has vertices $M(-6, 0)$, $P(0, 6)$, and $Q(2, -2)$.

   (a) Find the perimeter of $\triangle MPQ$.

   * (b) Find the length of the altitude to the longest side.

   * (c) Find the area of the triangle.

* 9. Find the values of $b$ such that the triangle whose vertices are $(-6, 0)$, $(0, 6)$, and $(b, -b)$ is equilateral.

10. Given the points $A(-1, 6)$, $B(1, 4)$, and $C(7, -2)$. Find $AB$ and $BC$. Prove that $B$ is between $A$ and $C$.

11. Prove for the points $D(-4, -6)$, $E(-1, -2)$, and $F(3, 1)$ that $E$ is not between $D$ and $F$.

+ 12. In the rectangular solid on the left below, one corner is at the origin and $A$, $B$, and $C$ are on the $x$-, $y$-, and $z$-axes, respectively. $P'$ is the projection of $P$ into the $xy$-plane.

   (a) Find $OP'$.     (b) Find $OP$.     (c) Find $CP'$.

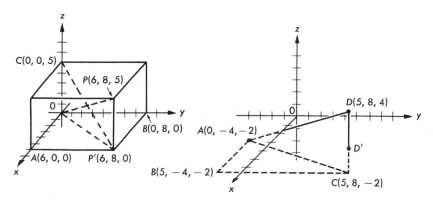

+ 13. For the figure on the right above

   (a) Find $AB$, $BC$, $AC$, $DC$, and $AD$.

   (b) Show that $AD^2 = (5 - 0)^2 + (8 + 4)^2 + (4 + 2)^2$.

+ 14. Find the distance from the origin to the point $P(a, b, c)$. Does the resulting formula change if $a$, $b$, or $c$ is a negative number? [*Hint:* Use the figure of Problem 13 above to help you.]

*+ 15. Show with a diagram similar to the figure of Problem 14 above that the distance $PQ$ between $P(x_1, y_1, z_1)$ and $Q(x_2, y_2, z_2)$ is given by the formula

$$PQ = \sqrt{(x_1 - x_2)^2 + (y_1 - y_2)^2 + (z_1 - z_2)^2}.$$

**+ 16.** Find the distance $PQ$ if the coordinates of $P$ and $Q$ are given by:

    (a) $P(4, -1, -5)$;   $Q(7, 3, 7)$.

    (b) $P(0, 4, 5)$;       $Q(-6, 2, 3)$.

    (c) $P(3, 0, 7)$;       $Q(-1, 3, 7)$.

    (d) $P(-3, 4, -5)$;  $Q(6, -8, 3)$.

    (e) $P(1, 2, 3)$;       $Q(2, 3, 4)$.

**+ 17.** Prove that the triangle with vertices $A(2, 0, 8)$, $B(8, -4, 6)$, and $C(-4, -2, 4)$ is isosceles.

**\*+ 18.** Show that $\triangle ABC$ is a right triangle if its vertices are

$$A(2, 4, 1), \quad B(11, -8, 1), \quad \text{and} \quad C(2, 4, 21).$$

**\*+ 19.** The figure $ABCD$ has vertices $A(3, 2, 5)$, $B(1, 1, 1)$, $C(4, 0, 3)$, and $D(6, 1, 7)$.

    (a) Show that its opposite sides are congruent.

    (b) Is $ABCD$ necessarily a parallelogram?

**20.** In a very carefully planned city the streets are laid out with numbered avenues running north-south and numbered streets running east-west, as in the diagram below, and in such a way that they form congruent squares. If you get into a taxi at the corner of 2nd Street and 6th Avenue and direct the driver to take you to 10th Street and 12th Avenue by the shortest possible route, what is the distance (in number of blocks) that you travel? Is this the shortest distance between the two points? Explain.

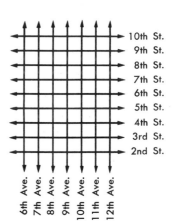

# 13-7.   THE MID-POINT FORMULA.   THE POINT DIVIDING A SEGMENT IN A GIVEN RATIO

Consider a segment $\overline{P_1P_2}$, on the $x$-axis:

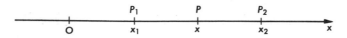

Let $P$ be the mid-point, let the coordinates of our three points be as shown in the figure, and suppose that $x_1 < x_2$. It is then rather easy to see how to express $x$ in terms of $x_1$ and $x_2$. We want

$$P_1P = PP_2.$$

Since

$$P_1P = |x - x_1| = x - x_1$$

and

$$PP_2 = |x_2 - x| = x_2 - x,$$

our first equation means that

$$x - x_1 = x_2 - x \qquad \text{or} \qquad x = \frac{x_1 + x_2}{2}.$$

This formula also works when $x_2 < x_1$. (Proof? If we interchange $x_1$ and $x_2$, the problem is unchanged and so is the formula.)

Once we have a mid-point formula for segments on the $x$-axis, it is easy to pass to the general case.

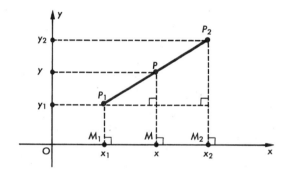

Here, if $P$ is the mid-point of $\overline{P_1P_2}$, then $M$ is the mid-point of $\overline{M_1M_2}$. (Why?) Therefore

$$x = \frac{x_1 + x_2}{2}.$$

In the same way, we get

$$y = \frac{y_1 + y_2}{2}.$$

To sum up we state the following theorem.

**Theorem 13–5.   The Mid-Point Formula**

Given $P_1 = (x_1, y_1)$ and $P_2 = (x_2, y_2)$. The mid-point of $\overline{P_1P_2}$ is the point

$$P = \left( \frac{x_1 + x_2}{2}, \frac{y_1 + y_2}{2} \right).$$

Consider now a more general problem. Given a segment $\overline{P_1P_2}$ on the x-axis, and a positive real number $r$.

We want to find the coordinate of the point $P$ which divides $P_1P_2$ in the ratio $r$ to 1. That is, we want

$$\frac{P_1P}{PP_2} = r, \quad \text{or} \quad P_1P = rPP_2.$$

If $x_1 < x_2$, as in the figure, this means that

$$x - x_1 = r(x_2 - x), \quad \text{or} \quad x + rx = x_1 + rx_2,$$

or

$$x = \frac{x_1 + rx_2}{1 + r}.$$

Note that for $r = 1$, this ought to give the coordinate of the mid-point. (Does it?)

For the case $x_2 < x_1$, the formula is exactly the same, but its derivation is slightly different. (We use $P_1P = x_1 - x$, $PP_2 = x - x_2$, and get the same answer.)

As in the case of the mid-point, we can easily pass to the general case. If

$$\frac{P_1P}{PP_2} = r,$$

then

$$\frac{M_1M}{MM_2} = r,$$

because $\triangle P_1PQ \sim \triangle P_1P_2Q_2$. Therefore it follows that

$$x = \frac{x_1 + rx_2}{1 + r}.$$

In exactly the same way, we obtain

$$y = \frac{y_1 + ry_2}{1 + r}.$$

Thus we have the following theorem.

**Theorem 13–6**

If $P$ is between $P_1$ and $P_2$, and

$$\frac{P_1P}{PP_2} = r,$$

then

$$P = \left(\frac{x_1 + rx_2}{1 + r}, \frac{y_1 + ry_2}{1 + r}\right).$$

## Problem Set 13–7

1. Find the coordinates of the mid-point of each segment in the figure.

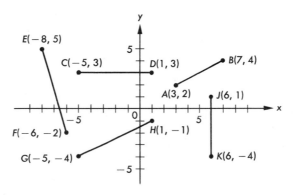

2. Use the mid-point formula to find the coordinates of the mid-point of the segment joining each pair of the following points.
   (a)  $(6, 0)$      and  $(10, 2)$.
   (b)  $(5, 7)$     and  $(11, 17)$.
   (c)  $(12, 3)$     and  $(3, 2)$.
   (d)  $(-5, 6)$   and  $(6, -5)$.
   (e)  $(\sqrt{2}, -\sqrt{3})$   and  $(\sqrt{18}, \sqrt{75})$.
   (f)  $(\frac{5}{4}, -\frac{5}{3})$   and  $(\frac{3}{4}, \frac{2}{3})$.
   (g)  $(a, 0)$      and  $(0, b)$.
   (h)  $(a, b)$     and  $(c, d)$.

3. If $A(3, 15)$ and $C(13, 0)$ are the end points of a segment and $B$ is a point of $\overline{AC}$, find the coordinates of $B$ given that the ratio $AB/BC$ equals

   (a) 4.        (b) $\frac{2}{3}$.

   (c) $\frac{1}{4}$.        (d) $\frac{3}{2}$.

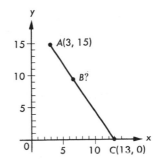

4. Given the points $P(5, 2)$ and $R(20, 14)$, and $Q$ between $P$ and $R$. Find the coordinates of $Q$ if $PQ/QR$ equals

(a) $\frac{1}{2}$.        (b) 2.        (c) $\frac{1}{3}$.        (d) 4.

5. What are the coordinates of the two points that trisect the segment having end points $(2, -3)$ and $(8, 9)$?

6. If the vertices of a triangle are $A(5, -1)$, $B(1, 5)$, and $C(-3, 1)$, what are the lengths of its medians?

7. The vertices of a quadrilateral are $A(0, 0)$, $B(5, 1)$, $C(7, 4)$ and $D(2, 3)$. Show that the two diagonals have the same mid-point. Is the quadrilateral a parallelogram? Why?

8. Given $P(-3, -4)$, $M(b, -1)$, and $Q(7, b)$. Find $b$ so that $M$ will be the mid-point of $\overline{PQ}$.

9. Given $G(-5, 8)$, $K(2, a)$, and $H(b, 1)$. Find $a$ and $b$ so that $K$ will be the mid-point of $\overline{GH}$.

10. A line segment has mid-point $M(3, -5)$, and one end point is $A(2, -4)$. What are the coordinates of $B$, the other end point?

11. Given the quadrilateral whose vertices are $A(3, -2)$, $B(-3, 4)$, $C(1, 8)$, and $D(7, 4)$. $W$, $X$, $Y$, $Z$ are the mid-points of $\overline{AB}$, $\overline{BC}$, $\overline{CD}$, and $\overline{DA}$, respectively.

(a) Find the coordinates of $W$, $X$, $Y$, $Z$.

(b) Find the perimeter of $\square WXYZ$.

(c) Find the slopes of $\overline{WX}$ and $\overline{YZ}$.

12. Prove that the diagonals of $\square PQRS$ have the same mid-point and are perpendicular to each other, given that the vertices are $P(2, 1)$, $Q(7, 4)$, $R(4, 9)$, and $S(-1, 6)$.

* 13. Using coordinates, prove that two of the medians of the triangle with vertices at $(m, 0)$, $(-m, 0)$, and $(0, 3m)$ are perpendicular to each other.

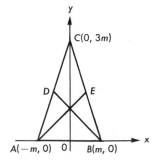

* 14. $A(-3, 2)$ and $B(5, 12)$ are two of the vertices of $\triangle ABC$. A line through $G$, the mid-point of $\overline{AB}$, and parallel to $\overline{AC}$, intersects $\overline{BC}$ at $H(10, 2)$. Find the coordinates of $C$, the third vertex.

+ **15.** Given the figure, determine the coordinates of the mid-point of each of the segments $\overline{AO}$, $\overline{BO}$, $\overline{CO}$, $\overline{AB}$, $\overline{BC}$, and $\overline{AC}$.

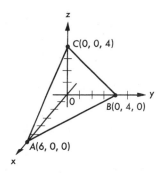

+ **16.** In the figure, $\overline{P'Q'}$ is the projection of $\overline{PQ}$ into the $xy$-plane, $\overline{PK} \parallel \overline{P'Q'}$, $\overline{P'A} \parallel y$-axis, $\overline{AQ'} \parallel x$-axis, $M$ is the mid-point of $\overline{PQ}$, $M'$ is the projection of $M$, $H$ is the mid-point of $\overline{QK}$, and $B$ and $C$ are mid-points of $\overline{AP'}$ and $\overline{AQ'}$, respectively.

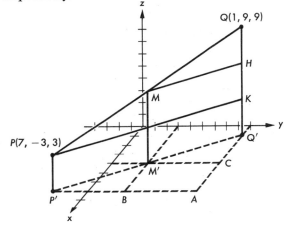

(a) Why is $\overline{PP'} \parallel \overline{MM'} \parallel \overline{QQ'}$?

(b) Why is $M'$ the mid-point of $\overline{P'Q'}$?

(c) Find the coordinates of $P'$, $Q'$, $A$, and $K$.

(d) Find the coordinates of $B$, $C$, $H$, and $M'$.

(e) Find the coordinates of $M$, the mid-point of $\overline{PQ}$.

+ **17.** State a general formula for the coordinates of the mid-point $M$ of the segment joining $P(x_1, y_1, z_1)$ and $Q(x_2, y_2, z_2)$, based upon your observations in solving Problem 16.

+ **18.** Find the coordinates of the mid-point of a segment joining the points:

(a)  $(3, 5, 0)$                                 and  $(1, 1, 8)$.

(b)  $(8, 5, 3)$                                 and  $(0, 0, -5)$.

(c)  $(-6, 2, 4)$                               and  $(6, -2, -4)$.

(d)  $(3\sqrt{2}, 2\sqrt{15}, -5\sqrt{3})$   and  $(-\sqrt{2}, 0, \sqrt{27})$.

*+  **19.** In Problem 16, find the coordinates of the two points which trisect $\overline{PQ}$.

*+  **20.** In Problem 16, find the perimeters of $\triangle BMM'$ and $\triangle AQQ'$.    Is $\triangle BMM' \sim \triangle AQQ'$?

## 13–8.   THE USE OF COORDINATE SYSTEMS IN PROVING GEOMETRIC THEOREMS

We shall now see how coordinate systems can be put to work in proving geometric theorems.  The main purpose of this section is to illustrate a certain method of working on geometry.  The method will be easier to understand if the first illustrations that we deal with are simple ones.  For this reason, we shall first apply the method to some theorems that we already know.

### Theorem A

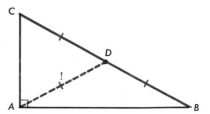

The mid-point of the hypotenuse of a right triangle is equidistant from the vertices.

The first step in applying coordinate methods is to choose the coordinate system in such a way as to make the algebra as simple as possible.  A good choice for this problem is the one shown in the figure below.  That is, we put the origin at $A$, with $B$ and $C$ on the positive ends of the two axes.  Thus $B = (a, 0)$, $C = (0, b)$, as in the figure. Therefore $D = (a/2, b/2)$, by the Mid-point Formula.  Now

$$AD = \sqrt{\left(\frac{a}{2} - 0\right)^2 + \left(\frac{b}{2} - 0\right)^2},$$

and

$$BD = \sqrt{\left(a - \frac{a}{2}\right)^2 + \left(0 - \frac{b}{2}\right)^2}.$$

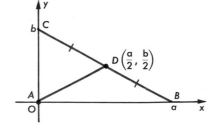

Therefore $AD = BD$.  This proves the theorem, because $BD = CD$ by definition of the mid-point.

Our choice of axes was not the only good choice.  The following figures suggest schemes which are just as easy.

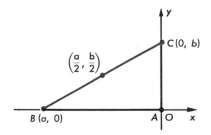
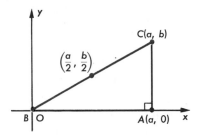

However, if you take the axes simply at random, you may turn an easy problem into a very hard one.

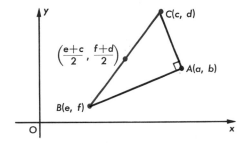

To start a proof, on the basis of this figure, you have to find a way to say, *algebraically*, that $\triangle ABC$ has a right angle at $A$.  This can be done, but it doesn't look very easy or very pleasant.

In using coordinate systems to prove things about parallelograms, we nearly always place the axes as shown at the right.  Given a parallelogram $\square ABCD$, we put the origin at $A$, with $B$ on the positive end of the $x$-axis and $C$ and $D$ in the upper half-plane. Now the slope of $\overline{AB}$ is 0, and $\overline{AB} \parallel \overline{CD}$.  Therefore the slope of $\overline{CD}$ is 0.  This gives

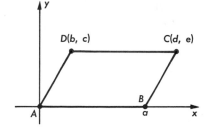

$$\frac{e - c}{d - b} = 0.$$

Therefore we can replace $e$ by $c$ in the figure.  (Why?)  We also claim that

$$d = a + b.$$

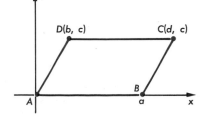

If $\overline{AD}$ and $\overline{BC}$ are not vertical, then they have slopes, and their slopes are the same. Thus

$$\frac{c - 0}{b - 0} = \frac{c - 0}{d - a},$$

$b = d - a$, and $d = a + b$. If $\overline{AD}$ and $\overline{BC}$ are vertical, then

$$b = 0, \qquad d = a, \qquad \text{and} \qquad d = a + 0 = a + b,$$

as before.

We can therefore label our figure as shown on the right.

Once we know about this scheme, many theorems about parallelograms become very easy.

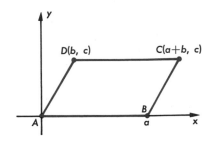

### Theorem B

If the diagonals of a parallelogram are congruent, then the parallelogram is a rectangle.

**Proof.** In the notation of the figure above, we have given that $AC = BD$. By the Distance Formula, this says that

$$\sqrt{(a + b - 0)^2 + (c - 0)^2} = \sqrt{(a - b)^2 + (0 - c)^2},$$

or

$$(a + b)^2 + c^2 = (a - b)^2 + c^2,$$

or

$$a^2 + 2ab + b^2 + c^2 = a^2 - 2ab + b^2 + c^2.$$

Therefore

$$4ab = 0.$$

Since $a > 0$, it follows that $b = 0$, and this means that $D$ is on the $y$-axis. Therefore $\angle DAB$ is a right angle, and $\square ABCD$ is a rectangle.

The following problem set is designed to give you some practice in the use of coordinate systems. In solving these problems, therefore, you should try to make the algebra do most of the work, using the illustrative examples of this section as a model.

## Problem Set 13–8

Prove the following theorems using the methods of coordinate geometry.

**1.** The diagonals of the rectangle on the left below are equal in length.

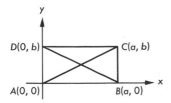
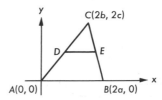

**2.** The segment between the mid-points of two sides of the triangle on the right above is parallel to the third side, and its length is one-half the length of the third side. [*Hint:* Since we will be finding the coordinates of mid-points and one-half of the base, it is convenient, but not necessary, to let the coordinates of $A$, $B$, and $C$ be as in the figure.]

**3.** The diagonals of a rhombus are perpendicular to each other. [*Hint:* Let the vertices be $(0, 0)$, $(a, 0)$, $(a + b, c)$ and $(b, c)$. Verify that the slopes are negative reciprocals.]

**4.** The median of a trapezoid is parallel to the bases, and its length is one-half the sum of the lengths of the bases.

**5.** The segment between the mid-points of the diagonals of a trapezoid is parallel to the bases and its length is one-half the difference of the lengths of the bases.

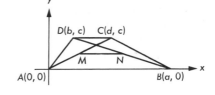

**6.** The segments joining, in order, the mid-points of consecutive sides of a quadrilateral form a parallelogram. [*Note:* We can select our axes so that one vertex is $(0, 0)$ and a side of the figure is along the $x$-axis, no matter how "tipped" the figure may be.]

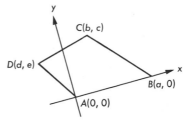

**7.** The segments joining, in order, the mid-points of consecutive sides of an isosceles trapezoid form a rhombus.

**8.** In $\triangle ABC$, if $\overline{CM}$ is the median to $\overline{AB}$, then

$$AC^2 + BC^2 = \tfrac{1}{2}AB^2 + 2CM^2.$$

[*Hint:* Choose the mid-point of $\overline{AB}$ at $(0, 0)$.]

**9.** In any triangle, the square of a side opposite an acute angle is equal to the sum of the squares of the other two sides minus twice the product of one of those sides and the projection of the other on it. To prove: $AC^2 = AB^2 + BC^2 - 2AB \cdot DB$. At what point in the calculation do you need the hypothesis that $\angle B$ is acute?

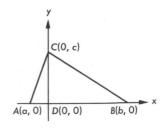

**10.** The sum of the squares of the sides of a parallelogram is equal to the sum of the squares of the diagonals.

* **11.** In any quadrilateral the sum of the squares of the sides is equal to the sum of the squares of the diagonals plus four times the square of the length of the segment between the mid-points of the diagonals.

+ **12.** Prove that the four diagonals of a rectangular solid are congruent and intersect at a common mid-point.

## 13–9.    THE GRAPH OF A CONDITION

By a *graph* we mean a figure lying in the plane, that is, a set of points. Thus angles, triangles and half-planes are graphs, and so are segments, rays and lines.

The term "graph" is usually used when we are describing a figure by stating a condition which is satisfied by all points of the given figure, and by no other points. Here are some examples.

| Condition | Graph |
|---|---|
| 1.  $y > 0$. | The half plane above the $x$-axis. |
| 2.  $x > 0$. | The half plane to the right of the $y$-axis. |
| 3.  $x = 0$. | The $y$-axis. |
| 4.  $x > 0$ and $y > 0$. | The first quadrant. |
| 5.  $x = 1$. | The vertical line through $(1, 0)$. |
| 6.  $x = 3$. | The vertical line through $(3, 0)$. |
| 7.  $1 < x < 3$. | The infinite strip lying between the lines described by Conditions 5 and 6. |

The seven graphs are shown on p. 407.

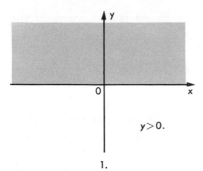

$y > 0.$

1.

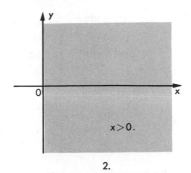

$x > 0.$

2.

$x = 0.$

3.

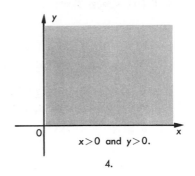

$x > 0$ and $y > 0.$

4.

$x = 1.$

5.

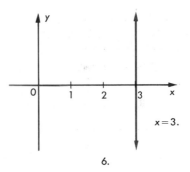

$x = 3.$

6.

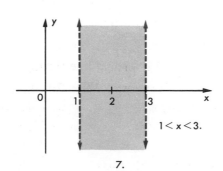

$1 < x < 3.$

7.

In each of these cases, we say that the figure is the *graph* of the condition that describes it. Thus each of the seven figures on p. 407 is the *graph* of the indicated condition.

*To repeat:* the *graph of a condition* is the set of all points that satisfy the condition.

This term is most often used when the condition is stated algebraically in terms of coordinates, as in the above examples. When the condition is stated in the form of an equation, we naturally speak of the figure as the graph of the equation. For example, the vertical line through $(1, 0)$ is the graph of the equation $x = 1$. Similarly, the first of the seven figures is called the graph of the inequality $y > 0$.

## Problem Set 13–9

**1.** On the same set of axes, sketch the graphs of the following conditions.

    (a) $x = 5$.      (b) $x < -2$.     (c) $y \geq 4$.     (d) $y = 0$.

**2.** Sketch on one pair of axes the set of points described by the following conditions:

    (a) $|x| = 2$.         (b) $|y| < 1$.        (c) $|x| \geq 3$.

**3.** Sketch the union of the graphs of $x = 3$ and $y = 2$. What is their intersection?

**4.** Given the conditions: (i) $x$ is a positive number and (ii) $y$ is a positive number.

    (a) Sketch the union of their graphs.

    (b) Sketch the intersection of their graphs.

**5.** Sketch the intersection of the graphs of these four conditions:

$$x \geq 0, \qquad x \leq 6, \qquad y \geq 0, \qquad y \leq 4.$$

Describe the intersection in words.

**6.** State the conditions which describe the region sketched on the right.

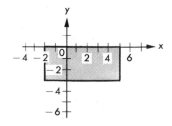

7. Sketch the graph and find the area of the intersection of the sets of all points satisfying the conditions

$$-1 \le x \le 3 \quad \text{and} \quad -2 \le y \le 5.$$

8. The distance from a point $P(x, y)$ to $A(1, 0)$ is equal to the distance from $P$ to $B(7, 0)$. Write an equation which expresses this condition. How many such points $P$ are there? Sketch the set of all such points $P$.

9. Write an equation for the set of all points $P(x, y)$ which are equidistant from the points $A(0, 6)$ and $B(6, 0)$. Sketch the graph.

* 10. Sketch the graph of $y = |x|$.

* 11. Sketch the graph of $y = -|x|$.

+ 12. A point $P(x, y)$ is between the point $A(1, 3)$ and the point $B(8, 6)$. Use the distance formula and the definition of "between" to write an equation expressing this condition on $P$.

*+ 13. If $P = (x, y)$, $A = (a, c)$, and $B = (b, d)$, what condition on the points $P$, $A$, and $B$ is expressed by

$$\sqrt{(x - a)^2 + (y - c)^2} + \sqrt{(x - b)^2 + (y - d)^2}$$
$$= \sqrt{(a - b)^2 + (c - d)^2} \ ?$$

*+ 14. On the same set of axes, sketch the set of all points $P(x, y)$ satisfying the conditions:

(a) $\sqrt{(x - 3)^2 + (y + 2)^2} + \sqrt{(x - 7)^2 + (y - 1)^2} = 5.$

(b) $\sqrt{(x - 3)^2 + (y + 2)^2} = \sqrt{(x - 7)^2 + (y - 1)^2}.$

*+ 15. In the figure, plane $E$ is parallel to the $xz$-plane and plane $F$ is parallel to the $yz$-plane. $E$ and $F$ intersect in $\overleftrightarrow{AB}$. $\overleftrightarrow{CG}$ is in plane $E$, $\overleftrightarrow{CH}$ is in plane $F$, and both lines are in the $xy$-plane.

(a) What are the coordinates of $C$?

(b) What equation gives the condition of which plane $E$ is the graph? of which plane $F$ is the graph?

(c) $\overleftrightarrow{AB}$ is the graph of what condition?

(d) Point $C$ is the graph of what condition?

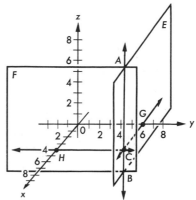

*+ **16.** In a three-dimensional coordinate system what are the graphs of each of the following conditions?

(a) $z = 0$.

(b) $x = 0$.

(c) $y = 0$.

(d) $y = 3$.

(e) $z = 5$.

(f) $|y| = 2$.

(g) $x = 0$ and $y = 0$.

(h) $x = 3$ and $z = 0$.

(i) $|y| = 2$ and $z = 0$.

(j) $x = 3$ and $y = 2$.

## 13–10.  HOW TO DESCRIBE A LINE BY AN EQUATION

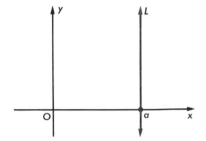

It is easy to describe a vertical line by an equation.

If the line intersects the $x$-axis at $(a, 0)$, then it is the graph of the equation $x = a$.

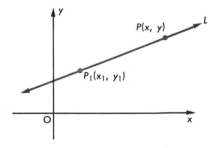

For nonvertical lines, we need to use the slope. Suppose that the line $L$ passes through the point $P_1 = (x_1, y_1)$, and has slope $m$. If $P = (x, y)$ is any *other* point of $L$, then

$$\frac{y - y_1}{x - x_1} = m,$$

because all segments of $L$ have slope $m$. Of course, this equation is not satisfied when $x = x_1$ and $y = y_1$, because in this case the fraction on the left becomes the nonsensical expression $0/0$, which is not equal to $m$ (or equal to anything else). But this is easily fixed: multiplying by $x - x_1$, we get

$$y - y_1 = m(x - x_1).$$

This operation *adds a point to the graph:* the new equation is satisfied for every point of $L$ other than $P_1$, because the old one was. And the new equation is also satisfied for $P_1$ itself, because when $x = x_1$ and $y = y_1$ we get $0 = m \cdot 0$, which is a true statement.

We write this result as a theorem.

**Theorem 13–7**

Let $L$ be a line with slope $m$, passing through the point $(x_1, y_1)$. Then every point $(x, y)$ of $L$ satisfies the equation

$$y - y_1 = m(x - x_1).$$

Note that this theorem does *not* say that $L$ is the graph of the equation. And in fact, we haven't proved this yet; we have proved only half of it. When we say that $L$ is the graph of the equation, this means two things:

    (1)   every point of $L$ satisfies the equation, and

    (2)   every point that satisfies the equation is on $L$.

So far, we have proved (1). We shall now prove (2).

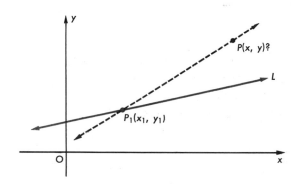

Suppose that $P(x, y)$ is a point for which

$$y - y_1 = m(x - x_1).$$

If $x = x_1$, then $y = y_1$, and $P$ is on $L$. If $x \neq x_1$, then $\overline{P_1 P}$ is not vertical, and its slope is

$$\frac{y - y_1}{x - x_1} = m.$$

Therefore $\overleftrightarrow{P_1 P}$ and $L$ have the same slope. Therefore these lines are parallel or the same. They cannot be parallel, because $(x_1, y_1)$ is on both of them. Therefore $\overleftrightarrow{P_1 P}$ is $L$, and $P$ lies on $L$.

This gives us a theorem which is simpler and also says more than the preceding theorem.

### Theorem 13–8

The graph of the equation

$$y - y_1 = m(x - x_1)$$

is the line which passes through the point $(x_1, y_1)$ and has slope $m$.

The equation given in this theorem is called the *point-slope* form of the equation of the line.

If we know the coordinates of two points of a line, it is easy to find an equation for it.

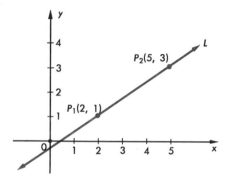

Suppose, for example, that the line passes through the points

$$P_1(2, 1) \quad \text{and} \quad P_2(5, 3).$$

Then its slope is

$$m = \frac{3 - 1}{5 - 2} = \frac{2}{3}.$$

Using $P_1(2, 1)$ and $m = \frac{2}{3}$, in the point-slope form, we get

$$(1) \qquad y - 1 = \tfrac{2}{3}(x - 2).$$

We can simplify, obtaining an equivalent equation:

$$3y - 3 = 2x - 4,$$
$$(2) \qquad 2x - 3y = 1.$$

Note, however, that although equation (2) is "simpler" than equation (1), it is not as easy to interpret. Using Theorem 13–8, we can tell immediately that the graph of (1) is the line through $(2, 1)$ with slope $\frac{2}{3}$. This is not so obvious for the simplified form (2).

Given an equation in the point-slope form, it is easy to draw its graph. Take, for example,

$$y - 3 = 2(x + 1).$$

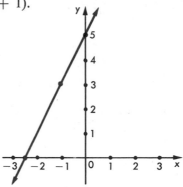

You can see immediately that the graph contains the point $(-1, 3)$. To draw the line, we merely need to know one more point of it. (Why?) Setting $x = 0$, we get

$$y - 3 = 2(0 + 1),$$

or

$$y = 5.$$

Therefore $(0, 5)$ is on the graph. We can now use a ruler, because we knew at the start that the graph had to be a line. As a practical matter, however, it is a very good idea to check our work by calculating the coordinates of a third point. For example, setting $y = 0$, we get

$$0 - 3 = 2(x + 1),$$

which gives

$$x = -\tfrac{5}{2}.$$

Therefore $(-\tfrac{5}{2}, 0)$ is on the graph, just as the figure suggests.

The following theorem is an easy consequence of Theorem 13–8.

**Theorem 13–9**

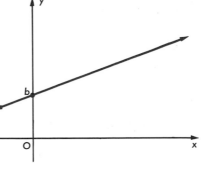

The graph of the equation

$$y = mx + b$$

is the line which passes through the point $(0, b)$ and has slope $m$.

The reason is that our equation can be written in the form

$$y - b = m(x - 0).$$

The equation $y = mx + b$ is called the *slope-intercept* form. For many purposes, it is the most convenient form.

We can now draw the graph of the equation

$$y = |x|$$

by the following method.  First we draw on the left below the graphs of the equations $y = x$ and $y = -x$.

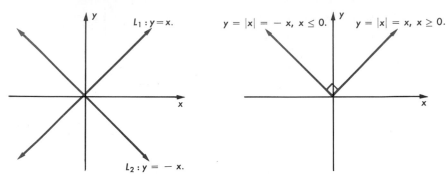

We remember that $|x|$ is defined by the following conditions:

(1)   For $x \geq 0$,     $|x| = x$.
(2)   For $x \leq 0$,     $|x| = -x$.

This means that to the right of the $y$-axis, our graph lies on the line $L_1$ but not on $L_2$.  To the left of the $y$-axis, our graph is on the line $L_2$ but not on $L_1$.  The graph therefore looks like the one on the right above.

It is easy to see that the two rays are perpendicular.  Therefore the graph of $y = |x|$ is a right angle.

## Problem Set 13–10

1. The equations below are written in point-slope form.  For each equation determine the slope and the coordinates of two points of its graph, and sketch the graph.

    (a) $y - 3 = 2(x - 4)$.          (b) $y - 1 = \frac{2}{3}(x - 6)$.
    (c) $y + 6 = -\frac{1}{4}(x - 8)$.          (d) $y - 5 = 3x$.
    (e) $y = -2(x + 3)$.

2. Write an equation of the line through point $P$ and having slope m, given that

    (a) $P = (4, 1)$     and  $m = 3$.      (b) $P = (\frac{1}{2}, -4)$  and  $m = -2$.
    (c) $P = (8, 2)$     and  $m = \frac{3}{4}$.      (d) $P = (-4, 0)$  and  $m = \frac{5}{4}$.
    (e) $P = (-6, 5)$  and  $m = 0$.

3. For each pair of points, first find the slope of the line which contains them, and then write an equation of the line.

(a)  (5, 2)        and  (2, 8).
(b)  (2, 4)        and  (4, 5).
(c)  (0, 0)        and  (1, 5).
(d)  (2, 7)        and  (−8, 5).
(e)  (−6, 0)       and  (0, 4).
(f)  (9, −15)      and  (12, −18).
(g)  (−4, −13)  and  (19, 33).
(h)  ($\sqrt{2}, \sqrt{8}$)  and  ($-\sqrt{8}, -\sqrt{2}$).

4. Joan and Al were comparing their solutions to homework problems. The problem was:

"Write an equation of the line through the points (2, −5) and (8, 7)."

Joan had the equation $y + 5 = 2(x - 2)$ and Al had $y - 7 = 2(x - 8)$. Whose answer was correct? Explain.

5. For each of the equations below, written in slope-intercept form, determine the slope and the $y$-intercept, and sketch the graph.

(a) $y = 2x + 6$.                    (b) $y = -2x + 6$.
(c) $y = \frac{2}{3}x$.                      (d) $y = 2x - 6$.
(e) $y = \frac{2}{3}x - 6$.

6. Find an equation of the line with slope equal to −5 and containing the point (0, 4).

7. Write an equation of the line through the point (7, −6) and parallel to the line whose equation is
$$y = \tfrac{1}{2}x + 1.$$

8. Write an equation of the line through the point (−2, 0) and perpendicular to the line whose equation is
$$y = -\tfrac{2}{3}x + 6.$$

9. On one set of axes draw the graphs of the equations
$$y = 3, \qquad y = x + 3, \qquad y - 3 = -\tfrac{5}{3}(x - 8).$$

(a) What are the coordinates of the three points at which the lines intersect?
(b) Find the area of the triangular region bounded by the three lines.

\* **10.** On one set of axes draw the graphs of the equations

$$y = -\tfrac{1}{2}x + 4, \qquad y = \tfrac{3}{4}x + 4, \qquad y + 1 = -\tfrac{4}{3}(x - 10).$$

(a) What are the coordinates of the three points at which the lines intersect?

(b) Find the area of the triangular region bounded by the three lines.

\* **11.** Sketch the graph of $x = |y|$.

\* **12.** Sketch the graph of $|x| + |y| = 4$.

+ **13.** Using the point-slope form of the equation of a line, prove that the equation of the line through the points $(a, 0)$ and $(0, b)$ can be written

$$\frac{x}{a} + \frac{y}{b} = 1 \qquad (a, b \neq 0).$$

Explain why this form is referred to as the "intercept form."

+ **14.** Use Problem 13 to write an equation of the line whose $x$-intercept is 5 and whose $y$-intercept is 3. Check your equation by using the slope-intercept form or the point-slope form.

\*+ **15.** In a three-dimensional coordinate system,

$$3x + 6y + 2z = 12$$

is the equation of a plane which intersects each axis. What are the coordinates of the intercepts?

\*+ **16.** In the figure on the right, plane $K$ intersects the axes at the points shown. The equation of plane $K$ is

$$6x + 4y + 9z = 36.$$

(a) Find the equations of the intersections of plane $K$ with each coordinate plane.

(b) Show that the equation of $K$ may be written as

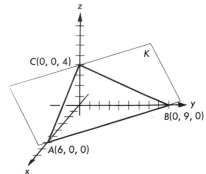

$$\frac{x}{6} + \frac{y}{9} + \frac{z}{4} = 1.$$

\*+ **17.** Write an equation of the plane determined by the three points:

(a) $(5, 0, 0)$, $(0, 3, 0)$, and $(0, 0, 4)$.

(b) $(12, 0, 0)$, $(0, 4, 0)$, and $(0, 0, -3)$.

(c) $(5, 0, 0)$, $(0, -3, 0)$, and $(0, 0, 10)$.

[*Hint:* See Problems 13 and 16 above. You need not prove that your equations are correct.]

*+ **18.** For each of the following equations determine the intercepts. Sketch the three-dimensional graph of each equation.

       (a) $4x + 3y + 2z = 12$.

       (b) $14x + 35y + 10z = 70$.

       (c) $9x - 7y + 21z = 63$.

       (d) $6x + 5z = 30$.

*+ **19.** In the figure $\overleftrightarrow{AB}$, $\overleftrightarrow{CD}$, and $\overleftrightarrow{EF}$ are the projections of $\overrightarrow{PQ}$ into the $xy$-plane, the $yz$-plane, and the $xz$-plane, respectively.

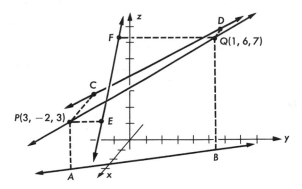

(a) Find the coordinates of $A$, $B$, $C$, $D$, $E$, $F$.

(b) Find the equations of $\overleftrightarrow{AB}$, $\overleftrightarrow{CD}$, and $\overleftrightarrow{EF}$ in their respective coordinate planes.

## HONORS PROBLEM

Given $\triangle ABC$ with vertices $A(a, a')$, $B(b, b')$, and $C(c, c')$ such that $0 < a < c < b$ and $0 < a' < b' < c'$.

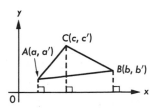

Prove that

$$a\triangle ABC = \tfrac{1}{2}[a(b' - c') + b(c' - a') + c(a' - b')].$$

What happens to the formula on the right if $A$ and $B$ are interchanged? $A$ and $C$? $B$ and $C$?

## Chapter Review

1. What are the coordinates of the projection of the point (5, 2) into the x-axis? into the y-axis?

2. What is the fourth vertex of a rectangle that has three vertices at

$$(-1, -1), \quad (3, -1), \quad \text{and} \quad (3, 5)?$$

3. Find the perimeter and area of a triangle whose vertices are (3, 2), (3, −4), and (9, −4).

4. Given $\triangle ABC$ with vertices $A(-3, -5)$, $B(3, 3)$, and $C(13, -9)$.

   (a) Find the coordinates of the mid-point of each side.

   (b) Find the length of each median.

   (c) Write the equation of the line containing each median, in the point-slope form.

5. The vertices of a quadrilateral are the points $A(-1, 1)$, $B(4, 3)$, $C(6, -2)$, $D(1, -4)$.

   (a) Prove that $\square ABCD$ is a parallelogram.

   (b) Show that its diagonals are perpendicular.

   (c) Are its diagonals congruent?

6. A line having slope $\frac{2}{3}$ contains the point $(0, -6)$. What is the y-coordinate of the point on the line whose x-coordinate is 12?

7. Using the methods of coordinate geometry, prove that the diagonals of an isosceles trapezoid are congruent, if the trapezoid is not a parallelogram.

8. Prove that the triangle whose vertices are $A(-3, 7)$, $B(2, -2)$, and $C(11, 3)$ is an isosceles right triangle.

9. One end point of a segment is the point $(-1, 8)$, and the mid-point of the segment is $(4, 2)$. Find the coordinates of the other end point.

10. A triangle has vertices $A(5, 7)$, $B(2, 0)$, and $C(5, -3)$. Find the altitude to the longest side. Find the area of the triangle.

11. A segment has end points $(4, -2)$ and $(13, 13)$. Find the coordinates of the points that trisect the segment.

12. Write an equation for the set of all points $P(x, y)$ that are equidistant from the points $A(0, 8)$ and $B(12, -8)$.

13. Write the equation of the line through the point $(0, 5)$ and parallel to the line $y = 2x - 13$.

14. Write the equation of the line through the point $(6, -1)$ that is perpendicular to the line $y = 3x + 1$.

15. On one set of axes draw the graphs of the equations $x = 9$, $y = x$, $y - 1 = -\frac{1}{2}(x - 1)$.

 (a) Find the coordinates of the intersections of the lines.

 (b) Find the area of the triangular region bounded by the lines.

# 14 | Circles and Spheres

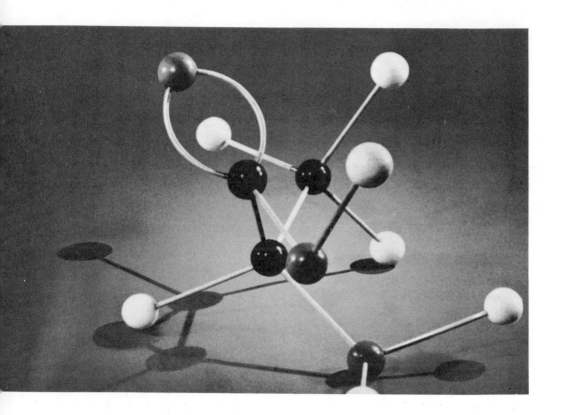

## 14–1.  BASIC DEFINITIONS

Roughly speaking, a circle is the boundary of a round region in a plane; and a sphere is the surface of a round ball in space.

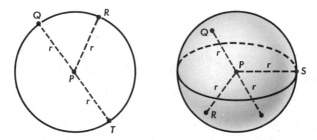

The following definitions state the same ideas in more precise language.

**Definition**

> Let $P$ be a point in a given plane, and let $r$ be a positive number. The *circle with center P and radius r* is the set of all points of the plane whose distance from $P$ is equal to $r$.

**Definition**

> Let $P$ be a point, and let $r$ be a positive number. The *sphere with center P and radius r* is the set of all points of space whose distance from $P$ is equal to $r$.

Two or more spheres or circles with the same center are called *concentric*.

In the figure, $P$ is the common center of the three concentric circles.

A *chord* of a circle is a segment whose end points lie on the circle.

In the figure, $\overline{AB}$ is a chord.

A line which intersects the circle in two points is called a *secant* of the circle.

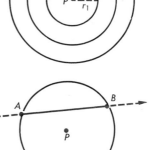

Thus every chord determines a secant, and every secant contains a chord.

Similarly, a *chord* of a sphere is a segment whose end points lie on the sphere. And a *secant* of a sphere is a line which intersects the sphere in two points.

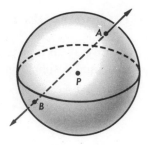

A *diameter* of a circle or sphere is a chord containing the center.

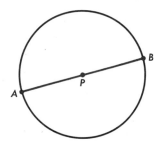

A *radius* of a circle is a segment from the center to a point of the circle. (Similarly for spheres.) The point *A* is called the *outer end* of the radius $\overline{PA}$.

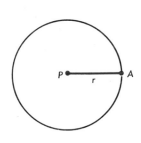

Note that we are using the word *radius* in two senses, to mean either a segment or a number, but it ought to be clear from the context which meaning is intended. Similarly, if a circle has radius *r*, we shall speak of the number 2*r* as *the diameter* of the circle. Of course, the number 2*r* is the length of every chord through the center.

To repeat: In the figure on the right, *r* is *the radius;* $\overline{PB}$ is *a radius;* $\overline{PA}$ is *a radius;* 2*r* is *the diameter;* $\overline{AB}$ is *a diameter;* and $\overline{PC}$ is *a radius* with *C* as its *outer end.*

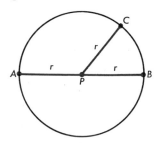

**Theorem 14–1**

The intersection of a sphere with a plane through its center is a circle with the same center and the same radius.

To see why this is so, we merely need to recall the definition of a sphere and the definition of a circle. Given a sphere $S$ with center $P$ and radius $r$, and a plane $E$. Then $S$ is the set of all points of space whose distance from $P$ is equal to $r$. The intersection of $S$ and $E$ is the set of all points of $E$ whose distance from $P$ is equal to $r$. This is a circle with the same center $P$ and the same radius $r$.

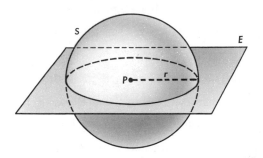

Knowing this, we can state the following definition.

**Definition**

The intersection of a sphere with a plane through its center is called a *great circle* of the sphere.

There is another reason for this term: the great circles are the *largest* circles that lie on the sphere. For example, if we draw meridians and parallels in the usual way, as on globes, then the equator is a great circle, but the other parallels of latitude are not. The other parallels of latitude are all smaller than the equator, becoming very small near the North and South Poles.

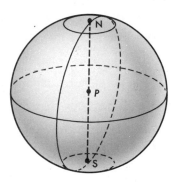

# Problem Set 14–1

1. Complete: The set of all points _____ at a given distance from a given point is called a _____.

2. Complete: A diameter of a circle is a _____ which contains the _____ of the circle.

3. The sentence below contains the word "diameter" twice. Explain how "diameter" is used each time.

   > Although a circle may have only one diameter, a circle actually does have infinitely many diameters.

4. In the statement of Theorem 14–1, what does "radius" mean?

5. Indicate whether each statement is true or false.

   (a) A diameter of a circle is a secant of the circle.

   (b) All radii of a sphere are congruent.

   (c) Every diameter of a sphere is the diameter of a great circle.

   (d) A radius is a chord of the circle.

   (e) A secant of a sphere intersects the sphere in exactly one point.

   (f) A chord of a circle contains exactly two points of the circle.

   (g) A sphere and a great circle of the sphere have the same center and the same radius.

6. Which of the following statements do you think are true?

   (a) If a radius bisects a chord of a circle, then it is perpendicular to the chord.

   (b) The intersection of a line with a circle may be empty.

   (c) Two circles may intersect in exactly three points.

   (d) A line may intersect a circle in exactly one point.

   (e) Two spheres may intersect in exactly one point.

   (f) Two spheres may intersect in a circle.

   (g) The secant which is the perpendicular bisector of a chord of a circle contains the center of the circle.

   (h) If a line intersects a circle in one point, it intersects the circle in two points.

7. If $\overline{AB}$ and $\overline{CD}$ are two diameters of a circle, then $\overline{AC} \cong \overline{BD}$ and $\overline{AC} \parallel \overline{BD}$.

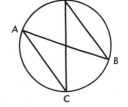

8. Prove that the diameters of a circle are the longest chords of the circle. [*Hint:* If $c$ is the length of any other chord, is $c < 2r$?]

9. If $\overline{AB}$ and $\overline{CD}$ are two diameters of a sphere, then the figure $ACBD$ is a rectangle.

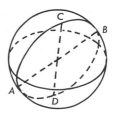

10. Prove: If each of two congruent chords of a circle has an end point in common with a diameter and they intersect the circle on opposite sides of the diameter, then the chords determine congruent angles with the diameter.

## 14–2.  TANGENT LINES TO CIRCLES

Throughout this section, we shall be talking about circles in a fixed plane.

### Definitions

The *interior* of a circle is the set of all points of the plane whose distance from the center is less than the radius. The *exterior* of a circle is the set of all points of the plane whose distance from the center is greater than the radius.

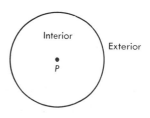

Thus every point of the plane is in the interior, or in the exterior, or on the circle. Frequently we shall say for short that a point is *inside* the circle, or *outside* the circle. (Remember that $0 < r$ because $r > 0$. Therefore the center is automatically in the interior.)

### Definitions

A *tangent* to a circle is a line (in the same plane) which intersects the circle in one and only one point. This point is called the *point of tangency*, or *point of contact*. We say that the line and the circle are *tangent* at this point.

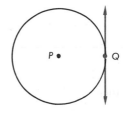

Every circle has a tangent at each of its points. We can see this from the following theorem

### Theorem 14–2

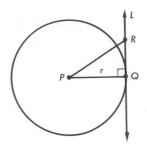

A line perpendicular to a radius at its outer end is tangent to the circle.

**Proof.** Let $L$ be perpendicular to the radius $\overline{PQ}$ at $Q$. We need to show that no other point of $L$ lies on the circle.

Let $R$ be any other point of $L$. By the First Minimum Theorem (Theorem 7–7), the shortest segment from $P$ to $L$ is the perpendicular segment. Therefore $PR > PQ$. Therefore $PR > r$, and $R$ is not on the circle; $R$ is in the exterior.

The converse is also true.

### Theorem 14–3

Every tangent to a circle is perpendicular to the radius drawn to the point of contact.

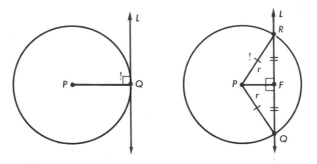

The figure on the left shows the situation as it actually occurs. The figure on the right illustrates the indirect proof which we give below.

**Proof.** Given that $L$ is tangent to the circle $C$ at the point $Q$. Suppose that $L$ is not perpendicular to $\overline{PQ}$. We shall show that this assumption leads to a contradiction.

Let $F$ be the foot of the perpendicular from $P$ to $L$. Then $F \neq Q$. Let $R$ be a point on the ray opposite to $\overrightarrow{FQ}$, such that $FR = FQ$. Then $\triangle PFR \cong \triangle PFQ$. (Why?) Therefore $PR = PQ = r$, and $R$ lies on the circle. Therefore $L$ intersects the circle in two points instead of in one. This is impossible, because $L$ is a tangent line. Therefore our supposition is false, and $L \perp \overline{PQ}$ at $Q$, which was to be proved.

In the figure on the left below, the two circles are *internally tangent*. In the figure on the right, the two circles are *externally tangent*.

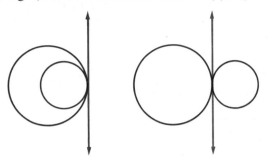

## Definition

Two circles are *tangent* if they are tangent to the same line at the same point. If two tangent circles are coplanar, and their centers are on the same side of their common tangent, then they are *internally tangent*. If two tangent circles are coplanar, and their centers are on opposite sides of their common tangent, then they are *externally tangent*.

## Problem Set 14–2A

1. Draw a circle with center $P$ and radius $PQ = 1\frac{1}{2}$ in. Locate a point $A$ such that $PA = 2$ in., and a point $B$ such that $PB = 1$ in. Now complete the following statements:

   (a) $A$ lies in the _____ of the circle because _____.

   (b) $B$ lies in the _____ of the circle because _____.

   (c) The circles with radii $\overline{PA}$, $\overline{PQ}$ and $\overline{PB}$ are called _____.

2. Describe how you can construct a tangent to a circle at a given point of the circle if you are given the center of the circle.

3. $E$ is a point in the exterior of a circle. How many tangents to the circle contain $E$? Make a sketch.

4. Prove: Given two concentric circles, every chord of the greater circle which is tangent to the smaller circle is bisected at its point of tangency. [*Hint:* Draw $\overline{PA}$, $\overline{PQ}$, and $\overline{PB}$.]

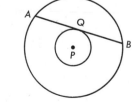

5. Prove that the tangents to a circle at the end points of a diameter are parallel.

**6.** One arrangement of three circles having
different radii so that each circle is tangent to the other two is shown in this
figure. Make sketches showing at least
three other arrangements.

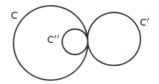

**7.** Prove the following theorem:

> If two circles are tangent, their centers are collinear with their
> point of tangency.

[*Hint:* Draw their common tangent.]

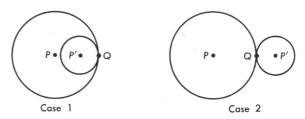

Case 1                    Case 2

**8.** Prove that if two congruent circles are externally tangent, any point
equidistant from their centers is on their common tangent.

**9.** The distance of a point $E$ from the center, $A$, of a circle is 20. The
radius of the circle is 5. A line through $E$ is tangent to the circle at $B$.
Find $EB$.

**10.** In the figure, each of the circles with centers
$A$, $B$, and $C$ is tangent to the other two. If
$AB = 10$, $AC = 14$ and $BC = 18$, find the
radius of each circle. [*Hint:* Let the radius of
one circle equal $x$.]

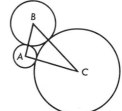

**11.** Given the figure in which the circles are
tangent, $P$ and $P'$ are the centers of the
circles, and $\overleftrightarrow{PB}$ and $\overleftrightarrow{P'A}$ are tangents at
$B$ and $A$, respectively. Given that the
radii are 9 and 6, find $PB$ and $P'A$.

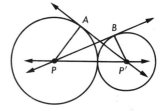

**12.** Two concentric circles have diameters of 10 and 26. Tangents to the
smaller circle pass through the ends of a diameter of the larger circle.
Find the length of the segment along each tangent which has an end
point on each circle.

* **13.** Given: In the figure on the left below, $\overline{AB}$ is a diameter of the circle with center $P$. $L$ is tangent to the circle at $T$. $\overline{AD}$ and $\overline{BC}$ are each perpendicular to $L$. Prove: $PD = PC$.

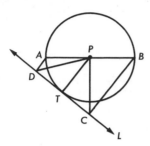 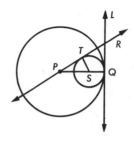

* **14.** In the figure on the right above, the circles with centers $P$ and $S$ are both tangent to line $L$ at $Q$. A secant of the larger circle passes through $P$, is tangent to the smaller circle at $T$, and intersects $L$ at $R$. Given that the radii of the circles are 8 and 3, find $QR$.

* **15.** In a circle with center $P$, $\overline{AB}$ is a diameter and $\overline{AC}$ is any other chord. A secant through $P$ parallel to $\overline{AC}$ intersects the tangent at $C$ in a point $D$. Prove that $\overleftrightarrow{DB}$ is tangent to the circle at $B$. [*Hint:* Introduce $\overline{PC}$.]

The following theorems are easy to prove.

**Theorem 14–4**

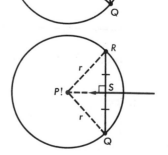

The perpendicular from the center of a circle to a chord bisects the chord.

**Theorem 14–5**

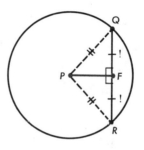

The segment from the center of a circle to the mid-point of a chord is perpendicular to the chord.

**Theorem 14–6**

In the plane of a circle, the perpendicular bisector of a chord passes through the center.

Proof? (If you don't see how to use any of the preceding theorems, try using Theorem 6–2.)

### Corollary 14–6.1

No circle contains three collinear points.

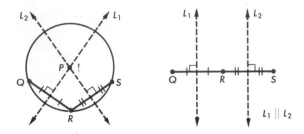

**Proof.**  If three points $Q$, $R$, $S$ of the circle were collinear, then the perpendicular bisectors of the chords $\overline{QR}$ and $\overline{RS}$ would be parallel. This is impossible, because both of these lines pass through the center.

### Definition

Circles with congruent radii are called *congruent*.

Note that this definition of *congruent circles* fits in with the use of the word *congruent* for segments, angles, and triangles.  The underlying idea, in each case, is that two figures are congruent if they have the same size and shape.

### Theorem 14–7

In the same circle or in congruent circles, chords equidistant from the center are congruent.

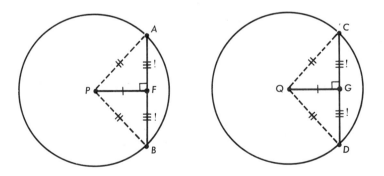

Proof?  (In the figures above, some of the marks are based on Theorem 14–4.)

**Theorem 14–8**

In the same circle or in congruent circles, any two congruent chords are equidistant from the center.

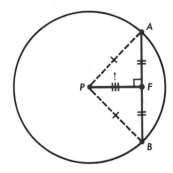
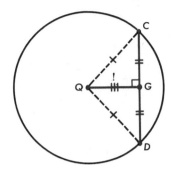

Proof?

Finally, we observe:

**Theorem 14–9**

If a line intersects the interior of a circle, then it intersects the circle in two and only two points.

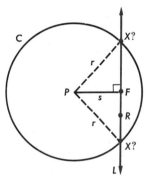

**Proof.** As in the figure, let $C$ be a circle of radius $r$, let $L$ be a line, and suppose that $L$ contains a point $R$ of the interior of $C$. Then $PR < r$. Let $F$ be the foot of the perpendicular from $P$ to $L$, and let $PF = s$.

(1) If $X$ is on both $L$ and $C$, then $\triangle PFX$ has a right angle at $F$, and so

$$r^2 = s^2 + FX^2.$$

Therefore

$$FX = \sqrt{r^2 - s^2}.$$

(2) If $X$ is a point of $L$, and $FX = \sqrt{r^2 - s^2}$, then $X$ is on $C$. The reason is that

$$PX^2 = PF^2 + FX^2$$
$$= s^2 + (r^2 - s^2)$$
$$= r^2.$$

But $r^2 - s^2 > 0$, because $r > s$. Thus, by the Point-Plotting Theorem, there are exactly two points $X$ of $L$ such that $FX = \sqrt{r^2 - s^2}$. Therefore exactly two points of $L$ are on $C$, which was to be proved.

## Problem Set 14–2B

1. State the theorem or corollary which justifies each conclusion below. Refer to the figure, in which $P$ is the center of the circle.

(a) If $\overline{PN} \perp \overline{CD}$, then $CN = ND$.

(b) Points $A$, $Q$, and $B$ are noncollinear.

(c) If $PM = PN$, $\overline{PM} \perp \overline{AB}$, and $\overline{PN} \perp \overline{CD}$, then $\overline{AB} \cong \overline{CD}$.

(d) If $\overline{AB} \cong \overline{CD}$, $\overline{PM} \perp \overline{AB}$, and $\overline{PN} \perp \overline{CD}$, then $PM = PN$.

(e) If $\overleftrightarrow{RT}$ is a tangent, $\overleftrightarrow{RT} \perp \overline{PQ}$.

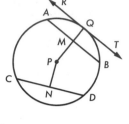

(f) If $M$ is in the interior of the circle, then $\overleftrightarrow{MQ}$ intersects the circle in exactly one point other than $Q$.

2. In a circle whose radius is 10 in., a chord is 6 in. from the center. How long is the chord?

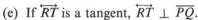

3. A diameter and a chord of a circle have a common end point. If the length of the diameter is 40 and the length of the chord is 24, how far is the chord from the center of the circle?

4. A chord 16 in. long is 15 in. from the center of a circle. What is the radius of the circle?

5. In the figure, $P$ is the center of the circle,

$$\overline{PD} \perp \overline{AC}, \qquad \overline{PE} \perp \overline{BC},$$

and

$$PD = PE.$$

Prove that $\angle DBA \cong \angle EAB$.

6. Prove: In any circle, the mid-points of all chords congruent to a given chord form a circle concentric with the given circle and with a radius equal to the distance of any one of the chords from the center.

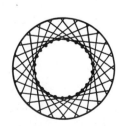

7. Prove: In a circle, if two chords which have a common end point determine congruent angles with a diameter from the same point, then the chords are congruent.

8. Given an arc of a circle, as in the figure at the right, explain how you could find the center and radius of the circle.

9. In a circle a chord 12 in. long is parallel to a tangent and bisects the radius drawn to the point of tangency. How long is the radius?

10. A chord 18 in. long is perpendicular to a radius of a circle. The distance from the intersection of chord and radius to the outer end of the radius is 3 in. Find the length of the radius.

11. For each part of this problem answer in the following way.

Write "extra" if more information is given than is needed to get a numerical answer. Write "not enough" if not enough information is given. Write "OK" if just enough information is given to allow a numerical solution. Write "contradictory" if the given information is contradictory.

[*Note:* You do not need to solve; just decide whether or not you can.]
In the figure $P$ is the center of the circle and $\overline{AB} \perp \overline{CD}$.

(a) $AF = 5, AB = $ ?   (b) $PB = 7, CD = $ ?   (c) $AC = 9, PB = $ ?

(d) $CF = 3, FP = 2, PD = 6, CD = $ ?

(e) $PB = 13, PF = 5, AB = $ ?

(f) $AB = 16, CD = 20, CF = 4, PB = $ ?

(g) $CF = 7, PB = 17, FB = 10, CD = $ ?

(h) $CD = 30, AB = 24, AC = $ ?

(i) $PB = 25, FB = 20, CF = 10, AC = $ ?

(j) $PD = 12, CF = 6, AB = $ ?

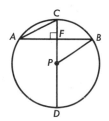

* 12. Prove: If two congruent chords (not diameters) of a circle intersect on a diameter, they determine congruent angles with the diameter.

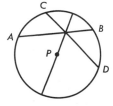

* 13. Two circles, of unequal radii, intersect at points $R$ and $S$. $M$ is the midpoint of $\overline{PP'}$, the segment between the centers of the circles. A line through $R$ is perpendicular to $\overline{MR}$ and intersects the circles again at $A$ and $B$. Prove that $AR = BR$.

* 14. Prove the following theorem.

Any three noncollinear points lie on a circle.

## 14–3.  TANGENT PLANES TO SPHERES

If you have really learned the preceding section, you will have no trouble with this one.  The reason is that the relation between spheres and planes in space is very much like the relation between circles and lines in a plane.  There is, therefore, a very close analogy between the definitions and theorems in the preceding section and the definitions and theorems in this one.

**Definitions**

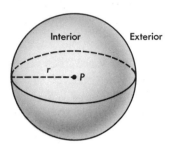

The *interior* of a sphere is the set of all points of space whose distance from the center is less than the radius.  The *exterior* of a sphere is the set of all points of space whose distance from the center is greater than the radius.

Thus every point of space is in the interior, or in the exterior, or on the sphere.  Frequently we shall say for short that a point is *inside* the sphere, or *outside* the sphere.

(Remember that $0 < r$ because $r > 0$.  Therefore the center is automatically in the interior.)

**Definitions**

A *tangent plane* to a sphere is a plane which intersects the sphere in exactly one point.  This point is called the *point of tangency*, or *point of contact*.  We say that the plane and the sphere are *tangent* at this point.

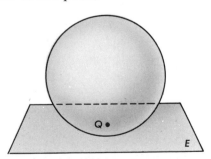

In the figure above, the plane $E$ is tangent to the sphere at $Q$.  Note that $Q$ does not appear to be on the "edge" of the sphere.  (When a round ball rests on a table, and we look at it from above, we can't see the point on which it is resting.)

Every sphere has a tangent plane at each of its points. We can see this from the following theorem.

### Theorem 14–10

A plane perpendicular to a radius at its outer end is tangent to the sphere.

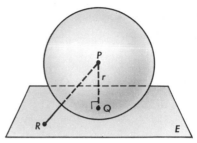

**Proof.** Let $E$ be perpendicular to the radius $\overline{PQ}$ at $Q$. We need to show that no other point of $E$ lies on the sphere.

Let $R$ be any other point of $E$. By the Second Minimum Theorem (Theorem 8–10) the shortest segment from $P$ to $E$ is the perpendicular segment. Therefore $PR > PQ$. Therefore $PR > r$, and $R$ is not on the sphere; $R$ is in the exterior.

The converse is also true.

### Theorem 14–11

Every tangent plane to a sphere is perpendicular to the radius drawn to the point of contact.

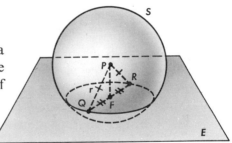

**Proof.** Given that $E$ is tangent to $S$ at the point $Q$. Suppose that $E$ is not perpendicular to $\overline{PQ}$. We shall show that this assumption leads to a contradiction. The figure illustrates the indirect proof.

Let $F$ be the foot of the perpendicular from $P$ to $E$. Then $F \neq Q$. Let $R$ be a point on the ray opposite to $\overrightarrow{FQ}$, such that $FR = FQ$. Then $\triangle PFR \cong \triangle PFQ$. (Why?) Therefore $PR = PQ = r$, and $R$ lies on the sphere. Therefore $E$ intersects the sphere in a point other than $Q$. This is impossible, because $E$ is a tangent plane.

In this proof, and several times before, we have drawn figures in which the intersection of a plane and a sphere appears to be a circle. Before proceeding with our investigation of tangent planes, we show that these figures are right.

## Theorem 14–12

If a plane intersects the interior of a sphere, then the intersection of the plane and the
sphere is a circle. The center
of this circle is the foot of the
perpendicular from the center
of the sphere to the plane.

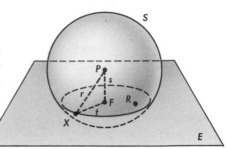

**Proof.** The notation is that of the figure. Given that the plane $E$
intersects the interior of the sphere $S$ in a point $R$. Let $F$ be the foot
of the perpendicular from $P$ to $E$. We need to show that the intersection of $E$ and $S$ is a circle with center at $F$.

Now $PR < r$, because $R$ is in the interior. By the Second Minimum
Theorem, $PF \leq PR$. Therefore $PF < r$. Let $PF = s$.

(1) Let $X$ be any point in the intersection of $E$ and $S$. Then $\triangle PFX$
has a right angle at $F$. Therefore

$$s^2 + FX^2 = r^2, \qquad \text{and} \qquad FX = \sqrt{r^2 - s^2}.$$

Therefore $X$ lies on the circle with center $F$ and radius $t = \sqrt{r^2 - s^2}$.

Therefore the intersection of $E$ and $S$ *lies in* the circle with center
$F$ and radius $t = \sqrt{r^2 - s^2}$.

This doesn't necessarily mean that the intersection *is* the circle. To
complete the proof, we need to show that every point of the circle lies
in the intersection.

(2) Let $X$ be any point of the circle in $E$ with center $F$ and radius
$t = \sqrt{r^2 - s^2}$. By the Pythagorean Theorem,

$$\begin{aligned}
PX^2 &= t^2 + s^2 \\
&= (r^2 - s^2) + s^2 \\
&= r^2.
\end{aligned}$$

Therefore $PX = r$, and $X$ lies on the sphere.

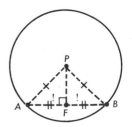

## Theorem 14–13

The perpendicular from the center of a
sphere to a chord bisects the chord.

Proof? (It is the same as the proof of Theorem 14–4.)

**Theorem 14–14**

The segment from the center of a sphere to the mid-point of a chord is perpendicular to the chord.

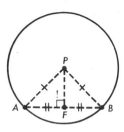

The proof is like that of Theorem 14–5.

## Problem Set 14–3

1. Complete: If a plane intersects a sphere, the intersection is either a _____ or a _____.

2. Complete: If a line intersects a sphere, the intersection is either _____ or _____.

3. Can three points of a sphere ever be collinear? Explain.

4. Sphere $S$ is tangent to plane $E$ at $A$. $P$ is the center of $S$, and $B$, $C$, $D$ lie in $E$. What is the relationship of $\overleftrightarrow{PA}$ to $\overleftrightarrow{AB}$, $\overleftrightarrow{AC}$ and $\overleftrightarrow{AD}$? Explain.

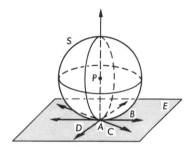

5. In a sphere having a radius of 15, the distance of a chord from the center is 9. How long is the chord?

6. A chord of a sphere is 12 in. long and is 6 in. from the center of the sphere. Find the radius of the sphere.

7. Prove: If two diameters of a sphere are perpendicular, the figure formed by the segments joining their end points in succession is a square.

8. Find the radius of the circle formed by a plane 4 in. from the center of a sphere whose diameter is 10 in.

9. Given a sphere and three points on it. Explain how to determine the center and the radius of the circle which contains the points. Explain how to determine the center and radius of the sphere.

10. Explain why any two great circles of a sphere intersect at the end points of a diameter of the sphere.

**11.** Prove the following theorem.

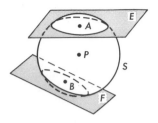

If two planes intersect a sphere and their distances from the center are equal, then the intersections are either two points or two congruent circles.

* **12.** Given: Plane $E$ intersects sphere $S$. $P$ is the center of $S$. $A, B, C, M$ are in $E$. $A$ and $B$ are in $S$.

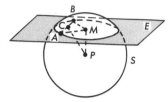

$\overline{PM} \perp E$.

$\overline{AM} \perp \overline{MB}$.

$AC = BC$.

$AM = PM$.

$AB = 5$.

Find: The radius of the sphere, $m \angle APB$, and $PC$.

*+ **13.** Two great circles are said to be perpendicular if they lie in perpendicular planes. Show that for every two great circles there is one other great circle perpendicular to both. If two great circles on the earth are meridians (through the poles), what great circle is their common perpendicular?

*+ **14.** In the figure, $P$ and $P'$ are the centers of spheres $S$ and $S'$. $A$ and $B$ are two points of the intersection of the two spheres. $\overleftrightarrow{AB}$ and $\overleftrightarrow{PP'}$ intersect at $M$. $\overleftrightarrow{PA}$ is tangent to $S'$ at $A$.

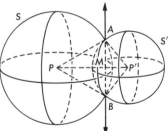

(a) Describe the intersection of spheres $S$ and $S'$.

(b) If the radius of $S$ is 12 and $PA = AB$, find the radius of $S'$ and the distance between the centers of the spheres.

## 14–4.  ARCS OF CIRCLES

We started this chapter with a discussion of circles, and then proceeded to give an analogous discussion of spheres. In the rest of the chapter, however, we shall be concerned only with circles, because the corresponding theory for spheres is too hard for a first course in geometry.

In the figure below, ∠APB is a *central angle* of the circle C.

### Definition

A *central angle* of a circle is an angle whose vertex is the center of the circle.

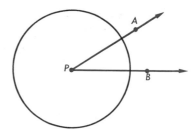

In the next figure, the curve in color is the *minor arc* $\overset{\frown}{AB}$, and the black curve is the *major arc* $\overset{\frown}{AB}$. In each case, A and B are the *end points* of the arc.

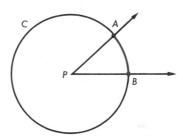

### Definitions

Let C be a circle with center P, and let A and B be points which lie on C but are not the end points of a diameter. Then the *minor arc* $\overset{\frown}{AB}$ is the union of A, B and all points of C that are in the interior of ∠APB. The *major arc* $\overset{\frown}{AB}$ is the union of A, B and all points of C that lie in the exterior of ∠APB. In each case, A and B are the *end points* of the arc $\overset{\frown}{AB}$.

If A and B are the end points of a diameter, then we get two arcs, each of which is called a *semicircle*.

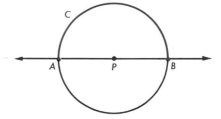

### Definition

Let C be a circle, and let A and B be the end points of a diameter. A *semicircle* $\overset{\frown}{AB}$ is the union of A, B, and the points of C that lie in a given half-plane with $\overleftrightarrow{AB}$ as edge. The points A and B are the *end points* of the semicircle.

Note that the notation $\overset{\frown}{AB}$ for arcs is always ambiguous, because every two points A and B of a circle are the end points of two different arcs of the circle. The easiest way to avoid this ambiguity is to pick another point X of the arc, and denote the arc by $\overset{\frown}{AXB}$.

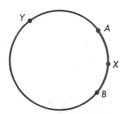

For example, in the figure above, $\overset{\frown}{AXB}$ is the minor arc, drawn in color, and $\overset{\frown}{AYB}$ is the major arc, drawn black. When it is clear from the context which arc is meant, we may simply write $\overset{\frown}{AB}$.

We now want to define the *degree measures* of arcs, in the way suggested by the labels in the following figures.

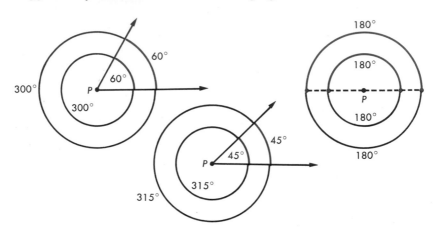

Note that the degree measure of an arc does not depend on the size of the circle. On the pairs of concentric circles above, corresponding arcs have the same measure. Note also that as an arc gets longer (on the fixed circle) its measure gets bigger. Thus a major arc always has measure greater than 180.

These ideas are conveyed by the following definition.

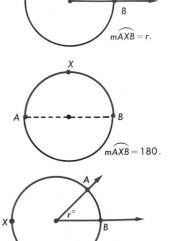

**Definition**

(1) The *degree measure* of a minor arc is the measure of the corresponding central angle.

(2) The *degree measure* of a semicircle is 180.

(3) The *degree measure* of a major arc is equal to 360 minus the measure of the corresponding minor arc.

Hereafter, the degree measure of an arc will be referred to simply as its measure. The measure of an arc $\overset{\frown}{AB}$ will be denoted by $m\overset{\frown}{AB}$.

The following theorem looks reasonable, but its proof is surprisingly tedious.

**Theorem 14–15.**   The Arc Addition Theorem

If $B$ is a point of $\overset{\frown}{AC}$, then

$$m\overset{\frown}{ABC} = m\overset{\frown}{AB} + m\overset{\frown}{BC}.$$

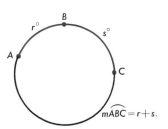

We omit the proof of this statement, and shall regard it, for practical purposes, as a postulate. Note that when $\overset{\frown}{ABC}$ is a minor arc, our formula follows immediately from the Angle Addition Postulate. There are, however, other cases that we would need to consider in a complete proof.

## Problem Set 14–4

1. In the figure, $A$ and $B$ are the end points of a diameter.

   (a) Name the semicircles.

   (b) Name the minor arcs.

   (c) Name the major arcs.

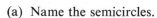

2. In the figure on the left below, $P$ is the center of the circle and $RQ = PS$. Find $m\overset{\frown}{RQ}$; $m\overset{\frown}{RS}$; $m\overset{\frown}{SRQ}$; $m\overset{\frown}{RSQ}$.

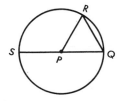
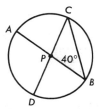

3. In the figure on the right above, diameters $\overline{AB}$ and $\overline{CD}$ intersect at $P$. If $m\angle ABC = 40$, find the measure of each minor arc of the circle.

4. Prove: If $\overline{GH}$ and $\overline{MK}$ are two diameters of a circle, then $m\overset{\frown}{GK} = m\overset{\frown}{HM}$.

**5.** In this figure, which arc has the greatest measure?

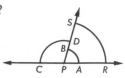

**6.** Prove: The bisector of a central angle of a circle bisects the corresponding minor arc.

**7.** Given: $\widehat{AB}$ is a semicircle with center $C$.

$\widehat{PQ}$ is concentric with $\widehat{AB}$.

$\overline{EC} \perp \overline{AB}$ and $\overline{DC} \perp \overline{CF}$.

Prove: $m\widehat{AD} + m\widehat{QT} = m\widehat{EF} + m\widehat{RS}$.

**8.** Two points on a circle determine a minor arc and a major arc. If the measure of the major arc is 40 less than 4 times the measure of the minor arc, find the measure of each arc.

## 14–5.  INSCRIBED ANGLES AND INTERCEPTED ARCS

In each of the figures below, $\angle x$ is said to be *inscribed* in the arc which is drawn in color.

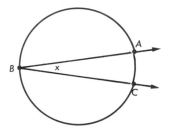 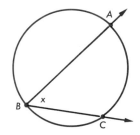

This idea can be described in words, quickly and easily.

### Definition

An angle is *inscribed* in an arc if

(1) the sides of the angle contain the end points of the arc and

(2) the vertex of the angle is a point, but not an end point, of the arc.

Of course, if $D$ is any point of $\widehat{ABC}$ other than $A$ or $C$, then $\widehat{ABC} = \widehat{ADC}$, and so $\angle ADC$ is also inscribed in the same arc.  In the figure on the right, all the angles shown are inscribed in the arc $\overarc{AC}$ which is drawn in color. The figure looks as though these angles were all congruent, and in fact, this is always the case, as we shall soon see.

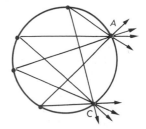

In each of the figures below, the angle *intercepts* the arc or arcs drawn in color.

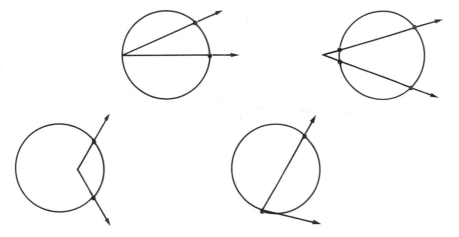

But in the following figure, we do *not* say that the angle intercepts the arc drawn in color.

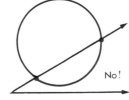

In the following definition, we allow the first four of these cases but rule out the fifth one.

## Definition

An angle *intercepts* an arc if

(1) the end points of the arc lie on the angle,

(2) all other points of the arc are in the interior of the angle, and

(3) each side of the angle contains an end point of the arc.

### Theorem 14–16

The measure of an inscribed angle is half the measure of its intercepted arc.

**Restatement.** Let $\angle A$ be inscribed in an arc $\overset{\frown}{BAC}$ of a circle, intercepting the arc $\overset{\frown}{BC}$. Then

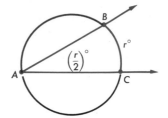

$$m\angle A = \tfrac{1}{2}m\overset{\frown}{BC}.$$

**Proof.** *Case* 1. We consider first the case in which $\angle A$ contains a diameter of the circle. By Corollary 9–13.3,

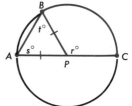

$$r = s + t.$$

By the Isosceles Triangle Theorem, $t = s$. Therefore

$$s = \frac{r}{2}.$$

This proves the theorem, in Case 1, because $s = m\angle A$ and $r = m\overset{\frown}{BC}$.

Now we know that the theorem holds in Case 1. We shall use this fact to show that it holds in every case.

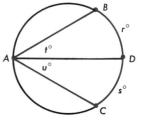

*Case* 2. Suppose that $B$ and $C$ are on opposite sides of the diameter through $A$, like this:

We know by Case 1 that

$$t = \frac{r}{2}, \qquad u = \frac{s}{2}.$$

Therefore, by addition

$$t + u = \tfrac{1}{2}(r + s).$$

But

$$t + u = m\angle A \qquad \text{and} \qquad r + s = m\overset{\frown}{BDC}.$$

(Reason, in each case?) Therefore $m\angle A = \tfrac{1}{2}m\overset{\frown}{BC}$, as before.

*Case* 3.   Suppose, finally, that *B* and *C* are on the same side of the diameter through *A*.  Then

$$r + s = m\widehat{BCD}$$

and

$$t + u = m\angle BAD.$$

By Case 1,

$$t + u = \tfrac{1}{2}(r + s),$$

and

$$u = \tfrac{1}{2}s.$$

Therefore

$$t = \tfrac{1}{2}r,$$

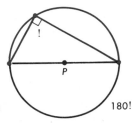

and $m\angle A = \tfrac{1}{2}m\widehat{BC}$, as before.  (Reasons, for each step?)

Theorem 14–16 has two important corollaries.

### Corollary 14–16.1

Any angle inscribed in a semicircle is a right angle.

The proof is obvious: such an angle always *intercepts* a semicircle, and $90 = \tfrac{1}{2} \cdot 180$.

### Corollary 14–16.2

Every two angles inscribed in the same arc are congruent.

Again this is obvious: they intercept the same arc.

### Definitions

A quadrilateral is *inscribed in* a circle if the vertices of the quadrilateral lie on the circle.  If each side of the quadrilateral is tangent to the circle, then the quadrilateral is *circumscribed about* the circle.

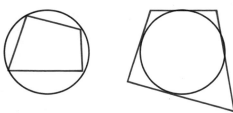

## Problem Set 14–5

**1.** Given the figure.

(a) Name the arc in which $\angle z$ is inscribed.

(b) Name the arc which $\angle x$ intercepts.

(c) Name the arc which $\angle z$ intercepts.

(d) Name the angle inscribed in $\overset{\frown}{BCA}$.

(e) Name the arc which $\angle BAD$ intercepts.

(f) Name the angle inscribed in $\overset{\frown}{CBD}$.

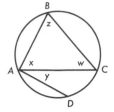

**2.** Given the figure with $\overrightarrow{AS}$ tangent at $S$.

(a) Name the arc(s) intercepted by $\angle x$.

(b) Name the arc(s) intercepted by $\angle z$.

(c) Name the arc(s) intercepted by $\angle y$.

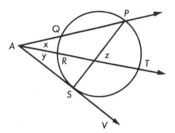

**3.** In the figure on the left, $P$ is the center of the circle. If $m \angle B = 35$, find $m \angle A$ and $m \angle P$.

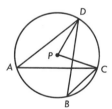
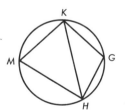

**4.** In the figure on the right above, if $m \angle M = 75$, $m\overset{\frown}{MK} = 90$, and $m\overset{\frown}{GH} = 70$, find the measures of all other arcs and angles.

**5.** If $m \angle RQS = 45$ and $P$ is the center, prove that $\overline{RP} \perp \overline{SP}$.

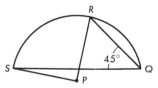

**6.** $\overline{AB}$ is a diameter of a circle and $C$ and $D$ are points of the circle on opposite sides of $\overline{AB}$ such that $BC = BD$. Prove that

$$\triangle ABC \cong \triangle ABD.$$

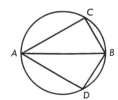

7. Given: $P$ is the center of semicircle $\widehat{AB}$; $\overline{PR}$
   bisects $\overline{AC}$ and $\overline{PQ}$ bisects $\overline{BC}$.

   Prove: $\overline{PR} \perp \overline{PQ}$.

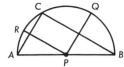

8. Prove: If two circles are tangent internally such that the smaller circle contains the center of the larger circle, then any chord of the larger circle having one end point at the point of tangency is bisected by the smaller circle.

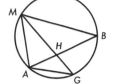

9. Given the figure with $m\widehat{AG} = m\widehat{BG}$. Prove that

$$\triangle MHB \sim \triangle MAG.$$

10. Prove: In any circle, parallel chords intercept arcs having equal measures.

11. Prove the following theorem.

   In a circle, a diameter perpendicular to a chord bisects each arc determined by the end points of the chord.

12. Prove: If an angle inscribed in a circular arc is a right angle, the arc is a semicircle.

13. In semicircle $\widehat{ACB}$, $\overline{CD} \perp \overline{AB}$ at $D$. Prove that $CD$ is the geometric mean of $AD$ and $DB$.

14. Given that

   (a) $AD = 9$ and $DB = 4$, find $CD$.

   (b) $AB = 25$ and $AD = 5$, find $CD$.

   (c) $AD = 32$ and $CD = 8$, find $DB$.

   (d) $AD = 3$ and $DB = 1$, find $CD$.

   (e) $AB = 25$ and $CD = 12$, find $AD$ and $DB$.

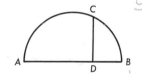

$\dfrac{ad}{cd} = \dfrac{cd}{db}$

Figure for Problems 13 and 14

* 15. In a circle, if diameter $\overline{AB}$ is perpendicular to chord $\overline{CD}$ at $E$, prove that
   $CD^2 = 4AE \cdot BE$.

16. Prove the following theorem.

   The opposite angles of an inscribed quadrilateral are supplementary.

17. In the figure, if $m\angle P = 60$ and $m\widehat{PSR} = 128$, what is $m\angle Q$, $m\angle R$, and $m\angle S$?

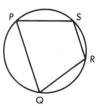

Figure for Problems 16 and 17

\* **18.** In the figure, $\overline{AB}$ is a diameter of the smaller of two concentric circles. $\overline{AP}$ and $\overline{BQ}$ are tangent to the smaller circle at $A$ and $B$, respectively. Prove that $\overline{AB}$ and $\overline{PQ}$ intersect at the center of the circles.

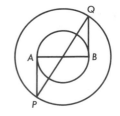

\* **19.** If an isosceles triangle is inscribed in a circle, the measure of the arc intercepted by the vertex angle is twice the difference of the measures of the exterior angle at the base of the triangle and a base angle.

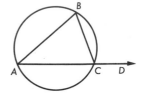

\* **20.** $\triangle ABC$ is inscribed in a circle. Chord $\overline{AE} \perp \overline{BC}$ and chord $\overline{CD} \perp \overline{AB}$. Prove that $\overset{\frown}{BD} \cong \overset{\frown}{BE}$.

\* **21.** Two congruent circles are tangent externally at $T$. Diameter $\overline{PQ}$ is parallel to diameter $\overline{SR}$, with $S$ and $Q$ on opposite sides of $\overleftrightarrow{PR}$. Prove that $\square PQRS$ is a rhombus.

## 14–6.   CONGRUENT ARCS

### Definition

In the same circle, or in congruent circles, two arcs are called *congruent* if they have the same measure.

Note that here, as always, the intuitive meaning of the word *congruent* is that the two figures have the same size and shape; one can be moved so as to coincide with the other.

### Theorem 14–17

In the same circle or in congruent circles, if two chords are congruent, then so are the corresponding minor arcs.

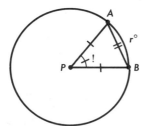
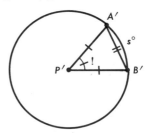

**Proof.**  The notation of the proof is that of the figure.  We need to show that $r = s$.  By SSS,

$$\triangle APB \cong \triangle A'P'B'.$$

Therefore  $m\angle APB = m\angle A'P'B'$.   Since  $m\widehat{AB} = m\angle APB$ and $m\widehat{A'B'} = m\angle A'P'B'$, we have $r = s$, and $\widehat{AB} \cong \widehat{A'B'}$.

### Theorem 14–18

In the same circle or in congruent circles, if two arcs are congruent, then so are the corresponding chords.

In the proof, there are three cases to consider, because the two congruent arcs may be minor arcs, major arcs, or semicircles.  The following figure suggests the proof for the second of these cases.

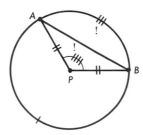 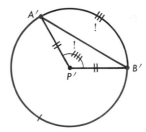

We get $AB = A'B'$, by using SAS.

### Theorem 14–19

Given an angle with its vertex on a circle, formed by a secant ray and a tangent ray.  The measure of the angle is half the measure of the intercepted arc.

**Proof.**  In the notation of the figure, we have

$$x + y = 90, \qquad 2y + z = 180;$$

and we want to show that

$$x = \tfrac{1}{2}z.$$

This is easy, because

$$x = 90 - y$$

and

$$z = 180 - 2y.$$

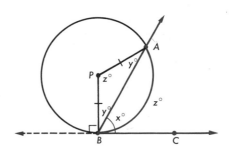

## Problem Set 14–6

**1.** In the figure on the left below, $\overline{AB} \cong \overline{CD}$. Prove that $\widehat{AC} \cong \widehat{BD}$.

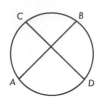 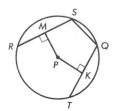

**2.** In the circle on the right above with center $P$, $PM = PK$ and $\overline{PM}$ and $\overline{PK}$ are perpendicular to chords $\overline{RS}$ and $\overline{QT}$, respectively. Prove that $\widehat{RS} \cong \widehat{QT}$.

**3.** $\overrightarrow{KH}$ and $\overrightarrow{KG}$ are tangent to the circle at $H$ and $G$. If the measure of the major arc $\widehat{GH}$ is 242, find $m \angle DGH$ and $m \angle GHK$.

**4.** In the figure for Problem 3, why is $\angle KHG \cong \angle KGH$?

**5.** In the figure for Problem 3, if $m \angle K = 60'$ show that the measure of major arc $\widehat{GH}$ is twice the measure of minor arc $\widehat{GH}$.

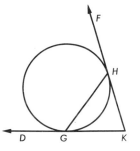

**6.** Prove: If two tangents to a circle intersect each other, they form an isosceles triangle with the chord joining the points of tangency.

**7.** Prove the following theorem.

> If two arcs are congruent, then any angle inscribed in one of the arcs is congruent to any angle inscribed in the other arc.

**8.** In the figure on the left below, $\widehat{AD} \cong \widehat{CB}$. Prove that $\square ADBC$ is an isosceles trapezoid.

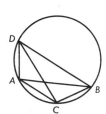 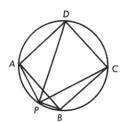

**9.** In the figure on the right above square $\square ABCD$ is inscribed in a circle and $P$ is any point of $\widehat{AB}$ other than $A$ or $B$. Prove that $\overline{PC}$ and $\overline{PD}$ trisect $\angle APB$.

10. In the figure, $\overleftrightarrow{PA}$ and $\overrightarrow{PD}$ are tangents at
A and D, respectively.  If

$$m\widehat{AD} = 70, \qquad m\widehat{BC} = 170$$

and

$$m\angle TAB = 40,$$

find the measure of each angle and each
minor arc of the figure.

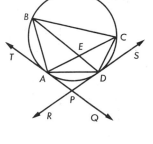

11. $\overline{AB}$ is a diameter of the circle in which chord $\overline{DE}$ is
parallel to tangent $\overleftrightarrow{CB}$.

(a) Given $m\widehat{BD} = 64$.  Find the measure of each
angle and each minor arc of the figure.

(b) Given that $AE = 16$ and the radius of the
circle is 10, find the length of each segment.

(c) Using the information of part (b), find the
area of $\square ADBE$.

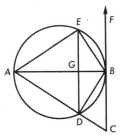

12. Given an angle with its vertex on a circle, formed by a secant ray and a
tangent ray.  Prove that the mid-point of the intercepted arc is equidistant
from the sides of the angle.

* 13. Two noncongruent circles are tangent at a point $T$.  A secant, $L$, through
$T$ intersects the larger circle at $A$ and the smaller circle at $B$.  Prove that
the tangents at $A$ and $B$ are parallel.  [*Note:* There are two cases: (a) the
circles are internally tangent; (b) the circles are externally tangent.]

14. In the figure, $\overleftrightarrow{PR}$ and $\overleftrightarrow{QS}$ are tangents
and $\overline{PQ}$ is a diameter.  Given that

$$m\widehat{MQ} = 120 \qquad \text{and} \qquad RQ = 8,$$

find the radius of the circle.

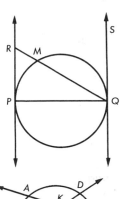

15. Prove the following theorem.

The measure of an angle formed by
two secants of a circle intersecting
at a point in the interior of the circle
is one-half the sum of the measures
of the arcs intercepted by the angle
and its vertical angle.

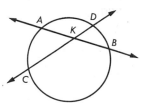

[*Hint:* Prove $m\angle DKB = \frac{1}{2}(m\widehat{DB} + m\widehat{AC})$.  First introduce $\overline{BC}$.]

**16.** In the figure for Problem 15, given that

    (a) $m\widehat{DB} = 40$ and $m\widehat{AC} = 90$, find $m\angle AKC$.

    (b) $m\widehat{AD} = 100$ and $m\widehat{BC} = 170$, find $m\angle BKC$.

    (c) $m\widehat{AC} = 130$ and $m\angle DKB = 75$, find $m\widehat{DB}$.

    (d) $m\widehat{ACD} = 310$ and $m\widehat{BC} = 200$, find $m\angle AKC$.

    (e) $m\widehat{BAC} = 180$ and $m\angle DKB = 57$, find $m\widehat{AD}$.

**17.** Prove the following theorem.

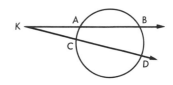

    The measure of an angle formed by two secants of a circle intersecting at a point in the exterior of the circle is one-half the difference of the measures of the intercepted arcs.

    [*Hint:* Prove $m\angle K = \frac{1}{2}(m\widehat{BD} - m\widehat{AC})$.  First introduce $\overline{BC}$.]

**18.** In the figure for Problem 17, given that

    (a) $m\widehat{BD} = 70$ and $m\widehat{AC} = 30$, find $m\angle K$.

    (b) $m\widehat{BD} = 126$ and $m\widehat{AC} = 18$, find $m\angle K$.

    (c) $m\widehat{AC} = 50$ and $m\angle K = 22$, find $m\widehat{BD}$.

    (d) $m\widehat{AB} = 80$, $m\widehat{BD} = 80$, and $m\widehat{CD} = 190$, find $m\angle K$.

    (e) $m\angle K = 28$, $m\widehat{ABD} = 166$, and $m\widehat{ACB} = 290$, find $m\widehat{CD}$.

**19.** Verify that the theorem of Problem 17 holds if the words "two secants" are replaced by "a secant and a tangent" or by "two tangents."

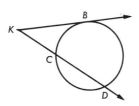
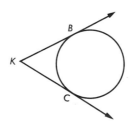

**20.** Two tangents to a circle form an angle whose measure is 72.  What is the number of degrees in each intercepted arc?

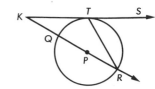

**21.** Given that $\overleftrightarrow{KS}$ is tangent to the circle at $T$ and secant $\overleftrightarrow{KR}$ contains $P$, the center of the circle.  If $m\angle K = 35$, find $m\widehat{QT}$ and $m\angle STR$.

**22.** Given two tangents to a circle intersecting at $K$. If the measure of one of the intercepted arcs is 4 times the measure of the other arc, what is the measure of $\angle K$?

**23.**

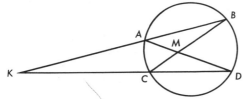

In the figure, if $m\widehat{BD} = 70$ and $m\angle DMB = 4m\angle K$, find $m\widehat{AC}$ and $m\angle K$.

*+ **24.** Given the figure, find the ratio of $x$ to $y$ which will make

$$m\angle DMB = 2m\angle K.$$

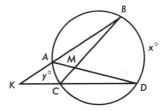

* **25.** Given a circle and a point $P$ in its exterior. A line through $P$ is tangent to the circle at $T$. A secant containing $P$ intersects the circle at $Q$ and $R$, with $Q$ between $R$ and $P$. The bisector of $\angle QTR$ intersects $\overline{RQ}$ at $S$. Prove that

$$PT = PS.$$

* **26.** Given: $\overline{AD}$ and $\overline{DB}$ are diameters of congruent, tangent circles. $\overleftrightarrow{BC}$ is a tangent at $C$.

Prove: $m\widehat{AC} = m\widehat{DC} + m\widehat{DE}$.

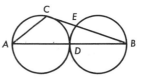

## 14–7.    SECANT AND TANGENT SEGMENTS.   THE POWER OF A POINT WITH RESPECT TO A CIRCLE

### Definition

If $\overleftrightarrow{QA}$ is tangent to a circle at $A$, then $\overline{QA}$ is called a *tangent segment* from $Q$ to the circle.

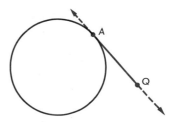

## Theorem 14-20

The two tangent segments to a circle from a point of the exterior are congruent and determine congruent angles with the segment from the exterior point to the center.

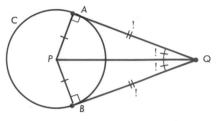

**Restatement.**    Given a circle $C$ with center $P$, and a point $Q$ of the exterior of $C$. If $\overline{QA}$ and $\overline{QB}$ are tangent to $C$ at $A$ and $B$, then $QA = QB$ and $\angle PQA \cong \angle PQB$.

**Proof.**    $PA = PB$, because $A$ and $B$ are on the circle; and $PQ = PQ$. By Theorem 14–3, $\angle A$ and $\angle B$ are right angles. By the Hypotenuse-Leg Theorem (Theorem 7–4) we have

$$\triangle PQA \cong \triangle PQB.$$

Therefore $QA = QB$ and $\angle PQA \cong \angle PQB$, which was to be proved.

Consider now the case of two *secant* lines to a circle, through the same point of the exterior.

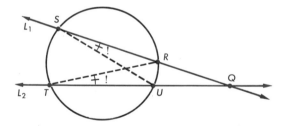

In the figure, $\overline{QS}$ and $\overline{QT}$ are called *secant segments* to the circle. To be exact:

## Definitions

If a segment intersects a circle in two points, and exactly one of these is an end point of the segment, then the segment is called a *secant segment* to the circle.

The next theorem says that in the figure above we always have

$$QR \cdot QS = QU \cdot QT.$$

That is, the product of the "two distances" from $Q$ to the circle is completely determined by the given circle and the point $Q$, and does not change when we choose different secant lines.

**Theorem 14–21.**   The Power Theorem

Given a circle $C$, and a point $Q$ of its exterior. Let $L_1$ be a secant line through $Q$, intersecting $C$ in points $R$ and $S$; and let $L_2$ be another secant line through $Q$, intersecting $C$ in points $U$ and $T$. Then

$$QR \cdot QS = QU \cdot QT.$$

**Proof.**   Consider the triangles $\triangle QSU$ and $\triangle QTR$. They have $\angle Q$ in common. And $\angle QSU \cong \angle QTR$, because they are inscribed in the same arc $\overset{\frown}{RSU} = \overset{\frown}{RTU}$. By the AA Corollary (12–3.1), we have

$$\triangle QSU \sim \triangle QTR.$$

Therefore

$$\frac{QS}{QT} = \frac{QU}{QR},$$

and

$$QR \cdot QS = QU \cdot QT,$$

which was to be proved.

Thus the product $QR \cdot QS$ is determined when the circle $C$ and the exterior point $Q$ are named. This number is called the *power of $Q$ with respect to $C$*.

Theorem 14–22 is going to say that in the figure below, in which $\overline{QT}$ is a tangent segment, we have

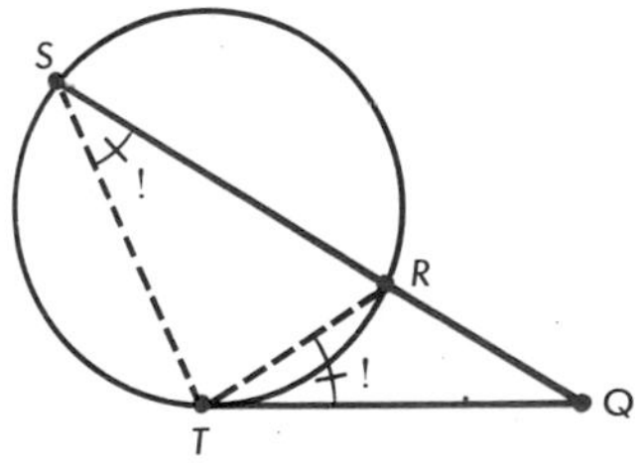

$$QR \cdot QS = QT^2.$$

This equation means that

$$QT = \sqrt{QR \cdot QS}.$$

Thus $QT$ is the geometric mean of
$QR$ and $QS$. The theorem is easier to state than the preceding one.

**Theorem 14–22**

Given a tangent segment $\overline{QT}$ to a circle, and a secant line through $Q$, intersecting the circle in points $R$ and $S$. Then

$$QR \cdot QS = QT^2.$$

In other words, the square of the length of a tangent segment is the power of its outer end point with respect to the circle.

**Proof.** $\overparen{TR}$ is the arc intercepted by $\angle QST$ and $\angle QTR$. The main steps in the proof are as follows:

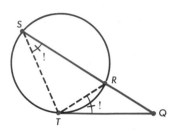

(1) $m\angle QST = \frac{1}{2}m\overparen{TR}$.

(2) $m\angle QTR = \frac{1}{2}m\overparen{TR}$.

(3) $\angle QST \cong \angle QTR$.

(4) $\angle Q \cong \angle Q$.

(5) $\triangle QST \sim \triangle QTR$.

(6) $\dfrac{QS}{QT} = \dfrac{QT}{QR}$.

(7) $QR \cdot QS = QT^2$.

What are the reasons for each step?

The next theorem states that in the figure below we have

$$QR \cdot QS = QU \cdot QT.$$

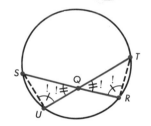

### Theorem 14–23

Let $\overline{RS}$ and $\overline{TU}$ be chords of the same circle, intersecting at $Q$. Then

$$QR \cdot QS = QU \cdot QT.$$

Again we give only the main steps in the proof:

(1) $\angle U \cong \angle R$.

(2) $\angle SQU \cong \angle TQR$.

(3) $\triangle SQU \sim \triangle TQR$.

(4) $\dfrac{QS}{QT} = \dfrac{QU}{QR}$.

(5) $QR \cdot QS = QU \cdot QT$.

This theorem enables us to define the power of a point with respect to a circle for the case in which the point lies *inside* the circle. We have found that the product $QR \cdot QS$ is determined when the circle $C$ and the point $Q$ are named; this number does not change when we choose different chords containing $Q$. We can therefore define the *power of $Q$ with respect to $C$* as the number $QR \cdot QS$.

## Problem Set 14–7

**1.** Prove: If the measure of the angle determined by two tangent segments to a circle from a point of the exterior is 60, then the tangent segments form an equilateral triangle with the chord joining the points of tangency.

**2.** A point $P$ is 13 in. from the center of a circle with a 10-in. diameter. How long are the tangent segments from the point $P$?

**3.** The sum of the lengths of two tangent segments to a circle from the same exterior point is equal to the diameter of the circle. Find the measure of the angle determined by the tangent segments.

**4.** Given: Circles $C$ and $C'$ are both tangent to $L$ at $T$. $P$ is any point (except $T$) of $L$. $\overline{PA}$ and $\overline{PB}$ are tangent segments.

Prove: $PA = PB$.

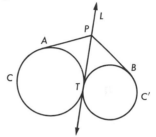

**5.** The sides of $\square ABCD$ are tangent to the circle, as shown in the figure. Prove that

$$AB + DC = AD + BC.$$

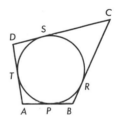

**6.** Two tangent segments to a circle from a point in the exterior determine an angle of 60°. If the diameter of the circle is 10, how long are the tangent segments?

**7.** If the tangent segments of Problem 6 determine an angle of 120°, how long are the tangent segments?

**8.** In the figure, $\overline{QR}$ and $\overline{QS}$ are tangent segments to the circle whose center is $P$. $\overline{QP}$ intersects the circle at $M$. Prove that $M$ is equidistant from the tangent segments.

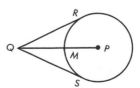

**9.** Two chords of a circle intersect. The segments of one chord have lengths 4 and 6. If the length of one segment of the other chord is 3, find the length of the remaining segment.

**10.** Find the power of $Q$ (see figure) with respect to $C$ given that

(a)  $QS = 9$  and  $QR = 5.$

(b)  $QS = 3$  and  $SR = 12.$

(c)  $QU = 7$  and  $QT = 5.$

(d)  $QT = 1$  and  $TU = 13.$

(e)  $QR = 4$  and  $SR = 14.$

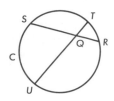

**11.** One inch from the end of a 37-in. diameter of a circle, the diameter intersects a chord 4 in. from one end of the chord. How long is the chord?

**12.** In the figure, $AB = 25$, $AE = 18$, and $DC = 27$. Find $EB$, $DE$, and $EC$.

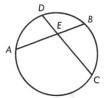

**13.** Find the power of $Q$ (see figure) with respect to $C$ given that:

(a)  $QR = 4$      and  $QS = 13.$

(b)  $QR = 6$      and  $RS = 8.$

(c)  $QT = 17$     and  $UT = 9.$

(d)  $QU = \sqrt{14}$ and $QT = \sqrt{56}.$

(e)  $QS = 23$     and  $RS = 17.$

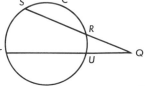

**14.** In the figure, if $PA = 6$, $PB = 15$ and $PC = 8$, what is $PD$?

**15.** In the figure, if $PB = 24$, $AB = 16$, and $PD = 16$, what is $PC$?

**16.** In the figure, if $PD = 20$, $CD = 12$, and $AB = 27$, what is $PB$?

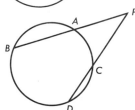

Figure for Problems 14, 15, 16

**17.** In the figure, $\overline{QT}$ is a tangent segment. Find the power of $Q$ with respect to $C$ given that

(a)  $QR = 4$, $QS = 9$, and $QT = 6.$

(b)  $QS = 13$     and  $RS = 9.$

(c)  $QT = 8$      and  $RS = 12.$

(d)  $QR = \sqrt{6}$ and $QS = \sqrt{54}.$

(e)  $QS = \sqrt{17}$ and $QT = \sqrt{13}.$

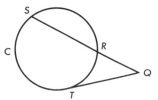

**18.** In the figure (p. 459), $\overline{PA}$ is a tangent segment. Given that $PB = 5$ and $PC = 20$, find $PA$.

**19.** $\overline{PA}$ is a tangent segment.    If $PA = 8$ and $PB = 7$, what is $PC$?

**20.** $\overline{PA}$ is a tangent segment.  Given $PA = 16$ and $BC = 24$.  Find $PC$.

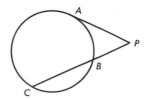

Figure for Problems 18, 19, 20

**21.** Given the figure on the right below with both circles tangent to $L$ at $T$. $P$ is any point of $L$ other than $T$.  Prove that

$$PM \cdot PR = PK \cdot PS.$$

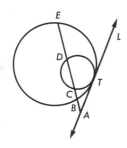
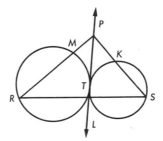

**22.** In the figure on the left above, $A$ is any point of $L$ except $T$, the common point of tangency of the circles.  Prove that

$$\frac{AB}{AD} = \frac{AC}{AE}.$$

**23.** If a common tangent of two circles intersects the line of centers at a point between the centers, it is called a *common internal tangent*.  If it does not intersect the line of centers at a point between the centers, it is called a *common external tangent*.

In this figure, $\overleftrightarrow{AB}$ is a common external tangent, and $\overleftrightarrow{CD}$ is a common internal tangent.

Given two circles, how many common external tangents and how many common internal tangents are there if

(a) the circles do not intersect as in the figure?

(b) the circles are externally tangent?

(c) the circles intersect in two points?

(d) the circles are internally tangent?

(e) the circles are concentric?

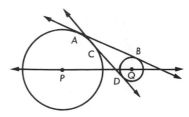

**24.** Two circles have radii 5 and 17 and a common external tangent segment of length 16. What is the distance between their centers?

**25.** The radii of two circles are 3 and 8, and the distance between their centers is 13. Find the length of their common external tangent segment. [*Hint:* Introduce a line through $Q$ perpendicular to $\overline{AP}$.]

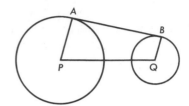

**26.** The distance between the centers of two circles, having radii of 3 and 6, is 18. How long is the common internal tangent segment?

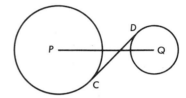

+ **27.** Prove that the common external tangent segments of two circles are congruent.

* **28.** Prove: If two circles and a line intersect in the same point, or points, then the line bisects each common external tangent segment of the circles.

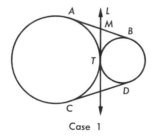
Case 1

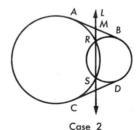
Case 2

*+ **29.** Prove: The common internal tangents of two nonintersecting circles and the line of centers of the circles meet at the same point.

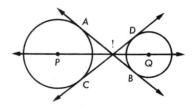

[*Hint:* Use an indirect proof. Draw radii. Use similarity and proportions.]

+ **30.** Prove that the common internal tangent segments of two nonintersecting circles are congruent.

* **31.** $\overline{DB}$ is a diameter of a circle. A tangent through $D$ and a secant through $B$ intersect at a point $A$. The secant also intersects the circle at $C$. Prove that $DB^2 = AB \cdot BC$.

* **32.** $\overline{RS}$ is a diameter of a circle. $L_1$ is the tangent to the circle at $R$, and $L_2$ is the tangent at $S$. A line through $Q$, any point of $L_1$ other than $R$, is tangent to the circle at $P$ and intersects $L_2$ at $T$. Prove that

$$a \square QRST = \tfrac{1}{2} RS \cdot QT.$$

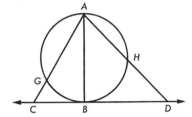

*+ **33.** In the figure, $\overline{AB}$ is a diameter and $\overleftrightarrow{CD}$ is the tangent at $B$. Prove that

$$AC \cdot AG = AD \cdot AH.$$

## 14–8.  CIRCLES IN A COORDINATE PLANE

If we set up a coordinate system in the plane, it is easy to see what the equation of a circle is. Take first the case where the center is the origin.

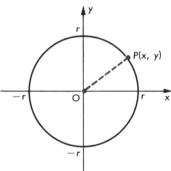

The circle with center at $O$ and radius $r$ is defined by the condition

$$OP = r.$$

Letting $P$ have coordinates $(x, y)$, we use the distance formula, and write our equation algebraically as

$$\sqrt{(x - 0)^2 + (y - 0)^2} = r,$$

or

$$x^2 + y^2 = r^2.$$

If the center is the point $Q(a, b)$, then the circle is defined by the condition

$$QP = r.$$

Algebraically, we have

$$\sqrt{(x - a)^2 + (y - b)^2} = r,$$

or

$$(x - a)^2 + (y - b)^2 = r^2.$$

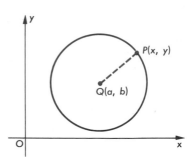

## Theorem 14–24

The graph of the equation

$$(x - a)^2 + (y - b)^2 = r^2$$

is the circle with center $(a, b)$ and radius $r$.

We can apply this theorem forward or backward.

(1) If we know the center and the radius, we can write an equation for the circle. For example, the circle with center $(3, 1)$ and radius 2 is the graph of the equation

$$(x - 3)^2 + (y - 1)^2 = 4.$$

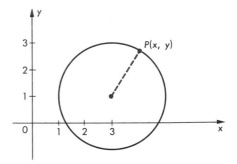

(2) Given an equation of the type dealt with in Theorem 14–24, we can tell what the center and radius of the circle must be. For example, given

$$(x + 1)^2 + (y - 2)^2 = 9,$$

we know that the center is $(-1, 2)$ and the radius is 3.

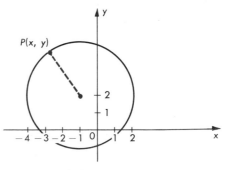

So far, so good. But suppose that our second equation for the circle has fallen into the hands of somebody who likes to "simplify"

every equation that he sees. He would have "simplified" the standard form, getting

$$x^2 + 2x + 1 + y^2 - 4y + 4 = 9,$$

and then

$$x^2 + y^2 + 2x - 4y - 4 = 0.$$

Sometimes we will find equations of circles given in forms like this. To find out what their graphs are, we need to "unsimplify" them to get back to the standard form

$$(x - a)^2 + (y - b)^2 = r^2.$$

The method is that of completing the square. First we rearrange the terms so as to bring together the terms involving $x$ and those involving $y$, and we move the constant terms to the other side of the equals sign. This gives

$$x^2 + 2x \quad + y^2 - 4y \quad = 4.$$

We now want to add something to the first two terms to complete a perfect square. That is, we want

$$x^2 + 2x + (?) = (x - a)^2.$$

Since

$$(x - a)^2 = x^2 - 2ax + a^2,$$

we must have $a = -1$, $a^2 = 1$. What we need to add, therefore, is 1. (The rule is simple: we take half the coefficient of $x$, and square the result.) In the same way, we see that to get a perfect square, we should add 4 to the terms involving $y$.

Since we are adding a total of 5 on the left, we should also add a total of 5 on the right. This gives

$$x^2 + 2x + 1 + y^2 - 4y + 4 = 4 + 5,$$

or

$$(x + 1)^2 + (y - 2)^2 = 9,$$

which is in the standard form. From the standard form we can tell that the graph is the circle with center at $(-1, 2)$ and radius 3.

If in the standard form $(x - a)^2 + (y - b)^2 = r^2$ we multiply out and rearrange the terms, we obtain

$$x^2 + y^2 - 2ax - 2by + a^2 + b^2 - r^2 = 0.$$

This has the form

$$x^2 + y^2 + Ax + By + C = 0,$$

where

$$A = -2a, \qquad B = -2b, \qquad C = a^2 + b^2 - r^2.$$

Thus we have the following theorem.

## Theorem 14–25

Every circle is the graph of an equation of the form

$$x^2 + y^2 + Ax + By + C = 0.$$

It might seem reasonable to suppose that the converse is also true. That is, we might think that the graph of an equation of this form is always a circle. But this is not true at all. Consider, for example, the equation

$$x^2 + y^2 = 0.$$

Here $A = B = C = 0$. If $x$ and $y$ satisfy this equation, then $x$ and $y$ are both zero. Therefore the graph contains only one point, namely, the origin.

Consider next the equation

$$x^2 + y^2 + 1 = 0.$$

Here $A = B = 0$ and $C = 1$. Since $x^2 \geq 0$ and $y^2 \geq 0$ for every $x$ and $y$, it follows that $x^2 + y^2 + 1 \geq 1$ for every $x$ and $y$. Therefore $x^2 + y^2 + 1$ is never equal to 0 for any $x$ and $y$. Therefore the graph of our equation *contains no points at all;* the graph is the empty set.

The next theorem tells us that, in fact, the only possible graphs are the circle that we would normally expect and the two peculiar possibilities that we have just discussed.

## Theorem 14–26

The graph of the equation

$$x^2 + y^2 + Ax + By + C = 0$$

is (1) a circle, (2) a point, or (3) the empty set.

**Proof.**  In our general equation, we shall complete the square for the terms involving $x$, and also for the terms involving $y$, just as we did in the example that we worked out above.  This gives

$$x^2 + Ax \qquad + y^2 + By \qquad = -C,$$

$$x^2 + Ax + \left(\frac{A}{2}\right)^2 + y^2 + By + \left(\frac{B}{2}\right)^2 = -C + \left(\frac{A}{2}\right)^2 + \left(\frac{B}{2}\right)^2,$$

$$\left(x + \frac{A}{2}\right)^2 + \left(y + \frac{B}{2}\right)^2 = \frac{A^2 + B^2 - 4C}{4}.$$

There are now three possibilities.

(1) If the fraction on the right is positive, then it has a square root. The graph is then the circle with center

$$(a, b) = \left(-\frac{A}{2}, -\frac{B}{2}\right)$$

and radius

$$r = \tfrac{1}{2}\sqrt{A^2 + B^2 - 4C}.$$

(2) If the fraction on the right is 0, then the graph is the point

$$\left(-\frac{A}{2}, -\frac{B}{2}\right).$$

(3) If the fraction on the right is negative, then the graph is the empty set, because the left-hand side can never be negative.

## Problem Set 14–8

[*Note:* Problems in this problem set should be solved by methods of coordinate geometry when a choice of methods exists.]

1. Write the equation of the circle whose center is at the origin and whose radius is

    (a) 4.         (b) 7.         (c) $\frac{2}{3}$.

    (d) 11.       (e) $\sqrt{15}$.      (f) $\pi$.

2. Given the circle whose equation is $x^2 + y^2 = 25$, which of the following points are points of the circle?

    (a) $(0, -5)$        (b) $(3, -4)$          (c) $(3, 2)$

    (d) $(24, 1)$       (e) $(\sqrt{8}, -\sqrt{17})$      (f) $(2\sqrt{3}, \sqrt{13})$

3. Given the circle whose equation is $x^2 + y^2 = 36$. Which of the following points are in its interior, which are in its exterior, which are on the circle?

(a) $(3, 3\sqrt{3})$        (b) $(4, -5)$        (c) $(-6, 0)$        (d) $(5, -3)$

(e) $(-4, -4)$        (f) $(2\sqrt{2}, 2\sqrt{7})$        (g) $(\frac{9}{2}, \frac{7}{4})$        (h) $(-2\sqrt{6}, 4)$

4. Find the radius and write the equation of the circle whose center is at the origin and which contains the point

(a) $(0, -4)$.        (b) $(3, 5)$.        (c) $(-2, 7)$.        (d) $(2, \sqrt{17})$.

5. Write the equation of each circle with center and radius as given.

(a) $(2, 5)$; 4        (b) $(-3, 0)$; 6

(c) $(-4, -6)$; $\sqrt{21}$        (d) $(0, 7)$; $\frac{5}{3}$

6. A circle whose center is the point $(2, 3)$ contains the point $(6, 6)$. Write its equation.

7. A circle with center at $(-4, 0)$ passes through the point $(2, -1)$. Write its equation.

8. The end points of a diameter of a circle are $(-6, 2)$ and $(6, -2)$. Find its center and its radius, and write its equation.

9. Write the equation of the circle having a diameter with end points $(5, 8)$ and $(-1, -4)$.

10. Determine the center and radius of each circle:

(a) $x^2 + y^2 = 16$.        (b) $x^2 + y^2 - 9 = 0$.

(c) $(x - 3)^2 + (y - 7)^2 = 8$.        (d) $(x + 4)^2 + (y - 5)^2 = 36$.

(e) $(x - 2)^2 + y^2 = 13$.        (f) $4x^2 + 4y^2 = 36$.

(g) $9x^2 + 9y^2 - 25 = 0$.        (h) $3x^2 + 3(y - 1)^2 = 12$.

(i) $2(x + 5)^2 + 2(y - 4)^2 - 14 = 0$.

(j) $5x^2 + 5y^2 - 7 = 0$.

11. Find the center and radius of the circle whose equation is

$$x^2 - 6x + 9 + y^2 - 8y + 16 = 4.$$

12. Find the center and radius of the circle whose equation is

$$x^2 + y^2 + 8x - 2y - 8 = 0.$$

13. Sketch the graph of the equation

$$x^2 + y^2 - 8x + 6y = 11.$$

**14.** Sketch the graph of the equation

$$x^2 + y^2 - 4x + 8y + 4 = 0.$$

**15.** Sketch the graph of the equation

$$x^2 + y^2 + 6x - 2y = -10.$$

**16.** Write the equation of the circle with center at $(-3, 4)$ which is tangent to the $x$-axis.

**17.** Write the equation of the circle tangent to both the $x$- and $y$-axes, given that its radius is 3 and its center is in the fourth quadrant.

**18.** Identify the geometric figures characterized by the following equations:
(a) $x^2 + y^2 = 15.$
(b) $x^2 + y^2 + 14x - 16y + 104 = 0.$
(c) $x^2 + 6x - 2y - x^2 + 2 = 0.$
(d) $x^2 + y^2 + 10x - 4y + 33 = 0.$
(e) $2x^2 + 2y^2 + 12x + 9 = 0.$
(f) $x^2 + y^2 + 4x - 10y + 29 = 0.$

**19.** In the circle whose equation is $x^2 + y^2 = 49$, a chord is perpendicular to a diameter at the point $(0, 4)$. Find the length of the chord and determine the coordinates of its end points.

**20.** Prove that the perpendicular bisector of the segment with end points $(a, 0)$ and $(0, a)$ contains the center of the circle whose equation is $x^2 + y^2 = a^2$.

**21.** Given the circle whose equation is $x^2 + y^2 = 225$ and the points $A(-15, 0)$ and $B(9, 12)$.
(a) Show that $\overline{AB}$ is a chord of the circle.
(b) Find the mid-point of $\overline{AB}$.
(c) Find the equation of the perpendicular bisector of $\overline{AB}$.
(d) Show that the perpendicular bisector of $\overline{AB}$ contains the center of the circle.

* **22.** Given the circle whose equation is $x^2 + y^2 - 8x - 4y - 5 = 0$ and the points $D(-1, 2)$ and $E(8, 5)$.
(a) Show that $\overline{DE}$ is a chord of the circle.
(b) Show that the perpendicular bisector of $\overline{DE}$ contains the center of the circle.
(c) Find the distance from the center of the circle to $\overline{DE}$.

**23.** Find the area of a square inscribed in the circle whose equation is $x^2 + y^2 = 144$.

\* **24.** Find the area of a square inscribed in the circle whose equation is $x^2 + y^2 + 8x - 10y + 5 = 0$.

**25.** A chord of the circle $x^2 + y^2 = 72$ is tangent to the circle $x^2 + y^2 = 18$. Find the length of the chord.

\*+ **26.** If the chord of Problem 25 is tangent to the smaller circle at the point $(-3, -3)$, find the equation of the line determined by the chord and find the coordinates of the end points of the chord.

**27.** Find the length of the tangent segments from the point $(13, 0)$ to the circle whose equation is $x^2 + y^2 = 25$.

**28.** Find the length of the tangent segments from the point $(16, 12)$ to the circle whose equation is $x^2 + y^2 = 100$.

\* **29.** Find the length of the tangent segments from the point $(-8, 3)$ to the circle whose equation is $x^2 + y^2 - 14x + 10y + 10 = 0$.

\*+ **30.** Given the circle whose equation is $x^2 + y^2 = 36$. For what values of $a$ is the point $(a, a + 4)$ in the interior of the circle?

\*+ **31.** Show that the two circles whose equations are $x^2 + y^2 = 16$ and $x^2 + y^2 - 20x + 64 = 0$ are externally tangent.    What are the coordinates of their point of tangency?

\*+ **32.** Show that the two circles whose equations are $x^2 + y^2 + 8x + 6y = 0$ and $x^2 + y^2 - 16x - 12y = 0$ are externally tangent. Find the equation of the line through their point of contact which is their common tangent.

\*+ **33.** Given the circle whose equation is $x^2 + y^2 + 16x + 12y = 125$.

   (a) Find the equation of the circle with radius 5 which is internally tangent to the given circle at $(4, 3)$.

   (b) Find the equation of their common tangent.

\*+ **34.** Find the equation of the circle which is tangent to all four of the circles characterized by these four equations:

$$x^2 + y^2 + 10x = 0.$$
$$x^2 + y^2 - 10x = 0.$$
$$x^2 + y^2 + 10y = 0.$$
$$x^2 + y^2 - 10y = 0.$$

*+  **35.** Using a scale of about 1 inch = 1 unit, make a careful sketch of the circles having the following equations:

$$(x - 1)^2 + (y - 1)^2 = 1.$$
$$(x + 1)^2 + (y - 1)^2 = 1.$$
$$(x - 1)^2 + (y + 1)^2 = 1.$$
$$(x + 1)^2 + (y + 1)^2 = 1.$$

(a) Find the equation of the circle which has each of the given circles as an internally tangent circle.

(b) Find the equation of the circle which has each of the given circles as an externally tangent circle.

## Chapter Review

**1.** Make sure that you know how to define each of the following terms.

| | | |
|---|---|---|
| Circle | Great circle | Intercepted arc |
| Sphere | Outer end | Central angle |
| Chord | Point of contact | Major arc |
| Secant | Interior of a circle | Minor arc |
| Tangent | Internally tangent | Semicircle |
| Radius | Externally tangent | Tangent segment |
| Diameter | Inscribed angle | |

**2.** Complete: Two circles, or two spheres, with the same center are called _____.

**3.** Complete: The intersection of a plane and a sphere is _____ or _____ or _____.

**4.** Complete: The intersection of a line and a circle is _____ or _____ or _____.

**5.** Complete: A point is in the exterior of a circle if it is in _____ and its distance from the center is _____.

**6.** Complete: An angle inscribed in a major arc is always an _____ angle, and an angle inscribed in a minor arc is always an _____ angle; an angle inscribed in a semicircle is a _____ angle.

**7.** Complete: If two chords of a circle intersect at a point of its interior, the power of the point with respect to the circle is _____.

8. In the figure, $\overleftrightarrow{AB}$ is tangent to the circle. If $m\widehat{BD} = 128$, $m\widehat{DE} = 38$, and $m\widehat{CE} = 104$, what are the measures of the six angles?

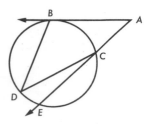

9. In the figure, $\overleftrightarrow{AB}$ is tangent to the circle. If $AC = 9$ and $CE = 7$, what is $AB$?

**Figure for Problems 8, 9, 10**

10. In the figure, if $BD = CD = 15$ and $m\widehat{BC} = 120$, what is the radius of the circle?

11. In the figure, if $RP = 8$, $MP = 6$ and $PQ = 3$, what is $KQ$?

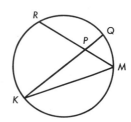

12. In the figure, if $MR = MK$, $m\widehat{MK} = 140$ and $m\widehat{MQ} = 26$, what is $m\angle RPK$?

**Figure for Problems 11 and 12**

13. Indicate for each of the statements below whether it is true or false.

(a) The measure of a central angle is equal to the measure of its intercepted arc.

(b) If two arcs are congruent, an inscribed angle of one arc is congruent to an inscribed angle of the other arc.

(c) If two angles which are inscribed in two arcs are congruent, then the arcs are congruent.

(d) A point which is the mid-point of two chords of a circle is the center of the circle.

(e) In a circle, if $m\widehat{AB} = \frac{1}{2}m\widehat{AC}$, then the chord of $\widehat{AB}$ is one-half as long as the chord of $\widehat{AC}$.

(f) A secant which bisects two chords of a circle is perpendicular to each of the chords.

(g) If a line bisects a chord of a circle, then it bisects the minor arc of the chord.

(h) If two chords of a circle are not congruent, the shorter chord is closer to the center.

(i) A tangent to a circle at the mid-point of an arc is parallel to the chord of the arc.

(j) The center of an arc is the point that bisects the arc.

(k) Two tangents to a circle at the ends of a diameter are parallel.

(l) Two tangents to the same circle may be perpendicular to each other.

14. Given the circle with center $P$ and $\overline{CB} \parallel \overline{PQ}$. If
    $m \angle BCP = 55$, what is $m\widehat{BQ}$ and $m\widehat{AD}$?

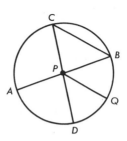

15. If $\overline{AB}$ is a diameter of a circle with center $P$, and $X$ and $Y$ are points of
    the circle such that $\overrightarrow{XY}$ bisects $\angle AXB$, prove that $\overrightarrow{PY} \perp \overline{AB}$.

16. Prove that it is impossible for the lengths of the
    segments of two intersecting chords of a circle
    to be four consecutive integers.

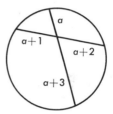

17. In searching an ancient ruin an archeologist found a piece of the rim of
    an old wheel. In order to restore the wheel he needed the diameter. He
    marked three points, $A$, $B$, $C$, on the rim so that chord $\overline{AB}$ was congruent
    to chord $\overline{AC}$. If $AB = 15$ in. and $BC = 24$ in., what was the diameter
    of the wheel?

18. Write the equation of the circle with center at $(0, 0)$ and radius 4.

19. Give the center and radius of the circle whose equation is $x^2 + 10x + y^2 + 16 = 0$.

20. A quadrilateral is inscribed in a circle. If the measures of two of its angles
    are 68 and 143, what are the measures of the other two angles?

21. A circular hole 40 in. in diameter is cut in a sheet of plywood and a
    spherical globe 50 in. in diameter is set into the hole. How far below the
    top surface of the plywood will the sphere extend?

22. The circle which has as its diameter side $\overline{AB}$ of
    equilateral triangle $\triangle ABC$ intersects the other
    two sides of $\triangle ABC$ at $D$ and $E$. If the diam-
    eter of the circle is 16, find the area of the in-
    scribed quadrilateral $\square ABED$.

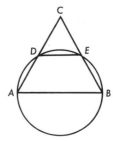

\* **23.** In the figure, $\overline{AB}$ is a diameter of the circle. If $AB = 8$, $AQ = 4$ and $PQ = 12$, what are $PB$ and $PR$?

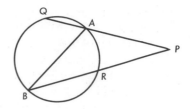

**24.** Prove that tangent segments to all of the circles which are tangent to a line at the same point from any other point of the line are congruent.

\* **25.** Given that $A$, $B$, $C$ are points of a circle such that $m\widehat{AB} = m\widehat{AC} = m\widehat{BC} = 120$. $P$ is any point of $\widehat{AB}$. Prove that $PA + PB = PC$. [*Hint:* Introduce a line through $A$ and parallel to $\overline{PB}$.]

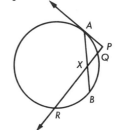

\* **26.** In the figure, $\overrightarrow{PA}$ is tangent to the circle at $A$. $AP = PX = XB$. If $PQ = 1$ and $QR = 8$, what is $AX$?

## HONORS PROBLEMS

**(a)** One of the first facts that a student of astronomy learns is that the latitude of a position on the earth is the same as the angle of Polaris (the North Star) above the horizon when observed from that position. Show why this is so by proving the following theorem. The physical situation is described by the following symbolism: $\overleftrightarrow{NS}$ is the earth's axis, the circle is a meridian, $C$ is the center, $E$ is on the equator, $O$ is the observer, $\overleftrightarrow{OH}$ is the horizon, and $m\angle POH$ is the elevation of Polaris.

Given: The circle with center $C$.

Radius $\overline{CE} \perp \overleftrightarrow{NS}$.

$\overleftrightarrow{OH}$ is tangent at $O$.

$\overrightarrow{OP} \parallel \overleftrightarrow{NS}$.

Prove: $m\widehat{OE} = m\angle POH$.

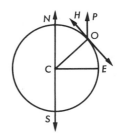

**(b)** Two noncongruent circles intersect in two points, $X$ and $Y$. A secant through $X$ intersects the larger circle at $A$ and the smaller circle at $B$. A secant through $Y$ intersects the larger circle at $C$ and the smaller circle at $D$. Prove that $\overline{AC} \parallel \overline{BD}$.

(c) On the bridge of a ship at sea, the captain asked the new, young officer standing next to him to determine the distance to the horizon. The officer took pencil and paper, and in a few moments came up with an answer. On the paper he had written the formula $d = \frac{5}{4}\sqrt{h}$.

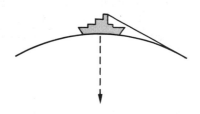

Show that this formula is a good approximation of the distance, in miles, to the horizon, if $h$ is the height, in feet, of the observer above the water. (Assume the radius of the earth to be 4000 mi.) If the bridge was 88 ft above the water, what was the distance to the horizon?

# 15 | Characterizations and Constructions

## 15–1. CHARACTERIZATIONS

You will remember that in Chapter 6 we proved a characterization theorem for the perpendicular bisector of a segment in a plane.

**Theorem 6–2**

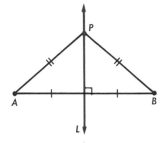

> The perpendicular bisector of a segment, in a plane, is the set of all points of the plane that are equidistant from the end points of the segment.

Briefly, we say that the points of the perpendicular bisector $L$ are *characterized* by the condition $PA = PB$. By this we mean that (1) every point of $L$ satisfies the condition $PA = PB$, and (2) every point of the plane that satisfies the condition $PA = PB$ is on $L$.

Similarly, we showed in Chapter 8 that the perpendicular bisecting plane of a segment $\overline{AB}$ is characterized by the condition $PA = PB$. (Here, of course, $P$ can be any point in space.)

Characterizations appear not only in theorems but also in definitions. For example, the sphere with center $P$ and radius $r$ is, by definition, the set of all points $Q$ such that $PQ = r$. Thus we say that the sphere is characterized by the condition

$$PQ = r.$$

*A word of caution:* In the plane figure below, every point of $\overline{CD}$ is equidistant from $A$ and $B$.

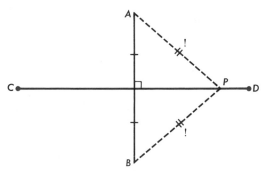

But the segment $\overline{CD}$ is *not* characterized by the condition $PA = PB$, because this condition is satisfied by many points that are not on $\overline{CD}$, namely, all points of the line $\overleftrightarrow{CD}$. Similarly, in the following figure, every point of $\overparen{AB}$ lies at a distance 1 from $P$. But $\overparen{AB}$ is not characterized by the condition $PQ = 1$, because all other points of the circle satisfy the same condition.

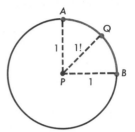

This is why the restatement of a characterization theorem usually appears in two parts:

(1) Every point of the given set satisfies the given condition.

(2) Conversely, every point that satisfies the given condition is in the given set.

See, for example, the restatements of Theorems 6–2 and 8–6.

## Problem Set 15–1

In Problems 1–8 a characterization statement is accompanied by a representative sketch. You are to decide whether each statement is really a characterization. If it is, answer "true." If it is not, write a corrected statement and make a corrected sketch. In the sketches, the required set of points is a solid figure, whereas the dashed figures are those contained in the given conditions or necessary in the explanation.

1. The set of all points in a plane $E$ which are equidistant from each of two parallel lines in $E$ is the perpendicular bisector, in $E$, of any segment perpendicular to the two lines and having an end point in each of them.

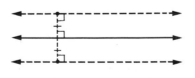
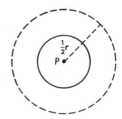

2. The set of all points which are mid-points of radii of a given circle is a circle concentric with the given circle and with a radius equal to one-half the radius of the given circle.

3. The set of all points in a plane which are 1 in. from a given line is a line parallel to the given line at a distance of 1 in.

4. The set of all points which are 1 in. from a given line is a cylindrical surface with 1-in. radius and the given line as axis.

5. The set of all points which are centers of circles tangent to a given line at a given point of the line is a ray perpendicular to the line at the given point.

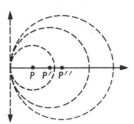 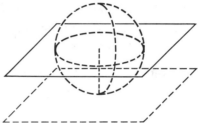

6. The set of all points which are centers of spheres of radius $r$, tangent to a given plane is a plane parallel to the given plane at a distance equal to $r$.

7. The set of all points in a plane which are vertices of the right angles of right triangles having the same segment as hypotenuse is a circle with the hypotenuse as its diameter minus the end points of the diameter.

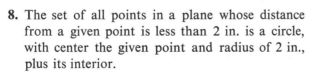

8. The set of all points in a plane whose distance from a given point is less than 2 in. is a circle, with center the given point and radius of 2 in., plus its interior.

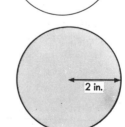

In Problems 9 through 20 make a sketch and describe the required set of points.

9. The set of all points equidistant from two given points.

10. The set of all points which are the mid-points of all chords of a circle having a given length.

**11.** The set of all points which are mid-points of chords of a circle having a given point of the circle as one common end point.

**12.** The set of all points which are 1 in. from a given segment 4 in. long and also are 2 in. from the mid-point of the segment.

**13.** The set of all points $A$, in a plane, for which $\triangle ABC$, which has a given segment $\overline{BC}$ as base, has a given area.

**14.** The set of all points in a plane which are centers of circles tangent to a given circle at a given point of the circle.

**15.** The set of all points in the exterior of a circle of diameter 6 which are end points of tangent segments of length 4.

**16.** The set of all points in a plane which are $\frac{1}{2}$ in. from a segment, $\overline{AB}$, of length 2 in.

**17.** The set of all points which are $\frac{1}{2}$ in. from a segment, $\overline{AB}$, of length 2 in.

**18.** The set of all points in a plane which are centers of circles of a given radius that contain a given point.

**19.** The set of all points in a plane which are 3 in. from each of two points 5 in. apart.

**20.** The set of all points which are 3 in. from a given plane and also are 5 in. from a given point of the plane.

**21.** Given a circle $C$ with center $P$, and a point $A$ in the plane of $C$. Let $B$ be that point of the intersection of $\overleftrightarrow{AP}$ and $C$ such that $P$ is not between $A$ and $B$. Then $AB$ is the *distance of the point A from the circle C.*

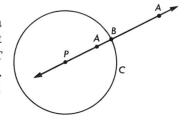

Describe the set of all points in a plane whose distance from a circle equals the radius of the circle.

**22.** Describe the set of all points in a plane whose distance from a circle is a fixed distance less than the radius.

+ **23.** Sometimes the solution to a characterization problem requires a discussion of various cases. Consider, for example, the following problem and its solution, which you should complete by filling in the blanks.

Describe the set of all points in a plane at a given distance from a given point and equidistant from two given parallel lines.

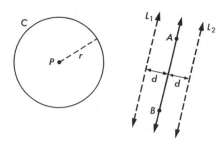

**Solution**

(1) The set of all points at a distance $r$ from point $P$ is the _____ $C$ with center $P$ and radius $r$.

(2) The set of all points equidistant from parallel lines $L_1$ and $L_2$ is $\overleftrightarrow{AB}$, the _____ of a segment between $L_1$ and and $L_2$ perpendicular to both of them.

(3) The required set is the intersection of $C$ and $\overleftrightarrow{AB}$.

    (i) If $C$ and $\overleftrightarrow{AB}$ do not intersect, the required set is _____.

    (ii) If $C$ and $\overleftrightarrow{AB}$ are _____, the required set contains exactly one point.

    (iii) If $\overleftrightarrow{AB}$ contains a point in the _____ of $C$, the required set contains exactly _____ points.

+ **24.** Describe the set of all points in a plane equidistant from two given points and equidistant from two given parallel lines.

+ **25.** Describe the set of all points in a plane at a given distance from a given point and at a given distance from a given line.

+ **26.** Describe the set of all points in a plane which are centers of circles tangent to a given line at a given point of the line and are centers of circles of a given radius tangent to the same given line.

+ **27.** Describe the set of all points which are at a given distance from a given plane and are at a given distance from a given point of the given plane.

## 15–2.  THE USE OF CHARACTERIZATIONS IN COORDINATE GEOMETRY

In coordinate geometry, we use characterizations continually.  For example, in the figure the line $L$ is the graph of the equation

$$x + y = 1.$$

(Why?)  This means that the line is *characterized* by the condition $x + y = 1$; every point $(x, y)$ of $L$ satisfies this condition, and no other point $(x, y)$ satisfies it.

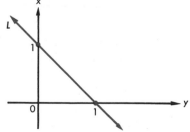

Similarly, in the next figure, the circle is characterized by the condition

$$(x - 1)^2 + y^2 = 1.$$

(Why?) In fact, every time we say that a figure is the graph of a certain equation, this means that the equation is a characterization of the graph. Most of the time, our work in coordinate geometry depends on the fact that the figures

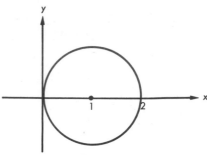

that we are working with are characterized by simple equations.

## Problem Set 15–2

[*Note:* The following notation is frequently used to describe sets in coordinate geometry.

$$\{(x, y) \mid x + y = 1 \text{ and } x = 1\}.$$

It means "The set of all ordered pairs $(x, y)$ such that $x + y = 1$ and $x = 1$." It is, of course, the single pair $(1, 0)$. Therefore we could write $\{(x, y) \mid x + y = 1 \text{ and } x = 1\} = \{(1, 0)\}$.]

1. Sketch each of the following sets (that is, sketch the graphs).
    (a) $\{(x, y) \mid x = 3\}$
    (b) $\{(x, y) \mid y = -2\}$
    (c) $\{(x, y) \mid y = x - 2\}$
    (d) $\{(x, y) \mid x + y = 0\}$

2. Sketch each of the following sets.
    (a) $\{(x, y) \mid x > -1\}$
    (b) $\{(x, y) \mid y \leq 0\}$
    (c) $\{(x, y) \mid x < y\}$
    (d) $\{(x, y) \mid x + y \geq 1\}$

3. Make a sketch and describe by an equation the set of all points $P(x, y)$ which are equidistant from $A(5, 0)$ and $B(1, 0)$.

4. Make a sketch and describe by an equation the set of all points $P(x, y)$ which are equidistant from $C(2, 2)$ and $D(2, -8)$.

5. Make a sketch and describe by an equation the set of all points $P(x, y)$ which are equidistant from the lines given by $x = -3$ and $x = 7$.

6. Sketch each of the following sets.
    (a) $\{(x, y) \mid x^2 + y^2 = 25\}$
    (b) $\{(x, y) \mid x^2 + y^2 = 8\}$
    (c) $\{(x, y) \mid (x - 1)^2 + y^2 = 4\}$
    (d) $\{(x, y) \mid x^2 + (y + 1)^2 = 9\}$

7. Sketch and describe the set of all points $P(x, y)$ which are equidistant from the points $A(0, 5)$ and $B(5, 0)$.

8. Sketch each of the following sets and describe each in the briefest way possible.

(a) $\{(x, y) \mid x = 3 \text{ and } y = 6\}$
(b) $\{(x, y) \mid x = y \text{ and } x = 5\}$
(c) $\{(x, y) \mid x^2 + y^2 = 16 \text{ and } x = -4\}$
(d) $\{(x, y) \mid x^2 + y^2 = 25 \text{ and } y = 3\}$
(e) $\{(x, y) \mid y = -2 \text{ and } |x| = 7\}$
(f) $\{(x, y) \mid |x| = 3 \text{ and } |y| = 5\}$

+ 9. What is the difference between the following two sets?

(a) $\{(x, y) \mid x = 4 \text{ and } y = 5\}$      (b) $\{(x, y) \mid x = 4 \text{ or } y = 5\}$

*+ 10. Make a sketch and describe by an equation the set of all points $P(x, y)$ which are twice as far from $(8, 0)$ as from $(2, 0)$.

*+ 11. Sketch the following set: $\{(x, y) \mid -1 \leq x \leq 5 \quad \text{and} \quad 0 \leq y \leq 4\}$.

*+ 12. Sketch the following set:

$$\{(x, y) \mid (x - 3)^2 + y^2 = 25 \quad \text{or} \quad (x + 6)^2 + y^2 = 52\}.$$

## 15–3.   CONCURRENCE THEOREMS

### Definition

Two or more lines are *concurrent* if there is a single point which lies on all of them. The common point is called the *point of concurrency*.

 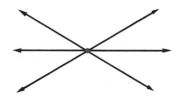

Of course, it is easy for *two* lines in the same plane to be concurrent. This is what we expect, when we draw two lines at random: if two lines happen to be parallel, and we rotate one of them even a little bit, they become concurrent.

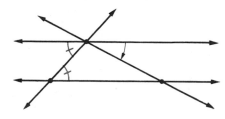

But for *three* lines to be concurrent is another matter. We normally expect three lines in a plane to contain a triangle.

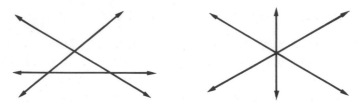

If they happen to be concurrent, and we move one of them even a little bit, the chances are that the lines will not be concurrent any more.

Under certain conditions, however, we can show that three lines must be concurrent. Our first theorem of this kind is the following.

**Theorem 15–1.**   The Perpendicular Bisector Concurrence Theorem

The perpendicular bisectors of the sides of a triangle are concurrent. Their point of concurrency is equidistant from the vertices of the triangle.

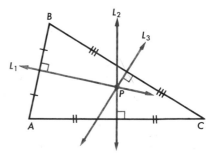

**Proof.**   Given $\triangle ABC$. Let $L_1$, $L_2$, and $L_3$ be the perpendicular bisectors of $\overline{AB}$, $\overline{AC}$, and $\overline{BC}$. If $L_1$ and $L_2$ were parallel, then $\overleftrightarrow{AB}$ and $\overleftrightarrow{AC}$ would be parallel. (Why?) But $\overleftrightarrow{AB}$ intersects $\overleftrightarrow{AC}$. Therefore $L_1$ intersects $L_2$ at a point $P$.

By the characterization theorem for perpendicular bisectors (Theorem 6–2), we have $PA = PB$, because $P$ is on $L_1$. By the same theorem, $PA = PC$, because $P$ is on $L_2$. Therefore $PB = PC$. By the same theorem, this means that $P$ is on $L_3$.

Thus the perpendicular bisectors are concurrent, and their point of intersection is equidistant from the vertices.

**Corollary 15–1.1**

Every three noncollinear points lie on one and only one circle.

(They lie on the circle with center $P$ and radius $PA = PB = PC$.)

**Corollary 15–1.2**

Two different circles can intersect in at most two points.

(In the proof, you need Corollaries 14–6.1 and 15–1.1.)

So far we have used the term *altitude* (for a triangle) in two senses: it may mean (1) a perpendicular segment from a vertex of the triangle to the opposite side, or (2) the length of such a perpendicular segment. In the following theorem, we use the word altitude in yet a third sense: here it means (3) a *line* through one vertex of the triangle, perpendicular to the opposite side.

**Theorem 15–2.** The Altitude Concurrence Theorem

The three altitudes of a tri- angle are always concurrent.

The proof is easy, provided you use the device shown on the right.

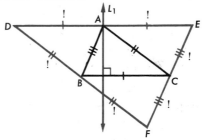

**Proof.** Given $\triangle ABC$, through each vertex we draw a line parallel to the opposite side. No two of these three lines are parallel. (Why?) Therefore they determine a triangle $\triangle DEF$.

We know that opposite sides of a parallelogram are congruent. By two applications of this theorem, we get

$$AD = BC = AE.$$

Therefore *the altitude through $A$ to $\overleftrightarrow{BC}$ is the perpendicular bisector of $\overline{DE}$.* For the same reasons, the other two altitudes of $\triangle ABC$ are the perpendicular bisectors of the other two sides of $\triangle DEF$. By Theorem 15–1, these three lines are concurrent.

Note that this theorem would become false if we interpreted the word *altitude* in the old sense to mean a segment. The perpendic- ular *segments* do not necessarily intersect at all. It is the *lines* that are always concurrent.

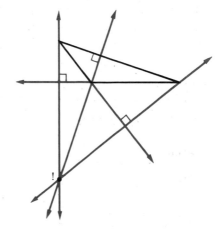

## Problem Set 15–3

1. Copy each of the following triangles on your paper and construct the three perpendicular bisectors of the sides and the three altitudes of each triangle, showing the points of concurrency.

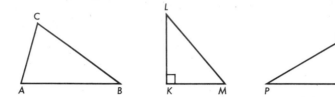

2. The point of concurrency of the altitudes of a triangle is called the *orthocenter*.

   (a) In what kind of triangle is the orthocenter a vertex of the triangle?

   (b) In what kind of triangle does the orthocenter coincide with the point of concurrency of the perpendicular bisectors?

3. Three points lie on a circle. The points are joined with segments forming a triangle. Where will the perpendicular bisectors of the segments be concurrent?

4. Given three noncollinear points, where is the point in their plane equidistant from all three? Why must the points be noncollinear?

5. Sketch and describe the set of all points equidistant from each of three noncollinear points.

6. Given a right triangle, where is the point in its plane equidistant from its vertices?

7. The altitude to the hypotenuse of an isosceles right triangle has length 7. What is the area of the triangle?

8. Given any angle ∠ *BAC*. Describe the set of all points of the interior which are equidistant from the sides of the angle. You should be able to prove your answer. (Warning: this set is neither a ray nor a line.)

9. A quadrilateral is *cyclic* if its four vertices lie on a circle. Prove that the perpendicular bisectors of the four sides and the perpendicular bisectors of the two diagonals of a cyclic quadrilateral are concurrent.

*+ 10. Find equations for the perpendicular bisectors of the sides of △*ABC* (see figure on the left, top of p. 485) and show that they are concurrent, given *A*(3, 4), *B*(5, 8), and *C*(−1, 10).

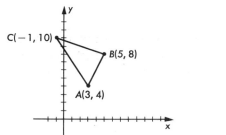

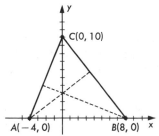

*+ **11.** Given the figure on the right above, find equations for the altitudes through $A$ and $B$ of $\triangle ABC$ and show that they intersect on the $y$-axis.

## HONORS PROBLEM

The following instructions were found on an old map.

"Start from the crossing of King's Road and Queen's Road. Proceed due north on King's Road and find a large pine tree and then a maple tree. Return to the crossroads. Due west on Queen's Road there is an elm, and due east on Queen's Road there is a spruce. One magical point is the intersection of the elm-pine line with the maple-spruce line. The other magical point is the intersection of the spruce-pine line with the elm-maple line. The treasure lies where the line through the two magical points meets Queen's Road."

A search party found the elm 4 mi from the crossing, the spruce 2 mi from the crossing, and the pine 3 mi from the crossing, but could find no trace of the maple. Nevertheless, they were able to locate the treasure from the instructions. Show how they could do this.

One member of the party remarked on how fortunate they were to have found the pine still standing. The leader laughed and said, "We didn't need the pine tree." Show that he was right.

## 15–4.   THE ANGLE BISECTORS OF A TRIANGLE

The next thing that we want to prove is that the angle bisectors of a triangle are always con-current.

To get this result, however, we first need to learn some more about

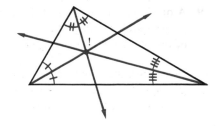

angle bisectors.  What we need is a characterization.  This is given in the following theorem.

### Theorem 15–3

The bisector of an angle, minus its end point, is the set of all points of the interior of the angle that are equidistant from the sides.

**Restatement.**    (1) If $P$ is in the interior of $\angle BAC$, and $P$ is equidistant from $\overleftrightarrow{AB}$ and $\overleftrightarrow{AC}$, then $P$ is on the bisector of $\angle BAC$.

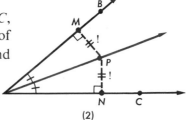

(1)

(2) If $P$ is on the bisector of $\angle BAC$, and $P \neq A$, then $P$ is in the interior of $\angle BAC$ and is equidistant from $\overleftrightarrow{AB}$ and $\overleftrightarrow{AC}$.

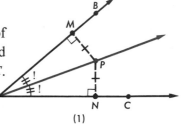

(2)

The figures illustrate the two parts of the restatement.  The notation of the proofs is that of the figures.

### Proof of (1)

| STATEMENTS | REASONS |
|---|---|
| 1.  $P$ is in the interior of $\angle BAC$. | Given. |
| 2.  $\overline{PM} \perp \overrightarrow{AB}$ and $\overline{PN} \perp \overrightarrow{AC}$. | Definition of the distance from a point to a line. |
| 3.  $\angle M$ and $\angle N$ are right angles. | Given. |
| 4.  $\angle M \cong \angle N$. | Right angles are congruent. |
| 5.  $PM = PN$. | Given. |
| 6.  $\triangle AMP \cong \triangle ANP$. | The Hypotenuse-Leg Theorem. |
| 7.  $\angle PAM \cong \angle PAN$. | Corresponding parts. |
| 8.  $\overrightarrow{AP}$ is the bisector of $\angle BAC$. | Steps 1 and 7, and the definition of the bisector of an angle. |

## Proof of (2)

| STATEMENTS | REASONS |
|---|---|
| 1. $P$ lies on the bisector of $\angle ABC$, and $P \neq A$. | Given. |
| 2. $P$ lies in the interior of $\angle BAC$. | Step 1 and the definition of angle bisector. |
| 3. $\angle PAM \cong \angle PAN$. | Definition of angle bisector. |
| 4. $\angle M \cong \angle N$. | Right angles are congruent. |
| 5. $PA = PA$. | Identity. |
| 6. $\triangle AMP \cong \triangle ANP$. | The SAA Theorem. |
| 7. $MP = NP$. | Corresponding parts. |

Steps 2 and 7 are the conclusions that we wanted.

Now we can prove our concurrence theorem:

**Theorem 15–4.**   The Angle Bisector Concurrence Theorem

The angle bisectors of a triangle are concurrent in a point which is equidistant from the three sides.

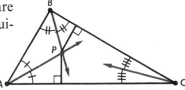

**Proof.**   Given $\triangle ABC$, let $P$ be the intersection of the bisectors of $\angle A$ and $\angle B$. Then $P$ is in the interior of $\angle A$, and in the interior of $\angle B$, and is therefore in the interior of $\angle C$. Hence

  (1)  $P$ is equidistant from $\overleftrightarrow{AC}$ and $\overrightarrow{AB}$;

  (2)  $P$ is equidistant from $\overleftrightarrow{AB}$ and $\overrightarrow{BC}$;

  (3)  $P$ is equidistant from $\overleftrightarrow{AC}$ and $\overleftrightarrow{BC}$;

  (4)  $P$ is on the bisector of $\angle C$.

  Reasons?

## Problem Set 15–4

**1.** A line intersects the sides of $\angle BAC$ in points $P$ and $Q$. Locate a point of $\overleftrightarrow{PQ}$ which is equidistant from $\overrightarrow{AB}$ and $\overrightarrow{AC}$.

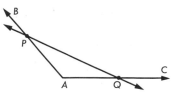

**2.** $\square ABCD$ is any convex quadrilateral.

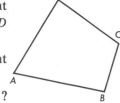

(a) Explain how to find a point which is equidistant from $\overleftrightarrow{AD}$ and $\overleftrightarrow{AB}$ and also equidistant from $D$ and $C$.

(b) Explain how to find a point which is equidistant from $\overleftrightarrow{AB}$, $\overleftrightarrow{AD}$, and $\overleftrightarrow{DC}$.

(c) Do the points of part (a) and part (b) coincide?

**3.** Describe the set of all points that are centers of circles tangent to both sides of a given angle.

**4.** Describe the set of all points in a plane which are equidistant from two intersecting lines.

**5.** Describe the set of all points in a plane which are equidistant from two intersecting lines and are 2 in. from the point of intersection.

**+ 6.** Describe the set of all points which are equidistant from two intersecting planes.

**+ 7.** Describe the set of all points of the interior of an angle which are equidistant from the sides of the angle and are at a given distance from a given line.

**8.** Prove that the bisectors of two consecutive angles of a parallelogram intersect at a point equidistant from a pair of opposite sides.

**9.** Prove the following theorem.

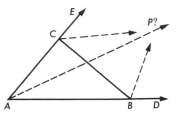

Given $\angle DAE$ and $A$-$C$-$E$ and $A$-$B$-$D$. Then the bisectors of the angles $\angle DAE$, $\angle DBC$, and $\angle ECB$ are concurrent.

**\* 10.** Describe the set of all points which are equidistant from all three of the lines determined by the sides of a triangle.

**+ 11.** Make sketches of several different convex quadrilaterals and carefully sketch in the bisectors of the angles. Are the four bisectors in each quadrilateral concurrent? In what special type of quadrilateral are the angle bisectors concurrent? Is there a general way of describing all quadrilaterals whose angle bisectors are concurrent?

**\*+ 12.** Given a pair of coordinate axes, show that the set of all points equidistant from the two axes is

$$\{(x, y) \mid y = x \text{ or } y = -x\}.$$

## 15–5.   THE MEDIAN CONCURRENCE THEOREM

A *median* of a triangle is a segment joining a vertex to the mid-point of the opposite side.  In the figure, $D$ is the mid-point of $\overline{BC}$, and $\overline{AD}$ is called the *median from A to $\overline{BC}$*.

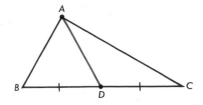

A carefully drawn figure suggests that the three medians of a triangle are always concurrent.  In fact, this is true.  It is much easier to prove, however, if we use a figure to make a further guess about *where* the point of intersection ought to be.  In the figure, it looks as though $AP = 2PD$, $BP = 2PE$, and $CP = 2PF$.  In fact, this is also true.

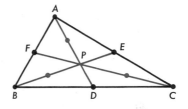

**Theorem 15–5.**   The Median Concurrence Theorem

The medians of every triangle are concurrent.  And their point of concurrency is two-thirds of the way along each median, from the vertex to the opposite side.

In the proof, it will be convenient to use a coordinate system.

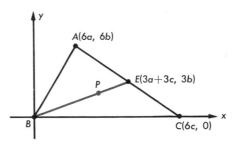

**Proof.**   We take the axes as indicated in the figure.  We use $6a$, $6b$, $6c$ to avoid fractions later.  $E$ is the mid-point of $\overline{AC}$; we get its coordinates by the mid-point formula (Theorem 13–5).

Now let $P$ be the point of the median $\overline{BE}$ such that $BP = 2PE$.  By Theorem 13–6 (which you should look up), we get

$$P = \left( \frac{0 + 2(3a + 3c)}{3}, \frac{0 + 2 \cdot 3b}{3} \right)$$

$$= (2a + 2c, 2b).$$

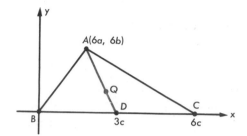

Now let $Q$ be the point of the median $\overline{AD}$ from $A$ to $\overline{BC}$ such that $AQ = 2QD$. Since $D = (3c, 0)$, we have

$$Q = \left( \frac{6a + 2 \cdot 3c}{3}, \frac{6b + 2 \cdot 0}{3} \right)$$

$$= (2a + 2c, 2b).$$

This means that $P = Q$, because a point is determined by its coordinates.

Similarly, it follows that the corresponding point of the median from $C$ to $\overline{AB}$ is the same point $P$. This proves the theorem.

**Definition**

The point of concurrency of the medians is called the *centroid* of the triangle.

## Problem Set 15–5

**1.** In the figure on the left below, medians $\overline{AE}$, $\overline{BF}$, and $\overline{CD}$ are concurrent at $Q$.

(a) If $AE = 9$, what is $AQ$?    (b) If $QD = 5$, what is $CD$?

(c) If $BQ = 12$, what is $QF$?    (d) If $QE = 4$, what is $AQ$?

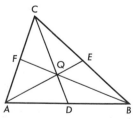    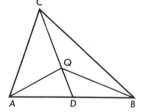

**2.** Given: The figure on the right above with median $\overline{CD}$ and $Q$ the centroid of $\triangle ABC$.

Prove: The altitude from $Q$ to $\overline{AB}$ is one-third the altitude from $C$ to $\overline{AB}$.

3. Using the figure for Problem 1, prove that $a \triangle AQB = a \square CEQF$.

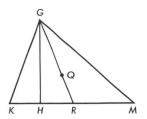

4. In $\triangle GKM$, centroid $Q$ is on median $\overline{GR}$, and $\overline{GH}$ is an altitude. Given that $QR = 4$ and $HR = 6$, what is $GH$?

+ 5. Given $\triangle ABC$ with vertices $A(6, 0)$, $B(0, 10)$, and $C(0, 0)$.

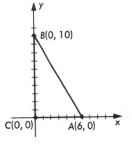

    (a) Find the coordinates of the point of concurrency of the perpendicular bisectors of the sides.

    (b) Find the coordinates of the orthocenter.

    (c) Find the distance from the orthocenter to the point of concurrency of the perpendicular bisectors.

+ 6. Given $\triangle ABC$ of Problem 5, find the coordinates of the centroid, and the distance from the centroid to the orthocenter.

*+ 7. Given $\triangle PQR$ with vertices $P(-6, 0)$, $Q(2, 0)$, and $R(0, 6)$. Find the distance between the centroid and the point of concurrency of the perpendicular bisectors of the sides.

*+ 8. Given $\triangle PQR$ of Problem 7, find the coordinates of the orthocenter and the distance from the orthocenter to the centroid.

## 15–6.  CONSTRUCTIONS WITH STRAIGHTEDGE AND COMPASS

Up to now, we have been doing geometry with a ruler and a protractor. In effect, our postulates tell us that we have an infinitely long ruler, with number labels on it. We use this "ruler" to draw lines and measure distances. We also have a protractor. With this we can measure angles, and we can also lay off angles with a given measure, starting at a given ray.

Probably this is the simplest way of doing geometry. There is another very important way, however. This is geometry with straightedge and compass. Under this scheme, we do not have a ruler with marks on it but only a straightedge (infinitely long, of course), so that, although we can draw straight lines, we cannot measure distances at all. We also have a compass. With this we can draw circles, with any given point as center and passing through any other given point. But we can't measure angles any more than we can measure distances.

This is the scheme developed by the Greek geometers of antiquity. (As a matter of fact, distance and angular measure are not mentioned in Euclid's *Elements* at all.) This scheme has considerable mathematical interest today and leads to some curious problems, when we try to find out what sort of figures we can draw with our straightedge and compass. The solutions to some of these problems are of practical value in mechanical drawing; and so professional draftsmen know them.

No matter which way we do geometry, we have certain physical drawing instruments and a corresponding mathematical theory. In each case, the mathematical theory is exact, but the results obtained with the physical drawing instruments are only approximate.

To justify our constructions with straightedge and compass, we need a theorem describing the way in which circles intersect each other. Suppose we have given two circles of radius $a$ and $b$, with $c$ as the distance between their centers.

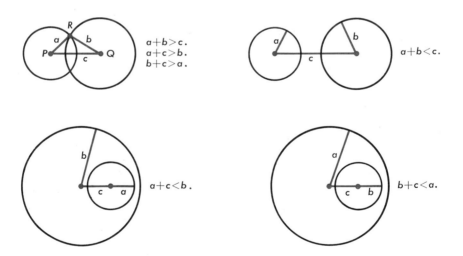

If the circles intersect in two points, as in the figure at the upper left, then each of the numbers $a$, $b$, and $c$ is less than the sum of the other two. We get these three inequalities by applying the Triangle Inequality (Theorem 7–8) to $\triangle PQR$ in three ways. On the other hand, if any one of these three inequalities works in the opposite way, the circles don't intersect at all, as the other three figures illustrate. And if the sum of two of our numbers is *equal* to the third, then the circles are tangent.

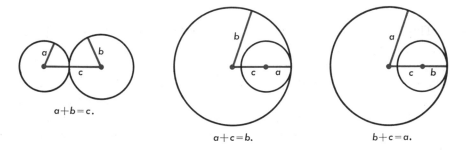

$a+b=c.$

$a+c=b.$

$b+c=a.$

This situation is described in the following theorem.

**Theorem 15–6.** The Two-Circle Theorem

Given two circles of radius $a$ and $b$, with $c$ as the distance between their centers. If each of the numbers $a$, $b$, and $c$ is less than the sum of the other two, then the circles intersect in two points, on opposite sides of the line through the centers.

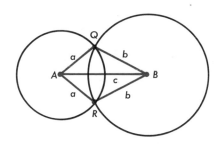

This is a theorem because it can be proved if we are willing to work hard enough. In the present chapter, however, we omit the proof and regard the statement as a postulate.

## 15–7. ELEMENTARY CONSTRUCTIONS

In this section and the next we shall show how the simplest constructions are done. All of these will, of course, be carried out in a given plane. They will appear later as steps in more difficult constructions.

**CONSTRUCTION 1.** To bisect a given angle.

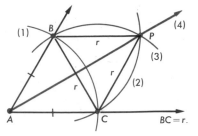

Given ∠*A*.

STEP 1. Using *A* as center, draw any circle. The circle will intersect the sides of ∠*A* in points *B* and *C*. Obviously *AB* = *AC*, as the marks on the figure indicate.

STEP 2. Draw the circle with center at *B* and radius *r* = *BC*.

STEP 3. Draw the circle with center at *C* and the same radius *r* = *BC*.

By the Two-Circle Theorem, these circles intersect in two points, lying on opposite sides of $\overleftrightarrow{BC}$. (The hypothesis of the Two-Circle Theorem must be satisfied, because each of the numbers *r*, *r*, and *r* is less than the sum of the other two.) Let *P* be the intersection point which is on the opposite side of $\overleftrightarrow{BC}$ from *A*, as in the figure.

STEP 4. Draw $\overrightarrow{AP}$.

By SSS we have △*PAB* ≅ △*PAC*. Therefore ∠*PAE* ≅ ∠*PAC*, and $\overrightarrow{AP}$ is the bisector.

(In drawing our two circles, in Steps 2 and 3, we could have used any radius greater than $\frac{1}{2}BC$. We cannot get into trouble unless we use a radius so small that the circles do not intersect at all.)

**CONSTRUCTION 2.** To copy a given angle on a given side of a given ray.

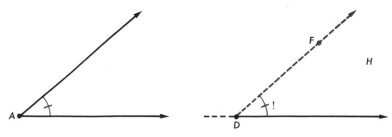

Given ∠*A*, a ray with end point *D*, and a half-plane *H*, with the given ray on its edge. We want to construct a ray $\overrightarrow{DF}$, with *F* in *H*, so as to get a second angle which is congruent to the first.

STEP 1.    Draw a circle with center at $A$, and with any radius $r$. The circle will intersect the sides of $\angle A$ in points $B$ and $C$.

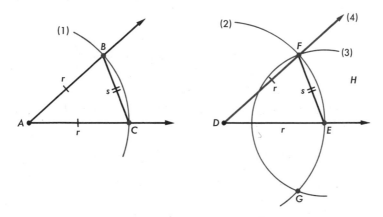

STEP 2.    Draw the circle with center at $D$ and radius $r = AB = AC$. This circle will intersect the given ray in a point $E$.

STEP 3.    Draw the circle with center at $E$ and radius $s = BC$.

These two circles will intersect in two points $F$ and $G$, on opposite sides of $\overleftrightarrow{DE}$. (*Query:* How do we know that each of the numbers $r$, $s$, and $r$ is less than the sum of the other two? This condition is what we need to apply the Two-Circle Theorem.) Let $F$ be the intersection point which lies in $H$, as in the figure.

STEP 4.    Draw $\overrightarrow{DF}$.

This is the ray that we wanted. By SSS, $\triangle FDE \cong \triangle BAC$. Therefore $\angle FDE \cong \angle BAC$, as desired.

**CONSTRUCTION 3.**    To copy a given triangle on a given side of a given ray.

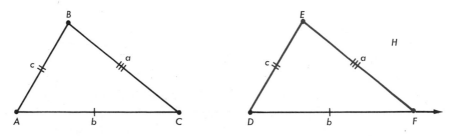

Given triangle $\triangle ABC$. We also have given a ray with end point $D$, and a half-plane $H$ containing the ray in its edge. We want to construct $\triangle DEF$, with $F$ on the given ray and $E$ in $H$, so that $\triangle DEF \cong \triangle ABC$.

STEP 1.  First we draw a circle with center at $\searrow D$ and radius $b = AC$. This circle intersects our ray in a point $F$, and $DF = AC$.

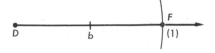

STEP 2.  Draw a circle with center $D$ and radius $c$.

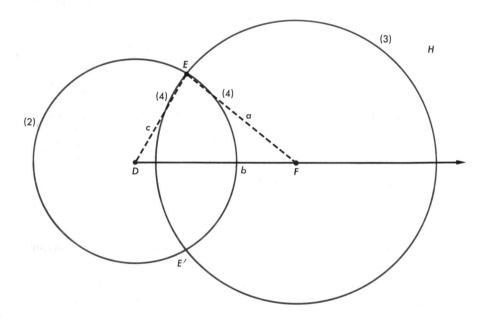

STEP 3.  Draw a circle with center $F$ and radius $a$. These two circles ought to intersect, as in the figure, in two points on opposite sides of $\overleftrightarrow{DF}$. And by the Two-Circle Theorem they *do* intersect in this way, because each of the numbers $a$, $b$ and $c$ is less than the sum of the other two. (Why?) As indicated in the figure, let $E$ be the intersection point that lies in $H$.

STEP 4.  Now draw the segments $\overline{DE}$ and $\overline{EF}$. By SSS we have $\triangle DEF \cong \triangle ABC$, which is what we wanted.

If you look again at Section 6–7, you will see that in the proof of SSS we had much the same problem as in Construction 3, namely, the problem of copying a given triangle on a given side of a given ray. It is worthwhile to compare the two methods. (In Section 6–7 we were using a ruler and a protractor instead of a straightedge and a compass. And we used SAS, instead of SSS, to show that our construction worked.)

## Problem Set 15–7

[*Note:* The problems of this set should be done with straightedge and compass.]

1. Draw a line horizontally across the top of your homework paper. Using the length of the segment $\overline{AB}$ below, mark off a scale (with a compass) at least 10 units long. Use this scale whenever necessary in solving the problems that follow.

$$A \text{———} B$$

Construct triangles with sides of the lengths given below.

(a) 5, 6, 8     (b) 3, 5, 7     (c) 4, 4, 5     (d) 6, 10, 8

2. Draw any obtuse triangle and construct the bisector of each of its angles.

3. Draw any scalene triangle $\triangle ABC$. Copy the triangle, on a given side of a given ray, by a method which depends on the ASA Postulate.

4. Construct an equilateral triangle with a side of length 5.

5. Construct an isosceles triangle having a base of length 8 and two congruent sides of length 5.

6. Prove that it is always possible to construct an equilateral triangle having a given segment as one of its sides.

7. Two lengths, $a$ and $b$, are given for the congruent sides and base, respectively, of an isosceles triangle to be constructed. What conditions on $a$ and $b$ are necessary to make the construction possible?

8. Draw any convex quadrilateral. Copy it on a given side of a given ray.

## 15–8.  ELEMENTARY CONSTRUCTIONS (CONTINUED)

CONSTRUCTION 4.  To construct the parallel to a given line through a given external point.

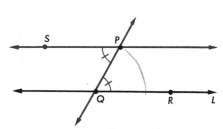

Given the line $L$, and the external point $P$. Let $Q$ and $R$ be any two points of $L$.

STEP 1.  Draw $\overleftrightarrow{PQ}$.

STEP 2.  By Construction 2, draw $\angle QPS$ congruent to $\angle PQR$, with $S$ on the opposite side of $\overleftrightarrow{PQ}$ from $R$. Then $\angle QPS$ and $\angle PQR$ are alternate interior angles. Then $\overrightarrow{PS} \parallel \overrightarrow{QR}$, which is what we wanted.

**CONSTRUCTION 5.**   To divide a segment into a given number of congruent segments.

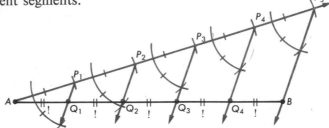

Given $\overline{AB}$, we want to divide $\overline{AB}$ into $n$ congruent segments.   (The figure shows the case $n = 5$.)

STEP 1.   Starting at $A$, draw any ray at all which does not lie on $\overleftrightarrow{AB}$.

STEP 2.   On this ray, lay off $n$ congruent segments $\overline{AP_1}$, $\overline{P_1P_2}$, ..., $\overline{P_{n-1}P_n}$ end to end.   (The length of these segments does not matter, so long as they have the same length.   We can therefore choose $P_1$ at random and lay off the rest of the segments with the compass, one at a time.)

STEP 3.   Draw $\overline{P_nB}$.

STEP 4.   Through the other points $P_1$, $P_2$, ..., $P_{n-1}$, draw rays parallel to $\overline{P_nB}$, intersecting $\overline{AB}$ in the points $Q_1$, $Q_2$, ..., $Q_{n-1}$.

Since our parallel lines intercept congruent segments on the transversal $\overleftrightarrow{AP_n}$, they also intercept congruent segments on the transversal $\overleftrightarrow{AB}$.   (This is Corollary 9–30.1.)   Therefore the points $Q_1$, $Q_2$, ..., $Q_{n-1}$ divide $\overline{AB}$ into $n$ congruent segments end to end.

**CONSTRUCTION 6.**   To construct the perpendicular bisector of a given segment.

Given $\overline{AB}$.

STEP 1.   Draw the circle with center at $A$ and radius $r = AB$.

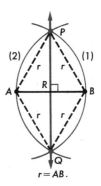

STEP 2.   Draw the circle with center at $B$ and radius $r = AB$.

The Two-Circle Theorem now applies, because each of the numbers $r$, $r$, and $r$ is less than the sum of the other two.   Therefore the circles intersect in two points $P$ and $Q$.

STEP 3.   Draw $\overleftrightarrow{PQ}$.

Since $P$ is equidistant from $A$ and $B$, $P$ lies on the perpendicular bisector of $\overline{AB}$. For the same reason, $Q$ lies on the perpendicular bisector. But two points determine a line. Therefore $\overleftrightarrow{PQ}$ *is* the perpendicular bisector of $\overline{AB}$.

Of course, there was no need to use circles of radius $r = AB$. Any larger radius would have worked as well. In fact, any radius greater than $\frac{1}{2}AB$ would have worked. (Reasons?)

Obviously, if we can construct the perpendicular bisecting line of a segment, we can construct the bisecting point. (This is the point $R$ in the preceding figure.) We note this as a sort of "corollary construction."

CONSTRUCTION 7. To construct the mid-point of a given segment.

The perpendicular bisector automatically gives us the mid-point.

CONSTRUCTION 8. To construct a perpendicular to a given line, through a given point.

*Case 1.* Given a line $L$ and a point $P$. Suppose first that $P$ is an external point. Let $Q$ be any point of $L$.

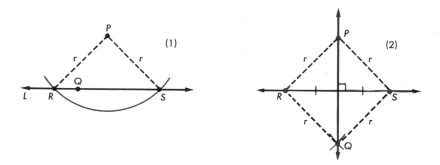

STEP 1. Draw a circle with center $P$ and radius $r > PQ$. Since $Q$ lies in the interior of the circle, it follows by Theorem 14–9 that $L$ intersects the circle in two points $R$ and $S$.

STEP 2. Construct the perpendicular bisector of $\overline{RS}$. This line passes through $P$, because $P$ is equidistant from $R$ and $S$.

Note that to draw the perpendicular bisector, we don't need to go through *all* of Construction 6; we only need to draw enough of each of our two circles to get an intersection point $Q$ different from $P$.

Therefore $\overleftrightarrow{PQ}$ must be the perpendicular bisector, because it contains two points which are equidistant from $R$ and $S$.

*Case 2.* If the point *P* lies on the line *L*, the construction is easier.

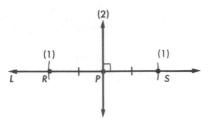

STEP 1.   Draw any circle with center at *P*, intersecting *L* in points *R* and *S*.

STEP 2.   Draw the perpendicular bisector of $\overline{RS}$.

This is it.


## Problem Set 15–8

[*Note:* The problems of this set should be done with straightedge and compass.]

1. Construct an isosceles right triangle.

2. Construct a rhombus, given the lengths of its diagonals.

3. Construct a parallelogram, given one of its angles, the length of a shorter side, and the length of the longer diagonal.

4. Construct a 60°-angle.

5. Construct a 30°-angle.

6. Construct a 15°-angle.

7. Construct a 75°-angle.

8. Construct an isosceles triangle, given the base and the altitude to the base.

9. Construct an equilateral triangle, given its altitude.

10. Given the vertex angle of an isosceles triangle, construct a base angle.

11. Construct an isosceles triangle, given a base angle and the altitude to the base.

12. Trisect a given segment.

13. Given a segment of length *a*, construct a segment of length $a\sqrt{2}$.

**14.** Given a segment of length $a$, construct a segment of length $a\sqrt{3}$.

**15.** Given two segments of lengths $a$ and $b$, construct a segment whose length is the geometric mean of $a$ and $b$. [*Hint:* See Problem 13 of Problem Set 14–5.]

**16.** Given a segment of length $a$, construct a segment of length $a\sqrt{6}$.

**17.** Construct a right triangle, given one acute angle and the length of the hypotenuse.

**18.** Construct a right triangle, given one acute angle and the altitude upon the hypotenuse.

**19.** Construct a triangle, given the lengths of two sides and the length of the median to the longer side.

**20.** Construct a parallelogram, given one angle, one side, and the altitude to that side.

**21.** Construct two circles internally tangent, given the radius of each circle.

**22.** Construct a circle tangent to both sides of an angle, given the angle and the radius of the circle.

**23.** Given the radius, construct three congruent circles each tangent to the other two.

**24.** Construct an equilateral triangle, given a segment whose length equals the perimeter of the triangle.

\* **25.** Construct a tangent to a circle from a point in the exterior of the circle. [*Hint:* Use Corollary 14–16.1.]

\* **26.** Construct an isosceles trapezoid, given the bases and a diagonal.

\* **27.** Construct an isosceles triangle, given the base and the altitude to one of the congruent sides. [*Hint:* Problem 25 should help.]

\* **28.** Construct a right triangle, given one acute angle and a segment whose length is the sum of the lengths of the legs. [*Hint:* How can you use a 45°-angle?]

\* **29.** Given two points, $A$ and $B$, of a line $L$. At $A$, a circle, $C$, is tangent to $L$. Construct a circle tangent to $L$ at $B$ and also tangent to circle $C$. [*Hint:* Analyze the diagram in which $Q$ is the center of the required circle.]

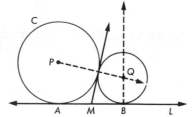

\* **30.** Construct a triangle, given the lengths of two sides and the length of the
median to the third side.

## HONORS PROBLEM

Given a segment $\overline{AB}$ and an angle $\angle C$. Construct the set of all
points $P$ in a plane such that $\angle APB \cong \angle C$.

## 15–9. INSCRIBED AND CIRCUMSCRIBED CIRCLES

In the figure below, the circle $C_1$ is *inscribed in* $\triangle ABC$, and the
circle $C_2$ is *circumscribed about* $\triangle ABC$.

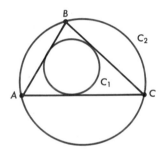

**Definitions**

If a circle is tangent to all three sides of a triangle, then we say
that the circle is *inscribed in* the triangle, and that the triangle is
*circumscribed about* the circle. If a circle contains all three of the
vertices of a triangle, then we sav that the circle is *circumscribed
about* the triangle, and that the triangle is *inscribed in* the circle.

It is a fact that every triangle is circumscribed about one circle and
inscribed in another. One way to see, roughly, why this is true is to
think of a little circle in the interior of a triangle, gradually swelling
up. At the stage where it can't swell up any more, it must be inscribed. Similarly, think of an adjustable steel hoop, gradually closing
in on the triangle from the outside. At the stage where it can't close
in any further, it must be circumscribed.

We shall now prove not only that the inscribed and circumscribed
circles exist, but also that they can be drawn with straightedge and
compass.

CONSTRUCTION 9. To circumscribe a circle about a given triangle.

Given $\triangle ABC$.

STEP 1. Construct the perpendicular bisectors of $\overline{AB}$ and $\overline{AC}$. These lines intersect in a point $P$. By Theorem 15–1, $P$ is equidistant from $A$, $B$, and $C$.

STEP 2. Draw the circle with center at $P$ and radius $r = PA$. Since $PB = PC = PA = r$, the circle contains not only $A$ but also $B$ and $C$.

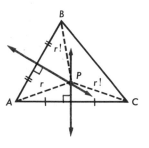

### Definition

The point of concurrency of the perpendicular bisectors of the sides of a triangle is called the *circumcenter* of the triangle.

We can also draw the inscribed circle.

CONSTRUCTION 10. To inscribe a circle in a given triangle.

Given $\triangle ABC$.

STEP 1. Bisect $\angle A$.

STEP 2. Bisect $\angle B$.

By Theorem 15–4, these bisectors meet in a point which is equidistant from all three sides of the triangle.

STEP 3. Drop a perpendicular from $P$ to $\overline{AC}$. Let $D$ be the foot of the perpendicular.

STEP 4. Draw the circle with center $P$ and radius $r = PD$.

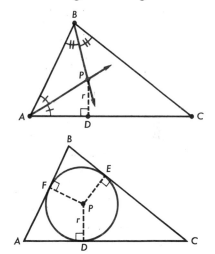

Now the circle is tangent to $\overleftrightarrow{AC}$ at $D$ because $\overleftrightarrow{AC}$ is perpendicular to the radius $\overline{PD}$. For the same reason, the circle is also tangent to the other two sides. We have therefore constructed the required circle.

### Definition

The point of concurrency of the angle bisectors of a triangle is called the *incenter* of the triangle.

## Problem Set 15–9

[*Note:* The problems of this set should be done with straightedge and compass.]

1. Construct an equilateral triangle.  Then construct its circumscribed circle and its inscribed circle.

2. Construct an isosceles right triangle.  Then construct its inscribed circle.

3. Given any scalene triangle, construct its circumscribed circle.

4. Given any scalene triangle, construct its inscribed circle.

5. Circumscribe a circle about a given square.

6. Given a rhombus, construct its inscribed circle.

7. Answer the following question by doing the construction.  Then prove your answer.

    How many chords will fit end to end in a circle if each chord is congruent to a radius of the circle?

8. Construct a right triangle, given one acute angle and the radius of the circumscribed circle.

9. Construct an isosceles triangle, given the base and the radius of the inscribed circle.

10. Construct an isosceles right triangle, given the radius of the circumscribed circle.

11. Construct an equilateral triangle, given the radius of the inscribed circle.

\* 12. Construct a right triangle, given a leg and the radius of the inscribed circle.

\* 13. Construct an isosceles triangle, given the vertex angle and the radius of the inscribed circle.

\* 14. Prove that the perimeter of a right triangle equals the sum of the diameter of its inscribed circle and twice the diameter of its circumscribed circle.

## 15–10.  THE IMPOSSIBLE CONSTRUCTION PROBLEMS OF ANTIQUITY

The ancient Greeks discovered all the constructions that you have studied so far, together with many others which are more difficult. There were some problems, however, that the best Greek mathematicians worked on for years without success.

To get an idea of how hard a construction problem can be, consider the problem of dividing a circle into 17 congruent arcs, end to end, with straightedge and compass.

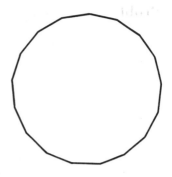

When you draw in the corresponding chords, you get a figure called a *regular polygon of 17 sides*, or, briefly, a *regular 17-gon*. This problem was well known, but remained unsolved, for over two thousand years. Finally the required construction was discovered, in the last century, by C. F. Gauss.

But some of the ancient Greek problems turned out to be harder than very hard: they were actually impossible.

## (1) THE ANGLE TRISECTION PROBLEM

Given any angle $\angle BAC$, we want to construct rays $\overrightarrow{AD}$ and $\overrightarrow{AE}$ (with $D$ and $E$ in the interior of $\angle BAC$) so that

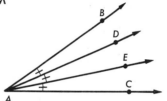

$$\angle BAD \cong \angle DAE \cong \angle EAC.$$

In this construction we are to use only a straightedge and a compass.

The first thing that most people try is to take $AB = AC$, draw $\overline{BC}$, and then trisect $\overline{BC}$, as shown on the right. This doesn't work; $\angle BAD$ and $\angle EAC$ can be shown to be congruent, but neither of these angles is congruent to $\angle DAE$. In fact, nobody has ever found a method that works.

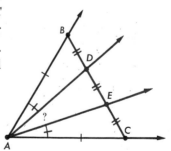

## (2) THE DUPLICATION OF THE CUBE.

A cube of edge $a$ has volume $a^3$. Given a segment of length $a$, we want to construct a segment of length $b$, such that a cube of edge $b$ has twice the volume of a cube of edge $a$. Algebraically, of course, this means that

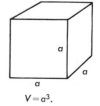

$V = a^3.$

$$b^3 = 2a^3, \quad \text{or} \quad b = a\sqrt[3]{2}.$$

Nobody had any luck with this problem either. There is a curious myth in connection with it. The story goes that the people of a certain Greek town were dying in large numbers from a plague, and consulted the oracle at Delphi to find out which god was angry and why. The oracle told them that the angry god was Apollo. The altar to Apollo, in the town, was a cube of solid gold. Apollo wanted his altar to be twice as big.

When the people got home from Delphi, they made a new altar, with edges twice as long as the edges of the old one. The plague then got worse instead of better, and the people realized that Apollo must have been thinking about the *volume* of his altar. (Of course, when the edge was doubled, the volume was multiplied by eight instead of two.) This raised the problem of the duplication of the cube, but the local mathematicians were unable to solve it. Thus the first attempt to apply mathematics to the problems of public health was a total failure.

(3) **SQUARING THE CIRCLE.** Given a circle, we want to construct a square which has the same area.

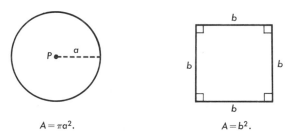

$$A = \pi a^2. \qquad\qquad A = b^2.$$

Algebraically, this means that $b = a\sqrt{\pi}$.

For over two thousand years, the best mathematicians tried to find ways to carry out these constructions with straightedge and compass. Finally it was discovered in modern times that all three problems were *impossible*.

*Impossibility* in mathematics does not mean the same thing as "impossibility" in everyday life, and so it calls for some explanation.

Frequently, when we say that something is impossible, we merely mean that it is very difficult, like finding a needle in a haystack. Often we mean that we don't *see* how to do it, and doubt that it can be done. Thus people used to say that flying machines were impossible, and people went right on saying this until somebody built an airplane and flew in it.

Mathematical impossibility is not like this. In mathematics, there are some things that really can't be done, and it is possible to *prove* that they can't be done.

(1) No matter how clever you are, you can't find a whole number between 2 and 3, because there isn't any such number.

(2) If this problem seems too trivial to be taken seriously, consider the following situation. We start with the integers, positive, negative, and zero. We are allowed to perform additions, subtractions, multiplications and divisions. Let us call a number "*constructible*" if we can get to it, starting with integers, in a finite number of such steps. For example, the following number is constructible:

$$\frac{\left(\frac{3}{7} + \frac{1}{5}\right) - \frac{1}{13}\left(\frac{4}{9} - \frac{5}{7}\right)}{\frac{1}{3}\left(\frac{1}{4} + \frac{1}{7}\right) - \frac{2}{3}\left(\frac{7}{5} - \frac{1}{2}\right)}.$$

Now suppose that the problem before us is to "*construct*" the number $\sqrt{2}$ by operations of this kind. This problem is impossible; that is, it cannot be solved. The reason is that the "constructible" numbers, under these rules, are the rational numbers, and $\sqrt{2}$ is not this kind of number. There is no use hunting for it among the "constructible numbers," because that isn't where it is.

Problems of constructibility with straightedge and compass are very much like this second illustration. Starting with a segment $\overline{AB}$, we find that there are certain segments that we can construct with straightedge and compass. For example, there are constructible segments of lengths $2AB$, $\frac{1}{2}AB$, $\sqrt{2}AB$, and $\frac{1}{10}AB$. But there is no constructible segment $\overline{CD}$ for which

$$CD^3 = 2AB^3.$$

This is what we mean when we say that the duplication of the cube with straightedge and compass is impossible.

The angle-trisection problem deserves some further discussion.

(1) *Some* angles can easily be trisected with straightedge and compass. For example, a right angle can be so trisected. And this means that trisection is possible for 45° angles, $22\frac{1}{2}$° angles, and many others. When we say that the angle-trisection problem is impossible, we mean that there are *some* angles for which the trisecting rays cannot be constructed.

(2) The angle-trisection problem becomes solvable if we relax the rules very slightly by allowing ourselves to make two marks on the straightedge.

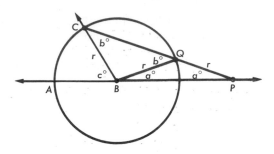

Given $\angle B$, and a straightedge with two marks on it. Let $r$ be the distance between the two marks. We first draw a circle with center at $B$ and radius $r$. This intersects our angle in two points $A$ and $C$.

We now lay down the straightedge so that (a) it passes through $C$. We then slide and rotate it in such a way that (b) one of the marks falls on a point $Q$ of the circle, and (c) the other mark falls on a point $P$ of the ray opposite to $\overrightarrow{BA}$.

We then have the situation shown in the figure. Since $\triangle QBP$ is isosceles with $QB = QP = r$, its base angles have the same measure $a$, as indicated; and similarly for $\triangle BCQ$.

Now the measure of an exterior angle of a triangle is the sum of the measures of the remote interior angles. Applying this theorem to $\triangle QBP$, we get $b = a + a = 2a$. Applying the same theorem to $\triangle BCP$, we get $c = b + a$. Therefore $c = 3a$. That is, $m\angle P = \frac{1}{3}m\angle ABC$.

We now copy $\angle P$ twice in the interior of $\angle ABC$:

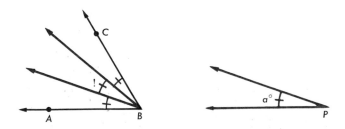

We have now trisected $\angle ABC$.

Of course, this procedure is not allowed by the old Greek rules for constructions with straightedge and compass.

## Problem Set 15–10

**1.** (a) What is the number such that the sum of 5 and the number equals 5 times the number? Prove your answer.

(b) What is the number such that 4 times the number divided by the number equals 5? Prove your answer.

**2.** Explain how to trisect a 135°-angle with straightedge and compass.

**3.** Prove that it is impossible to construct a triangle two of whose sides are 2 in. and 3 in. long and whose altitude to the third side is 4 in.

**4.** Given a square $\square ABCD$. $M$ and $N$ are mid-points of $\overline{DC}$ and $\overline{BC}$, respectively. $\overline{AM}$ and $\overline{AN}$ intersect $\overline{BD}$ at $R$ and $S$. Prove that $\overline{AM}$ and $\overline{AN}$ trisect $\overline{BD}$ but do *not* trisect $\angle DAB$.

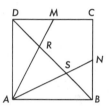

**5.** A carpenter is able to trisect any angle by using an instrument, called a *carpenter's square*, shown in the figure at the right. All the angles are right angles and $EF = CD = \frac{1}{2}AB$.

To trisect an angle $\angle PRQ$ with the carpenter's square, the carpenter first uses the longest edge to draw a ray $\overrightarrow{ST}$ parallel to $\overrightarrow{RP}$ at distance $EF$. Then placing the carpenter's square so that $\overline{DE}$ contains $R$, $A$ is on $\overrightarrow{ST}$, and $B$ is on $\overrightarrow{RQ}$, the carpenter knows that $\overrightarrow{RD}$ and $\overrightarrow{RA}$ trisect $\angle PRQ$. Prove that this is so.

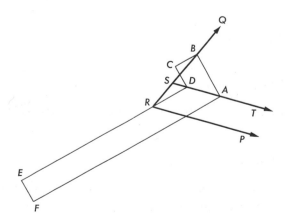

## Chapter Review

1. Describe the set of all points in a plane which are equidistant from two given parallel lines.

2. Describe the set of all points in a plane which are centers of circles tangent to a given circle at a given point of the circle.

3. Describe the set of all points in space which are at a given distance from a given point.

4. Given a line and a point not on the line in plane $E$. Describe the set of all points in $E$ which are a distance $d$ from the given line and also a distance $r$ from the given point.

5. Describe the set of all points which are at a given distance from a given point $P$, and equidistant from $P$ and another point $Q$.

6. Sketch each of the following sets.

   (a) $\{(x, y) \mid x = -1\}$        (b) $\{(x, y) \mid y = x\}$

   (c) $\{(x, y) \mid y = 2\}$        (d) $\{(x, y) \mid y < x\}$

7. Sketch and describe with an equation the set of all points equidistant from the points $A(-5, 0)$ and $B(3, 0)$.

8. Sketch and describe with an equation the set of all points at distance 3 from the graph of the equation $y = 0$. (Use of the $\pm$ sign is not allowed).

9. Construct a fairly large scalene triangle. Then find by construction the orthocenter, the centroid, and the incenter of the triangle.

10. Construct a rhombus, given one angle and a segment whose length equals the perimeter of the rhombus.

+ 11. Given $\triangle ABC$ with vertices $A(-4, 6)$, $B(0, -3)$, and $C(4, 6)$.

   (a) Prove that $\triangle ABC$ is isosceles.

   (b) Determine the coordinates of its centroid.

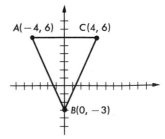

+ 12. Given $\triangle PQR$ with vertices $P(-4, 7)$, $Q(8, 7)$, and $R(8, 2)$, find the coordinates of its orthocenter.

+ **13.** Given $\triangle EFG$ with vertices $E(-2, 0)$, $F(4, 6)$, and $G(10, 0)$.

    (a) Find the coordinates of the circumcenter.

    (b) Write an equation of the circumscribed circle.

*+ **14.** Find the coordinates of the centroid of the triangle whose vertices are $A(-5, 0)$, $B(9, 0)$, and $C(5, 8)$.

**15.** Let $A$ be the center of a circle with radius $a$, and let $B$ be the center of a circle with radius $b$, both circles lying in the same plane. If $a + b > AB$, must the circles intersect? Why?

**16.** $\square ABCD$ is a trapezoid with bases $\overline{AB}$ and $\overline{DC}$. Under what conditions will there exist a point $P$, in the plane of the trapezoid, equidistant from $A$, $B$, $C$, and $D$?

**17.** Given two parallel lines $L_1$ and $L_2$ and a transversal $T$. Describe the set of all points equidistant from $L_1$, $L_2$, and $T$.

* **18.** Construct a parallelogram, given one side, one acute angle, and the longer diagonal.

* **19.** Construct a right triangle, given one acute angle and the radius of the inscribed circle.

* **20.** Given a segment whose length is the sum of the lengths of a diagonal and a side of a square. Construct the square.

* **21.** Given a segment whose length is the difference of the lengths of a diagonal and a side of a square. Construct the square.

# 16 | Areas of Circles and Sectors

## 16–1. POLYGONS

A polygon is a figure formed by fitting together segments end to end, like this:

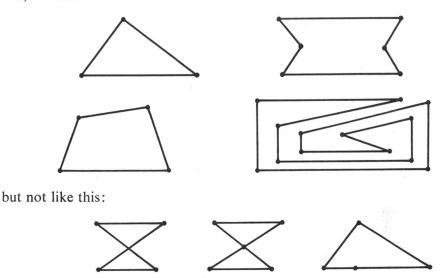

but not like this:

The idea illustrated by the figures is formally stated in the following definition.

### Definitions

Let $P_1, P_2, \ldots, P_n$ be a sequence of $n$ distinct points in a plane, with $n \geq 3$. Suppose that the $n$ segments $\overline{P_1P_2}$, $\overline{P_2P_3}$, ..., $\overline{P_{n-1}P_n}$, $\overline{P_nP_1}$ have the following properties:

(1) No two of the segments intersect except at their end points.

(2) No two segments with a common end point are collinear.

Then the union of the $n$ segments is called a *polygon*. The points $P_1, P_2, \ldots, P_n$ are called the *vertices* of the polygon, and the segments $\overline{P_1P_2}$, $\overline{P_2P_3}$, ..., $\overline{P_{n-1}P_n}$, $\overline{P_nP_1}$ are called its sides. The *angles* of the polygon are $\angle P_nP_1P_2$, $\angle P_1P_2P_3$, and so on. For short, we often denote the angles by $\angle P_1$, $\angle P_2$, and so on. The sum of the lengths of the sides is called the *perimeter*.

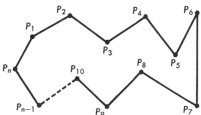

513

At this point, you should look again at the seven figures at the beginning of this section, and make sure that you see why our definition of a polygon allows the first four figures, but rules out the last three. (Remember that the points $P_1, P_2, \ldots, P_n$ are all required to be different.)

A polygon with $n$ sides is called an $n$-*gon*. Thus we might refer to triangles and quadrilaterals as 3-*gons* and 4-*gons*, although these terms are seldom used. Similarly, 5-gons are called *pentagons*, 6-gons are *hexagons*, 8-gons are *octagons*, and 10-gons are *decagons*. Some of the other $n$-gons (for small numbers $n$) also have special names taken from the Greek, but these are not very commonly used.

Each side of a polygon lies on a line, and each line, of course, separates the plane into two half-planes.

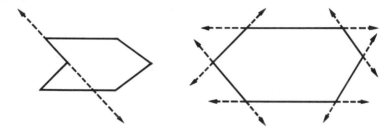

It can easily happen (as in the figure on the left) that each of these half-planes contains points of the polygon. If this does *not* happen for any side of the polygon (as in the figure on the right), then the polygon is called *convex*. We repeat this briefly as a definition.

### Definition

A polygon is *convex* if no two points of it lie on opposite sides of a line containing a side of the polygon.

This use of the term "convex" is natural: if a polygon is convex, then the polygon plus its interior forms a *convex set* in the sense defined in Chapter 3. When we speak of the area of a convex polygon we mean the area of the corresponding convex polygonal region.

## Problem Set 16–1

1. In this figure, no two segments intersect except at their end points, and no two segments with a common end point are collinear. Yet the figure is not a polygon. Why?

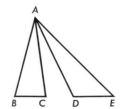

**2.** Which of the figures below are hexagons? Which are convex hexagons?

(a)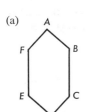

(b)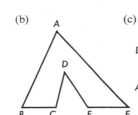

(c)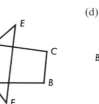

(d)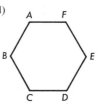

(e)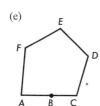

(f)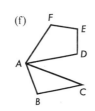

(g)

(h)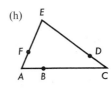

**3.** Give a precise explanation of why this figure is not a convex polygon.

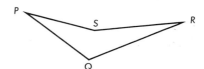

**4.** Name the angles of each polygon.

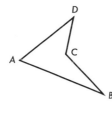

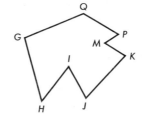

**5.** Is a polygon that has all its sides congruent and all its angles right angles necessarily a square?

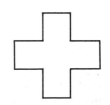

**6.** A segment whose end points are two nonconsecutive vertices of a polygon is called a *diagonal* of the polygon.

(a) Name all the diagonals of each of the polygons shown below.

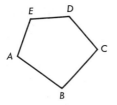

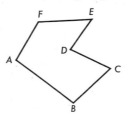

(b) How many diagonals has a polygon with 3 sides? 4 sides? 5 sides? 6 sides? 7 sides?

(c) How many diagonals has a polygon with 103 sides? $n$ sides?

7. Calculate the sum of the measures of the angles of a convex pentagon; of a convex hexagon. [*Hint:* Draw all the diagonals from *one* vertex.]

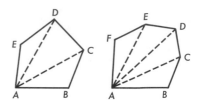

8. In a convex polygon all the diagonals from *one* vertex are drawn. How many triangles result if the polygon has 4 sides? 5 sides? 6 sides? 11 sides? 35 sides? $n$ sides?

9. Verify the following generalization.

*The sum of the measures of the angles of a convex polygon of n sides is $(n - 2)180$.*

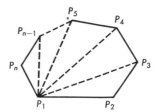

10. Find the sum of the measures of the angles of a convex octagon; decagon; 12-gon; 15-gon; 20-gon.

11. What is the number of sides of a convex polygon if the sum of the measures of its angles is 900? 1260? 1980? 2700? 4140?

+ 12. Using the figure on the right, verify the statement of Problem 9.

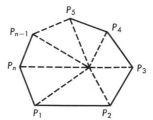

13. Determine the sum of the measures of the exterior angles of a convex pentagon; of a convex octagon.

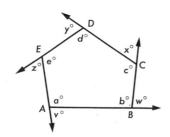

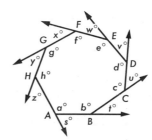

**14.** Verify the following generalization.

*The sum of the measures of the exterior angles of a convex polygon of n sides is 360.*

+ **15.** State a definition of the *interior* of a convex polygon. (See the definition of interior of a triangle.)

+ **16.** Discuss the truth or falsity of the following statements.

(a) The union of any convex polygon with its interior is a polygonal region.

(b) The boundary of every polygonal region is a polygon.

*+ **17.** Given a correspondence $P_1P_2P_3 \cdots P_n \leftrightarrow Q_1Q_2Q_3 \cdots Q_n$ between two polygons. If the corresponding sides are congruent and the corresponding angles are congruent, must the two polygons be similar? Must their perimeters be equal? Must they enclose regions having equal areas?

Support your answer with logical reasoning and/or examples.

## HONORS PROBLEM

That a polygon separates the points of the plane into two sets, called the interior and exterior of the polygon, seems a rather obvious fact. It is, however, provable from our postulates, though its proof is quite difficult. Show that this theorem is important to the solution of the following popular puzzle. Three houses, *A, B, C,* are each to be connected to three outlets, one for gas, *G,* one for water, *W,* and one for electricity, *E.*

A     B     C
.     .     .

G     W     E
.     .     .

The challenge is to draw paths, one from each house to each outlet, without letting any two paths intersect. The whole figure is to lie in a plane.

## 16–2.   REGULAR POLYGONS

**Definition**

A polygon is *regular* if (1) it is convex, (2) all of its sides are congruent, and (3) all of its angles are congruent.

For example, an equilateral triangle is a regular 3-gon, and a square is a regular 4-gon.

We can construct regular *n*-gons with any number of sides by the following method. We begin with a circle, with center $Q$ and radius $r$.

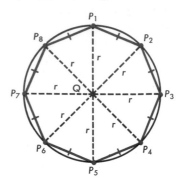

We first divide the circle into $n$ congruent arcs, end to end. Each of the arcs then has measure $360/n$. (The figure shows the case $n = 8$.) For each little arc, we draw the corresponding chord. This gives us a polygon, with vertices $P_1$, $P_2, \ldots, P_n$. It is easy to see that the polygon is convex. The sides are all congruent because the small arcs are.

If we draw the radii from $Q$ to the vertices, we get a set of isosceles triangles. By SSS, all these triangles are congruent. Therefore all the angles of our polygon are congruent. (The measure of each angle is twice the measure of each base angle of each of our isosceles triangles.) Therefore our polygon is regular.

It is a fact that every regular polygon can be constructed by this method. That is, every regular polygon is inscribed in a circle. We shall not stop to prove this statement because we won't need it. We shall be using regular polygons only in the study of circles, and all the regular polygons that we talk about will be constructed by the method that we have just described.

The center $Q$ of the circle in which the polygon is inscribed is called the *center* of the polygon. Since all the small isosceles triangles in the figure above are congruent, they have the same base $e$ and the same altitude $a$. The number $a$ is the distance from the center to each of the sides.

### Definition

The distance $a$ from the center of a regular polygon to each of the sides is called the *apothem* of the polygon.

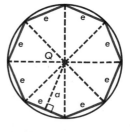

The perimeter is denoted by $p$. Obviously

$$p = ne.$$

It is easy to calculate the area of the region formed by the polygon plus its interior. Each of our isosceles triangles has area $\frac{1}{2}ae$. There are $n$ triangles. Therefore the area is $A_n = n \cdot \frac{1}{2}ae = \frac{1}{2}ap$.

## Problem Set 16–2

1. What quadrilateral, if any, is equilateral but not regular? equiangular but not regular?

2. Sketch a polygon which has all its sides congruent and all its angles right angles, but is not regular.

3. The figure represents part of a regular $n$-gon inscribed in a circle with center $Q$.

   (a) What is $m \angle P_5QP_6$?

   (b) What is $m \angle QP_5P_6 + m \angle QP_6P_5$?

   (c) Why is $\angle QP_6P_5 \cong \angle QP_5P_4$?

   (d) Why is $m \angle P_4P_5P_6 = m \angle P_4P_5Q + m \angle QP_5P_6$?

   (e) Show that $m \angle P_4P_5P_6 = 180 - \dfrac{360}{n}$.

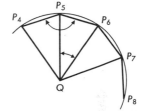

4. Determine the measure of each angle of a regular polygon of 5 sides; 9 sides; 12 sides; 15 sides; 17 sides; 24 sides. (See Problem 3.)

5. How many sides has a regular polygon if the measure of an exterior angle is 72? 45? 36? 24? $17\frac{1}{7}$?

6. How many sides has a regular polygon if the measure of one of its angles is $128\frac{4}{7}$? 140? 144? 160?

7. How would you construct a regular octagon with only a compass and an unmarked straightedge?

8. How would you construct a regular hexagon with only a compass and an unmarked straightedge?

9. The perimeter of a regular polygon is 48 and its apothem is 6. What is the area of the polygon?

10. Determine the area of a regular hexagon which has a side 10 in. long.

11. A side of a regular hexagon inscribed in a circle is 4. What is the radius of the circle and the apothem of the hexagon?

12. Prove that the area of a regular hexagon of side $s$ is given by the formula $\frac{3}{2}\sqrt{3}\, s^2$.

13. $\square ABCD$ is any quadrilateral having each of its sides tangent to a circle of diameter 9. If the perimeter of $\square ABCD$ is 56, what is $a\square ABCD$?

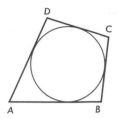

+ 14. Determine the area of a regular polygon of 9 sides, given that the length of one side is 8.  (Remember the trigonometric ratios!)

+ 15. Determine the area of a regular polygon of 15 sides, given that the length of one side is 4.

* 16. Prove that each side of a regular octagon inscribed in a circle of radius 1 has a length of $\sqrt{2 - \sqrt{2}}$.

## HONORS  PROBLEM

A problem commonly faced in architectural design is that of covering a surface with regular polygonal regions.  For example, a plane can be covered by congruent square regions placed four at a vertex, as shown here.

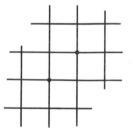

(a) How many equilateral triangular regions must be placed at a vertex to cover a plane?

(b) What other class of regular polygonal regions can be used to cover a plane?  How many would be needed at a vertex?

(c) Two regular octagons and one square will exactly cover the part of a plane around a point when arranged as shown.  What other combinations of three regular polygonal regions (two of which are alike) will accomplish this? You should be able to find two other combinations.

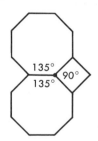

(d) Investigate whether there are other possibilities of covering a plane by regular polygonal regions.  A table of measures of angles of regular polygons would be helpful in discovering workable combinations.

# 16–3.  THE CIRCUMFERENCE OF A CIRCLE.
## THE NUMBER $\pi$

In this section and the next one, we shall consider regular $n$-gons for various values of $n$. As usual, we denote the side, apothem, and perimeter of a regular $n$-gon inscribed in a circle of radius $r$ by $e$, $a$, and $p$.

Let $C$ be the circumference of a circle. It seems reasonable to suppose that if you want to measure $C$ approximately, you can do it by inscribing a regular polygon with a large number of sides and then measuring the perimeter of the polygon. That is, the perimeter $p$ ought to be a good approximation of $C$ when $n$ is large. In other words, once we decide how close to $C$ we want $p$ to be, we should be able to get $p$ this close to $C$ merely by making $n$ large enough. We describe this situation in symbols by writing

$$p \to C,$$

and we say that $p$ approaches $C$ as a limit.

We cannot prove this, however; and the reason why we cannot prove it is rather unexpected. The reason is that so far, we have no mathematical definition of what is meant by the circumference of a circle. (We can't get the circumference merely by adding the lengths of segments, the way we did to get the perimeter of a polygon, because a circle doesn't contain any segments, even very short ones. In fact, Corollary 14–6.1 tells us that no circle contains even *three* points which are collinear.)

But the remedy is easy: we take the statement

$$p \to C$$

as our definition of $C$.

**Definition**

> The *circumference* of a circle is the limit of the perimeters of the inscribed regular polygons.

We now want to define the number $\pi$, in the usual way, as the ratio of the circumference to the diameter. But to be sure that this definition makes sense, we first need to know that the ratio $C/2r$ is the same for all circles, regardless of their size. In fact, this is true.

**Theorem 16–1**

> The ratio of the circumference to the diameter is the same for all circles.

**Proof.**   Given a circle with center $Q$ and radius $r$, and a circle with center $Q'$ and radius $r'$. In each circle we inscribe a regular $n$-gon.

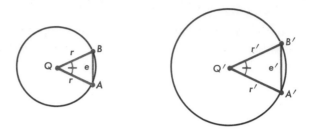

In the figure, we show only one side of each $n$-gon, with the corresponding isosceles triangle. The two central angles are congruent, as the marks indicate, because the measure of each is $360/n$. Also, the including sides are proportional: $r'/r = r'/r$. By the SAS Similarity Theorem,

$$\triangle BQA \sim \triangle B'Q'A'.$$

Therefore

$$\frac{e'}{r'} = \frac{e}{r}, \qquad \frac{ne'}{r'} = \frac{ne}{r}, \qquad \text{and} \qquad \frac{p'}{r'} = \frac{p}{r},$$

where $p$ and $p'$ are the perimeters of the two $n$-gons.  Now

$$p \to C \qquad \text{and} \qquad p' \to C',$$

by definition.  Therefore

$$\frac{p}{r} \to \frac{C}{r} \qquad \text{and} \qquad \frac{p'}{r'} \to \frac{C'}{r'}.$$

Since $\dfrac{p}{r}$ and $\dfrac{p'}{r'}$ are equal, their limits are the same:

$$\frac{C}{r} = \frac{C'}{r'}, \qquad \text{and} \qquad \frac{C}{2r} = \frac{C'}{2r'},$$

which was to be proved.

The ratio $C/2r$ is denoted by $\pi$. Since this is the same for all circles, the formula

$$C = 2\pi r$$

holds for all circles.

The number $\pi$ is not rational.  In fact, it cannot be calculated exactly by any of the ordinary methods of algebra.  On the other hand, it can be approximated, as closely as we please, by rational numbers. Some of the useful approximations are

$$3, \quad 3.14, \quad 3\tfrac{1}{7}, \quad 3.1416, \quad \tfrac{355}{113}, \quad 3.14159265358979.$$

It is not hard to convince yourself, by making physical measurements, that $\pi$ is a little more than 3. But to get a very close approximation requires the use of very advanced mathematics.

## Problem Set 16–3

1. A regular polygon is inscribed in a circle, then another regular polygon with one more side than the first is inscribed, and so on endlessly, each new polygon having one more side than the previous one.
   (a) What is the limit of the apothem?
   (b) What is the limit of the length of a side?
   (c) What is the limit of the measure of an angle of the polygon?
   (d) What is the limit of the perimeter of the polygon?

2. The diameter of a bicycle wheel is 28 in. How far does the bicycle travel with each revolution of the wheel? (Which approximation of $\pi$ makes the computation easiest?)

3. Which is the closer approximation to $\pi$, 3.14 or $3\tfrac{1}{7}$?

4. The circumference of a log is 62.8 in. How long is the side of a cross section of the largest square beam that can be cut from the log? (Use 3.14 for $\pi$.)

5. What is the radius of a circle whose circumference is $\pi$?

6. A circular swimming pool 35 ft in diameter is to be enclosed by a fence in the shape of a square. The total length of the fence is to be twice the circumference of the pool. How long will the fence be along one side of the square?

7. The side of a square is 8 in. long. Find the circumference of its inscribed circle; of its circumscribed circle.

8. The length of a side of an equilateral triangle is 12. What is the circumference of its inscribed circle? of its circumscribed circle?

9. The earth is approximately 93,000,000 mi from the sun. The path of the earth around the sun is nearly circular. Calculate how far we travel each year "in orbit" with respect to the sun. What is a close estimate of our speed (in miles per hour) in this orbit?

10. The radius of the earth is approximately 4000 mi. As the earth rotates, objects on its surface are constantly traveling at various speeds with respect to the earth's axis, depending upon the latitude of each object. What is the approximate speed, in miles per hour, of an object near the equator? What is the speed of an object at latitude 45°N?

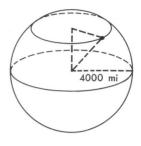

11. A side of a regular hexagon is 6. What is the circumference of its circumscribed circle? of its inscribed circle?

12. The radii of three circles are 1 ft, 10 ft, and 10,000 ft. The radius of each circle is increased by 1 ft, so that the new radii are, respectively, 2 ft, 11 ft, and 10,001 ft. Determine the increase in the circumference of each circle, due to the increase of the radius.

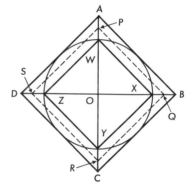

* 13. Given the figure in which $\square ABCD$ is a square circumscribed about the circle, $\square WXYZ$ is a square inscribed in the circle, and $\overleftrightarrow{AC}$ and $\overrightarrow{BD}$ contain the diagonals of both squares. $\square PQRS$ is a square whose vertices are the mid-points of $\overline{AW}$, $\overline{BX}$, $\overline{CY}$, and $\overline{DZ}$. Determine whether the perimeter of $\square PQRS$ is less than, equal to, or greater than the circumference of the circle. Let the radius of the circle equal 1, and justify your answer by computation.

## 16–4.   THE AREA OF A CIRCLE

### Definition

A *circular region* is the union of a circle and its interior.

When we speak of "the area of a circle," we mean the area of the corresponding circular region. (This is the same sort of abbreviation that we use when we speak of "the area of a triangle," meaning the area of the corresponding triangular region.) We shall now get a formula for the area of a circle.

Given a circle of radius $r$, we inscribe in it a regular $n$-gon. As usual, the area of the $n$-gon is denoted by $A_n$; the perimeter is $p$ and the apothem is $a$. In Section 16–2, p. 518, we found that

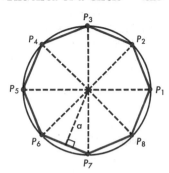

$$A_n = \tfrac{1}{2}ap.$$

In this situation there are three quantities involved, each depending on $n$. These are $p$, $a$, and $A_n$. To get our formula for the area of a circle, we must find out what limits these quantities approach as $n$ becomes very large.

(a) *What happens to $A_n$?* $A_n$ is always slightly less than the area $A$ of the circle, because there are always some points that lie inside the circle but outside the regular $n$-gon. However, the difference between $A_n$ and $A$ is very small when $n$ is very large, for, when $n$ is very large, the polygon almost fills up the interior of the circle. Thus, we expect that

$$A_n \to A. \tag{1}$$

But just as in the case of the circumference of the circle, this can never be proved, since we have not yet given any definition of the area of a circle. Here also, the remedy is easy:

**Definition**

> The *area of a circle* is the limit of the areas of the inscribed regular polygons.

Thus, $A_n \to A$ by definition.

(b) *What happens to $a$?* The apothem $a$ is always slightly less than $r$, because either leg of a right triangle is shorter than the hypotenuse. But the difference between $a$ and $r$ is very small when $n$ is very large. Thus

$$a \to r. \tag{2}$$

(c) *What happens to $p$?* By definition of $C$, we have

$$p \to C. \tag{3}$$

Fitting together results (2) and (3), we get

$$\tfrac{1}{2}ap \to \tfrac{1}{2}rC.$$

Therefore, since $A_n = \frac{1}{2}ap$, we have

$$A_n \to \tfrac{1}{2}rC.$$

But we knew from (1) that $A_n \to A$. Therefore

$$A = \tfrac{1}{2}rC.$$

Since $C = 2\pi r$, this gives

$$A = \tfrac{1}{2}r \cdot 2\pi r = \pi r^2.$$

Thus the familiar formula has finally become a theorem.

### Theorem 16–2

The area of a circle of radius $r$ is $\pi r^2$.

## Problem Set 16–4

**1.** Find the circumference and the area of a circle whose radius is 3; 5; $\sqrt{2}$; $\pi$.

**2.** Find the circumference and the area of a circle whose diameter is 6; 9; 2; $\pi\sqrt{12}$.

**3.** What is the radius of a circle whose area is $49\pi$? $20\pi$? 25? 16? $18\pi^3$?

**4.** What is the area of a circle whose circumference is $6\pi$? $16\pi$? 12? $2\pi$?

**5.** Compute the area of one face of an iron washer, given that its diameter is $1\frac{1}{4}$ in. and the diameter of the hole is $\frac{1}{2}$ in. (Use $3\frac{1}{7}$ for $\pi$.)

**6.** Prove the following theorem.

The ratio of the areas of two circles is equal to the square of the ratio of their radii.

**7.** Two circles have radii of 3 and 12, respectively. What is the ratio of their areas?

**8.** The circumferences of two circles are 7 and $4\pi$. What is the ratio of the areas of the circles?

**9.** The circumference of a circle and the perimeter of a square are each 20 in. Which has the greater area, the circle or the square? How much greater?

10. Given a square with a side of length 10, find the area of the region bounded by its inscribed and circumscribed circles.

11. In the figure, the diameter of each small semicircle equals the radius of the large semicircle. If the radius of the large semicircle is 2, what is the area of the shaded region?

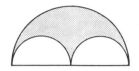

12. ▢$ABCD$ is a square whose side is $s$. $X$ and $Z$ are mid-points of $\overline{AD}$ and $\overline{BC}$, respectively. Circular arcs $\overarc{DY}$ and $\overarc{BY}$ have centers $X$ and $Z$, respectively. Determine the area of the shaded region.

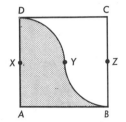

13. In a sphere of radius 10 in., sections are made by planes 4 in. and 5 in. from the center. Which section will have the greater area? Compute the ratio of the areas of the two sections.

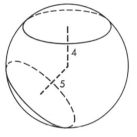

14. An *annulus* is a region bounded by two concentric circles. Find the area of the annulus bounded by the inscribed and circumscribed circles of an equilateral triangle with a side of length 6.

15. Given two concentric circles and a chord of the larger circle tangent to the smaller circle. Prove that the area of the annulus formed by the circles is equal to one-fourth the product of $\pi$ and the square of the length of the chord.

\* 16. The semicircles drawn in the figure have as diameters the sides of right triangle $\triangle ABC$. $x, y, z, m,$ and $n$ are the areas of the regions, as shown. Prove that $x + y = z$.

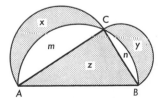

\* 17. The 12-gon shown here, with 8 of its vertices on a circle, has all sides congruent, and all its angles are right angles. Given that the length of each side is 4, find the area of the part of the circular region which is outside the polygon.

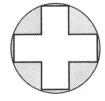

+ **18.** A circle with circumference $4\pi$ is inscribed in a rhombus with perimeter 20. Compute the total area of the regions bounded by the circle and the rhombus.

+ **19.** An isosceles trapezoid whose bases are 2 in. and 6 in. is circumscribed about a circle. Determine the area of that part of the trapezoid region which lies outside the circle.

\*+ **20.** A target on which an amateur can be expected to hit the bullseye as often as he can hit any of the rings is constructed in the following way. Let the distance between two parallel rays, $\overrightarrow{PM}$ and $\overrightarrow{AN}$, be $PA = r$, the radius of the bullseye. The circle with radius $r$ and center $P$ intersects $\overrightarrow{PM}$ at $Q$. Let the perpendicular to $\overrightarrow{PM}$ at $Q$ intersect $\overrightarrow{AN}$ at $B$. Then draw the circle with radius $PB = r$, and center $P$. This process is repeated, drawing perpen-

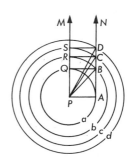

diculars at $R$ and $S$ and concentric circles with radii $PC = r_2$ and $PD = r_3$. Of course, more rings can be constructed.

(a) Express $r_1$, $r_2$, and $r_3$ in terms of $r$.

(b) Show that the areas of the bullseye and the three rings, namely, $a$, $b$, $c$, and $d$, are equal.

## 16–5.   LENGTHS OF ARCS AND AREAS OF SECTORS

To define the length of a circular arc, we use the same sort of scheme that we used to define the circumference of the whole circle. First we cut up the given arc $\overset{\frown}{AB}$ into $n$ congruent arcs, end to end. Then we draw the corresponding chords. Just as before, all the chords have the same length $e$, and the sum of their lengths is

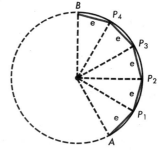

$$p = ne.$$

The *length* of $\overset{\frown}{AB}$ is defined to be the limit of $p$ as $n$ becomes larger and larger.

In the following discussion, it will be convenient to consider an entire circle as an arc of measure 360. The circumference can then be regarded as the length of an arc of measure 360.

**Theorem 16–3**

If two arcs have equal radii, then their lengths are proportional to their measures.

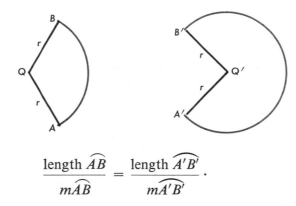

$$\frac{\text{length } \widehat{AB}}{m\widehat{AB}} = \frac{\text{length } \widehat{A'B'}}{m\widehat{A'B'}}.$$

In simple cases, it is easy to see why this is true. If you double the measure of an arc, this doubles the length; if you divide the measure by 7, this divides the length by 7, and so on. But a complete proof of the theorem is too difficult for this course. We shall therefore regard the theorem as a new postulate.

On the basis of this theorem, we can calculate the lengths of arcs.

**Theorem 16–4**

If an arc has measure $q$ and radius $r$, then its length is

$$L = \frac{q}{180} \cdot \pi r.$$

**Proof.**  Let $C$ be the circumference of a circle of radius $r$. By Theorem 16–3,

$$\frac{L}{q} = \frac{C}{360},$$

But $C = 2\pi r$. Therefore

$$\frac{L}{q} = \frac{2\pi r}{360},$$

and

$$L = \frac{q}{180} \cdot \pi r.$$

A *sector* is a region like one of these:

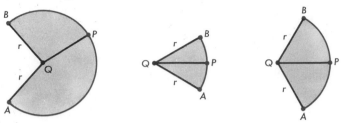

## Definitions

Let $\overset{\frown}{AB}$ be an arc of a circle with center $Q$ and radius $r$.  The union of all segments $\overline{QP}$, where $P$ is any point of $\overset{\frown}{AB}$, is called a *sector*.   $\overset{\frown}{AB}$ is called the *arc* of the sector, and $r$ is called its *radius*.

We define the area of a sector by the same sort of scheme that we used to define the area of a circle.  Using the same type of proofs, we obtain the following theorem.

## Theorem 16–5

The area of a sector is half the product of its radius and the length of its arc.

Briefly,

$$A = \tfrac{1}{2}rL.$$

There is an easy way to remember this formula.  The area of a sector in a circle of fixed radius $r$ ought to be proportional to the length of its arc.  (In fact, this is true.)  When the arc is the whole circle, the area is $\pi r^2 = \tfrac{1}{2}Cr$, where $C = 2\pi r$.  Therefore, for a sector with arc length $L$ and area $A$, we must have

$$\frac{A}{L} = \frac{\tfrac{1}{2}Cr}{C}, \quad \text{and} \quad A = \tfrac{1}{2}rL.$$

Using the formula for $L$ in Theorem 16–4, we get:

## Theorem 16–6

If a sector has radius $r$ and its arc has measure $q$, then its area is

$$A = \frac{q}{360} \cdot \pi r^2.$$

Note that for $q = 360$ the theorem says that $A = \pi r^2$, which is what it ought to say.

## Problem Set 16–5

1. The radius of a circle is 18. How long is an arc of 60°? of 90°? of 120°? of 150°? of 180°? of 270°?

2. What is the radius of a circle if the length of a 45°-arc is $3\pi$?

3. What is the radius of a circle if the length of a 72°-arc is $4\pi$?

4. Both $\overset{\frown}{AB}$ and $\overset{\frown}{CD}$ are arcs of 60°, but their lengths are not equal. $P$ is the center of both arcs. If $PA = 6$ and $AC = 3$, how long is $\overset{\frown}{AB}$ and how long is $\overset{\frown}{CD}$?

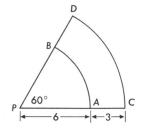

5. The length of a 60°-arc is 1 in. Find the radius of the arc and the length of the chord of the arc.

6. Explain the difference in meaning of arc measure and arc length.

7. The radius of a circle is 10. What is the area of a sector having an arc of 90°? of 72°? of 180°? of 216°? of 324°?

8. In a circle with radius 2, a sector has area $\pi$. What is the measure of the arc of the sector?

9. In a circle with radius 6, a sector has area $15\pi$. What is the length of the arc of the sector?

10. The minute hand of a large clock on the tower of a public building is 6 ft long. Find the distance traveled by the tip of the minute hand in 5 min. How many inches does the tip of the minute hand travel in 1 min?

11. In designing very tall buildings engineers must allow for the swaying motion which is typical of skyscraper structures. The height of the Empire State Building at the 102d floor is 1250 ft. If the building, at this height, describes an arc of $\frac{1}{2}°$, how far does it sway back and forth?

12. A *segment of a circle* is a region bounded by an arc of the circle and the chord of the arc. Describe a method of determining the area of a segment of a circle.

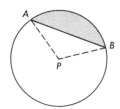

**13.** Find the area of a segment of a circle given that the radius, $r$, of the circle and the measure of the arc, $m\widehat{AB}$, are:

(a) $r = 12$;   $m\widehat{AB} = 60$.          (b) $r = 6$;     $m\widehat{AB} = 120$.

* **14.** Find the area of a segment of a circle given that the radius, $r$, of the circle and the measure of the arc, $m\widehat{AB}$, are:

(a) $r = 8$;   $m\widehat{AB} = 45$.          (b) $r = 10$;   $m\widehat{AB} = 30$.

* **15.** A regular octagon is inscribed in a circle of radius 6. Find the area of that part of the circular region that is outside the octagon.

* **16.** The radius of each circular arc which makes up this six-petal design is the same as the radius of the circle which contains the outer tips of all the petals. If the radius is 1, what is the area of the figure?

**17.** A continuous belt runs around two wheels as shown. The wheels have radii of 3 in. and 15 in. and the distance between their centers is 24 in. Find the length of the belt.

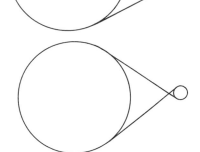

* **18.** A continuous belt runs around two wheels so that the wheels will turn in opposite directions. The wheels have radii of 3 in. and 9 in., and the distance between their centers is 24 in. Find the length of the belt.

## HONORS PROBLEM

Derive a formula for the area of an oval. Construct an oval in the following way. Let $\overline{AB}$ and $\overline{CD}$ be perpendicular diameters of a circle having radius $r$. With $A$ as center and $AB$ as radius swing an arc from $B$ intersecting $\overleftrightarrow{AC}$ at $G$. Similarly, with $B$ as center and $AB$ as radius, let $\widehat{AH}$ intersect $\overleftrightarrow{BC}$ at $H$. Finally, with $C$ as center and $CG$ as radius, draw $\widehat{GH}$. Find the area of the oval $ADBGH$.

# Chapter Review

1. Is a convex polygon a convex set?

2. Define a regular polygon.

3. A hexagon is circumscribed about a circle of diameter 10. If the perimeter of the hexagon is 28, what is the area of the hexagon?

4. Compare the apothem of a regular polygon and the radius of the inscribed circle.

5. Compare the apothem of a regular polygon and the radius of the circumscribed circle. (To prove your answer you may assume the length of an edge is $e$.)

6. A convex polygon has 13 sides. What is the sum of the measures of its 13 exterior angles?

7. How many sides does a convex polygon have if the sum of the measures of its angles is 1080?

8. What is the measure of each angle of a regular pentagon? hexagon? octagon? decagon?

9. What is the apothem of a regular polygon having area 225 and perimeter 60?

10. If the circumference of a circle is $C$ and its radius is $r$, what is the value of $C/r$?

11. What is the radius of a circle if its circumference is equal to its area?

12. The area of a circle is 6 times its circumference. What is its radius?

13. Two concentric circles have radii of 5 and 13. Find the radius of a circle whose area equals the area of the annulus bounded by the two given circles.

14. If the radius of one circle is 4 times the radius of another, what is the ratio of their diameters? of their circumferences? of their areas?

15. The circumferences of two circles are $6\pi$ and $10\pi$. What is the ratio of their areas?

16. Compare the areas of an equilateral triangle circumscribed about a circle and an equilateral triangle inscribed in the circle.

17. Show that the area of a circle is given by the formula $\frac{1}{4}\pi d^2$, where $d$ is the diameter of the circle.

**18.** Will more water flow through three 1-in. pipes or one 3-in. pipe? Prove your answer. (A pipe is measured by its inside diameter.)

**19.** Given that the length of a side of the equilateral triangle $\triangle ABC$ is 6 and $P$, $Q$, $R$ are mid-points of the sides. $\overset{\frown}{PQ}$, $\overset{\frown}{PR}$, and $\overset{\frown}{QR}$ have the vertices of the triangle as their centers. Find the area and the length of the boundary of the region $PQR$.

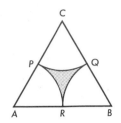

**20.** The area of a square equals the area of a circle with diameter 2. How long is a side of the square?

* **21.** The perimeter of a square is equal to the circumference of a circle. Which has the greater area? Find the ratio of the area of the square to the area of the circle.

* **22.** The square is inscribed in a 90°-sector of radius $r$. Derive a formula for the area of the shaded regions.

* **23.** Each vertex of figure $ABC$ is the center of the opposite arc. The figure has the interesting property that when rolled between two parallel lines which just touch it, it will always touch both lines, just as a circle will. Let the radius of each arc be $r$ and derive a formula for the area of figure $ABC$ and a formula for the perimeter of figure $ABC$.

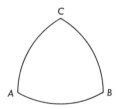

## HONORS PROBLEM

Have you ever seen a drill that can bore a square hole? Such a drill was invented in 1914. It is merely an adaptation of the triangular figure shown in Problem 23 above. The figure is known as the Reuleaux triangle, named after Franz Reuleaux (1829–1905), who was the first person to demonstrate its constant-width properties. You can design a drill to bore a square hole quite easily. Begin in the following way. Out of a piece of heavy cardboard carefully cut a square about 4 in. on a side. The resulting hole will be your trial square hole. Next, on a separate piece of cardboard, construct an equilateral triangle having a side the same length as a side of the square hole. With a compass, and using the triangle's vertices as centers, draw the necessary arcs. Cut out this Reuleaux triangle. You should find that the triangle will rotate in the hole, but that it will always maintain contact with each side of the square hole. Designing the drill is now up to you.

If you are interested in knowing more about curves of constant width, as well as other problems related to them, you should read Martin Gardner's "Mathematical Games" in *Scientific American*, February 1963, p. 148 ff., and the chapter on such curves in *The Enjoyment of Mathematics* by Rademacher and Toeplitz.

# 17 | Solids and Their Volumes

## 17-1. PRISMS

Suppose we have given two parallel planes and a polygonal region in one of them.

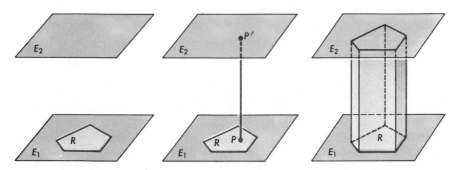

In the figures, the given region is $R$, lying in the plane $E_1$.

At each point $P$ of $R$, we set up a segment $\overline{PP'}$ perpendicular to $E_1$, joining $P$ to a point $P'$ of the second plane. The union of all these segments is called a *right prism*. The region $R$ is called its *lower base*, or simply its *base*. We can think of a right prism as the solid that is swept out as the base moves vertically upward from $E_1$ to $E_2$.

A solid like this is called a *right* prism because the segments that we set up are perpendicular to the plane of the base. We can form prisms of other kinds by setting up our segments in any fixed direction, which may or may not be perpendicular to the plane of the base. We allow this possibility in the following definition.

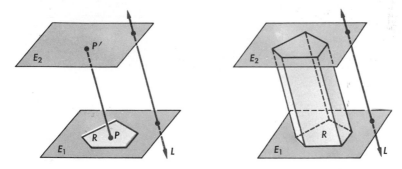

### Definition

Let $E_1$ and $E_2$ be two parallel planes, let $R$ be a polygonal region in $E_1$, and let $L$ be a line which intersects $E_1$ and $E_2$ but not $R$. For each point $P$ of $R$, let $\overline{PP'}$ be the segment which is parallel to $L$ and joins $P$ to a point $P'$ of $E_2$. The union of all the segments $\overline{PP'}$ is called a *prism*.

(Note that in the definition above we can't allow $L$ to intersect $R$, because then no segment through the intersection point would be parallel to $L$.)

**Definitions**

The polygonal region $R$ is called the *lower base*, or simply the *base* of the prism. The part of the prism that lies in $E_2$ is called the *upper base*. The distance between $E_1$ and $E_2$ is called the *altitude*. If $L$ is perpendicular to $E_1$ and $E_2$, then the prism is called a *right* prism.

Note that for right prisms the altitude is the distance $PP'$, but for nonright prisms the altitude is always less than $PP'$.

Prisms are described by their bases: a *triangular prism* is one whose base is a triangular region, and so on.

**Definition**

A *cross section* of a prism is the intersection of the prism with a plane parallel to the plane of the base (provided that this intersection is not empty.)

**Theorem 17–1**

All cross sections of a triangular prism are congruent to the base.

Of course the cross sections and the base are really triangular regions rather than triangles. When we say that they are congruent, we mean that the corresponding triangles are congruent.

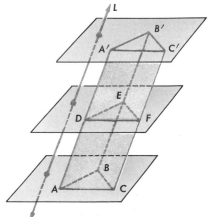

**Proof.** As in the figure, let the base be $\triangle ABC$ plus its interior, and let $D$, $E$, and $F$ be the points where the cross section intersects $\overline{AA'}$, $\overline{BB'}$, and $\overline{CC'}$. Then $\overline{AD} \parallel \overline{FC}$, because both these segments are parallel to $L$. And $\overline{DF} \parallel \overline{AC}$, by Theorem 10–1. Therefore $\square ADFC$ is a parallelogram. Therefore $DF = AC$.

[*Query:* Theorem 10–1 tells us what happens when two parallel planes are intersected by a third plane. Here our two parallel planes are the planes that contain $\triangle ABC$ and $\triangle DEF$. What is the third plane?]

In exactly the same way, we show that $DE = AB$ and $EF = BC$. By SSS we have $\triangle DEF \cong \triangle ABC$, which was to be proved.

### Corollary 17–1.1

The upper and lower bases of a triangular prism are congruent.

This is obvious, because the upper base is a cross section.

### Theorem 17–2.    The Prism Cross-Section Theorem

All cross sections of a prism have the same area.

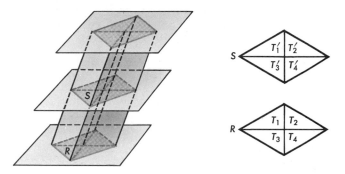

**Proof.**   Let $R$ be the base, and let $S$ be a cross section. Then the area of $R$ is the sum of the areas of a finite set of triangular regions. The area of $S$ is the sum of the areas of the corresponding triangular regions in $S$. Since congruent triangles have the same area, the sum is the same for $R$ and $S$.

### Corollary 17–2.1

The bases of a prism have the same area.

This is because the upper base is a cross section.

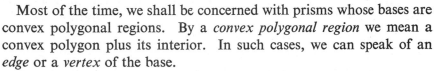

Most of the time, we shall be concerned with prisms whose bases are convex polygonal regions. By a *convex polygonal region* we mean a convex polygon plus its interior. In such cases, we can speak of an *edge* or a *vertex* of the base.

The figure above reminds us of the definition of a prism. In the figure, $A$ and $B$ are vertices of the base, and $\overline{AB}$ is an edge of the base.

The segments $\overline{AA'}$, $\overline{BB'}$ are called *lateral edges* of the prism. The parallelogram region determined by $\square AA'B'B$ is called a *lateral face* of the prism. We restate this in more exact language.

**Definition**

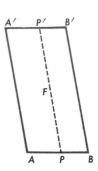

> If $A$ is a vertex of the base of a prism, and $A'$ is the corresponding point of the upper base, then $\overline{AA'}$ is a *lateral edge* of the prism. If $\overline{AB}$ is an edge of the base, and $F$ is the union of all segments $\overline{PP'}$ for which $P$ is in $\overline{AB}$, then $F$ is a *lateral face* of the prism.

**Theorem 17–3**

> The lateral faces of a prism are parallelogram regions.

To prove this, we need to know that $\overline{AA'} \parallel \overline{BB'}$ and $\overline{AB} \parallel \overline{A'B'}$. Reasons?

**Corollary 17–3.1**

> The lateral faces of a right prism are rectangular regions.

Proof? (We know that $L \perp E_1$ and $\overline{AA'} \parallel L$.)

**Definitions**

> The union of the lateral faces of a prism is called its *lateral surface*. The union of its lateral faces and its two bases is called its *total surface*.

**Definitions**

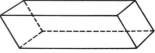

> A *parallelepiped* is a prism whose base is a parallelogram region.
> A *rectangular parallelepiped* is a right rectangular prism.

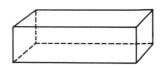

Thus all the faces of a parallelepiped (lateral, top, and bottom) are parallelogram regions. And all the faces of a rectangular parallelepiped are rectangular regions.

**Definition**

> A *cube* is a rectangular parallelepiped all of whose edges are congruent.

## Problem Set 17–1

1. (a) The prism shown here is called a _____
   _____ prism.

   (b) The region $ABCD$ is called _____.

   (c) $\overline{AA'}$ is called _____.

   (d) $\overline{HH'}$ is called _____.

   (e) If $\overline{AA'}$ were perpendicular to the plane
   of the base, then the prism would be
   called _____.

   (f) The parallelogram region $BB'C'C$ is called _____.

   (g) The union of the lateral faces is called _____.

   (h) If $\square ABCD$ were a parallelogram, the prism would be called _____.

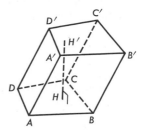

2. The figure on the left below, shows a right prism lying on a lateral face.
   Its bases are trapezoid regions. The lengths of the parallel edges of the
   base are 4 and 9, the lengths of the nonparallel edges are 5 and 6, and
   $BF = 12$. Find the area of the lateral surface of the prism.

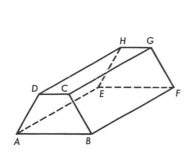
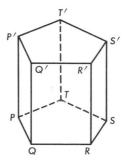

3. The altitude of the right pentagonal prism on the right above is 8 and
   the lengths of the edges of the base are 2, 5, 7, 7, and $8\frac{1}{2}$. Find the area
   of the lateral surface of the prism.

4. A right prism has a lateral edge of 3 and the perimeter of its base is 34.
   What is the area of its lateral surface?

5. Prove that the area, $S$, of the lateral surface of a right prism is given by
   the formula $S = hp$, where $h$ is the altitude of the prism and $p$ is the
   perimeter of the base.

6. Find the altitude of a right prism for which the area of the lateral surface
   is 143 and the perimeter of the base is 13.

7. If a lateral face of a prism is a rectangle, does it follow that all of the lateral faces will be rectangles?

8. The bases of this prism are equilateral triangles and its lateral faces are rectangular regions. Given that the length of an edge of the base is 6 and the altitude of the prism is 10, compute the area of the total surface of the prism.

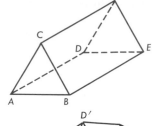

9. Prove that any two nonconsecutive lateral edges of a prism are coplanar and that the intersection of their plane with the prism is a parallelogram region. (First make a restatement in terms of the figure.)

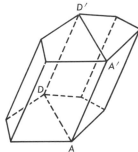

10. What is the area of the lateral surface of a cube with edge 5? What is the area of its total surface?

11. The edges of a cross section of a triangular prism are 3, 6, and $3\sqrt{3}$. How long are the edges of another cross section? What geometric figure will it be? What are the measures of its angles? Compute the area of a cross section of this prism.

12. The diagonal of a cube is $16\sqrt{3}$. Find the area of its total surface.

13. The dimensions of a rectangular parallelepiped are 4, 7, and 12. Compute its total surface area.

* 14. The dimensions of the base of a rectangular parallelepiped are 5 and 8, and its altitude is 12. A hole, extending from upper base to lower base, is in the shape of a right triangular prism whose bases are equilateral triangles having an edge of length 3. Determine the area of the total surface of the figure.

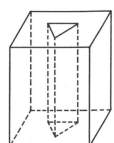

* 15. The base of a parallelepiped is a rectangular region 6 by 15. The end faces are square regions inclined 60° to the base. A plane perpendicular to a longer edge of the base intersects the parallelepiped in a rectangular region. Find the total surface area.

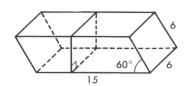

## 17–2.   PYRAMIDS

The pyramid with base $R$ and vertex $V$ is the solid shown below.

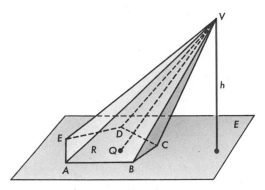

The pyramid is the union of all segments $\overline{VQ}$, where $Q$ is any point of the base.   Thus:

### Definitions

Given a polygonal region $R$ in a plane $E$, and a point $V$ not in $E$. The *pyramid with base $R$ and vertex $V$* is the union of all segments $\overline{VQ}$ for which $Q$ belongs to $R$.   The *altitude* of the pyramid is the (perpendicular) distance from $V$ to $E$.

Horizontal cross sections are defined in the same way for pyramids as for prisms.   That is, a *horizontal cross section* of a pyramid is the intersection of the pyramid with a plane parallel to the plane of the base (providing, as before, that the plane must actually intersect the pyramid).

As a horizontal plane moves upward from the base toward the vertex, it is obvious that the area of the cross section steadily decreases, until it finally becomes zero at the vertex.   In the following theorem, we obtain a formula which tells us exactly *how* the cross-sectional area changes when the base is triangular.

### Theorem 17–4

Every cross section of a triangular pyramid, between the base and the vertex, is a triangular region similar to the base.   If $h$ is the altitude, and $k$ is the distance from the vertex to the cross section, then the area of the cross section is equal to $k^2/h^2$ times the area of the base.

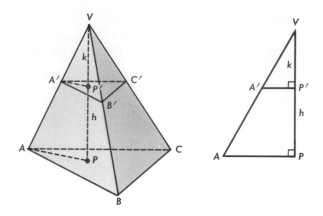

The notation of the proof is that of the figure. The base is the region determined by $\triangle ABC$. The triangle $\triangle A'B'C'$ is the corresponding triangle in the cross section. The segment $\overline{VP}$ is the perpendicular from $V$ to the plane of the base, with $VP = h$; and $\overline{VP'}$ is the perpendicular from $V$ to the plane of the cross section, with $\overline{VP'} = k$. The figure on the right shows $\triangle VAP$ and $\triangle VA'P'$ in their own plane. Note that $\angle P$ and $\angle P'$ (that is, $\angle VP'A'$) really are right angles, because $\overleftrightarrow{VP}$ is perpendicular to both of our two horizontal planes.

**Proof.**    The main steps are as follows.

$$(1)\quad \triangle VA'P' \sim \triangle VAP.$$

Since $\angle P$ and $\angle P'$ are right angles, and $\angle V \cong \angle V$, the similarity follows from the AA Corollary.

$$(2)\quad \frac{VA'}{VA} = \frac{k}{h},$$

because these are lengths of corresponding sides.
    In exactly the same way, using $\triangle VP'B'$ and $\triangle VPB$, we can show that

$$(3)\quad \frac{VB'}{VB} = \frac{k}{h}.$$

By the SAS Similarity Theorem, we get

$$(4)\quad \triangle VA'B' \sim \triangle VAB.$$

Therefore

$$(5)\quad \frac{A'B'}{AB} = \frac{VA'}{VA} = \frac{k}{h}.$$

In this situation, there is nothing special about $\overline{AB}$ in the base and $\overline{A'B'}$ in the cross section; the edges $\overline{BC}$ and $\overline{B'C'}$ are related in the same way. Therefore we have

$$(6) \qquad \frac{B'C'}{BC} = \frac{k}{h},$$

and

$$(7) \qquad \frac{A'C'}{AC} = \frac{k}{h}.$$

By the SSS Similarity Theorem 12–6, we have

$$(8) \quad \triangle A'B'C' \sim \triangle ABC.$$

This proves half of our theorem. The other half now follows from Theorem 12–9, because the ratio of each pair of corresponding sides is $k/h$.

It isn't just for triangular pyramids that cross-sectional areas behave in this way; no matter what the shape of the base may be, the ratio is always $k^2/h^2$, as before.

**Theorem 17–5**

In any pyramid, the ratio of the area of a cross section to the area of the base is $k^2/h^2$, where $h$ is the altitude of the pyramid and $k$ is the distance from the vertex to the plane of the cross section.

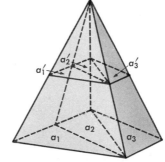

**Proof.** We cut up the base into little triangular regions $T_1, T_2, \ldots,$ $T_n$, as in the definition of a polygonal region. Let their areas be $a_1, a_2, \ldots, a_n$. In the figure we show the case $n = 3$. Let the areas of the corresponding triangular regions in the cross section be $a'_1, a'_2, \ldots, a'_n$. Then the area of the base is

$$A = a_1 + a_2 + \cdots + a_n,$$

and the area of the cross section is

$$A_k = a'_1 + a'_2 + \cdots + a'_n.$$

By the preceding theorem,

$$a'_1 = \frac{k^2}{h^2} a_1, \quad a'_2 = \frac{k^2}{h^2} a_2, \quad \ldots, \quad a'_n = \frac{k^2}{h^2} a_n.$$

Therefore

$$A_k = \frac{k^2}{h^2} (a_1 + a_2 + \cdots + a_2) = \frac{k^2}{h^2} A,$$

which was to be proved.

This theorem in turn enables us to prove the following.

### Theorem 17–6.   The Pyramid Cross-Section Theorem

If two pyramids have the same base area and the same altitude, then cross sections equidistant from the vertices have the same area.

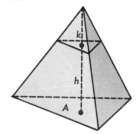
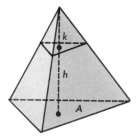

In the figure we show triangular pyramids, merely for the sake of simplicity.  But the proof is not restricted to this case, and neither is the theorem.

**Proof.**   As indicated in the figure, let the base area of each pyramid be $A$; let $h$ be the altitude of each, and let $k$ be the distance from each cross section to the vertex.   Then the cross-sectional areas are the same, because each of them is equal to $(k^2/h^2)A$.

## Problem Set 17–2

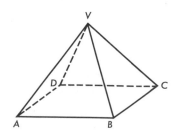

**1.** Like prisms, pyramids are named by the shapes of their bases.  This is a sketch of a rectangular pyramid.  Make sketches of triangular pyramids and square pyramids.

**2.** What is another name for a triangular pyramid?  (See Chapter 3.)

**3.** Make formal definitions for *lateral edge* and *lateral face* of a pyramid.

4. In pyramid $V$-$ABC$, $\triangle ABC$ is equilateral. A plane parallel to the base intersects the lateral edges in $D$, $E$, and $F$ such that $VE = \frac{1}{2}EB$.

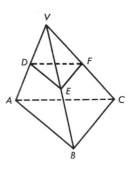

(a) What is $\dfrac{DV}{AV}$ ?

(b) What can you assert about $\triangle DEV$ and $\triangle ABV$? about $\triangle ABC$ and $\triangle DEF$?

(c) What is $\dfrac{DE}{AB}$ ?

(d) If $BC = 6$, what is $a\triangle DEF$?

5. The altitude of a square pyramid is 10 and a side of the base is 15. Find the area of a cross section at a distance 6 from the vertex.

6. The area of the base of a pentagonal pyramid is 72 sq. in. The altitude of the pyramid is 12 in. What is the area of a cross section 4 in. from the base?

7. A cross section of area 108 sq. in. is 9 in. from the vertex of a pyramid whose base has an area of 180 sq. in. Find the altitude of the pyramid.

8.

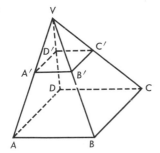
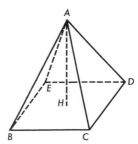

The two pyramids shown here, with the square pyramid on the left, have equal altitudes. Their bases are coplanar and the cross sections are coplanar. Given that $AB = 2\sqrt{6}$, $A'B' = 3\sqrt{2}$, and the area of the polygonal region $SUVWXYZ$ is 24, find the area of the cross section of the pyramid on the right.

9. A pyramid whose base is a regular polygon and whose vertex is equidistant from each vertex of the base is called a *regular pyramid*.

Prove that the altitude from the vertex of a regular pyramid to its base intersects the base at its circumcenter (that is, at a point equidistant from each vertex of the base).

**10.** One edge of the base of a regular square pyramid is 10 in. long, and the altitude of the pyramid is 12 in. Find the area of the lateral surface of the pyramid.

**11.** Prove that the lateral faces of a regular pyramid are bounded by congruent isosceles triangles.

**12.** The altitude of each lateral face of a regular pyramid is called the *slant height* of the pyramid. Show that the area of the lateral surface is one-half the product of the slant height and the perimeter of the base.

**13.** Find the area of the total surface of a regular pyramid whose altitude is 15 and whose base is a square with side 16.

**\* 14.** Find the total surface area of a regular hexagonal pyramid given that an edge of the base is 8 and the altitude of the pyramid is 12.

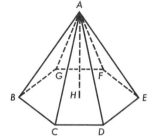

**+ 15.** Given any triangular pyramid *ABCD*. Describe a plane whose intersection with the pyramid is a parallelogram region.

### HONORS PROBLEM

Given a regular tetrahedron (a triangular pyramid) with an edge of 8. Find the area of a cross section that contains the point of concurrency of the four altitudes of the pyramid.

## 17–3. VOLUMES OF PRISMS AND PYRAMIDS. CAVALIERI'S PRINCIPLE

We shall now learn how to find the volumes of various solids. This process will involve many of the same ideas that we used in finding areas of polygonal regions. Our discussion, however, will be more informal than that in Chapter 11 and will not include a complete set of postulates adequate to justify everything we do, a step at a time. We shall, however, state the two main postulates which we use in getting numerical answers.

You remember that in Chapter 11 we took the area formula $A = e^2$ for squares, as a postulate, and then used a trick to get the area formula $A = bh$ for rectangles. For volumes of solids, our trick won't work, and so we use a stronger unit postulate.

**POSTULATE 23.**   The Unit Postulate

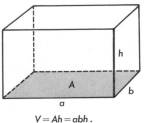

*The volume of a rectangular parallele-piped is the product of the altitude and the area of the base.*

$V = Ah = abh$.

Of course, any face of a rectangular parallelepiped can be regarded as the base. We always get the same answer for the volume, because in each case $Ah$ is the product of the lengths of any three edges with a common end point.

To understand what is happening in our next postulate, let us first think of a physical model. We can make an approximate model of a square pyramid by forming a stack of thin square cards, cut to the proper size:

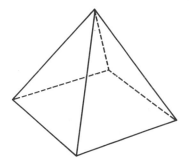
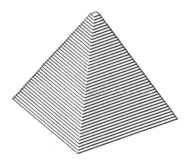

The figure on the left represents the exact pyramid, and the figure on the right is the approximate model made from cards.

Now suppose we drill a narrow hole in the model, from the top to some point of the base, and insert a thin rod so that it passes through every card in the model. We can then tilt the rod in any direction we want, keeping its bottom end fixed on the base. The shape of the model then changes, but its volume does not change. The reason is that its volume is simply the total volume of the cards, and this total volume does not change as the cards slide along each other.

The same principle applies more generally. Suppose we have two solids with bases in the same plane. We shall think of this plane as being horizontal. If all horizontal cross sections of the two solids at the same level have the same area, then the two solids have the same volume.

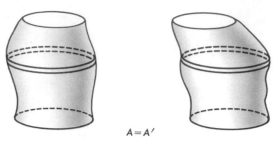

$$A = A'$$

This is true for the following reason. Let us again make a card model of each of the solids. Then each card in the first model has exactly the same volume as the corresponding card in the second model. By using very thin cards, we can make card models that are very close approximations to the given solids. In fact, we can make the approximation as close as we please, by using sufficiently thin cards. Therefore the volumes of the two solids with which we started are the same.

The principle involved here is called *Cavalieri's Principle*. We surely haven't proved it; we have merely been explaining why it is plausible. We therefore state it in the form of a postulate.

**POSTULATE 24.   Cavalieri's Principle**

*Given two solids and a plane. Suppose that every plane parallel to the given plane, intersecting one of the two solids, also intersects the other, and gives cross sections with the same area. Then the two solids have the same volume.*

Cavalieri's Principle is the key to the calculation of volumes, as we shall soon see.

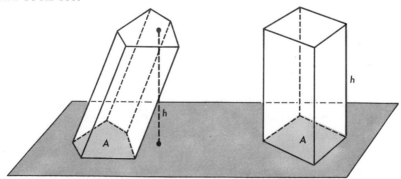

Figure for Theorem 17–7

### Theorem 17–7

The volume of any prism is the product of the altitude and the area of the base.

**Proof.** Let $h$ and $A$ be the altitude and the base area of the given prism. Consider a rectangular parallelepiped with the same altitude $h$ and base area $A$, and with its base in the same plane as the base of the given prism. We know by the Prism Cross-Section Theorem that all cross sections, for both prisms, have the same area $A$. By Cavalieri's Principle, this means that they have the same volume. Since the volume of the rectangular parallelepiped is $Ah$ by Postulate 23, the theorem follows.

### Theorem 17–8

If two pyramids have the same altitude and the same base area, and their bases lie in the same plane, then they have the same volume.

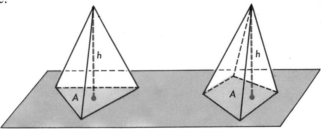

**Proof.** By the Pyramid Cross-Section Theorem, corresponding cross sections of the two pyramids have the same area. By Cavalieri's Principle, this means that the volumes are the same.

### Theorem 17–9

The volume of a triangular pyramid is one-third the product of its altitude and its base area.

**Proof.** Given a triangular pyramid, we form a triangular prism with the same base and altitude.

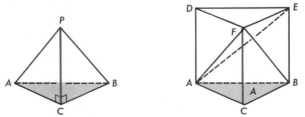

(We are free to use a *right* triangular prism, as in the figure. It doesn't matter, one way or the other.)

We now cut up our prism into three pyramids, as shown above on the right. We name these by naming their vertices, in any order. Thus our three new pyramids are *ADEF*, *ABEF*, and *AFBC*. Drawn separately, they look like this:

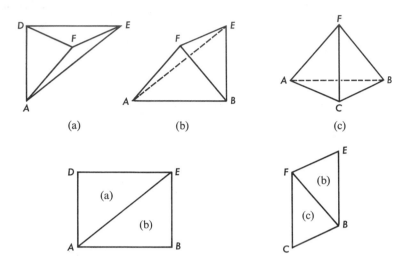

(1) *ADEF and ABEF have the same volume.*

> **Proof.** We can regard *F* as the vertex of each of the pyramids. Their bases are then the triangular regions determined by △*ADE* and △*ABE*. Since these triangles are congruent, we know that *ADEF* and *ABEF* have the same base area; and they have the same altitude, because the altitude of each of them is the distance from *F* to the plane that contains their bases. Therefore they have the same volume.

(2) *ABEF and AFBC have the same volume.*

> **Proof.** We can regard *A* as the vertex of each of the pyramids. Their bases are then the triangular regions determined by △*BEF* and △*FBC*. Since these triangles are congruent, we know that *ABEF* and *AFBC* have the same base area. And they have the same altitude, because the altitude of each of them is the distance from *A* to the plane that contains their bases. Therefore they have the same volume.

(3) *AFBC and the original pyramid PABC have the same volume.* (The proof is obvious: they have the same base and the same altitude.)

We are now almost done.  Let $a$ be the area of $\triangle ABC$, and let $h$ be the altitude of $PABC$.  Then the volume of our prism is $ah$.  If $V$ is the volume of each of our pyramids, then $3V = ah$.  Therefore

$$V = \tfrac{1}{3}ah,$$

which was to be proved.

The same result holds for pyramids in general.

### Theorem 17–10

The volume of a pyramid is one-third the product of its altitude and its base area.

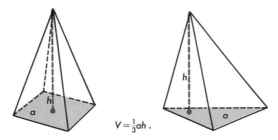

$V = \tfrac{1}{3}ah$ .

**Proof.**  Given a pyramid of altitude $h$ and base area $a$.  Take a triangular pyramid of the same altitude and base area, with its base in the same plane.  By the Pyramid Cross-Section Theorem, cross sections at the same level have the same area.  Therefore, by Cavalieri's Principle, the two pyramids have the same volume.  Therefore the volume of each of them is $\tfrac{1}{3}ah$, which was to be proved.

## Problem Set 17–3

1. The altitude of a rectangular parallelepiped is 7, and the dimensions of the base are 4 and 5.  Find its volume.

2. A rectangular metal can, 1 ft by 1 ft by 1 ft, is filled with water.  Given that 1 gallon of liquid has a volume of 231 cu. in., how many gallons of water does the can hold?

3. Certain silver ingots are cast in the shape of a right prism whose base (the end of the ingot) is a trapezoid.  The bases of the trapezoid are 3 in. and 4 in., and the height of the ingot is 2 in.  The length of the ingot is 1 ft. If the silver weighs 6 oz per cu. in., how much does one ingot weigh?

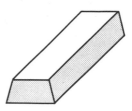

**4.** A lump of metal is submerged in a rectangular water tank 20 in. by 15 in., raising the level of the water 0.35 in. What is the volume of the metal?

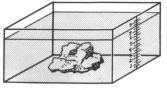

**5.** To calculate the cost of providing air-conditioning for a proposed construction project, a contractor has to compute the volume of air contained in a rectangular building as outlined in the figure. The building is 130 ft long and 42 ft wide. On both sides of the building the eaves are $9\frac{1}{2}$ ft high, and the highest point of the roof is 15 ft. Find the volume of the building.

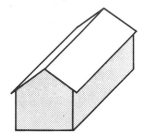

**6.** A right rectangular prism has an altitude of 18 in. and a base which measures 6 in. by 8 in. A plane determined by a diagonal of the base and a vertex of the upper base forms a pyramid with the faces of the prism. Find the volume of the pyramid.

**7.** Find the volume of a regular square pyramid whose altitude is 12 and whose base has an edge of 12. Also find the area of its lateral surface.

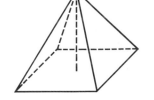

**8.** Derive a formula for the volume of a regular square pyramid whose lateral faces are equilateral triangles of side $s$.

**9.** If two regular square pyramids whose lateral faces are equilateral triangles are placed base to base, the resulting 8-sided solid is called a *regular octahedron*. Prove that the volume, $V$, of the regular octahedron whose edge is $e$ is given by the formula $V = \frac{1}{3}\sqrt{2}e^3$.

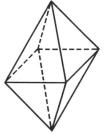

**10.** Compute the volume and the total surface area of a regular octahedron of edge 3.

**+ 11.** Prove that the volume of a regular octahedron is given by $V = \frac{1}{6}d_1d_2d_3$, where $d_1$, $d_2$, and $d_3$ are the lengths of its diagonals.

**12.** A cross section of a pyramid forms a small pyramid whose volume is 2 and whose altitude is 1. The volume of the large pyramid is 54. What is the altitude of this pyramid?

13. Pyramid *P-ABCDE* is pentagonal, and the area of its base is 64. Altitude *PF* equals 12. *V*, *W*, *X*, *Y*, and *Z* are midpoints of the lateral edges, as shown in the figure. Find the area of the cross section *VWXYZ*. (Why is it a cross section?) Find the volume of the smaller pyramid. What is the ratio of the volumes of the two pyramids?

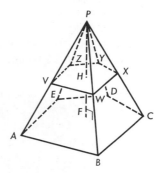

14. The part of a pyramid bounded by the base, a cross section, and the trapezoid regions of the lateral faces is called a *frustum* of a pyramid. In the figure for Problem 13, the vertices of the frustum are *A*, *B*, *C*, *D*, *E*, *V*, *W*, *X*, *Y*, and *Z*. Find the volume of this frustum.

\* 15. The area of a cross section of a pyramid is 20, and the area of the base of the pyramid is 45. If the altitude of the pyramid is 6, how far from the vertex is the cross section? What is the ratio of the volumes of the two pyramids?

\* 16. A plane parallel to the base of a regular square pyramid intersects the altitude at a point three-fourths the distance from the vertex to the base. The altitude of the pyramid is 16, and the edge of the base is 24. Find the area of the lateral surface of the frustum and the volume of the frustum.

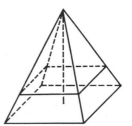

## HONORS PROBLEM

Show that the volume of a frustum is given by the formula

$$V = \tfrac{1}{3}h(B + B' + \sqrt{BB'}),$$

where *B* and *B'* are the areas of the bases and *h* is the altitude of the frustum.

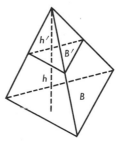

*Hint:* Let *h'* be the altitude of the small pyramid. Get the volumes of the two pyramids. Note that

$$\frac{h + h'}{h'} = \frac{\sqrt{B}}{\sqrt{B'}}$$

so that

$$\frac{h}{h'} = \frac{\sqrt{B} - \sqrt{B'}}{\sqrt{B'}} \quad \text{and} \quad h' = \frac{h\sqrt{B'}}{\sqrt{B} - \sqrt{B'}}.$$

ARCHIMEDES (287–212 B.C.)

Archimedes is generally regarded as the greatest mathematician of antiquity, and one of the three or four greatest of all time. He was the first man to determine the volume of a sphere. He made a very accurate computation of $\pi$. And the methods that he devised for solving area and volume problems placed him many centuries ahead of his time. He was able to calculate the areas of regions bounded by very complicated curves; and his achievements in this kind of geometry stood almost alone for eighteen hundred years. The next major step forward in the computation of areas and volumes was the discovery of the calculus, by Newton and Leibniz, in the seventeenth century.

Unlike most of the Greek mathematicians, Archimedes was interested in applications. Legend has it that when the Romans attacked his native city of Syracuse, in Sicily, he played a leading part in the city's defense, terrorizing the invaders with weapons of his own invention. He is said to have bombarded the Roman ships with large stones, fired from the biggest catapults that anybody has ever seen. It is also reported that he set the Roman fleet on fire, using mirrors to focus the concentrated rays of the sun on the ships. When the attack settled down into a siege, Archimedes could no longer help; he returned to his study, and went back to work on mathematics.

He died on the job. When the Romans finally captured Syracuse, a soldier found him in his house, drawing geometric figures in the sand on the floor. "*Don't disturb my circles!*" said Archimedes. These turned out to be his last words. The Roman general had given orders that Archimedes was not to be harmed. But nobody knows whether the soldier knew or cared who his victim was.

## 17–4. CYLINDERS AND CONES

If you remember how we formed a prism with a given polygonal region as base, you will see that the same process works just as well for bases which are not polygonal regions. Suppose, for example, that we start with two parallel planes $E_1$ and $E_2$, as before, but use a *circular* region in $E_1$ as base.

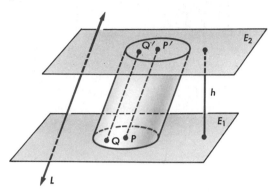

Exactly as before, we use a line $L$, intersecting $E_1$ and $E_2$ but not the base. And we form the union of all segments $\overline{QQ'}$, where $Q$ is in the base, $Q'$ is in $E_2$, and $\overline{QQ'} \parallel L$. The resulting solid is called a *circular cylinder*. There is no need to repeat the definitions of the altitude, cross sections, and so on, because these are exactly the same as the corresponding definitions for prisms. If $L \perp E_1$, then the cylinder is called a *right* cylinder.

Of course, you can get other kinds of cylinders by using other figures as bases. The circular cylinders, however, are the only ones that will be discussed in this book.

Similarly, the scheme that we used to form a pyramid can be used equally well when the base is not a polygonal region. If we use a circular region as base, the resulting solid is called a *circular cone*.

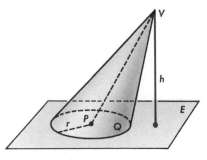

Using the definition of a pyramid as your model, you should not have any trouble writing the definition of a circular cone.

The following theorems on cylinders and cones are analogous to the corresponding theorems on prisms and pyramids. Their proofs are also very similar: the point is that the shape of the base never mattered very much in the first place. We therefore omit the details.

### Theorem 17–11

Every cross section of a circular cylinder is a circular region congruent to the base.

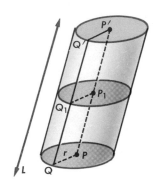

The proof is based on the fact that $P_1Q_1 = PQ = r$; this is true because $\overline{PQ}$ and $\overline{P_1Q_1}$ are opposite sides of the parallelogram $\square QQ_1P_1P$.

### Theorem 17–12

Every cross section of a circular cylinder has the same area as the base.

The next theorem is slightly more difficult.

### Theorem 17–13

Given a cone of altitude $h$, and a cross section made by a plane at a distance $k$ from the vertex. The area of the cross section is equal to $k^2/h^2$ times the area of the base.

In the notation of the figure on the following page, the main steps in the proof are as follows:

(1) $\triangle VPT \sim \triangle VP'T'$,

(2) $\dfrac{VP'}{VP} = \dfrac{VT'}{VT} = \dfrac{k}{h}$,

(3) $\triangle VP'Q' \sim \triangle VPQ$,

(4) $\dfrac{P'Q'}{PQ} = \dfrac{VP'}{VP} = \dfrac{k}{h}$    and    $P'Q' = \dfrac{k}{h}PQ$.

Thus, if $Q$ is on the circle with center $P$ and radius $r$ in the base, then $Q'$ is on the circle with center $P'$ and radius

$$r' = \frac{k}{h}PQ = \frac{k}{h}r$$

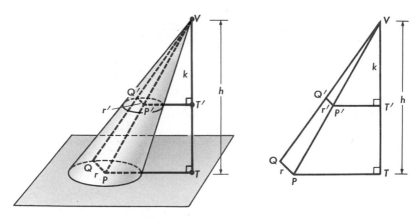

in the cross section.   Therefore the cross section is a circular region
of radius $r'$, and its area is

$$\pi \frac{k^2}{h^2} r^2 .$$

This is equal to $k^2/h^2$ times the area of the base.

We can now calculate the volumes of cylinders and cones, using
Cavalieri's Principle in the same way as we did for prisms and pyramids.

### Theorem 17–14

The volume of a circular cylinder is the product of its altitude
and the area of its base.

The proof is like that of Theorem 17–7.

### Theorem 17–15

The volume of a circular cone is one-third the product of its
altitude and the area of its base.

The proof is like that of Theorem 17–10.

## Problem Set 17–4

**1.** The base of a cylinder is a circular region of diameter 8.   The altitude of
the cylinder is also 8.   What is the volume of the cylinder?

**2.** A drainage tile is a cylindrical shell 21 in. long.   The inside and outside
diameters are 4.5 and 5.1 in.   Find the volume of clay needed to make
the tile.   (Use $3\frac{1}{7}$ for $\pi$.)

**3.**

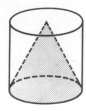 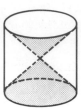

The two cylinders in the figure are identical. Compare the volume of the inscribed cone on the left with the volume of the two cones ("hour-glass" figure) on the right.

**4.** How long must a 1 in. (inside diameter) pipe be to hold one gallon of water? (The volume of one gallon is 231 cu. in. Use $3\frac{1}{7}$ for $\pi$.)

**5.** Find the volume of a circular cone whose altitude is 12 and whose base has a radius equal to 3.2.

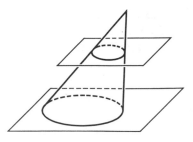

**6.** This figure represents a *right circular cone*. Define a right circular cone. Determine its altitude when its volume is $48\pi$ and the diameter of its base is 8.

**7.** A conical tank is $10\frac{1}{2}$ ft deep and its circular top has a radius of 5 ft. How many gallons of liquid will it hold? (1 cu. ft. will contain 7.48 gallons.)

**8.** In a cone the altitude is 9. A plane parallel to the plane of the base intersects the cone, cutting off a smaller cone at the top. The distance between the planes is 5.

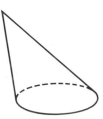

   (a) What is the ratio of the altitudes of the two cones?
   (b) What is the ratio of the radii of the bases of the cones?
   (c) What is the ratio of the areas of the bases?
   (d) What is the ratio of the volumes of the two cones?

9. The altitude of a cone is 5 in. A plane 2 in. from the vertex of the cone is parallel to the base of the cone. If the volume of the smaller cone is 24 cu. in., what is the volume of the larger cone?

10. A square pyramid is inscribed in a circular cone such that they have the same vertex and the base of the pyramid is inscribed in the base of the cone. The common altitude is 18 and a side of the square is 15. Find the volume of each.

11. A storage bin is shaped as in the figure. The radius of the cylindrical top is 7 ft. The over-all height of the bin is 26 ft and the altitude of the conical section is 12 ft. Find the capacity of the bin in bushels. (1 bushel has a volume of approximately 1.25 cu. ft.)

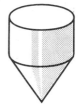

12. A conical surface stands inside a cylindrical surface. The base of the cone is the base of the cylinder, and the vertex of the cone lies in the upper base of the cylinder. Write a formula for the volume of the space bounded by the two surfaces and the upper base in terms of *r*, the radius of the base, and *h*, the altitude of the cylinder.

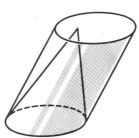

* 13. A plane intersects the figure of Problem 12 midway between the bases and parallel to them. Make a sketch of a top view of the intersection. If the radius of the cylinder is 4, what is the area of the intersection of the plane with the space between the two surfaces?

14. In the figure the right circular conical surface is inscribed in the right circular cylinder. Plane *E* is parallel to the base of the cylinder 14 inches above the base. The altitude of the cone is 21 inches and the radius of the base is 6 inches. Find the area of the intersection of plane *E* with the space between the two surfaces.

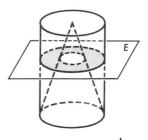

+ 15. A frustum of a cone has an altitude of 8 and the radii of its upper and lower bases are 4 and 6. What is its volume? (See Problem 14 of Problem Set 17–3.)

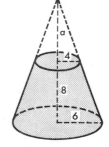

## 17–5.   THE VOLUME AND THE SURFACE AREA OF A SPHERE

By the volume of a sphere we mean, of course, the volume of the solid which is the union of the sphere and its interior.

So far, in our calculation of volumes, our best weapon has been Cavalieri's Principle.  To use the Principle for the problem of the sphere, we shall need to find another solid with the same cross-sectional areas at every level.  Therefore our first step should be to find the areas of the cross sections of our sphere.  This is easy.  Given a sphere of radius $r$, the horizontal cross sections are circular regions. If the cross section is at a distance $s$ from the center, and its radius is $t$, then we know by the Pythagorean Theorem that

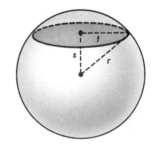

$$t^2 = r^2 - s^2.$$

Therefore the area of the cross section at distance $s$ is

$$A_s = \pi t^2$$
$$= \pi(r^2 - s^2)$$
$$= \pi r^2 - \pi s^2.$$

This last formula has a geometric meaning: it is the area of the ring-shaped region lying inside a circle of radius $r$ and outside a circle of radius $s$, as shown on the right. A figure such as this is called an *annulus* (which is simply the Latin word for *ring*).

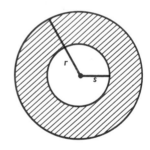

$$A = \pi r^2 - \pi s^2.$$

We shall now form a solid that has regions like this as its cross sections.

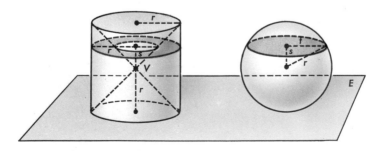

We take a horizontal plane $E$, tangent to the sphere. In this plane we take a circular region of radius $r$. Using this as base, we form a right circular cylinder of altitude $2r$. Let $V$ be the mid-point of the axis of the cylinder, that is, of the vertical segment joining the centers of the bases. We form two cones with $V$ as vertex, and with the top and bottom of the cylinder as bases.

The solid lying inside the cylinder and outside the cones is a solid of the sort we were looking for: each of its cross sections is an annulus, and the cross sections at distance $s$ from $V$ have area $\pi(r^2 - s^2)$. Therefore the volume of this solid is the same as the volume of the sphere.

But the volume of the new solid is easily calculated: it is equal to the volume of the cylinder minus the volumes of the cones. This gives

$$\pi r^2 \cdot 2r - 2 \cdot \tfrac{1}{3}\pi r^2 r$$
$$= 2\pi r^3 - \tfrac{2}{3}\pi r^3$$
$$= \tfrac{4}{3}\pi r^3.$$

Thus we have proved the following theorem.

### Theorem 17–16

The volume of a sphere of radius $r$ is $\tfrac{4}{3}\pi r^3$.

There is a trick which enables us to use this result to find the area of the sphere itself, that is, of the surface. Given a sphere of radius $r$, we form a slightly larger sphere of radius $r + h$. The solid lying between the two spheres is called a *spherical shell*, and looks like the figure below. Let the surface area of the sphere be $A$, and let the volume of the shell be $V$. Then $V$ is approximately $Ah$, and if $h$ is small, the approximation is good. (For example, if you had a round ball of radius one foot, and painted it with a very thin coat of paint, say, one-hundredth of an inch thick, then the total volume of the paint you used would be about $\tfrac{1}{100}A$.) Thus $V/h$ is approximately $A$ when $h$ is small. And as $h \to 0$, we have

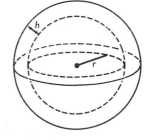

$$\frac{V}{h} \to A.$$

But we can calculate $V/h$ exactly, and see what it approaches as $h \to 0$. Now $V$ is the difference of the volumes of the two spheres.

Therefore

$$V = \tfrac{4}{3}\pi(r + h)^3 - \tfrac{4}{3}\pi r^3$$
$$= \tfrac{4}{3}\pi[(r + h)^3 - r^3]$$
$$= \tfrac{4}{3}\pi[r^3 + 3r^2h + 3rh^2 + h^3 - r^3]$$
$$= \tfrac{4}{3}\pi[3r^2h + 3rh^2 + h^3].$$

[You should check that $(r + h)^3$ really is equal to $r^3 + 3r^2h + 3rh^2 + h^3$.] Therefore

$$\frac{V}{h} = \tfrac{4}{3}\pi(3r^2 + 3rh + h^2)$$
$$= 4\pi r^2 + h(4\pi r + \tfrac{4}{3}\pi h).$$

As $h \to 0$, the entire second term approaches zero. Therefore

$$\frac{V}{h} \to 4\pi r^2.$$

Since we also know that

$$\frac{V}{h} \to A,$$

it follows that

$$A = 4\pi r^2.$$

Thus we have proved the following theorem.

**Theorem 17–17**

The surface area of a sphere of radius $r$ is

$$A = 4\pi r^2.$$

Note the rather interesting fact that the area of the sphere is exactly four times the area of a cross section through the center.

## Problem Set 17–5

**1.** Find the surface-area and the volume of a sphere whose radius equals 4.

**2.** In a sphere of diameter 4 which is greater, its surface-area or its volume?

**3.** In a sphere of diameter 10 which is greater, its surface-area or its volume?

**4.** What is the diameter of a sphere for which its volume is equal to its surface-area?

**5.** A spherical storage tank has a radius of 7 ft. How many gallons will it hold? (Use $3\frac{1}{7}$ for $\pi$.)

**6.** An ice cream cone is 5 inches deep and 2 inches across at the top. Two hemispherical scoops of ice cream, also of diameter 2 inches, are placed on top of the cone. If the ice cream is allowed to melt into the cone, will it overflow?

**7.** A large storage building is in the shape of a hemisphere. If it took 13 gallons of paint to cover the floor, how many gallons can one expect to need to paint the exterior of the building?

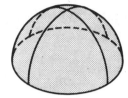

**8.** The volumes of a sphere and a circular cylinder are equal and the diameter of the sphere equals the diameter of a base of the cylinder. Determine the altitude of the cylinder in terms of the diameter of the sphere.

**9.** The diameter of a certain sphere is equal to the radius of a second sphere.

(a) What is the ratio of their radii?

(b) What is the ratio of their surface-areas?

(c) What is the ratio of their volumes?

**10.** The diameter of a certain sphere is one-third the radius of a second sphere. Answer the questions of Problem 9 for these spheres.

**11.** Archimedes (287–212 B.C.) showed that the volume of a sphere is two-thirds the volume of the smallest right circular cylinder that can contain it. Verify this.

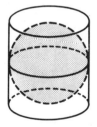

**12.** The moon's diameter is approximately one-fourth the diameter of the earth. Compare the volumes of the moon and the earth.

**13.** About three-fourths of the earth's surface is covered with water. How many millions of square miles of the earth's surface are land? (Use 8000 mi as the diameter and 3.14 as an approximation of $\pi$.)

**14.** In the figure, the sphere is inscribed in the right circular cone. $\overline{AB}$ is a diameter of the base and $C$ is the vertex of the cone. $\triangle ABC$ is equilateral. Find the volume of the cone in terms of $r$, the radius of the sphere.

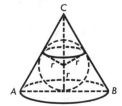

\* **15.** The volume of one sphere is one-half the volume of another sphere. What is the ratio of their radii?

\* **16.** The city engineer, who was 6 feet tall, walked up to inspect the new spherical water tank. His head just touched the tank when he stood at a place 18 feet from the point where the tank rested on the ground. Knowing that the city used 10,000 gallons of water per hour, he immediately figured how many hours a full tank should last. How did he do it and what was his result?

\*+ **17.** Using the method by which the formula for the surface-area of a sphere was derived (Theorem 17–17), show that the area of the lateral surface of a right circular cylinder is $2\pi ra$, where $r$ is the radius of a base and $a$ is the altitude.

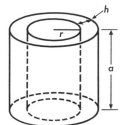

## HONORS  PROBLEM

A sphere and a right circular cylinder have equal volumes. The radius of the sphere equals the radius of the base of the cylinder. Compare the surface-area of the sphere with the area of the total surface of the cylinder.

## Chapter Review

**1.** Without looking back through the chapter try to write down and identify all of the formulas for area and volume covered in this chapter.

**2.** Complete each sentence with the appropriate terms:
   (a) The bases of every prism are _____ and _____.
   (b) The lateral faces of a prism are _____ regions.
   (c) The lateral surface of a prism is the _____ of the _____ of the prism.
   (d) If the base of a prism is a parallelogram, the prism is called a _____.
   (e) If two triangular pyramids have congruent bases, the volumes of the pyramids are proportional to the _____.

**3.** Complete each sentence with the appropriate terms:
   (a) In a right prism, each lateral edge is _____ to the base.
   (b) A cross-section of a pyramid is the _____ of the pyramid and a plane _____ to the base.

(c) The areas of two cross-sections of a pyramid are proportional to the _____ of their _____ from the vertex of the _____ .

(d) If a cone and a cylinder have congruent bases and equal altitudes, the volume of the cylinder is _____ the volume of the cone.

(e) The volumes of two spheres are proportional to the _____ of their radii and the surface-areas are proportional to the _____ of their radii.

4. The base of a right prism is a regular hexagonal region. An edge of the base is 2 in. long and a lateral edge of the prism is 7 in. long. Find the area of the lateral surface of the prism. Find the area of a cross-section 5 in. above the base.

5. Two jars of the same brand of strawberry jam stand on a shelf in a supermarket. The taller jar is twice the height of the other jar, but its diameter is one-half as much as the diameter of the shorter jar. The taller jar costs 23 cents and the shorter jar costs 43 cents. Which is the better buy?

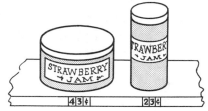

6. What is the volume of a cone if the altitude is 6 and the diameter of the base is 10?

7. The volume of a square pyramid is 384 cu. in. and its altitude is 8 in. How long is an edge of the base? What is the area of the lateral surface of the pyramid? (Assume that the projection of the vertex is the center of the base.)

8. The bases of a hemisphere and a cone are congruent circles and are coplanar. A plane through the vertex of the cone is parallel to the plane of the bases and is tangent to the hemisphere. What is the ratio of the volume of the cone to the volume of the hemisphere?

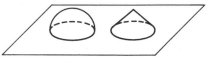

9. The base of a tetrahedron is a triangle whose sides have lengths 10, 24, and 26. The altitude of the tetrahedron is 20. Find the area of a cross section whose distance from the base is 15.

10. Given that the diameter of a sphere is 18, find its volume and surface-area.

11. The volume of a cone is 400 cu. in. and the radius of its base is 5 in. Find its altitude.

12. A spherical ball of radius 3 in. has a hollow center of radius 2 in. What is the volume of the shell?

13. Prove that the volume of a sphere is given by the formula $\frac{1}{6}\pi d^3$, where $d$ is the diameter.

14. The volume of a pyramid whose altitude is 12 in. is 432 cu. in. Find the area of a cross-section 3 in. above the base.

15. Given two cones. The altitude of the first is one-half that of the second and the radius of the base of the first is one-half that of the second. Compare their volumes.

16. A sphere is inscribed in a right circular cylinder, such that it is tangent to both bases. What is the ratio of the volume of the sphere to the volume of the cylinder?

17. A cylindrical can with radius 12 in. and height 25 in. is filled with water. A sphere of diameter 20 in. is submerged in the can of water and then removed. What volume of water remains in the can?

* 18. A rectangular parallelepiped whose base is 12 by 20 is inscribed in a sphere of diameter 25. Find the volume of the part of the sphere outside the parallelepiped.

* 19. The base of a right circular cone has a diameter of 12 in. and the altitude of the cone is 12 in. The cone is filled with water. A sphere is lowered into the cone until it fits snugly. Exactly one-half of the sphere remains out of the water. After the sphere is removed, how much water remains in the cone?

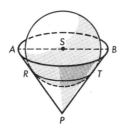
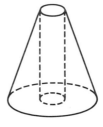

* 20. The altitude of a right circular cone is 15 and the radius of its base is 8. A cylindrical hole of diameter 4 is drilled through the cone, with its axis along the axis of the cone, leaving a solid as shown in the figure. What is the volume of this solid?

## HONORS PROBLEM

Given a rectangle $\square ABCD$. $\overline{PQ}$ is a segment not in the plane of $\square ABCD$ such that $\overline{PQ} \parallel \overline{AB}$. Draw $\overline{PA}, \overline{PD}, \overline{QB}$, and $\overline{QC}$. The length of a perpendicular from any point on $\overline{PQ}$ to the plane of $\square ABCD$ is $h$. Let $AD = a$, $AB = b$, and $PQ = c$. Prove that the volume of the solid $ABCDPQ$ equals

$$\tfrac{1}{6}ah(2b + c).$$

# *Postulates and Theorems*

# Postulates

---

*Postulate 1. The Distance Postulate.* To every pair of different points there corresponds a unique positive number.

*Postulate 2. The Ruler Postulate.* The points of a line can be placed in correspondence with the real numbers in such a way that
(1) to every point of the line there corresponds exactly one real number;
(2) to every real number there corresponds exactly one point of the line; and
(3) the distance between any two points is the absolute value of the difference of the corresponding numbers.

*Postulate 3. The Ruler Placement Postulate.* Given two points $P$ and $Q$ of a line, the coordinate system can be chosen in such a way that the coordinate of $P$ is zero and the coordinate of $Q$ is positive.

*Postulate 4. The Line Postulate.* For every two points there is exactly one line that contains both points.

*Postulate 5*
(a) Every plane contains at least three noncollinear points.
(b) Space contains at least four noncoplanar points.

*Postulate 6.* If two points of a line lie in a plane, then the line lies in the same plane.

*Postulate 7. The Plane Postulate.* Any three points lie in at least one plane, and any three noncollinear points lie in exactly one plane.

*Postulate 8.* If two different planes intersect, then their intersection is a line.

*Postulate 9. The Plane Separation Postulate.* Given a line and a plane containing it. The points of the plane that do not lie on the line form two sets such that
(1) each of the sets is convex, and
(2) if $P$ is in one of the sets and $Q$ is in the other, then the segment $\overline{PQ}$ intersects the line.

*Postulate 10. The Space Separation Postulate.* The points of space that do not lie in a given plane form two sets, such that
(1) each of the sets is convex, and
(2) if $P$ is in one of the sets and $Q$ is in the other, then the segment $PQ$ intersects the plane.

*Postulate 11. The Angle Measurement Postulate.* To every angle $\angle BAC$ there corresponds a real number between 0 and 180.

*Postulate 12. The Angle Construction Postulate.* Let $\overrightarrow{AB}$ be a ray on the edge of the half-plane $H$. For every number $r$ between 0 and 180 there is exactly one ray $\overrightarrow{AP}$, with $P$ in $H$, such that $m\angle PAB = r$.

*Postulate 13. The Angle Addition Postulate.* If $D$ is in the interior of $\angle BAC$, then $m\angle BAC = m\angle BAD + m\angle DAC$.

*Postulate 14.* *The Supplement Postulate.* If two angles form a linear pair, then they are supplementary.

*Postulate 15.* *The SAS Postulate.* Every SAS correspondence is a congruence.

*Postulate 16.* *The ASA Postulate.* Every ASA correspondence is a congruence.

*Postulate 17.* *The SSS Postulate.* Every SSS correspondence is a congruence.

*Postulate 18.* *The Parallel Postulate.* Through a given external point there is only one parallel to a given line.

*Postulate 19.* *The Area Postulate.* To every polygonal region there corresponds a unique positive real number.

*Postulate 20.* *The Congruence Postulate.* If two triangles are congruent, then the triangular regions determined by them have the same area.

*Postulate 21.* *The Area Addition Postulate.* Suppose that the region $R$ is the union of two regions $R_1$ and $R_2$. Suppose that $R_1$ and $R_2$ intersect in at most a finite number of segments and points. Then $aR = aR_1 + aR_2$.

*Postulate 22.* *The Unit Postulate.* The area of a square region is the square of the length of its edge.

*Postulate 23.* *The Unit Postulate.* The volume of a rectangular parallelepiped is the product of the altitude and the area of the base.

*Postulate 24.* *Cavalieri's Principle.* Given two solids and a plane. Suppose that every plane parallel to the given plane, intersecting one of the two solids, also intersects the other, and gives cross sections with the same area. Then the two solids have the same volume.

# Theorems

***Theorem 2–1.*** *The Point-Plotting Theorem.* Let $\overrightarrow{AB}$ be a ray, and let $x$ be a positive number. Then there is exactly one point $P$ of $\overrightarrow{AB}$ such that $AP = x$.

***Theorem 2–2.*** Every segment has exactly one mid-point.

***Theorem 3–1.*** If two different lines intersect, their intersection contains only one point.

***Theorem 3–2.*** If a line intersects a plane not containing it, then the intersection contains only one point.

***Theorem 3–3.*** Given a line and a point not on the line, there is exactly one plane containing both.

***Theorem 3–4.*** Given two intersecting lines, there is exactly one plane containing both.

***Theorem 4–1.*** If two angles are complementary, then both are acute.

***Theorem 4–2.*** Every angle is congruent to itself.

***Theorem 4–3.*** Any two right angles are congruent.

***Theorem 4–4.*** If two angles are both congruent and supplementary, then each is a right angle.

***Theorem 4–5.*** Supplements of congruent angles are congruent.

***Theorem 4–6.*** Complements of congruent angles are congruent.

***Theorem 4–7.*** *The Vertical Angle Theorem.* Vertical angles are congruent.

***Theorem 4–8.*** If two intersecting lines form one right angle, then they form four right angles.

***Theorem 5–1.*** Every segment is congruent to itself.

***Theorem 5–2.*** Every angle has exactly one bisector.

***Theorem 5–3.*** *The Isosceles Triangle Theorem.* If two sides of a triangle are congruent, then the angles opposite these sides are congruent.

***Theorem 5–4.*** If two angles of a triangle are congruent, then the sides opposite them are congruent.

***Theorem 6–1.*** In a given plane, through a given point of a given line, there is one and only one line perpendicular to the given line.

***Theorem 6–2.*** *The Perpendicular Bisector Theorem.* The perpendicular bisector of a segment, in a plane, is the set of all points of the plane that are equidistant from the end-points of the segment.

***Theorem 6–3.*** Through a given external point there is at least one line perpendicular to a given line.

*Theorem 6–4.* Through a given external point there is at most one line perpendicular to a given line.

*Theorem 6–5.* If $M$ is between $A$ and $C$ on a line $L$, then $M$ and $A$ are on the same side of any other line that contains $C$.

*Theorem 6–6.* If $M$ is between $B$ and $C$, and $A$ is any point not on $\overleftrightarrow{BC}$, then $M$ is in the interior of $\angle BAC$.

*Theorem 7–1.* If $a = b + c$ and $c > 0$, then $a > b$.

*Theorem 7–2.* *The Exterior Angle Theorem.* An exterior angle of a triangle is greater than each of its remote interior angles.

*Theorem 7–3.* *The SAA Theorem.* Every SAA correspondence is a congruence.

*Theorem 7–4.* *The Hypotenuse-Leg Theorem.* Given a correspondence between two right triangles. If the hypotenuse and one leg of one of the triangles are congruent to the corresponding parts of the second triangle, then the correspondence is a congruence.

*Theorem 7–5.* If two sides of a triangle are not congruent, then the angles opposite them are not congruent, and the larger angle is opposite the longer side.

*Theorem 7–6.* If two angles of a triangle are not congruent, then the sides opposite them are not congruent, and the longer side is opposite the larger angle.

*Theorem 7–7.* *The First Minimum Theorem.* The shortest segment joining a point to a line is the perpendicular segment.

*Theorem 7–8.* *The Triangle Inequality.* The sum of the length of any two sides of a triangle is greater than the length of the third side.

*Theorem 7–9.* *The Hinge Theorem.* If two sides of one triangle are congruent, respectively, to two sides of a second triangle, and the included angle of the first triangle is larger than the included angle of the second, then the third side of the first triangle is longer than the third side of the second.

*Theorem 7–10.* *The Converse Hinge Theorem.* If two sides of one triangle are congruent respectively to two sides of a second triangle, and the third side of the first triangle is longer than the third side of the second, then the included angle of the first triangle is larger than the included angle of the second.

*Theorem 8–1.* If $B$ and $C$ are equidistant from $P$ and $Q$, then every point between $B$ and $C$ is equidistant from $P$ and $Q$.

*Theorem 8–2.* If a line is perpendicular to each of two intersecting lines at their point of intersection, then it is perpendicular to the plane that contains them.

*Theorem 8–3.* Through a given point of a given line there passes a plane perpendicular to the given line.

*Theorem 8–4.* If a line and a plane are perpendicular, then the plane contains every line perpendicular to the given line at its point of intersection with the given plane.

*Theorem 8–5.* Through a given point of a given line there is only one plane perpendicular to the line.

*Theorem 8–6.* *The Perpendicular Bisecting Plane Theorem.* The perpendicular bisecting plane of a segment is the set of all points equidistant from the end points of the segment.

*Theorem 8–7.* Two lines perpendicular to the same plane are coplanar.

*Theorem 8–8.* Through a given point there passes one and only one *plane* perpendicular to a given *line*.

*Theorem 8–9.* Through a given point there passes one and only one *line* perpendicular to a given *plane*.

*Theorem 8–10.* *The Second Minimum Theorem.* The shortest segment to a plane from an external point is the perpendicular segment.

*Theorem 9–1.* Two parallel lines lie in exactly one plane.

*Theorem 9–2.* Two lines in a plane are parallel if they are both perpendicular to the same line.

*Theorem 9–3.* Let $L$ be a line and let $P$ be a point not on $L$. Then there is at least one line through $P$, parallel to $L$.

*Theorem 9–4.* If two lines are cut by a transversal, and one pair of alternate interior angles are congruent, then the other pair of alternate interior angles are also congruent.

*Theorem 9–5.* *The AIP Theorem.* Given two lines cut by a transversal. If a pair of alternate interior angles are congruent, then the lines are parallel.

*Theorem 9–6.* Given two lines cut by a transversal. If a pair of corresponding angles are congruent, then a pair of alternate interior angles are congruent.

*Theorem 9–7.* Given two lines cut by a transversal. If a pair of corresponding angles are congruent, then the lines are parallel.

*Theorem 9–8.* *The PAI Theorem.* If two parallel lines are cut by a transversal, then alternate interior angles are congruent.

*Theorem 9–9.* If two parallel lines are cut by a transversal, each pair of corresponding angles are congruent.

*Theorem 9–10.* If two parallel lines are cut by a transversal, the interior angles on the same side of the transversal are supplementary.

*Theorem 9–11.* In a plane, if two lines are each parallel to a third line, then they are parallel to each other.

*Theorem 9–12.* In a plane, if a line is perpendicular to one of two parallel lines it is perpendicular to the other.

*Theorem 9–13.* For every triangle, the sum of the measures of the angles is 180.

*Theorem 9–14.* Each diagonal separates a parallelogram into two congruent triangles.

*Theorem 9–15.* In a parallelogram, any two opposite sides are congruent.

*Theorem 9–16.* In a parallelogram, any two opposite angles are congruent.

*Theorem 9–17.* In a parallelogram, any two consecutive angles are supplementary.

*Theorem 9–18.* The diagonals of a parallelogram bisect each other.

*Theorem 9–19.* Given a quadrilateral in which both pairs of opposite sides are congruent. Then the quadrilateral is a parallelogram.

*Theorem 9–20.* If two sides of a quadrilateral are parallel and congruent, then the quadrilateral is a parallelogram.

*Theorem 9–21.* If the diagonals of a quadrilateral bisect each other, then the quadrilateral is a parallelogram.

*Theorem 9–22.* The segment between the mid-points of two sides of a triangle is parallel to the third side and half as long.

*Theorem 9–23.* If a parallelogram has one right angle, then it has four right angles, and the parallelogram is a rectangle.

*Theorem 9–24.* In a rhombus, the diagonals are perpendicular to one another.

*Theorem 9–25.* If the diagonals of a quadrilateral bisect each other and are perpendicular, then the quadrilateral is a rhombus.

*Theorem 9–26.* The median to the hypotenuse of a right triangle is half as long as the hypotenuse.

*Theorem 9–27.* *The 30-60-90 Triangle Theorem.* If an acute angle of a right triangle has measure 30, then the opposite side is half as long as the hypotenuse.

*Theorem 9–28.* If one leg of a right triangle is half as long as the hypotenuse, then the opposite angle has measure 30.

*Theorem 9–29.* If three parallel lines intercept congruent segments on one transversal $T$, then they intercept congruent segments on every transversal $T'$ which is parallel to $T$.

*Theorem 9–30.* If three parallel lines intercept congruent segments on one transversal, then they intercept congruent segments on any other transversal.

*Theorem 10–1.* If a plane intersects two parallel planes, then it intersects them in two parallel lines.

*Theorem 10–2.* If a line is perpendicular to one of two parallel planes it is perpendicular to the other.

*Theorem 10–3.* Two planes perpendicular to the same line are parallel.

*Theorem 10–4.* Two lines perpendicular to the same plane are parallel.

*Theorem 10–5.* Parallel planes are everywhere equidistant.

*Theorem 10–6.* All plane angles of the same dihedral angle are congruent.

*Theorem 10–7.* If a line is perpendicular to a plane, then every plane containing the line is perpendicular to the given plane.

*Theorem 10–8.* If two planes are perpendicular, then any line in one of them, perpendicular to their line of intersection, is perpendicular to the other plane.

*Theorem 10–9.* If a line and a plane are not perpendicular, then the projection of the line into the plane is a line.

***Theorem 11–1.*** The area of a rectangle is the product of its base and its altitude.

***Theorem 11–2.*** The area of a right triangle is half the product of its legs.

***Theorem 11–3.*** The area of a triangle is half the product of any base and the corresponding altitude.

***Theorem 11–4.*** The area of a trapezoid is half the product of its altitude and the sum of its bases.

***Theorem 11–5.*** The area of a parallelogram is the product of any base and the corresponding altitude.

***Theorem 11–6.*** If two triangles have the same base $b$ and the same altitude $h$, then they have the same area.

***Theorem 11–7.*** If two triangles have the same altitude $h$, then the ratio of their areas is equal to the ratio of their bases.

***Theorem 11–8.*** *The Pythagorean Theorem.* In a right triangle, the square of the hypotenuse is equal to the sum of the squares of the legs.

***Theorem 11–9.*** If the square of one side of a triangle is equal to the sum of the squares of the other two sides, then the triangle is a right triangle, with its right angle opposite the longest side.

***Theorem 11–10.*** *The Isosceles Right Triangle Theorem.* In an isosceles right triangle, the hypotenuse is $\sqrt{2}$ times as long as each of the legs.

***Theorem 11–11.*** If the base of an isosceles triangle is $\sqrt{2}$ times as long as each of the two congruent sides, then the angle opposite the base is a right angle.

***Theorem 11–12.*** In a 30-60-90 triangle, the longer leg is $\sqrt{3}/2$ times as long as the hypotenuse.

***Theorem 12–1.*** *The Basic Proportionality Theorem.* If a line parallel to one side of a triangle intersects the other two sides in distinct points, then it cuts off segments which are proportional to these sides.

***Theorem 12–2.*** If a line intersects two sides of a triangle, and cuts off segments proportional to these two sides, then it is parallel to the third side.

***Theorem 12–3.*** *The AAA Similarity Theorem.* Given a correspondence between two triangles. If corresponding angles are congruent, then the correspondence is a similarity.

***Theorem 12–4.*** If $\triangle ABC \sim \triangle DEF$, and $\triangle DEF \cong \triangle GHI$, then $\triangle ABC \sim \triangle GHI$.

***Theorem 12–5.*** *The SAS Similarity Theorem.* Given a correspondence between two triangles. If two pairs of corresponding sides are proportional, and the included angles are congruent, then the correspondence is a similarity.

***Theorem 12–6.*** *The SSS Similarity Theorem.* Given a correspondence between two triangles. If corresponding sides are proportional, then the correspondence is a similarity.

***Theorem 12–7.*** In any right triangle, the altitude to the hypotenuse separates the triangle into two triangles which are similar to each other and to the original triangle.

**Theorem 12–8.** Given a right triangle and the altitude to the hypotenuse.
(1) The altitude is the geometric mean of the segments into which it separates the hypotenuse.
(2) Each leg is the geometric mean of the hypotenuse and the segment of the hypotenuse adjacent to the leg.

**Theorem 12–9.** If two triangles are similar, then the ratio of their areas is the square of the ratio of any two corresponding sides.

**Theorem 12–10.** For every $\angle A$, $(\sin \angle A)^2 + (\cos \angle A)^2 = 1$.

**Theorem 12–11.** For every $\angle A$, $\tan \angle A = \dfrac{\sin \angle A}{\cos \angle A}$.

**Theorem 12–12.** If $\angle A$ and $\angle B$ are complementary, then $\sin \angle B = \cos \angle A$ and $\cos \angle B = \sin \angle A$.

**Theorem 13–1.** On a nonvertical line, all segments have the same slope.

**Theorem 13–2.** Two nonvertical lines are parallel if and only if they have the same slope.

**Theorem 13–3.** Two nonvertical lines are perpendicular if and only if their slopes are negative reciprocals of each other.

**Theorem 13–4.** *The Distance Formula.* The distance between the points $(x_1, y_1)$ and $(x_2, y_2)$ is $\sqrt{(x_2 - x_1)^2 + (y_2 - y_1)^2}$.

**Theorem 13–5.** *The Mid-Point Formula.* Given $P_1 = (x_1, x_2)$ and $P_2 = (y_1, y_2)$. The mid-point of $\overline{P_1P_2}$ is the point $P = \left( \dfrac{x_1 + x_2}{2}, \dfrac{y_1 + y_2}{2} \right)$.

**Theorem 13–6.** If $P$ is between $P_1$ and $P_2$, and $\dfrac{P_1P}{PP_2} = r$, then

$$P = \left( \frac{x_1 + rx_2}{1 + r}, \frac{y_1 + ry_2}{1 + r} \right).$$

**Theorem 13–7.** Let $L$ be a line with slope $m$, passing through the point $(x_1, y_1)$. Then every point $(x, y)$ of $L$ satisfies the equation $y - y_1 = m(x - x_1)$.

**Theorem 13–8.** The graph of the equation $y - y_1 = m(x - x_1)$ is the line which passes through the point $(x_1, y_1)$ and has slope $m$.

**Theorem 13–9.** The graph of the equation $y = mx + b$ is the line which passes through the point $(0, b)$ and has slope $m$.

**Theorem 14–1.** The intersection of a sphere with a plane through its center is a circle with the same center and the same radius.

**Theorem 14–2.** A line perpendicular to a radius at its outer end is tangent to the circle.

**Theorem 14–3.** Every tangent to a circle is perpendicular to the radius drawn to the point of contact.

**Theorem 14–4.** The perpendicular from the center of a circle to a chord bisects the chord.

*Theorem 14–5.* The segment from the center of a circle to the mid-point of a chord is perpendicular to the chord.

*Theorem 14–6.* In the plane of a circle, the perpendicular bisector of a chord passes through the center.

*Theorem 14–7.* In the same circle or in congruent circles, chords equidistant from the center are congruent.

*Theorem 14–8.* In the same circle or in congruent circles, any two congruent chords are equidistant from the center.

*Theorem 14–9.* If a line intersects the interior of a circle, then it intersects the circle in two and only two points.

*Theorem 14–10.* A plane perpendicular to a radius at its outer end is tangent to the sphere.

*Theorem 14–11.* Every tangent plane to a sphere is perpendicular to the radius drawn to the point of contact.

*Theorem 14–12.* If a plane intersects the interior of a sphere, then the intersection of the plane and the sphere is a circle. The center of this circle is the foot of the perpendicular from the center of the sphere to the plane.

*Theorem 14–13.* The perpendicular from the center of a sphere to a chord bisects the chord.

*Theorem 14–14.* The segment from the center of a sphere to the mid-point of a chord is perpendicular to the chord.

*Theorem 14–15. The Arc Addition Theorem.* If $B$ is a point of $\overset{\frown}{AC}$, then
$$m\overset{\frown}{ABC} = m\overset{\frown}{AB} + m\overset{\frown}{BC}.$$

*Theorem 14–16.* The measure of an inscribed angle is half the measure of its intercepted arc.

*Theorem 14–17.* In the same circle or in congruent circles, if two chords are congruent, then so are the corresponding minor arcs.

*Theorem 14–18.* In the same circle or in congruent circles, if two arcs are congruent, then so are the corresponding chords.

*Theorem 14–19.* Given an angle with its vertex on a circle, formed by a secant ray and a tangent ray. The measure of the angle is half the measure of the intercepted arc.

*Theorem 14–20.* The two tangent segments to a circle from a point of the exterior are congruent and determine congruent angles with the segment from the exterior point to the center.

*Theorem 14–21. The Power Theorem.* Given a circle $C$, and a point $Q$ of its exterior. Let $L_1$ be a secant line through $Q$, intersecting $C$ in points $R$ and $S$; and let $L_2$ be another secant line through $Q$, intersecting $C$ in points $U$ and $T$. Then $QR \cdot QS = QU \cdot QT$.

*Theorem 14–22.* Given a tangent segment $\overline{QT}$ to a circle, and a secant line through $Q$, intersecting the circle in points $R$ and $S$. Then $QR \cdot QS = QT$ .

**Theorem 14–23.** Let $\overline{RS}$ and $\overline{TU}$ be chords of the same circle, intersecting at $Q$. Then $QR \cdot QS = QU \cdot QT$.

**Theorem 14–24.** The graph of the equation $(x - a)^2 + (y - b)^2 = r^2$ is the circle with center $(a, b)$ and radius $r$.

**Theorem 14–25.** Every circle is the graph of an equation of the form
$$x^2 + y^2 + Ax + By + C = 0.$$

**Theorem 14–26.** The graph of the equation $x^2 + y^2 + Ax + By + C = 0$ is (1) a circle, (2) a point, or (3) the empty set.

**Theorem 15–1.** *The Perpendicular Bisector Concurrence Theorem.* The perpendicular bisectors of the sides of a triangle are concurrent. Their point of concurrency is equidistant from the vertices of the triangle.

**Theorem 15–2.** *The Altitude Concurrence Theorem.* The three altitudes of a triangle are always concurrent.

**Theorem 15–3.** The bisector of an angle, minus its end point, is the set of all points of the interior of the angle that are equidistant from the sides.

**Theorem 15–4.** *The Angle Bisector Concurrence Theorem.* The angle bisectors of a triangle are concurrent in a point which is equidistant from the three sides.

**Theorem 15–5.** *The Median Concurrence Theorem.* The medians of every triangle are concurrent. And their point of concurrency is two-thirds of the way along each median, from the vertex to the opposite side.

**Theorem 15–6.** *The Two-Circle Theorem.* Given two circles of radius $a$ and $b$, with $c$ as the distance between their centers. If each of the numbers $a$, $b$, and $c$ is less than the sum of the other two, then the circles intersect in two points, on opposite sides of the line through the centers.

**Theorem 16–1.** The ratio of the circumference to the diameter is the same for all circles.

**Theorem 16–2.** The area of a circle of radius $r$ is $\pi r^2$.

**Theorem 16–3.** If two arcs have equal radii, then their lengths are proportional to their measures.

**Theorem 16–4.** If an arc has measure $q$ and radius $r$, then its length is

$$L = \frac{q}{180} \cdot \pi r.$$

**Theorem 16–5.** The area of a sector is half the product of its radius and the length of its arc.

**Theorem 16–6.** If a sector has radius $r$ and its arc has measure $q$, then its area is

$$A = \frac{q}{360} \cdot \pi r^2.$$

**Theorem 17–1.** All cross sections of a triangular prism are congruent to the base.

**Theorem 17–2.** *The Prism Cross-Section Theorem.* All cross sections of a prism have the same area.

*Theorem 17–3.* The lateral faces of a prism are parallelogram regions.

*Theorem 17–4.* Every cross section of a triangular pyramid, between the base and the vertex, is a triangular region similar to the base. If $h$ is the altitude, and $k$ is the distance from the vertex to the cross section, then the area of the cross section is equal to $k^2/h^2$ times the area of the base.

*Theorem 17–5.* In any pyramid, the ratio of the area of a cross section to the area of the base is $k^2/h^2$, where $h$ is the altitude of the pyramid and $k$ is the distance from the vertex to the plane of the cross section.

*Theorem 17–6. The Pyramid Cross-Section Theorem.* If two pyramids have the same base area and the same altitude, then cross sections equidistant from the vertices have the same area.

*Theorem 17–7.* The volume of any prism is the product of the altitude and the area of the base.

*Theorem 17–8.* If two pyramids have the same altitude and the same base area, and their bases lie in the same plane, then they have the same volume.

*Theorem 17–9.* The volume of a triangular pyramid is one-third the product of its altitude and its base area.

*Theorem 17–10.* The volume of a pyramid is one-third the product of its altitude and its base area.

*Theorem 17–11.* Every cross section of a circular cylinder is a circular region congruent to the base.

*Theorem 17–12.* Every cross section of a circular cylinder has the same area as the base.

*Theorem 17–13.* Given a cone of altitude $h$, and a cross section made by a plane at a distance $k$ from the vertex. The area of the cross section is equal to $k^2/h^2$ times the area of the base.

*Theorem 17–14.* The volume of a circular cylinder is the product of its altitude and the area of its base.

*Theorem 17–15.* The volume of a circular cone is one-third the product of its altitude and the area of its base.

*Theorem 17–16.* The volume of a sphere of radius $r$ is $\frac{4}{3}\pi r^2$.

*Theorem 17–17.* The surface area of a sphere of radius $r$ is $A = 4\pi r^2$.

# List of Symbols

Following are short explanations of the symbols used in this book, with references to the pages where fuller explanations are given.

| SYMBOLS | MEANING | FOR DEFINITION SEE PAGE |
|---|---|---|
| $=$ | Equals; is equal to; is the same as | 15 |
| $\neq$ | Is not equal to; is different from | |
| $<$ | Is less than: | |
| | for numbers | 22 |
| | for segments | 185 |
| | for angles | 185 |
| $\leq$ | Is less than or equal to: | |
| | for numbers | 22 |
| $>$ | Is greater than: | |
| | for numbers | 22 |
| $\geq$ | Is greater than or equal to: | |
| | for numbers | 22 |
| $\sqrt{a}$ | The positive square root of $a$ | 23 |
| $\lvert a \rvert$ | The absolute value of $a$ | 26 |
| $AB$ | The distance between points $A$ and $B$ | 31 |
| $\overleftrightarrow{AB}$ | The line containing points $A$ and $B$ | 41 |
| $\overline{AB}$ | The segment whose end points are $A$ and $B$ | 41 |
| $\overrightarrow{AB}$ | The ray having end point $A$ and containing $B$ | 41 |
| $\angle BAC$ | The angle whose sides are $\overrightarrow{AB}$ and $\overrightarrow{AC}$ | 75 |
| $m\angle BAC$ | The measure of $\angle BAC$ | 82 |
| $\triangle ABC$ | The triangle whose vertices are $A$, $B$, and $C$ | 76 |
| $\square ABCD$ | The quadrilateral whose vertices are $A$, $B$, $C$ and $D$ | 144 |
| $A\text{-}B\text{-}C$ | $B$ is between $A$ and $C$ | 39, 78 |
| $\angle A \cong \angle B.$ | $\angle A$ and $\angle B$ are congruent. | 88 |
| $\overline{AB} \cong \overline{CD}.$ | The segments $\overline{AB}$ and $\overline{CD}$ are congruent. | 112 |
| $ABC \leftrightarrow DEF$ | The correspondence which matches $A$ with $D$, $B$ with $E$, and $C$ with $F$ | 106 |
| $\triangle ABC \cong \triangle DEF.$ | The correspondence $ABC \leftrightarrow DEF$ is a congruence. | 113 |
| $\triangle ABC \sim \triangle DEF.$ | The correspondence $ABC \leftrightarrow DEF$ is a similarity. | 327 |

| <small>SYMBOLS</small> | <small>MEANING</small> | <small>FOR DEFINITION<br>SEE PAGE</small> |
|---|---|---|
| $\perp$ | Is perpendicular to: | |
| | for lines | 87 |
| | for a line and a plane | 213 |
| | for planes | 277 |
| $\parallel$ | Is parallel to: | |
| | for lines | 229 |
| | for a line and a plane | 269 |
| | for planes | 269 |
| $aR$ | The area of the region $R$ | 293 |
| $\angle A\text{-}BC\text{-}D$ | The dihedral angle with $\overleftrightarrow{BC}$ as edge, and with sides containing $A$ and $D$ | 276 |
| $m\angle A\text{-}BC\text{-}D$ | The measure of $\angle A\text{-}BC\text{-}D$ | 277 |
| $\overarc{AB}$ | The arc whose end points are $A$ and $B$ | 439 |
| $m\overarc{AB}$ | The degree measure of $\overarc{AB}$ | 440 |
| $\sin r°$ | sine of $\angle A$ if $m\angle A = r$ | 353 |
| $\cos r°$ | cosine of $\angle A$ if $m\angle A = r$ | 353 |
| $\tan r°$ | tangent of $\angle A$ if $m\angle A = r$ | 354 |

The following symbols are frequently used for the terms described or defined in Section 2–1, although most of them are not used in the text.

| | |
|---|---|
| $\{a, b, c\}$ | The set whose elements are $a$, $b$, and $c$ |
| $\{a \mid a > 2\}$ | The set of all numbers greater than 2 |
| $\emptyset$ | The empty set |
| $A \cup B$ | The union of sets $A$ and $B$ |
| $A \cap B$ | The intersection of sets $A$ and $B$ |
| $A \subset B$ | Set $A$ is a subset of set $B$ |
| $x \in A$ | $x$ is an element of set $A$ |

Marking of figures and the use of exclamation marks (!) to convey information are discussed on pp. 128, 129, 140.

# Index

# Index